PHYSICAL MECHANICS

UNIVERSITY PHYSICS SERIES

A Group of Text Books for Intermediate and
Advanced Courses

WALTER C. MICHELS, PH.D.

CONSULTING EDITOR

Introduction to Optics. FOURTH EDITION. *By* John K.
Robertson, F.R.S.C., *Professor of Physics, Queen's
University.*

Principles of Electricity. THIRD EDITION. *By* Leigh
Page, Ph.D., *Late Professor of Mathematical Physics,
Yale University;* and Norman Isley Adams, Jr., Ph.D.,
Professor of Physics, Yale University.

Introduction to Mathematical Physics. *By* William
Band, *Professor of Physics, Washington State University.*

Modern Atomic and Nuclear Physics. *By* C. Sharp Cook,
U. S. Naval Radiological Defense Laboratory, California.

Physical Mechanics. THIRD EDITION. *By* R. Bruce
Lindsay, Ph.D., *Hazard Professor of Physics, Brown
University.*

PHYSICAL MECHANICS

BY

ROBERT BRUCE LINDSAY

Hazard Professor of Physics in Brown University

THIRD EDITION

D. VAN NOSTRAND COMPANY, INC.

PRINCETON, NEW JERSEY

TORONTO　　　　　　　　　　　　　　　LONDON

NEW YORK

D. VAN NOSTRAND COMPANY, INC.
120 Alexander St., Princeton, New Jersey (*Principal office*)
24 West 40 Street, New York 18, New York

D. VAN NOSTRAND COMPANY, LTD.
358, Kensington High Street, London, W.14, England

D. VAN NOSTRAND COMPANY (Canada), LTD.
25 Hollinger Road, Toronto 16, Canada

First Edition May 1933
Ten Reprintings
Second Edition May 1950
Four Reprintings
Third Edition September 1961
Reprinted June 1962

PREFACE TO THE THIRD EDITION

The fundamental purpose of the third edition of this book is the same as that of the two previous editions, published in 1933 and 1950 respectively—to serve as the basis of an intermediate course in mechanics for college and university students who have taken a substantial course in elementary general physics and college mathematics through calculus and introductory differential equations. The aim is still to stress the fundamental concepts and principles of mechanics and their use in all branches of physics.

The revision has provided a welcome opportunity to introduce a substantial amount of new material to strengthen the appropriateness of the word "physical" in the title. The material on kinetic theory of gases has been consolidated in a separate chapter and has been considerably expanded in respect to transport properties and elementary statistical mechanics as a basis for the principles of thermodynamics. New sections on dispersion, group velocity and wave pulses have been added to the development of wave propagation. The treatment of special relativity and elementary quantum mechanics has been elaborated and new chapters on these subjects have been added at the end of the volume. Chapter 1 has been strengthened by the addition of elementary illustrative material on the impulse-momentum and work-kinetic-energy theorems. Vector differential operator notation has been introduced where it could serve the purpose of economy as well as introducing the reader to more advanced treatises. Attention has been paid to modern developments by the inclusion of sections on collisions of nuclear particles as well as artificial satellites and ballistic missiles.

About sixty new problems have been added, including many that materially extend the scope of application of the text.

The author desires to express his deep appreciation to Professor Walter C. Michels, Consulting Editor for the University Physics Series, for helpful criticism and advice, as well as to many users of the book who have contributed useful suggestions and corrections of errors. Grateful acknowledgment is made to the National Bureau of Standards and in particular to Dr. Chester H. Page of that institution for permission to use Figure 2.10 of the Heyl apparatus for the measurement of the gravitational constant.

R. B. LINDSAY

Providence, Rhode Island
June 1961

v

CONTENTS

CHAPTER 1

THE ELEMENTAL CONCEPTS OF MECHANICS

1·1. What is Mechanics? Mechanics is the science of motion. Since motion is probably the most obvious of all physical phenomena, it is not surprising that the field of physics dealing with it has received careful attention by physicists from the very earliest times. The evolution of mechanics as we know it today has been a long protracted process involving the introduction and discarding of many different notions. The ideas of Galileo, Huygens and Newton, developed mainly during the seventeenth century, proved so successful in the description of the observed large-scale motions of bodies that it became only natural to attempt the explanation of other physical phenomena like heat and light in terms of mechanical principles. This has further enhanced the importance of mechanics in the evolution of physics.

It should be made clear at the beginning that mechanics is not an explanation of *why* bodies move. It seeks the simplest possible description of *how* bodies move. It is true that this description does not content itself with ordinary, common-sense observation expressed in terms of everyday language. Rather, it involves the construction of what has come to be called a physical theory of motion, a logical structure in which certain general but plausible principles are postulated without proof. From these principles physicists can deduce mathematically *all* the possible motions of bodies. The latter can then be compared with actually observed motions, and the extent of the agreement between the theoretically predicted results and those observed is treated as a measure of the success of the theory.[1] In particular if the theory is able to predict a result which has not previously been observed and subsequent test leads to agreement with the prediction, confidence in the success of the theory is considerably enhanced. From this standpoint, theoretical mechanics has proved to be a highly successful physical theory and it is therefore hardly surprising that up to very recent times it has been the endeavor of physicists to cast all physical theories into mechanical form, that is, to reduce the description of all natural phenomena in the last analysis to the motions of particles

---

[1] For a discussion of the nature of a physical theory cf. Lindsay and Margenau, *Foundations of Physics*, Wiley, New York, 1936 (Dover Publications Inc, New York, 1957), Chap. I.

or continuous media of appropriate properties.   This procedure has been attended with considerable success, though the satisfactory application of it to certain modern problems like the structure of atoms has demanded modifications in the fundamental postulates leading to the generalization of classical mechanics which is called quantum mechanics.

It is the aim of the present volume to set forth the fundamental principles of classical mechanics and to illustrate them with many applications to concrete physical problems of all kinds, not only large-scale observed motions but also phenomena described in terms of the motion of hypothetical particles like molecules, atoms and electrons. In this way, it is hoped that the reader will secure a proper perspective on the value of mechanics as a tool in general physical description.

1·2. Fundamental Definitions.   Since mechanics is the science of motion, the question at once arises: *what moves*, and what are the *simplest elements* in terms of which its *motion* may be described? A careful analysis of the first question indicates that a logically consistent answer is really very hard to find; the usual statement that it is matter which moves is not very helpful, since we do not know precisely what matter is, though we are now well acquainted with many of its properties. However, in order to avoid too much of a philosophical discussion, in this book we shall adopt the simple assumption (recognizing, of course, its shortcomings) that the fundamental entity in mechanics is the *material particle* and that all gross bodies whose changes in position with respect to their surroundings we denominate by the term *motion*, are aggregates of such particles.   At the present stage the simplest and most profitable view which the student can take of such a particle is that it is a geometrical point with the important added non-geometrical property of *inertia*, the quantitative measure of which we shall later define as its *mass*.   We shall also assume that particles may have certain relations with respect to each other, e.g., gravitation, electrical attraction or repulsion, etc.

We shall therefore begin our study of mechanics with a discussion of the motion of a single particle.   Now the elements in terms of which we describe motion are first of all *position* in *space* and *time*.   The thoughtful student will undoubtedly wish to examine closely these fundamental concepts.[1]   All that we can well say here is that space and time are strictly *modes* of *perception*, ways in which we as human beings distinguish objects and events.   Each individual thus possesses his own space and time.   But for practical purposes there has been devised a kind of public space in which we all agree to conceive the

---

[1] See H. Poincaré, *Foundations of Science*, trans. by G. B. Halsted, a work which should be in the library of every student of physics.   Cf. also Lindsay and Margenau, *Foundations of Physics*, Chap. II.

objects of perception to be placed, and a public time in which events take place.   This public space, which is likewise that used in elementary mechanics, is Euclidean and three dimensional.   There is one very important fact concerning the position of an object, such as a particle, in this space: we can never know more than its position with respect to other particles, which, of course, may include ourselves as observers. When we speak of the position of a particle, what we really imply is a method of *reaching* that particle, starting from some *given* position. Hence position is wholly relative, and implies an arbitrary set of particles or bodies as a *reference* system.   In mechanics this reference system will vary.   For many problems it will consist of a point or points on the surface of the earth; for others it will be the sun; while the most general system of this kind is provided by the so-called " fixed " stars. This latter system is known as the *primary inertial system*.

   There are many ways of representing mathematically the position of a particle.   The two most common ways are (1) by means of *rectangular coördinates* and (2) by a *vector*.   Consulting Fig. 1·1,

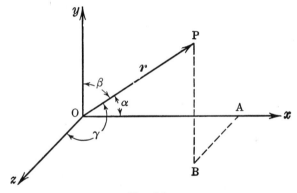

FIG. 1·1

the point P may have its position referred to a set of three mutually perpendicular planes intersecting at the point O and in the lines Ox, Oy and Oz (the so-called coördinate axes) respectively, by means of the three perpendicular distances from P to the yz, xz and xy planes respectively.   These three distances, usually denoted by x, y and z for convenience, are called the *rectangular coördinates* of the point P in the reference system O-xyz; and the three values are in themselves sufficient to determine the position of the point.[1]

---

[1] The axes indicated in Fig. 1·1 form what is called a *right-handed set* in the sense that the positive direction of the z axis is fixed by the direction of advance of a right-handed screw rotated in the xy plane from the positive direction of the x axis to that of the y axis through the angle between them.   Interchange of the y and z axes leads to a *left-handed set*, useful for some purposes.   We shall use right-handed axes in this book.

But it is clear that the point P is also completely specified by its *distance* r from the point O and the *direction* of this line with respect to the three coördinate axes, the latter being given by the angles α, β, γ which the line OP makes with these axes.   Such a line OP with definite length and in a specified direction is called a *vector*, for it is a physical quantity which has both *magnitude* (i.e., as given by its length) and *direction* (as given by the three angles).   We may say that the vector **OP** completely determines the position of the point P and the particle located there in the given reference system.   We shall call **OP** $=$ **r** the position vector corresponding to the position P.[1]   It might at first be thought that the specification of P by means of a vector involves the use of four independent quantities, viz., r and the angles α, β and γ; whereas the rectangular coördinates are but three in number.   However the student will at once recall that α, β, γ are not independent but are connected by the relation

$$\cos^2 \alpha + \cos^2 \beta + \cos^2 \gamma = 1. \tag{1·2–1}$$

As a matter of fact it follows from an examination of the figure that the following connection holds between the rectangular coördinates and the angles, viz.:

$$x = r \cos \alpha, \quad y = r \cos \beta, \quad z = r \cos \gamma, \tag{1·2–2}$$

whence, since $x^2 + y^2 + z^2 = r^2$, the identity (1·2–1) follows immediately. The rectangular projection of a vector on a given line is termed the *rectangular component* (usually more simply *component*) of the vector along the given line and is equal in magnitude to the product of the magnitude of the vector by the cosine of the angle between the positive directions of the vector and the line.   Thus it develops that the rectangular coördinates of P are the components of the vector **OP** along the three coördinate axes respectively (see Sec. 1·3).   We shall find that both methods of locating P are useful, both when P may be considered as lying in a plane and also when three dimensions are essential.   The method of specifying position known as *spherical* coördinates will be dealt with later.

Specification of position by *distance*, of course, demands the introduction of a unit of *length*.   In the metric system this is the *meter*, which is the distance between two marks on a bar of platinum carefully preserved at the International Bureau of Metric Standards, St. Cloud, near Paris.[2]   The common unit is the centimeter (cm) which is 1/100 of a meter.   The British unit is the foot, which is 1/3 of the Standard Yard,

---

[1] Note the use of boldface type for the designation of vector quantities.

[2] The meter has been officially redefined by international agreement as of October, 1960, to be 1,650,763.73 wave lengths of the orange-red line of krypton 86.

the latter being the distance between two marks on a metal bar preserved in London. The United States and the British Commonwealth have agreed (as of July, 1959) to redefine an international yard and make it equal 0.9144 meter.

We must next consider the element of *time*. All physical events, including the motion of particles and bodies, are said to take place in time. The time to which mechanical motions are referred is the *public* time, which is arbitrarily related to the observed motions of the heavenly bodies, and it has been agreed in mechanics to take as a unit of this time 1/86,400 of a mean solar day. The mean solar day is the time (averaged over one year) between two successive transits of the sun across a given meridian. The unit of time thus defined is called the mean solar second.[1] Actually when in theoretical mechanics it is stated, for example, that the position of a particle is a function of the time, this really means that the position can be most conveniently represented as dependent on an independent variable which can take on an aggregate of values capable of being put into one-to-one correspondence with the real number continuum or, if we like, the points on a line. From this standpoint an interval of time is represented simply as the interval between two real numbers or two points on a line. However, in actual practice these two values are made to correspond with two readings on a clock which registers public time. This is the modern point of view which replaces Newton's definition of "absolute" time as "flowing uniformly." For the latter definition is clearly circular. Nevertheless it is also evident that Newton felt the necessity for the *continuity* of the abstract time of physics as opposed to the discreteness of the time of perception.

Time like space is relative, and Einstein has shown that it is necessary to modify the common notion regarding the simultaneity of two events. The Einstein modifications are of practical importance only for particles moving with very high velocities, e.g., close to that of light (see Chap. 14).

The development of physical concepts suitable for physical description, e.g., for use in building a theory like mechanics, affords a problem of great interest in what may be called the foundations of physics. Already much thought has been given to this question. One of the most striking points of view is that of P. W. Bridgman,[2] who stresses what may be called the *operational* standpoint. According to this every

---

[1] Astronomers use also the mean sidereal second, which is 1/86,400 of the mean sidereal day or 365.25/366.25 of the mean solar second. By international agreement reached in October, 1960, the second has been redefined as 1/31,556,925.9747 of the tropical year 1900. The tropical year is defined as the interval of time between two successive passages of the sun through the vernal equinox.

[2] P. W. Bridgman, *The Logic of Modern Physics*, Macmillan, New York, 1927. This has much material which will prove very fascinating for the mature student. Cf. also R. B. Lindsay, *Philosophy of Science*, **4**, 456, 1937, for a critique of operationalism.

physical concept possesses meaning only in so far as there exists a laboratory operation or set of operations by which a number may be attached to the symbol representing the concept.

1·3. Displacement and Velocity. When a particle changes its position, it is said to undergo a *displacement*. Since this may be treated

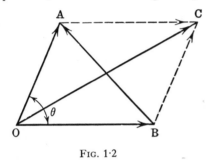

FIG. 1·2

as a change in the position vector of the particle, it is essential that we introduce some considerations on the properties of vectors. Let us consider the two vectors **OA** and **OB** in the above figure (Fig. 1·2). Through B draw the line parallel to and in the same direction as **OA**; through A draw the line parallel to and in the same direction as **OB**. Let these two lines intersect at C. Then the vector **OC** will be defined as the *sum* or *resultant* of the two vectors **OA** and **OB**. Thus we have the *vector* equation

$$\mathbf{OA} + \mathbf{OB} = \mathbf{OC}. \qquad (1\text{·}3\text{–}1)$$

The sum of the two vectors may be looked upon as that diagonal of the parallelogram with **OA** and **OB** as adjacent sides which is included by these two sides. We may also consider the resultant as the third

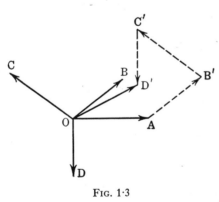

FIG. 1·3

side of the triangle formed by **OB** and **BC**, where **BC** is equal in magnitude to **OA** and parallel thereto. This point of view is particularly valuable when we desire to find the sum of several vectors: we merely lay off at the end of the first vector a line equal in magnitude to and in the same direction as the second vector. We repeat in turn for all the vectors, and the resultant will be the vector from the origin to the end of the line last drawn, thus completing a polygon.

(Consult the figure — Fig. 1·3 — where **OD′** is the sum of **OA**, **OB**, **OC** and **OD**, the four vectors being taken for convenience in the same plane, although this is not necessary for the application of the method.)

Reverting to the simpler case of two vectors, we must be careful to note that eq. (1·3–1) is not an *algebraic* but a *vector* equation. The *magnitude* of the resultant **OC** is given by the cosine law, i.e.,

$$|\mathbf{OC}|^2 = |\mathbf{OA}|^2 + |\mathbf{OB}|^2 + 2|\mathbf{OA}|\cdot|\mathbf{OB}| \cos \theta, \qquad (1·3–2)$$

where the bars indicate absolute value or magnitude.

We are now in a position to discuss the subtraction of two vectors. Consulting Fig. 1·2 once more, we are led to define the vector **BA** as the *difference* between **OA** and **OB**, for it is the vector which when added to **OB** (by the preceding rule) yields **OA**. We thus have the vector equation

$$\mathbf{OA} - \mathbf{OB} = \mathbf{BA}. \qquad (1·3–3)$$

The magnitude of the difference vector will again be obtained from the cosine law, i.e.,

$$|\mathbf{AB}|^2 = |\mathbf{OA}|^2 + |\mathbf{OB}|^2 - 2|\mathbf{OA}|\cdot|\mathbf{OB}| \cos \theta. \qquad (1·3–4)$$

A very important illustration of the addition of vectors is afforded by the resolution of the position vector **r** corresponding to a given point (Sec. 1·2) into its components along three mutually perpendicular lines, i.e., the rectangular components x, y, z. If we consult again Fig. 1·1, the law of vector addition gives us at once the vector equation

$$\mathbf{OP} = \mathbf{OA} + \mathbf{AB} + \mathbf{BP}, \qquad (1·3–5)$$

where $\mathbf{OP} = \mathbf{r}$, while $|\mathbf{OA}| = x$, $|\mathbf{BP}| = y$ and $|\mathbf{AB}| = z$. If now we denote by **i**, **j**, **k** vectors of *unit* magnitude along the x, y and z directions respectively, we may write

$$\mathbf{OA} = \mathbf{i}x, \quad \mathbf{BP} = \mathbf{j}y, \quad \mathbf{AB} = \mathbf{k}z,$$

whence (1·3–5) becomes

$$\mathbf{r} = \mathbf{i}x + \mathbf{j}y + \mathbf{k}z. \qquad (1·3–6)$$

This mode of representing vectors in terms of their rectangular components is of considerable utility.

It is now in order to discuss the *displacement* of a particle. Consulting Fig. 1·4 we note that the particle is conceived at first to be at the point P_1 and at a short time interval Δt later to be at the point P_2. If the displacement has taken place along the line P_1P_2 it is best represented by the vector element

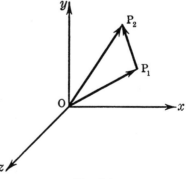

FIG. 1·4

$\mathbf{P_1P_2}$ which is equal to the difference between the vectors giving the respective positions P_2 and P_1, i.e., we have

$$\mathbf{P_1P_2} = \mathbf{OP_2} - \mathbf{OP_1} = \mathbf{r_2} - \mathbf{r_1}, \qquad (1\cdot3\text{--}7)$$

where $\mathbf{r_1}$ and $\mathbf{r_2}$ are the position vectors corresponding to the positions P_1 and P_2 respectively. We shall then write

$$\mathbf{P_1P_2} = \Delta\mathbf{r} \qquad (1\cdot3\text{--}8)$$

as a simplified expression for the displacement. We shall now *define* $\dfrac{\Delta\mathbf{r}}{\Delta t}$ as the *average velocity* of displacement from P_1 to P_2. It is the average time rate of change of position of the particle from its original position P_1 to its final position P_2. It will be noted that we have here confined our attention to an elementary displacement. But we can easily apply the same method to any finite displacement along any path whatever by considering the path to be made up of a great number of such elementary displacements.

The *instantaneous velocity* of the particle *at* the position P_1 is then defined as follows:

$$\lim_{\Delta t=0}\frac{\Delta\mathbf{r}}{\Delta t} = \frac{d\mathbf{r}}{dt} = \mathbf{v}, \qquad (1\cdot3\text{--}9)$$

which, of course, assumes that the derivative actually exists. This will be the case in all the problems in mechanics which we shall study. It is clear that velocity like displacement is a vector quantity; its magnitude is often referred to as the *speed* and will be denoted simply by v. It is a quantity having the dimensions of distance divided by time. In the metric system it will commonly be expressed in cm/sec, while in the British system the unit is the foot/sec.

It is often convenient to resolve a velocity into components along the x, y and z axes in a coördinate system. We shall denote these three components by v_x, v_y and v_z respectively. Let Δx, Δy, Δz be the components of $\Delta\mathbf{r}$ along the coördinate axes, i.e.,

$$\Delta x = |\Delta\mathbf{r}|\cos\xi,$$

$$\Delta y = |\Delta\mathbf{r}|\cos\eta, \qquad (1\cdot3\text{--}10)$$

$$\Delta z = |\Delta\mathbf{r}|\cos\zeta,$$

where ξ, η and ζ are the angles $\Delta\mathbf{r}$ makes with the three axes respectively.

Eq. $(1\cdot3\text{--}10)$ can be understood by actually drawing the projections in a figure like Fig. 1·4. This is a somewhat involved problem in perspective. It can be materially simplified without real loss in generality by placing one end of $\Delta\mathbf{r}$ at the origin of the system of coördinates.

Then Fig. 1·1 and eqs. (1·2–2) at once apply, with $\mathbf{r}$ replaced by $\Delta\mathbf{r}$, the angles, α, β, γ by ξ, η, ζ respectively and x, y, z by Δx, Δy, Δz, respectively.   There follows

$$\lim_{\Delta t=0}\frac{\Delta x}{\Delta t} = \frac{dx}{dt} = \dot{x} = v_x,$$

$$\lim_{\Delta t=0}\frac{\Delta y}{\Delta t} = \frac{dy}{dt} = \dot{y} = v_y, \qquad (1\cdot3\text{–}11)$$

$$\lim_{\Delta t=0}\frac{\Delta z}{\Delta t} = \frac{dz}{dt} = \dot{z} = v_z.$$

Attention should be called to the use of the dot to indicate differentiation with respect to the time.   Two dots will indicate the second derivative, etc.   This notation will be used throughout the book because of its simplicity.   It will be noted that v_x, v_y and v_z are no longer vectors, for they are the magnitudes of the *components* of the vector velocity along the coördinate axes.   Since

$$\cos^2\xi + \cos^2\eta + \cos^2\zeta = 1,$$

we have

$$|\mathbf{v}|^2 = v^2 = v_x{}^2 + v_y{}^2 + v_z{}^2. \qquad (1\cdot3\text{–}12)$$

The representation of a velocity vector in terms of its components is termed the *resolution* of the vector.   From another point of view we can consider the vector as compounded of three mutually perpendicular vectors of magnitudes equal to the components v_x, v_y and v_z respectively, by the general method of summation of vectors discussed in the first part of this section.   For velocity vectors follow the same rules for addition and subtraction as position and displacement vectors. Thus corresponding to eq. (1·3–6) we shall have here

$$\mathbf{v} = \dot{\mathbf{r}} = \mathbf{i}v_x + \mathbf{j}v_y + \mathbf{k}v_z. \qquad (1\cdot3\text{–}13)$$

In fact the student should realize that the vector formulas we have been using in this section are perfectly general in form, i.e., hold for vectors in general.   Anyone interested in vector analysis as a branch of mathematics may turn with profit to a text like that of J. G. Coffin, *Vector Analysis*, Wiley, New York, 2nd ed., 1911.[1]

   There is, indeed, one important point to note concerning the composition of vector velocities by the parallelogram or polygon rule, namely, that in using the latter in this case we are really making an assumption of a very fundamental nature, though one not often emphasized in elementary texts.   The assumption is that the velocities are mutually independent, i.e., the fact that a particle has the velocity $\mathbf{v}_1$ does not

---

[1] Cf. also H. B. Phillips, *Vector Analysis*, Wiley, New York, 1933.

influence the imposition of a velocity $\mathbf{v}_2$ at the same time.   This mutual independence is not universal in physics,[1] but where the assumption is justified, as in the present instance, it introduces marked simplification. The hypothesis is usually referred to as the principle of superposition. We shall meet with other illustrations.

1·4. Linear and Angular Motion.   The notions of displacement and velocity developed in the preceding sections are quite general. But there is a particular method of measuring displacement and velocity which is often of such great use that special mention must be made of it

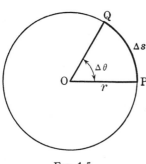

here preparatory to the more thorough discussion of Chapters 2 and 3.   Let us consider the special case of the motion of a particle in a circle.   Examining the figure (Fig. 1·5) we note that the motion of the particle from P to Q may be described either by the *distance* Δs traveled along the circumference or by the *angle* $\Delta \theta$ through which the line joining the position of the particle to the center of the circle is displaced.   In physics the common unit of such angular displacement is the *radian*, which is the angle at the center of a circle subtended by an arc equal in length to the radius.   It follows immediately that the one displacement may be expressed in terms of the other by the relation

$$\Delta s = r\,\Delta \theta. \qquad (1\text{·}4\text{–}1)$$

FIG. 1·5

If the displacement from P to Q takes place in an interval of time Δt, the *average* angular velocity during the displacement may be defined as $\Delta \theta / \Delta t$ and the instantaneous angular velocity at P will then be

$$\omega = \lim_{\Delta t=0}\frac{\Delta \theta}{\Delta t} = \frac{d\theta}{dt} = \dot{\theta}, \qquad (1\text{·}4\text{–}2)$$

expressed in radians per second.   From (1·4–1) it follows that the corresponding instantaneous velocity along the arc of the circle, viz., $v = \dfrac{ds}{dt} = \dot{s}$ is related to ω by the relation

$$v = r\omega, \qquad (1\text{·}4\text{–}3)$$

[1] The student may recall from elementary electrostatics that the mutual influence of two charged conductors is *not* independent of the presence of a third conductor.

where v will be expressed in cm/sec if r is in cm and ω in radians per sec. If the angular velocity is expressed, as is sometimes done, in revolutions per sec, say n in number, we have

$$\omega = 2\pi n, \tag{1·4–4}$$

and therefore

$$v = 2\pi n r, \tag{1·4–5}$$

expressions which the student will have frequent occasion to use.

It may be noted, of course, that the above relationships are strictly scalar in nature. Yet velocity along a curve is a vector, as we have seen. Is then angular velocity representable by a vector? It is, and the representation is usually made by a line drawn from the center of the circle O perpendicular to the plane of the motion directed in such a way that as one looks along the vector from O the sense of revolution is clockwise. Alternatively one may say that the direction of the vector is the direction of advance of a right-handed screw the sense of whose revolution is the same as that of the given motion. This provides a rule which it is particularly simple to remember. The length of the line is proportional to the magnitude of the angular velocity. As a matter of fact, *finite angular displacements* are not compoundable in the same way as linear displacement or velocity vectors, and hence we shall not consider them as vectors in this book. (See Problem 11 at the end of the chapter.) However, finite angular velocities *are* compoundable in the usual sense and as vectors turn out to be of importance in the motion of rigid bodies.

1·5. Acceleration. The definition of instantaneous velocity given in Sec. 1·3 implies that the velocity of a particle may change with the time. The time rate of change of velocity is called the *acceleration* of the particle and is one of the fundamental quantities of mechanics. Thus, if in the time element Δt the linear velocity of a particle has changed from $\mathbf{v}_1$ to $\mathbf{v}_2$, we have

$$\mathbf{a}_{av} = \frac{\mathbf{v}_2 - \mathbf{v}_1}{\Delta t} = \frac{\Delta \mathbf{v}}{\Delta t}, \tag{1·5–1}$$

and similarly

$$\mathbf{a}_{inst} = \lim_{\Delta t = 0} \frac{\Delta \mathbf{v}}{\Delta t} = \frac{d\mathbf{v}}{dt} = \dot{\mathbf{v}}. \tag{1·5–2}$$

Since $\mathbf{v}$, the instantaneous velocity, has been defined in Sec. 1·3 as $\dfrac{d\mathbf{r}}{dt}$, we can write

$$\mathbf{a} = \frac{d}{dt}\left(\frac{d\mathbf{r}}{dt}\right) = \frac{d^2\mathbf{r}}{dt^2} = \ddot{\mathbf{r}}, \tag{1·5–3}$$

thus defining **a** as the *second derivative* of the position vector **r** with respect to the time.   It is clear that acceleration is a vector since the difference between two velocities is a vector.   It may be observed that for this reason, even though the magnitude of the velocity of a particle may not change, it may nevertheless experience an acceleration due to change in the direction of its velocity.   The classical illustration of this is to be found in uniform motion in a circle.   We can treat this in simple fashion by an investigation of the adjacent figure (Fig. 1·6).   Let the particle move with constant angular velocity ω radians/second in the circle of

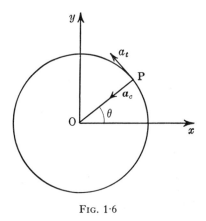

FIG. 1·6

radius r with center at O.   The position vector of point P on the circular path is (cf. 1·3–6)

$$\mathbf{r} = \mathbf{i}x + \mathbf{j}y = r(\mathbf{i} \cos \theta + \mathbf{j} \sin \theta). \tag{1·5–4}$$

Hence by differentiation with respect to the time, remembering that r is constant, the instantaneous velocity becomes

$$\mathbf{v} = \dot{\mathbf{r}} = r(-\mathbf{i} \sin \theta + \mathbf{j} \cos \theta)\dot{\theta}, \tag{1·5–5}$$

leading to the speed

$$v = |\mathbf{v}| = r\dot{\theta} = r\omega, \tag{1·5–6}$$

in agreement with (1·4–3).   A second time differentiation yields

$$\mathbf{a} = \dot{\mathbf{v}} = \ddot{\mathbf{r}} = r(-\mathbf{i} \cos \theta - \mathbf{j} \sin \theta)\dot{\theta}^2 + r(-\mathbf{i} \sin \theta + \mathbf{j} \cos \theta)\ddot{\theta}. \tag{1·5–7}$$

This is more conveniently written

$$\mathbf{a} = r\mathbf{i}(-\cos \theta \cdot \dot{\theta}^2 - \sin \theta \cdot \ddot{\theta}) + r\mathbf{j}(-\sin \theta \cdot \dot{\theta}^2 + \cos \theta \cdot \ddot{\theta}). \tag{1·5–8}$$

In the usual way the magnitude of the acceleration becomes

$$a = \sqrt{a_x^2 + a_y^2} = r\sqrt{\dot{\theta}^4 + \ddot{\theta}^2}. \tag{1·5–9}$$

To give a physical interpretation to (1·5–9) let us assume first that $\ddot{\theta} = 0$.   This means that $\dot{\omega} = 0$, i.e., there is no change in the magnitude of the angular velocity with the time.   We shall say that there is no *angular acceleration*, putting

$$\ddot{\theta} = \alpha, \tag{1·5–10}$$

for convenience.   Then

$$a = r\dot{\theta}^2 = r\omega^2. \tag{1·5–11}$$

Thus even when the angular speed ω is constant the particle still has an acceleration whose magnitude is given by (1·5–11). It remains to be ascertained what the direction of this acceleration is. From (1·5–8) (we are still considering $\ddot{\theta} = 0$) we have

$$a_x = -r\dot{\theta}^2 \cos\theta, \quad a_y = -r\dot{\theta}^2 \sin\theta. \qquad (1·5–12)$$

But these are precisely the components of a vector of magnitude $r\dot{\theta}^2$ directed along the radius r *toward* the center of the circle O. Hence the acceleration $\mathbf{a}$ is called the *centripetal* acceleration, with magnitude denoted by a_c.

It then develops that a particle moving in a circle is subject to two kinds of acceleration. Whether the angular velocity is constant or not, there always exists the centripetal acceleration with magnitude a_c. If in addition there is an angular acceleration α, there exists another acceleration of magnitude $r\alpha$. The direction of this can be seen from an examination of (1·5–8), since the components are, respectively,

$$-r \sin\theta \cdot \ddot{\theta}, \quad r \cos\theta \cdot \ddot{\theta}.$$

These are the components of a vector of magnitude $r\alpha$ directed tangentially to the circle at P in the direction in which P is moving (i.e., increasing θ). We therefore write

$$a_t = r\alpha, \qquad (1·5–13)$$

and refer to this acceleration as the *tangential* acceleration of P. It is clear from (1·5–9) that if a is the magnitude of the resultant acceleration

$$a = \sqrt{a_c^2 + a_t^2}. \qquad (1·5–14)$$

1·6. Concept of Inertia and Definition of Mass. So far we have concerned ourselves solely with *kinematics*, the geometry of motion. This treats particles essentially as geometrical points and neglects any differences that may exist between them. Actually two particles that look alike may move quite differently even when subjected to what appear to be identical conditions. To explain this the concept of *inertia* has been invented with *mass* as its quantitative measure. This is inextricably related with the mutual motion of two or more particles as will be made clear in the definition we shall now examine.[1]

Let us suppose that we have two particles A and B which are completely isolated from all others in the universe. Under their mutual action they will suffer accelerations which with reference to the primary

[1] Cf. Lindsay and Margenau, *Foundations of Physics*, pp. 91 ff.; also H. Poincaré, *Science and Hypothesis* (English translation in *Foundations of Science*), pp. 98 ff.; also Ernst Mach, *The Science of Mechanics* (English translation by Open Court Publishing Co., Chicago), pp. 216 ff.

inertial system we may denote by $\mathbf{a}_{AB}$ and $\mathbf{a}_{BA}$ respectively. Now all experiments which have ever been performed on actual bodies lead us to assume that in such a case as we are discussing, these accelerations are *opposite* in direction and that their ratio is a scalar *constant* which is independent of the relative positions of the particles, of their velocities (save when the latter approach in value the velocity of light) and the time. We shall extend this assumption by supposing that this ratio is also independent of the presence of other particles, where, of course, it is to be clearly understood (as the above notation indicates) that the accelerations in question are due *solely* to *mutual* action. The presence of other particles will indeed produce accelerations in A and B, but our assumption is that the ratio of the acceleration of A due to B to that of B due to A is not influenced by such. We thus have, no matter what the magnitudes of the individual accelerations may be,

$$\frac{\mathbf{a}_{AB}}{-\mathbf{a}_{BA}} = K_{BA}. \tag{1·6–1}$$

The constancy of this ratio may be looked upon as one of the most fundamental laws of mechanics. We are now free to give some interpretation to the magnitude of the constant K_{BA}. Let us take any other particle C. For the mutual actions of C and A, and C and B respectively we shall then have analogously to (1·6–1)

$$\frac{\mathbf{a}_{AC}}{-\mathbf{a}_{CA}} = K_{CA}, \quad \frac{\mathbf{a}_{BC}}{-\mathbf{a}_{CB}} = K_{CB}. \tag{1·6–2}$$

Now experiment indicates that the following relation holds between the three constants K_{BA}, K_{CA} and K_{CB}, namely,

$$K_{CB} = \frac{K_{CA}}{K_{BA}}. \tag{1·6–3}$$

The second of the relations (1·6–2) then becomes

$$K_{BA}\mathbf{a}_{BC} = -K_{CA}\mathbf{a}_{CB}. \tag{1·6–4}$$

The relation (1·6–4) indicates that we are able by choosing A as a standard particle to associate with every other particle a *constant which does not depend at all on the particle with which the one in question interacts.* Its importance will be emphasized if we give to it or some simple function of it a name. This may, of course, be done in a variety of ways, but we shall prefer to name the constant K_{BA} the *mass* of B relative to A, or more simply the mass of B, it being understood that A is to be taken as a reference particle. Thus we write $K_{BA} = m_B$, etc., so that (1·6–4) becomes

$$m_B\mathbf{a}_{BC} = -m_C\mathbf{a}_{CB}. \tag{1·6–5}$$

We make further the important assumption also suggested by experiment that if a particle B is influenced by several particles $C, D, E, \ldots$ its resultant acceleration will be the vector sum of the accelerations due to the particles independently, viz.,

$$\mathbf{a}_{B,CDE} = \mathbf{a}_{BC} + \mathbf{a}_{BD} + \mathbf{a}_{BE} + \cdots.$$

This is another illustration of the principle of superposition already mentioned in Sec. 1·3. We shall see in the next section that the foregoing definition of mass implies the important additive property that the mass of the particle formed by joining any two is equal to the sum of the individual masses. Indeed this may be looked upon as one reason for choosing the present definition, which is, of course, really arbitrary in nature.[1]

In order to measure mass by means of eq. (1·6–5) it is necessary to establish a *unit* by arbitrarily assigning unit mass to a certain volume of some substance. In the metric system the unit of mass is the *gram*, which is defined to be the one-thousandth part of the mass of a lump of platinum carefully preserved in Paris — the so-called standard kilogram. It was originally intended that the standard kilogram should be the mass of 1000 cubic centimeters of water at its maximum density. Actually there is a slight discrepancy so that the volume of one kilogram of water at maximum density is 1000.027 ± 0.001 cubic centimeters.[2] The British unit is the standard *pound*, whose relation to the kilogram is expressed in the statement that one kilogram is approximately equivalent to 2.205 pounds. The United States and the British Commonwealth have agreed (as of July, 1959) to introduce an international pound and define it as equal to 0.45359237 kilogram.

The definition of mass presented in this section is general in nature and the student will find it desirable to think out for himself certain special cases. For example, two particles may be conceived to be connected by a perfectly elastic spring which itself has no mass. When the spring is stretched and released the relation (1·6–1) will be verified irrespective of the extent of stretching. Moreover with other particles and springs, eq. (1·6–3) will also be verified. Other modes of interaction will occur to the mind, such as the mutual actions of gravitating and electrified particles. Our fundamental assumption is that in every case of this sort the relations (1·6–1) and (1·6–3) will be found to be satisfied.

The student is particularly urged to avoid such statements as " mass is the amount of matter in a body." It is becoming increasingly clear that the expression " amount of matter " without further qualification

---

[1] Thus we might have named $1/K_{BA}$ the mass of B with equal consistency.

[2] See R. T. Birge: " Probable Values of the General Physical Constants " in *Reviews of Modern Physics*, Vol. 1, p. 11, 1929.

is physically meaningless. The only logical definition of mass is that which enables us to establish a method of comparing masses. This is precisely the object of the definition of this section. Of course, it must be at once admitted that in practice masses are not usually compared in the ideal way indicated. For this purpose it is much more convenient to employ a balance, which utilizes the gravitational attraction of the earth for all bodies. The connection between this type of measurement and the logical definition of mass will be discussed later.

1·7. Force and the Laws of Motion. We are now in a position to introduce formally the fundamental laws of motion resulting from the experimental researches of Galileo and the more mature considerations of Huygens and Newton, the three greatest physicists of the 17th century. As a matter of fact we have already progressed far toward an understanding of these laws in the preceding section. For let us go back to eqs. (1·6–1) and (1·6–3) with the resulting equation (1·6–4). We were there led to a definition of mass, wherein mass and acceleration for two interacting particles B and C are connected by the relation

$$m_B \mathbf{a}_{BC} = -m_C \mathbf{a}_{CB}.$$

We now wish to attach further significance to this relation. It states that in the interaction of the two particles there is *something* which is the *same* in *magnitude* for *both* particles. This is, of course, the product of mass (as we have defined it) and acceleration. We shall now further *assume* that its value in any given case depends on the relative positions of the particles, though it may conceivably sometimes be a function of the relative velocities of the particles as well as of the time. It is convenient to express this dependence by introducing a new vector function[1] $\mathbf{F}_{BC}(x, y, z)$, where x, y, z are the coördinates of the one particle relative to the other, and placing

$$m_B \mathbf{a}_{BC} = \mathbf{F}_{BC}(x, y, z). \tag{1·7–1}$$

We now *define* the function $\mathbf{F}_{BC}$ as the *force* acting on the particle B due to the influence of the particle C. For C we have similarly

$$m_C \mathbf{a}_{CB} = \mathbf{F}_{CB}, \tag{1·7–2}$$

and the relation (1·6–5) shows us that

$$\mathbf{F}_{BC} = -\mathbf{F}_{CB}, \tag{1·7–3}$$

which means that the force on B due to C is equal and opposite in direction to the force on C due to B. It is to be noted that the *force*

---

[1] For simplicity of notation we shall express this here as a function of position only, and leave more complicated cases for later discussion.

is a vector and is moreover directed along the acceleration. Using the derivative notation we may write (1·7–1) in general form

$$\mathbf{F} = m\dot{\mathbf{v}} = m\ddot{\mathbf{r}} \qquad (1\cdot7\text{--}4)$$

if $\mathbf{v} = \dot{\mathbf{r}}$, as in Sec. 1·3. This may be called the " equation of motion " of the particle, which is thus obtained by placing the force equal to the product of mass and acceleration, i.e., the so-called *kinetic reaction*. It is fundamental in the solution of all problems in motion.

The definition of force given above is probably the only logically consistent one available in mechanics. For the notions of " push " and " pull " are too purely anthropomorphic for any exact use, though we shall probably continue to employ them for illustrative purposes.[1] In a later chapter we shall see how static force is related to the present definition. The only kind of motion in which we conceive *no* force to act is clearly that in which the acceleration is zero everywhere and at all times. This is either rest or uniform motion (i.e., with constant velocity) in a straight line. With this addition to our previous discussion we have developed the essential content of *Newton's three laws of motion*, stated by him in the following form:

(I) *Every body continues in its state of rest or of uniform motion in a straight line, except in so far as it is compelled by forces to change that state.*

(II) *Change of motion is proportional to the force and takes place in the direction of the straight line in which the force acts.*

(III) *To every action there is always an equal and contrary reaction; or, the mutual actions of any two bodies are always equal and oppositely directed along the same straight line.*

In comparing the first two formal statements with the discussion of the present section we must bear in mind that as a measure of the " motion " of a body, Newton used the product of mass and velocity, which in present day usage is termed the *momentum*, though Newton referred to it as " quantity of motion." Hence Newton's statement of the second law would logically be written in mathematical form

$$\mathbf{F} = \frac{d(m\mathbf{v})}{dt}. \qquad (1\cdot7\text{--}5)$$

However, if the mass remains constant in time, eq. (1·7–5) is equivalent to eq. (1·7–4). We shall in general prefer (1·7–4).

1·8. Units. The units of *mass* in the metric and British systems have been stated to be the *gram* and the *pound* respectively. The unit of *force* may be at once defined from eq. (1·7–1). Thus the force

[1] Cf. Lindsay and Margenau, *Foundations of Physics*, pp. 85 ff.

which corresponds to one gram of mass moving with an acceleration of one centimeter per second per second is the unit force in the metric or centimeter-gram-second (c.g.s.) system, and is called the *dyne*. Similarly the force associated with one *pound* of mass moving with an acceleration of one foot per second per second is called one *poundal*. Engineers rarely use this unit, preferring to define their unit of force in terms of weight. Thus they call the force with which the earth accelerates a body of mass one pound, a force of one pound. This is sometimes called the gravitational unit of force. Since it is experimentally true that *every* body in the neighborhood of the earth's surface experiences an approximately constant downward acceleration of " g " (about 32.2 feet/sec[2] or 980 cm/sec[2], though variable from place to place[1] within certain narrow limits) it follows that the pound of force or weight is equivalent to " g " poundals. The poundal has the advantage of being an absolute unit, while the pound of force (written in this text hereafter as pound weight and abbreviated to lb wt) varies in magnitude from place to place on the earth's surface, being greatest at the poles and least at the equator. While the student of mechanics is advised to use mainly the absolute units, he should be prepared to transfer his results into the engineering units, for the latter are the most widely used in daily life, at least in English-speaking countries. In the metric system there is an analogous usage, the gram of force or weight being defined as that force with which the earth accelerates a mass of one gram. The gram weight is then " g " dynes (g in metric units here, of course).

The reader will already have noted that the introduction of units is a matter of convention and bound to be arbitrary. For pure science usage the metric c.g.s. (centimeter-gram-second) system has been pretty generally adopted throughout the world. Engineers usually employ some kind of gravitational unit. Much pressure is being exerted on both engineers and scientists to adopt a uniform system. The one commonly urged for this purpose is the so-called m.k.s. (meter-kilogram-second) system. In this the meter is the unit of length, the kilogram the unit of mass, while the second remains the unit of time. The unit of force is the *newton* or one kilogram meter per second per second. It is clearly equal to 10^5 dynes and hence, so far as magnitude is concerned, a more practical unit than the dyne. Indeed, the m.k.s. system is sometimes called the absolute practical system. It has some advantages in connection with the relation between mechanical and electrical units. In the meantime the reader is advised against a slavish adherence to any particular system. The main thing to keep in mind

---

[1] The value of " g " at the poles is 983.21 cm/sec[2] while at the equator it is 977.99 cm/sec[2].

is the necessity for consistency: in the solution of numerical problems in mechanics, adopt at the start the system of units which seems most convenient and stick to it throughout the analysis.

1·9. The Third Law of Motion.   Combination of Masses.   The first two laws of motion were completely implied in the truly remarkable investigations of Galileo.   The third law was the peculiar contribution of Newton himself.   We note that it is already present by implication in eq. (1·6–5), and following upon the definition of force the complete mathematical statement of the law was given in eq. (1·7–3).   It thus appears as an even more fundamental law of motion than the first two. To state it again in words, it means that whenever one body is accelerated there must be another body accelerated in the opposite direction.   Thus accelerations never occur singly but always in pairs.   Stated in terms of force we may say that if a force acts on a given body, this body exerts an *equal* and *oppositely directed* force on some other body.   The significance of the law is perhaps most easily understood with reference to the push and pull forces with which we feel ourselves so familiar. When a book lies on the table we say it *presses down* on the table with a certain force: the law states then that the table *pushes up* with precisely the *same* force.   The locomotive pulls *forward* on a train of cars and the cars pull *back* on the locomotive with precisely the same force, irrespective of the actual state of motion of the whole train.   Newton called the two aspects of the force *action* and *reaction*, whence the formal statement of the law given above.

The recoil of a gun is another familiar illustration of the principle. That the latter is sometimes a matter of confusion is evident from the well known student paradox: " if action and reaction are equal and opposite, how can bodies ever move?"   The well-worn illustration of the horse pulling the wagon will suffice to clear up this point: the horse pulls forward on the wagon and the wagon pulls back on the horse with the same force, yet the wagon moves!   The answer is that the acceleration of the wagon is a function only of the forces acting *on* the wagon, which in this instance are the *forward* pull of the horse and the *backward* pull of the ground.   The force which the wagon *itself* exerts has nothing to do with *its* motion — this force concerns the motions of other bodies only, for example, the horse in our illustration.

In the previous section it was pointed out that the definition of mass there presented implies the additive property that the mass of two particles joined together is equal to the sum of the individual masses.   The truth of this statement is now seen to follow from the third law of motion.

Consider the three mass particles B, C and D and suppose that B and C have approached so closely to each other that they may effectively be considered as forming a single particle under the influence of D.   The equation (1·6–5) then becomes

$$m_{(C+B)}\mathbf{a}_{(C+B),D} = -m_D\mathbf{a}_{D,(C+B)}, \qquad (1\cdot9\text{–}1)$$

where $m_{(C+B)}$ denotes the joint mass of C and B considered as a single particle, and $\mathbf{a}_{(C+B),D}$ is the acceleration of the joint particle due to D. The left-hand side is equal by definition to the force which D exerts on the joint particle $C + B$.   Call this $\mathbf{F}_{(C+B),D}$.   By the use of the principle of superposition this may be considered as the resultant of the forces which D exerts on C and B separately.   Thus

$$\mathbf{F}_{(C+B),D} = \mathbf{F}_{CD} + \mathbf{F}_{BD}. \qquad (1\cdot9\text{–}2)$$

Now no matter what the mutual orientation of B, C, D is, the total force on C is the vector sum of the force due to D and that due to B and this is equal to the mass of C times the acceleration of C, since we have already assumed in the preceding section that the resultant acceleration is the vector sum of the individual accelerations.   There is a similar equation for B.   We may write them both as follows:

$$\mathbf{F}_{CD} + \mathbf{F}_{CB} = m_C\mathbf{a}_{C,BD}, \qquad (1\cdot9\text{–}3)$$

$$\mathbf{F}_{BD} + \mathbf{F}_{BC} = m_B\mathbf{a}_{B,CD}, \qquad (1\cdot9\text{–}4)$$

where $\mathbf{F}_{CB}$ and $\mathbf{F}_{BC}$ are respectively the force on C due to B and that on B due to C.   From the third law of motion, we have, of course, no matter of what character the action may be,

$$\mathbf{F}_{CB} + \mathbf{F}_{BC} = 0. \qquad (1\cdot9\text{–}5)$$

Hence if we add (1·9–3) and (1·9–4) having regard for (1·9–5) we get

$$\mathbf{F}_{CD} + \mathbf{F}_{BD} = m_C\mathbf{a}_{C,BD} + m_B\mathbf{a}_{B,CD}, \qquad (1\cdot9\text{–}6)$$

where $\mathbf{a}_{C,BD}$ and $\mathbf{a}_{B,CD}$ are respectively the accelerations of C due to B and D, and of B due to C and D.   For any arbitrary orientation of B, C and D these accelerations may be quite different.   However, since we are going to assume that B and C are to form the equivalent of a single particle, we must suppose that by the time we are considering them they move in such a way that their distance apart always remains within certain fixed limits, the upper of which is very small compared with the distance of either from D.   To specify exactly their mutual motion under this condition would demand a precise assumption with respect to the nature of the forces between them and this, of course, we desire to avoid since we wish our result to be as general as possible.

However, if we finally neglect small quantities of the second order, which is equivalent to assuming that the distance between B and C remains invariable, we may write

$$\mathbf{a}_{C,BD} = \mathbf{a}_{B,CD} = \mathbf{a}_{(C+B),D}. \tag{1·9-7}$$

Consequently eq. (1·9–6) becomes

$$\mathbf{F}_{CD} + \mathbf{F}_{BD} = (m_C + m_B)\mathbf{a}_{(C+B),D}. \tag{1·9-8}$$

It now follows from (1·9–1) and (1·9–2) that

$$m_{(C+B)}\mathbf{a}_{(C+B),D} = (m_C + m_B)\mathbf{a}_{(C+B),D},$$

whence

$$m_{(C+B)} = m_C + m_B, \tag{1·9-9}$$

and the additive property is thus confirmed.

The student may well inquire what attitude he should adopt toward the laws of motion, i.e., are they truly experimental laws or are they merely postulates — a part of the fundamental theory of mechanics? Careful consideration of this question by such men as K. Pearson, H. Poincaré, Ernst Mach, H. Hertz, and others indicates that the latter attitude is the more strictly logical one, for while the laws are of course *suggested* by experiment, no experiment can ever be devised to test them fully and unambiguously. They may be taken to represent our idea as to the most general and simple basis, compatible with experiment, for the development of mechanics. Beginning with them as *assumptions* we shall make various deductions which may then be checked by the results of the most careful experiments which can be carried out. We shall see in the course of our work that beside the three laws of Newton, other more compact formulations of the principles of mechanics are possible and very valuable for certain purposes.

1·10. Impulse and Momentum. Now that we have set up the fundamental principles of mechanics and have introduced the concepts of mass and force to supplement those of kinematics, it becomes important to see what we can do with them. In a sense everything that follows in this book is only an application of these basic ideas. It turns out, however, that there are some very simple but general conclusions we can draw at once from the principles so far set forth and these will prove fundamental to the detailed developments in subsequent chapters.

In the first place the question naturally arises: what is the cumulative effect of a resultant force on a particle? Of course from the equation of motion (1·7–4) this question might seem to be unnecessary and irrelevant, since the effect of the force is merely the acceleration it produces. But writing the equation of motion in the form (1·7–5) allows us to attach a somewhat broader meaning to the question. Suppose we wish to know what will happen to a particle after a resultant force has acted on it for a certain finite time. This might be called the time-cumulative effect of the force. Its natural measure is the time integral of the force over the interval in question, a quantity which has received the technical name impulse. From eq. (1·7–5) the impulse between times t_0 and t_1 becomes

$$\int_{t_0}^{t_1} \mathbf{F}\, dt = \int_{t_0}^{t_1} \frac{d(m\mathbf{v})}{dt}\, dt = \int_{(mv)_0}^{(mv)_1} d(m\mathbf{v}) = (m\mathbf{v})_1 - (m\mathbf{v})_0. \quad (1\cdot10\text{–}1)$$

If we assume that the mass of the particle remains constant in time, we can rewrite this as

$$\int_{t_0}^{t_1} \mathbf{F}\, dt = m\mathbf{v}_1 - m\mathbf{v}_0. \quad (1\cdot10\text{–}2)$$

In words this says that the impulse of the force over a given time interval is equal to the change in momentum experienced during this interval by the particle acted on by the force. This is known as the impulse-momentum theorem. Though perfectly general, it is often of particular interest for forces which are of short duration, commonly called impulsive, like the blow of a hammer. The name " impulse " comes from this type of example.

However, the significance of the theorem far transcends this special case and becomes most prominent when several particles are involved. We have already commented on the fact that we strictly speaking have no right to talk about forces except as acting between particles. Let us look again in this connection at eq. (1·6–5) describing the action and reaction of particles B and C. We rewrite the equation in somewhat simpler form

$$\frac{d(m_B\mathbf{v}_B)}{dt} = -\frac{d(m_C\mathbf{v}_C)}{dt}, \quad (1\cdot10\text{–}3)$$

where $\mathbf{v}_B$ is here the velocity of particle B in the presence of C, etc. We may at once integrate (1·10–3) with respect to the time and obtain

$$m_B\mathbf{v}_B + m_C\mathbf{v}_C = \text{const.} \quad (1\cdot10\text{–}4)$$

This says that in the interaction of the two particles the *total* momentum of the pair must remain constant, i.e., is conserved. This is a special case of a general conservation theorem we shall prove for an arbitrary number of interacting particles in Sec. 6·1. It is one of the most powerful theorems in mechanics, and we shall encounter many uses of it in subsequent chapters. The reader is probably already familiar with it from elementary physics, in connection with the collision of two billiard balls for example, or to take another illustration, the recoil of a gun which takes place in firing.   In the latter case the value of the constant is zero and hence the conservation theorem takes a particularly simple form, which permits the evaluation of the, muzzle velocity of the bullet from the recoil velocity, if the two masses are known.

Two important observations on (1·10–4) are in order here.   The first is that it of course holds as here developed only if the two particles B and C interact with each other and no other particles.   However, we shall generalize the result to systems of many particles in Chapter 6. The second observation is that (1·10–4) is independent of the *nature* of the interaction between the particles, i.e., whether it be a spring, a rubber band, gravitational attraction, or the exploding powder in the gun barrel in the example just given.

There is another simple interpretation of (1·10–4) which may with profit be mentioned here.   If we write each instantaneous velocity in terms of its appropriate position vector, the equation takes the form

$$m_B \frac{d\mathbf{r}_B}{dt} + m_C \frac{d\mathbf{r}_C}{dt} = \text{const.} \qquad (1\cdot10\text{–}5)$$

It is tempting to introduce an imaginary point P_c whose position vector in the frame of reference with respect to which B and C are supposed to be moving is denoted by $\bar{\mathbf{r}}$ defined as follows:

$$\bar{\mathbf{r}} = \frac{m_B \mathbf{r}_B + m_C \mathbf{r}_C}{m_B + m_C}. \qquad (1\cdot10\text{–}6)$$

In this notation (1·10–5) becomes

$$(m_B + m_C)\dot{\bar{\mathbf{r}}} = \text{const.} \qquad (1\cdot10\text{–}7)$$

Differentiation with respect to the time yields

$$(m_B + m_C)\ddot{\bar{\mathbf{r}}} = 0. \qquad (1\cdot10\text{–}8)$$

In words, the point P_c moves with constant velocity and as if all the mass were concentrated there.   It is called the *center of mass* of the system of two particles.   This also turns out to be an unusually fruitful concept for further applications (see Chapter 6 for details).

1·11. Work and Energy.   We next ask ourselves the question: what happens to a particle after it has moved a certain distance through space under the influence of the resultant force on it?   This will naturally be termed the space-cumulative effect of the force and will be measured by the space integral of the force.   Since this involves the product of two vectors, it is necessary to define the meaning of such a product.

Suppose we have two vectors **A** and **B**, written in terms of their rectangular components as follows [cf. (1·3–6)]:

$$\mathbf{A} = \mathbf{i}A_x + \mathbf{j}A_y + \mathbf{k}A_z,$$

$$\mathbf{B} = \mathbf{i}B_x + \mathbf{j}B_y + \mathbf{k}B_z. \tag{1·11–1}$$

We shall define the so-called *dot* or *scalar* product of **A** and **B** as

$$\mathbf{A} \cdot \mathbf{B} = A_x B_x + A_y B_y + A_z B_z. \tag{1·11–2}$$

It is clear that the commutative law holds.   Thus

$$\mathbf{A} \cdot \mathbf{B} = \mathbf{B} \cdot \mathbf{A}. \tag{1·11–3}$$

Moreover if **A**, **B**, **C** are any three vectors, the distributive law holds, viz.:

$$(\mathbf{A} + \mathbf{B}) \cdot \mathbf{C} = \mathbf{A} \cdot \mathbf{C} + \mathbf{B} \cdot \mathbf{C}. \tag{1·11–4}$$

The proof is left to the reader.   Since the magnitudes of **A** and **B** are given by (cf. Sec. 1·3 again)

$$A = |\mathbf{A}| = \sqrt{A_x{}^2 + A_y{}^2 + A_z{}^2},$$

$$B = |\mathbf{B}| = \sqrt{B_x{}^2 + B_y{}^2 + B_z{}^2}, \tag{1·11–5}$$

we may write (1·11–2) in the form

$$\mathbf{A} \cdot \mathbf{B} = AB\left(\frac{A_x B_x}{AB} + \frac{A_y B_y}{AB} + \frac{A_z B_z}{AB}\right). \tag{1·11–6}$$

But

$$A_x = A \cos \alpha_1, \quad A_y = A \cos \alpha_2, \quad A_z = A \cos \alpha_3,$$

$$B_x = B \cos \beta_1, \quad B_y = B \cos \beta_2, \quad B_z = B \cos \beta_3, \tag{1·11–7}$$

where $\cos \alpha_1$, $\cos \alpha_2$, $\cos \alpha_3$ are the direction cosines of **A** (cf. Sec. 1·2), and $\cos \beta_1$, $\cos \beta_2$, $\cos \beta_3$ are the direction cosines of **B**.   A fundamental theorem of analytic geometry gives

$$\cos \theta = \cos \alpha_1 \cos \beta_1 + \cos \alpha_2 \cos \beta_2 + \cos \alpha_3 \cos \beta_3 \tag{1·11–8}$$

as the cosine of the angle between the vectors **A** and **B**.   Hence (1·11–6) becomes

$$\mathbf{A} \cdot \mathbf{B} = AB \cos \theta. \tag{1·11–9}$$

This result is indeed sometimes used as the definition of the scalar product of the vectors **A** and **B**.

By the use of (1·11–9) we readily show the following properties of the unit vectors $\mathbf{i}, \mathbf{j}, \mathbf{k}$.

$$\mathbf{i}\cdot\mathbf{i} = \mathbf{j}\cdot\mathbf{j} = \mathbf{k}\cdot\mathbf{k} = 1,$$

$$\mathbf{i}\cdot\mathbf{j} = \mathbf{j}\cdot\mathbf{k} = \mathbf{k}\cdot\mathbf{i} = 0. \tag{1·11–10}$$

Reverting to the definition (1·11–2) we can assume that $\mathbf{A}$ and $\mathbf{B}$ are functions of the time and differentiate, obtaining

$$\frac{d}{dt}(\mathbf{A}\cdot\mathbf{B}) = \dot{A}_x B_x + A_x \dot{B}_x + \dot{A}_y B_y + A_y \dot{B}_y$$
$$+ \dot{A}_z B_z + A_z \dot{B}_z$$
$$= \dot{\mathbf{A}}\cdot\mathbf{B} + \mathbf{A}\cdot\dot{\mathbf{B}}, \tag{1·11–11}$$

where

$$\dot{\mathbf{A}} = \mathbf{i}\dot{A}_x + \mathbf{j}\dot{A}_y + \mathbf{k}\dot{A}_z, \tag{1·11–12}$$

it being assumed that $\mathbf{i}, \mathbf{j}, \mathbf{k}$ remain fixed as time passes.

We are now ready to consider the space integral of the force. We shall define it as follows:

$$\int_{\mathbf{r}_0}^{\mathbf{r}_1} \mathbf{F}\cdot d\mathbf{r}, \tag{1·11–13}$$

where $\mathbf{r}_0$ is the position vector of the particle at the beginning of its motion, and $\mathbf{r}_1$ is the position vector at the end of the motion. The infinitesimal displacement of the particle in the neighborhood of position vector $\mathbf{r}$ is denoted by $d\mathbf{r}$. The integrand is the space effect of the force during the displacement $d\mathbf{r}$, when the force has the (nearly) instantaneous value $\mathbf{F}$. The whole integral is then taken as the space cumulative effect of the force during the motion from $\mathbf{r}_0$ to $\mathbf{r}_1$. We shall call the integral in (1·11–13) the *work* done by the force on the particle during its displacement and denote it by W. Let us evaluate W for the important case in which the force is the *resultant* force acting on the particle. Then we may replace $\mathbf{F}$ by $m\ddot{\mathbf{r}}$ from the equation of motion (1·7–4) and get

$$W = \int_{\mathbf{r}_0}^{\mathbf{r}_1} m\ddot{\mathbf{r}}\cdot d\mathbf{r} = \int_{\mathbf{r}_0}^{\mathbf{r}_1} m\ddot{\mathbf{r}}\cdot\dot{\mathbf{r}}\, dt, \tag{1·11–14}$$

where we have replaced $d\mathbf{r}$ by $\dot{\mathbf{r}}\, dt$. Let us examine $\ddot{\mathbf{r}}\cdot\dot{\mathbf{r}}$. If we differentiate $\dot{\mathbf{r}}\cdot\dot{\mathbf{r}}$ with respect to time, we get from (1·11–11)

$$\frac{d}{dt}(\dot{\mathbf{r}}\cdot\dot{\mathbf{r}}) = 2\ddot{\mathbf{r}}\cdot\dot{\mathbf{r}}, \tag{1·11–15}$$

recalling that the scalar product is commutative. Hence (1·11–14) becomes

$$W = \frac{m}{2} \int d(\dot{\mathbf{r}} \cdot \dot{\mathbf{r}}) = \frac{m}{2} \int_{v_0}^{v_1} d(v^2), \qquad (1\cdot11\text{–}16)$$

where we have replaced $\dot{\mathbf{r}} \cdot \dot{\mathbf{r}}$ by v^2, since

$$\mathbf{v} = \dot{\mathbf{r}},$$

and have changed our limits to the initial and final speed values respectively. Now the integration in (1·10–19) can be readily carried out and yields

$$W = \tfrac{1}{2}mv_1{}^2 - \tfrac{1}{2}mv_0{}^2. \qquad (1\cdot11\text{–}17)$$

This reminds us of the impulse-momentum theorem (1·10–2) in that the work done by the resultant force appears as the *difference* between the values of a certain function of mass and velocity at the beginning and the end of the motion. The function here is $\tfrac{1}{2}mv^2$, a scalar quantity which was known in the 18th century as the *vis viva* of the particle but which during the 19th century came to be called the *kinetic* energy. We shall, in general, denote it by the symbol K. The theorem we have just proved then says that the work done by the resultant force acting on a particle is equal to the change in *kinetic energy* experienced. We call this result the *work-kinetic energy* theorem. We must be careful to note that it applies only to the work done by the *resultant* force. Actually a force can act on a particle and do no work on it at all. Thus to revert to (1·11–13) we see that if $\mathbf{F}$ is at right angles to the displacement $d\mathbf{r}$, we have

$$dW = \mathbf{F} \cdot d\mathbf{r} = 0.$$

In other words, whenever a force is perpendicular to the displacement of the particle its space cumulative effect is zero or it does no work. This, for example, is the case for the centripetal force discussed in Sec. 1·5. In general

$$dW = F\, dr \cos\theta, \qquad (1\cdot11\text{–}18)$$

where θ is the angle between $\mathbf{F}$ and $d\mathbf{r}$.

We must now consider the matter of units. The work done when a particle is moved one *centimeter* while acted upon by a force of one *dyne* in the direction of the motion is called an *erg*. Because of the smallness of this quantity, a larger unit is used. This is equal to 10^7 ergs and is called the *joule*. The student should verify that $\tfrac{1}{2}mv^2$ has the same dimensions and therefore the same units as work; i.e., dimensionally, *kinetic energy* and *work* are the same, as naturally they should be by definition. The absolute English unit of work and energy is the *foot poundal*; this is the work done when a particle is moved through a distance of one foot by a force of one poundal in the direction of the motion.   Engineers never use this unit; they prefer the *foot pound*, which is the work done in the motion of a particle through one foot under the action of a *pound of force* (lb wt).   From the relation between the two units of force we note that 32 foot poundals are equal to one foot pound.   In the m.k.s. system, mentioned in Sec. 1·8, the natural unit of work is the *Newton meter*.   But a moment's reflection shows us that the Newton meter is exactly equal to the joule.   This indicates one advantage of the m.k.s. system of units.

The rate at which work is done is called *power*.   Denoting the latter by P we have the general relation

$$P = \dot{W}. \qquad (1\cdot11\text{--}19)$$

The metric unit (which is the same here as the m.k.s. unit) is the *watt* or joule/sec, the *kilowatt* being 1000 watts.   In the English system the corresponding unit foot pound/sec has no name, but 550 foot pounds/sec is called one *horsepower* (hp).   The student is advised to note that the *kilowatt hour* and the *horsepower hour* are not units of power but units of work, equivalent respectively to 3.60×10^6 joules and 1.98×10^6 foot pounds.

By dividing by dt both sides of the relation

$$dW = \mathbf{F} \cdot d\mathbf{r}$$

we obtain

$$P = \mathbf{F} \cdot \dot{\mathbf{r}} = \mathbf{F} \cdot \mathbf{v}, \qquad (1\cdot11\text{--}20)$$

which is often a useful relation.

As in the case of impulse and momentum, the work-energy theorem gains its greatest significance when more than a single particle is involved. We shall illustrate this with the case of two particles, postponing the general case to Chapter 6.   Let us again denote the masses of the two particles by m_B and m_C respectively and let us suppose they act on each other with the interaction forces $\mathbf{F}_{BC}$ and $\mathbf{F}_{CB} = -\mathbf{F}_{BC}$.   Let us also assume that m_B is acted on by an external force (due ultimately of course to other particles) $\mathbf{F}_B$ and similarly m_C is acted on by the external force $\mathbf{F}_C$.   The equations of motion of m_B and m_C respectively then become

$$m_B \ddot{\mathbf{r}}_B = \mathbf{F}_B + \mathbf{F}_{BC}, \qquad (1\cdot11\text{--}21)$$

$$m_C \ddot{\mathbf{r}}_C = \mathbf{F}_C - \mathbf{F}_{BC}. \qquad (1\cdot11\text{--}22)$$

In line with eq. (1·11--14) we dot-multiply the first equation with $d\mathbf{r}_B$ and the second with $d\mathbf{r}_C$ and add, obtaining

$$m_B \ddot{\mathbf{r}}_B \cdot d\mathbf{r}_B + m_C \ddot{\mathbf{r}}_C \cdot d\mathbf{r}_C = \mathbf{F}_B \cdot d\mathbf{r}_B + \mathbf{F}_C \cdot d\mathbf{r}_C + \mathbf{F}_{BC} \cdot d(\mathbf{r}_B - \mathbf{r}_C).$$
$$(1\cdot11\text{--}23)$$

From the analysis used in going from (1·11–14) to (1·11–17) we can integrate both sides of (1·11–23) with the result

$$\tfrac{1}{2}m_B v_{B1}^2 + \tfrac{1}{2}m_C v_{C1}^2 - \tfrac{1}{2}m_B v_{B0}^2 - \tfrac{1}{2}m_C v_{C0}^2 = \int_{\mathbf{r}_{B0}}^{\mathbf{r}_{B1}} \mathbf{F}_B \cdot d\mathbf{r}_B$$

$$+ \int_{\mathbf{r}_{C0}}^{\mathbf{r}_{C1}} \mathbf{F}_c \cdot d\mathbf{r}_C + \int \mathbf{F}_{BC} \cdot d\mathbf{r}_{BC}, \quad (1 \cdot 11 – 24)$$

where we have written $\mathbf{r}_{BC} = \mathbf{r}_B - \mathbf{r}_C$ for the vector separation of B and C. The integration is to be thought of as conducted from the initial position of the system symbolized by the subscript 0 to the final position symbolized by the subscript 1.

Let us suppose that the force of interaction $\mathbf{F}_{BC}$ is a central force, i.e., directed along the line joining the two particles and dependent functionally on the separation distance. This is indeed the simplest way to interpret Newton's third law of motion. We therefore write

$$\mathbf{F}_{BC} = f(r_{BC})\mathbf{r}_{BC}, \quad (1 \cdot 11 – 25)$$

where $f(r_{BC})$ is some function of the separation distance r_{BC}. The reader is invited to show from the properties of the dot product that

$$\mathbf{r}_{BC} \cdot d\mathbf{r}_{BC} = r_{BC} dr_{BC}. \quad (1 \cdot 11 – 26)$$

Hence the third integral on the right-hand side in (1·11–24) becomes

$$\int \mathbf{F}_{BC} \cdot d\mathbf{r}_{BC} = \int f(r_{BC}) r_{BC} \, dr_{BC}. \quad (1 \cdot 11 – 27)$$

The fundamental theorem of the integral calculus guarantees that for the kind of functions $f(r_{BC})$ which correspond to interaction forces useful in mechanics (e.g., inverse square forces of the gravitational or Coulomb type), the integration in (1·11–27) can always be carried out and indeed

$$\int f(r_{BC}) r_{BC} \, dr_{BC} = -V(r_{BC}) + \text{const}, \quad (1 \cdot 11 – 28)$$

where $V(r_{BC})$ is another function of the separation distance r_{BC}.

The mathematical situation with respect to the other integrals in (1·11–24) is by no means so straightforward, since there is no assurance that for any arbitrary external forces $\mathbf{F}_B$ and $\mathbf{F}_C$ there exist functions like the V in (1·11–28) such that the integrals can be expressed in terms of them. Hence, for the moment let us simplify matters by assuming that the external forces vanish and hence no external work is done. We shall return to the more general case in Chapter 6. Eq. (1·11–24) then takes the form

$$\tfrac{1}{2}m_B v_{B1}^2 + \tfrac{1}{2}m_C v_{C1}^2 + V_1(r_{BC}) = \tfrac{1}{2}m_B v_{B0}^2 + \tfrac{1}{2}m_C v_{C0}^2 + V_0(r_{BC}),$$
$$(1\cdot11\text{–}29)$$

where $V_0(r_{BC})$ means the value of the function V when r_{BC} has its initial value and V_1 the corresponding value when r_{BC} has its final value.   Eq. (1·11–29) has the interesting physical meaning that when the two particles B and C move subject only to their mutual interaction, the total kinetic energy of the system plus the function V remains constant.   This evidently is another kind of conservation theorem, reminding us of conservation of momentum (1·10–4).   Since the kinetic energy enters into it, the conservation clearly has something to do with work.   Whenever we encounter conservation of any kind, i.e., the constancy of any physical quantity in the midst of the change involved in motion, it is very tempting to give the quantity a special name and focus careful attention on it in the subsequent development of the subject.   This we do in the present case by calling the quantity which remains constant in (1·11–29) the *total mechanical energy* of the two interacting particles.   We shall denote it by U and write

$$\tfrac{1}{2}m_B v_B^2 + \tfrac{1}{2}m_C v_C^2 + V(r_{BC}) = U. \qquad (1\cdot11\text{–}30)$$

The question arises: what shall we call V?   It has the same physical dimensions as the kinetic energy and it is therefore natural to interpret it as a kind of energy.   We shall label it the mutual *potential energy* of the two particles.   It depends only on the mutual separation of the two particles.

The eq. (1·11–29) then says that when two particles are subject only to their own interaction, which has the character of a central force, the total mechanical energy of the system remains constant, where this energy is made up of the sum of the kinetic energies of the particles and their mutual potential energy.   We shall have occasion to make much use of this conservation principle in subsequent chapters.   A simple illustration of it in the special case of straight-line motion will serve to emphasize here its interesting character and importance.

Let us take as one of the particles the earth itself and assume (what will later be demonstrated) that it can be replaced by a single particle with a mass equal to that of the earth and located at the center of the earth.   We then apply the principle of conservation of energy to the motion of a small mass particle above the surface of the earth, restricting indeed our attention to motion along a given radius of the earth extended.

We shall assume that the force between the particle and the earth is given by Newton's law of gravitation, which says that any two mass particles in the universe attract each other with a force varying directly as the product of the masses and universely as the square of the distance between them. Hence if r denotes the distance between the small particle of mass m and the center of the earth (of mass M), the magnitude of the force is

$$F = -\frac{GmM}{r^2}, \tag{1·11–31}$$

where G is the so-called constant of universal gravitation, and equal approximately to 6.67×10^{-8} dyne cm²/gm² (see Sec. 2·3). From (1·11–29) we now have

$$\int \mathbf{F} \cdot d\mathbf{r} = -GmM \int \frac{\mathbf{r}}{r^3} \cdot d\mathbf{r}$$

$$= -GmM \int \frac{dr}{r^2} = \frac{GmM}{r} + \text{const.} \tag{1·11–32}$$

Hence in this case

$$V(r) = -\frac{GmM}{r}. \tag{1·11–33}$$

Now

$$r = R + h, \tag{1·11–34}$$

where R is the radius of the earth and h is the height of the particle of mass m above the surface. Eq. (1·11–30) then becomes, if we denote the velocity of the particle by v and that of the earth by v_e,

$$\tfrac{1}{2}mv^2 + \tfrac{1}{2}Mv_e^2 - \frac{GmM}{R+h} = U. \tag{1·11–35}$$

We note that the potential energy here is negative, leading to the possibility that the total energy U may be also negative, with proper choice of conditions. To use (1·11–35) successfully we evidently need another relation between v and v_e. But this is immediately available from the conservation of momentum. If we confine our attention to the case in which the particle is ejected from the surface of the earth along a radius extended, we know that independently of the nature of the interaction the total momentum is always zero, since originally both the particle and the earth were at rest with respect to axes fixed in the ground. Hence we must always have

$$mv + Mv_e = 0, \tag{1·11–36}$$

or

$$v_e = -\frac{m}{M}v. \tag{1·11–37}$$

This indicates, of course, that when an object is ejected from the surface of the earth, the recoil velocity of the earth is very small indeed, due to the smallness of m/M with respect to unity. If we substitute from (1·11–37) into (1·11–35), the result is

$$\tfrac{1}{2}m(1 + m/M)v^2 = U + \frac{GmM}{R + h}. \qquad (1·11\text{–}38)$$

We may as well approximate by neglecting m/M compared with unity and write finally

$$\tfrac{1}{2}mv^2 = U + \frac{GmM}{R + h}. \qquad (1·11\text{–}39)$$

This equation enables us to discuss the velocity-distance relation of any particle ejected directly into the air from the surface of the earth (of course neglecting air resistance, wind resistance, etc.). For the simple case in which a ball is tossed into the air, h is always much smaller than R. Hence we write

$$\frac{GmM}{R\left(1 + \dfrac{h}{R}\right)} \doteq \frac{GmM}{R} - \frac{GmM}{R^2}h. \qquad (1·11\text{–}40)$$

But GmM/R^2 is the magnitude of the force with which the earth attracts a particle of mass m near the surface. This is simply mg where g is the acceleration of gravity. Hence (1·11–39) becomes

$$\tfrac{1}{2}mv^2 = U + \frac{GmM}{R} - mgh. \qquad (1·11\text{–}41)$$

Suppose the ball is tossed up so that it comes to rest for $h = h_0$. Then

$$U + \frac{GmM}{R} = mgh_0$$

and (1·11–41) becomes

$$\tfrac{1}{2}mv^2 = mgh_0 - mgh. \qquad (1·11\text{–}42)$$

The initial velocity of propulsion to achieve this result is thus

$$v = \sqrt{2gh_0}, \qquad (1·11\text{–}43)$$

in agreement with the usual elementary physics result.

However, (1·11–39) is much more general, since it allows us to follow a projectile or missile to any height above the surface. In fact we can use it to estimate the velocity with which it is necessary to eject a particle from the surface so that it will never return. The condition for this is clearly that v shall vanish when h becomes infinite. This means that $U = 0$. Hence the ejection velocity v_0 becomes

$$v_0 = \sqrt{\frac{2GM}{R}} \,. \tag{1·11–44}$$

If we substitute the values $M = 6.1 \times 10^{27}$ g and $R = 6.37 \times 10^8$ cm, together with the value of G given above, the result is

$$v_0 = 1.13 \times 10^6 \text{ cm/sec}$$

or in English units about 7 miles/sec. This figure is of interest in connection with the space age of missiles and rockets.

1·12. Résumé. With the ideas of the preceding sections in mind we are now prepared to take up some concrete illustrations which will develop our understanding of the laws of mechanics. In the next two chapters we shall discuss the motion of a particle under various conditions. The main problem we shall meet there will be the setting up and solution of the *equation* (or *equations*) *of motion*, which is only the mathematical expression of the second law, namely (1·7–4). The physics of the problem enters with the significant choice of the force **F** and the appropriate initial conditions of the motion, i.e., the so-called "boundary conditions," the initial or final position and velocity of the particle. The rest of the problem will be mathematical. But each illustration will be so arranged that the results will tie up intimately with the experience of our actual world. This will strengthen our grasp of the fundamental concepts already introduced in the present chapter and afford a preparation for the more elaborate treatment to follow. In Chapter 4 we shall show how the concept of energy can be used to particular advantage in the solution of mechanical problems.

There is one point about the use of the equation of motion which merits a general remark before the solution of specific problems is undertaken. We have already noted in Sec. 1·2 that position is relative and the same must be true of displacement, velocity and acceleration. It will therefore naturally occur to the thoughtful student to inquire whether the equation of motion (1·7–4) will retain its present simple form in *all* systems of reference. The answer to this is in the negative. The most general system in which the equation applies is that fixed relatively to the average position of the fixed stars, sometimes called the primary inertial system. Nevertheless, it is easy to show that the equation retains the same form in any system which moves *with constant velocity* (without rotation) with respect to the above mentioned system. For suppose x, y, z are the coördinates of a particle in the first reference system, while x', y', z' are the coördinates in a system moving in the

x direction with velocity v relative to the first. We then have the following relations connecting the coördinates in the two systems

$$x' = x - vt - a,$$
$$y' = y - b,$$
$$z' = z - c,$$
(1·12–1)

where a, b, c are constants giving the position of the origin of the second system relative to the first when $t = 0$. But it then follows at once that

$$\ddot{x}' = \ddot{x},$$
$$\ddot{y}' = \ddot{y},$$
$$\ddot{z}' = \ddot{z},$$
(1·12–2)

whence the accelerations are the same in the two systems. It must, of course, be noted that this result would *not* be true were the two systems *accelerated* relatively to each other.

Our discussion has, to be sure, neglected the effect of the transformation on the force side of the equation. But we recall from Sec. 1·7 that **F** is a function of the relative position coördinates of the interacting particles. Relative position coördinates are not altered by the transformation (1·12–1).

The considerations of the preceding two paragraphs form the content of what is usually called the Newtonian principle of relativity. Effectively this says that there is no mechanical means, that is, no means based on the use of Newton's laws of motion, by which one can detect motion at *constant* velocity relative to the primary inertial system. For example, no experiment such as throwing a ball around on a train moving at constant velocity can indicate whether or not the train is actually moving. It is only when the train speeds up or slows down, i.e., accelerates, that mechanical means can detect its motion.

One naturally inquires next, is there *any* physical way in which the relative motion of inertial systems, i.e., systems moving at constant velocity with respect to the primary inertial system, can be detected? The answer to this question is given by the Einstein theory of relativity, to be considered in Chapter 14.

PROBLEMS

1. Determine the expression for the distance between two points in a plane (a) in terms of rectangular coördinates, (b) in terms of polar coördinates, (c) in terms of oblique coördinates with the axes making an angle of $60°$ with each other.

2. The position of a point in a plane with respect to rectangular coördinate axes is given by (x, y). If the axes are rotated through angle ϕ, what are the new position coördinates?

3. The position of a point P in space with respect to rectangular coördinate axes is given by (x, y, z). If the axes are rotated with the origin held fixed, the position of the original point P is now given by (x', y', z'). Find the expressions for x', y', z', in terms of x, y, z and the direction cosines of the new axes with respect to the old axes.

4. Prove that the distance between any two points in three-dimensional space remains invariant under a rotation of axes as that discussed in Problem 3.

5. A flywheel of radius 1 meter starts from rest with a constant angular acceleration of 1 rev/sec². Find the resultant acceleration of a particle on the periphery at the end of 1 second.

6. Compare the instantaneous linear velocities relative to the ground of the hub of a wheel and the highest point of the rim.

7. A ship sails southeast at 15 mi/hr and the wind blows from the south at 10 mi/hr. In what position will a masthead pennant come to rest?

8. A boat is headed southwest with a speed of 10 knots, while another boat is headed due east with a speed of 15 knots. Find the relative velocity of the boats.

9. Two particles move with equal speeds v in opposite directions in the same circle. In what position will their relative velocity have a maximum magnitude and what will it be? What is the magnitude of the relative velocity when the position vectors of the two particles make the angle 45° with each other? Draw a diagram showing the actual relative velocities.

10. Particle A moves with a uniform velocity of 100 cm/sec in a direction making angles of 60° and 45° with the x and y axes respectively. Particle B has a constant velocity of 50 cm/sec along the z axis. Find the components along the x, y, and z axes respectively of the difference between the two velocities.

11. Show by a simple example that the resultant of two *finite* angular displacements depends in general on the order in which the displacements are performed. Are there exceptions? Show by a construction why it is plausible that the resultant of two *infinitesimal* angular displacements is independent of the order in which such displacements are performed.

12. On the simple Bohr theory of the structure of the hydrogen atom a negatively charged electron revolves in a circular orbit about a positively charged nucleus. Denoting the charge on the electron by $-e$, that on the nucleus by $+e$, and the mass of the electron by m, find the expression for the angular velocity ω of the electron corresponding to orbital radius a. Calculate ω for $a = 0.53 \times 10^{-8}$ cm, $m = 9 \times 10^{-28}$ grams, and $e = 4.80 \times 10^{-10}$ electrostatic units. (Hint: Use the electrostatic Coulomb law of force between point charges.)

13. A particle moves with uniform angular velocity in a circle of radius a. Derive the expressions for the rectangular components ($\dot{x}$ and $\dot{y}$) of the peripheral velocity in terms of the angular displacement θ from the x axis as polar axis. Find the similar expressions for $\ddot{x}$ and $\ddot{y}$.

14. A particle moves in a plane with respect to *fixed* rectangular axes. Express its velocity and acceleration components relative to a set of rectangular axes rotating about the same origin with constant angular velocity ω in terms of the corresponding components relative to the fixed axes. Specialize to the case where the particle is at rest in the fixed system.

15. A particle of mass 100 grams and traveling along the x axis in the direction of increasing x with the constant speed 100 cm/sec collides at the origin with a particle of mass 200 grams traveling along the y axis in the direction of increasing y with the constant speed 150 cm/sec. If the two particles lock together after the collision, find the velocity in direction and magnitude of the combined particles. Compare the kinetic energy after collision with that of the individual particles before collision.

16. Two particles of masses m_1 and m_2 respectively suffer acceleration due to their mutual interaction. Find the expression for their *relative* acceleration in terms of the actual acceleration of either particle in a fixed reference system. What does it become when either mass is very large compared with the other?

17. In Problem 12, derive the expression for the kinetic energy of the electron moving in the circular orbit of radius a.

18. A force $F = kte^{-at}$, where k and a are positive constants, acts on a particle of mass m constrained to move in the x direction. Find the change in momentum produced by the force in time t. If the particle starts from rest, how far will it go in a time t_0 equal to that at which the force attains its maximum value?

19. In Problem 18, if the particle starts from rest, find the kinetic energy attained in time t_0. Find the maximum kinetic energy attained and the time at which it is attained.

20. In Problem 18, if the particle starts from rest, find the instantaneous power at time t. Also find the average power over the time interval τ.

21. The center of a hurricane is located at a given instant at Lat. 40° N and Long. 70° W. If the center of the storm is moving due north at 30 miles per hour and the rotational velocity of the wind is 80 miles per hour 50 miles from the center what is the instantaneous speed and direction of the wind 50 miles from the center and at a point northeast of the center? Answer the same question for a point 50 miles from the center and northwest of it.

22. If mass is defined in such a way that

$$m_{AB} = \frac{\mathbf{a}_{AB}}{-\mathbf{a}_{BA}}$$

where m_{AB} means the mass of A relative to B, find the resulting equation of motion. With this definition of mass, if two particles are joined together, how will the masses compound to give the resultant mass? (Compare with eq. (1·6–4) and use the analysis of Sec. 1·9).

23. How fast must a 150-pound man run up a 20° inclined plane in order to exert 1 kilowatt of power against gravity?

24. A particle of mass m is subject to a harmonic force of the form $F_0 \sin \omega t$ acting along the x axis. Here $\omega = 2\pi\nu$, where ν is the frequency of the sinusoidal function and P is the period ($P = 1/\nu$). Find the change in momentum produced by this force in the time interval from $t = t_0$ to $t = t_1$. Find also the values of the time interval for which the change in momentum takes on maximum and minimum values.

Give a plot of the force, momentum, and displacement x as functions of time, assuming that the particle starts from rest at the origin.

25. In the preceding problem find the kinetic energy attained at time t, assuming that the particle starts from rest at the origin.

26. Solve Problems 24 and 25 for a force of the form $F = F_0 \, e^{-at} \sin \omega t$, where a is a positive constant.

27. Two particles A and B of mass 200 and 500 grams respectively move along the x axis under the influence of their mutual arbitrary interaction. Initially A is at the origin, but moving toward B with speed 20 cm/sec. Initially B is at $x = 1000$ cm and moving toward A with speed 10 cm/sec.

What is the initial position of the center of mass of the two particles? What is the initial velocity of the center of mass? Where will the center of mass be at the end of 2 seconds?

28. A particle of mass m_1 moves along the x axis with constant speed v_1, whereas a particle of mass m_2 moves along the y axis with constant speed v_2. If the particles are at $(x_0, 0)$ and $(0, y_0)$ respectively at time $t = 0$, find the path followed by the center of mass of the system and find its position at time t.

29. A particle of mass m very small compared with that of the earth is ejected vertically from the surface with a speed of 4 miles per second. How far will it rise (neglecting air and wind resistance)? What will be the total energy of the particle?

30. An alpha particle of mass 6.6×10^{-24} gram is fired in a straight line with a speed of 2×10^9 cm/sec directly at a nucleus of gold whose charge is Ne, where $N = 79$ and $e = 4.8 \times 10^{-10}$ e.s.u. How close to the nucleus will the alpha particle be stopped and how much work will be done in stopping it?

CHAPTER 2

RECTILINEAR MOTION OF A PARTICLE

2·1. Free Motion and the Uniform Field. As an introduction to the study of the motion of a particle, let us consider motion along a straight line. The simplest type of this is, of course, " free " motion, that is, motion without acceleration, i.e., under the influence of no force. The velocity is constant and the distance traveled in time t, assuming that the motion takes place along the x axis, is $x - x_0$, where

$$x = vt + x_0. \qquad (2\cdot1\text{–}1)$$

The velocity is v in magnitude and the original displacement of the particle at $t = 0$ is x_0.

From this trivial case we pass at once to the more important one in which the particle moves with a constant acceleration. We shall call this motion in a uniform (i.e., constant) field of force. If the mass of the particle is m, the equation of motion (1·7–4) when reduced to scalar form becomes[1]

$$m\ddot{x} = F_0, \qquad (2\cdot1\text{–}2)$$

where F_0 represents the constant force. The equation (2·1–2) may be written in the form $\dot{v} = F_0/m$, whence $dv = F_0/m \cdot dt$. Integrating both sides we get

$$v = \dot{x} = \int \frac{F_0}{m} dt = \frac{F_0}{m} t + c,$$

where c is a constant of integration. In value it is equal to v when $t = 0$, i.e., the initial velocity, which we may call v_0. So we have

$$v = \frac{F_0}{m} t + v_0. \qquad (2\cdot1\text{–}3)$$

A second integration in similar fashion gives the distance from the origin at time t, viz.,

$$x = \frac{1}{2}\left(\frac{F_0}{m}\right) t^2 + v_0 t + x_0, \qquad (2\cdot1\text{–}4)$$

[1] The motion being rectilinear, we are interested in its scalar magnitude only.

37

where we have already replaced the constant of integration by x_0, the initial displacement of the particle. This simple illustration shows clearly that in order to use for purposes of computation the integrated equation of motion, we must know the particle's displacement and velocity at some chosen instant (here $t = 0$). These are, so to speak, the boundary conditions of the motion, though they are usually referred to as the initial conditions.

By elimination of the time t between eqs. (2·1–3) and (2·1–4) the reader may show the existence of the following important relation between velocity and distance traveled, viz.,

$$v^2 = \frac{2F_0}{m}(x - x_0) + v_0^2. \tag{2·1–5}$$

The most important illustration of this type of motion is furnished by a particle falling freely under the influence of gravity near the earth's surface, neglecting the air resistance.[1] Then F_0 becomes the weight of the particle, which is numerically equal to mg, where g is the constant acceleration of gravity. We are here considering the *upward* direction as positive, while the weight is a downward force: Hence $F_0/m = -g$ and (2·1–4) becomes

$$x = -\tfrac{1}{2}gt^2 + v_0 t + x_0, \tag{2·1–6}$$

and (2·1–5) is now

$$v^2 = -2g(x - x_0) + v_0^2. \tag{2·1–7}$$

If we wish to discuss the height which a particle thrown into the air with initial upward velocity v_0 will attain, we merely substitute $v = 0$ in eq. (2·1–7), whence the height is given at once by

$$h = \frac{v_0^2}{2g}. \tag{2·1–8}$$

The same result follows from the application of eqs. (2·1–3) and (2·1–6). Incidentally the reader may easily show that the particle spends as long a time going up as it does coming down and that it reaches the ground with a downward velocity equal in magnitude to its original upward velocity. These facts are very neatly brought out by the construction of a space-time graph, plotting the coördinate x against the time t, by means of the equation (2·1–6). The result, of course, is a parabola as shown in Fig. 2·1, where the axis of abscissas is the time axis and the ordinates are values of the upward displacement. What may be called the space-time history of the particle from the instant it is projected upward to the time when it strikes the ground is

[1] We also neglect the small effect due to the rotation of the earth.   See end of Sec. 3·3.   Also Sec. 8·12.

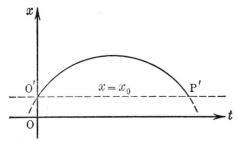

FIG. 2·1

completely given by the portion of the curve between O' and P'.
Moreover, the *slope* of the curve at each point yields the *instantaneous
velocity* of the particle at the corresponding time and place.   We shall
find this type of graph of value in the further study of problems in motion.

It has already been pointed out that in the above discussion we are
neglecting the effect of air resistance, in order to simplify the problem.
(See Sec. 2·7 for the more complicated case.)

There are some important examples of rectilinear motion under
the influence of gravity in which the particle is " constrained " to move
in a certain direction or with an acceleration which while constant
is different from " g."   Such cases logically belong to the discussion
in Chapter 9.   But the physical ideas involved are so common and so
important that we shall discuss here the problem of motion along an
inclined plane and the Atwood machine.

Consulting Fig. 2·2, which represents a plane inclined at an angle θ
to the horizontal, let a particle of mass m move without friction on this
plane.   The force of gravity is $m\mathbf{g}$, but this acts vertically downward
while the particle is constrained to move along the plane.   The net,
unbalanced force $\mathbf{F}$ which acts in the direction of the motion has therefore
the magnitude $mg \sin \theta$, and the equation of motion is

$$m\ddot{x} = mg \sin \theta, \qquad (2\cdot1-9)$$

where x is measured positively *down* the plane, for convenience.   The
results of the first part of this section will then follow in this case with
the substitution of $g \sin \theta$ for g.   For example, the application of
eq. (2·1–7) reveals the interesting fact that since $l \sin \theta = h$, where l is
the length and h the height of the plane, the velocity *along* the plane
acquired at the foot of the plane is equal to the velocity which would be
acquired were the particle to fall freely through a distance equal to the
height of the plane.   The *times* of fall for the same initial velocities are,
of course, different.   In fact, the reader should show that the time for
descent *along* the plane is to that down the height of the plane in the
ratio 1 : $\sin \theta$.

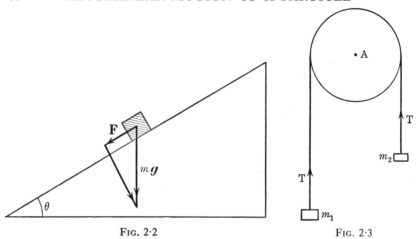

FIG. 2·2   FIG. 2·3

In the Atwood machine (shown diagrammatically in Fig. 2·3) there are two particles of mass m_1 and m_2 respectively at the ends of a flexible inextensible string wrapped around a frictionless peg, A. Suppose $m_1 > m_2$. We proceed to set up an equation of motion for each particle by determining the unbalanced force on each. The string pulls up on each mass particle with a force $\mathbf{T}$, the so-called " tension " in the string, which we shall assume is not altered when the latter passes over a perfectly smooth peg. The equations of motion therefore are

$$\left.\begin{aligned} m_1 g - T &= m_1 \ddot{x}_1 \\[1ex] m_2 g - T &= m_2 \ddot{x}_2 \end{aligned}\right\} \qquad (2 \cdot 1 – 10)$$

where x_1 and x_2 are the corresponding displacements of m_1 and m_2 measured downward. Now since the one mass rises with the same acceleration with which the other falls, we have

$$\ddot{x}_1 = - \ddot{x}_2 = \ddot{x}, \qquad (2 \cdot 1 – 11)$$

and hence by subtraction of the two equations in (2·1–10) there results

$$\ddot{x} = \frac{m_1 - m_2}{m_1 + m_2} \cdot g, \qquad (2 \cdot 1 – 12)$$

and the solution follows as in the previous cases. The tension in the string is evaluated by substitution from (2·1–12) into either of the equations (2·1–10). The utility of this device in studying the acceleration of gravity is evident from the fact that the actual acceleration of either particle may be made as small as desirable by choosing m_1 and m_2 sufficiently close together in magnitude.

2·2. Energy in the Uniform Field. The introduction of the concept of energy in Sec. 1·11 enables us to use this concept in the interpretation of some of the results obtained in Sec. 2·1. The work-kinetic energy theorem for a uniform field or constant force F_0 becomes, for motion along the x axis

$$\int_{x_0}^{x} F_0 \, dx = F_0(x - x_0) = \tfrac{1}{2}mv^2 - \tfrac{1}{2}mv_0^2. \qquad (2\cdot2\text{--}1)$$

This is of course identical with eq. (2·1–5) giving the relation between velocity and distance, but now it has a different interpretation. Rearranging, we have

$$\tfrac{1}{2}mv^2 - F_0 x = \tfrac{1}{2}mv_0^2 - F_0 x_0 = \text{const.} \qquad (2\cdot2\text{--}2)$$

From the definition of energy it is natural to interpret the constant as the total mechanical energy of the particle. Then $-F_0 x$ appears as the potential energy, which when added to the kinetic energy yields the total energy.

The simplest illustration of (2·2–2) is that of a particle in straight-line motion near the surface of the earth under the influence of gravity only and neglecting air and wind resistance. Then $F_0 = -mg$, and the energy equation takes the form

$$\tfrac{1}{2}mv^2 + mgx = U, \qquad (2\cdot2\text{--}3)$$

where U represents the total energy. The potential energy here is always positive and hence so is U. The initial conditions determine the application of (2·2–3) to special cases. Thus if the particle is ejected upward with velocity v_0 when $x = 0$, we have $U = \tfrac{1}{2}mv_0^2$. Then U will become zero when $x = h$, where

$$mgh = \tfrac{1}{2}mv_0^2, \qquad (2\cdot2\text{--}4)$$

and the height attained is precisely that given by eq. (2·1–8). When we are not interested in the precise temporal behavior of the particle (eq. 2·1–4) the energy equation yields valuable information without carrying through the complete integration of the equation of motion. The reader will see that the energy equation really corresponds to what may be called a first integral of the equation of motion.

Inclined-plane motion lends itself to similar treatment. Here $F_0 = -mg \sin \theta$ and the energy equation is

$$\tfrac{1}{2}mv^2 + mgx \sin \theta = U, \qquad (2\cdot2\text{--}5)$$

if x is measured positively *up* the plane. But

$$x \sin \theta = y,$$

where y is vertical distance above the lowest point on the plane.

Hence (2·2–5) takes the form

$$\tfrac{1}{2}mv^2 + mgy = U. \tag{2·2–6}$$

We at once see that if the particle starts from rest at the top of the plane, where $y = h$, the total energy is $U = mgh$ and the velocity attained at the foot of the plane is $\sqrt{2gh}$. As the potential energy decreases during fall the kinetic energy increases, the sum remaining constant.

The application of the energy principle to the Atwood machine is left as an exercise for the reader (Problem 18).

In the discussion of this section we have of course ignored what happens energywise when the particle dropped from height h at rest strikes the ground or floor. This is really a problem in collision, but it is not difficult to see that in the ideal case the motion is reversed and the particle starts upward with the same kinetic energy with which it hits. Similarly the particle which meets a horizontal surface after moving down the inclined plane will in the ideal case move along the horizontal with the kinetic energy which it gained in falling. In each example we have stressed the word " ideal " because in no actual case does the fact agree with the prediction. There is always a loss in mechanical energy in motion along or collision with physical surfaces. The appearance of heat in such cases is taken to mean that the mechanical energy of the particle has been transferred to kinetic energy of constituent parts of the surface (e.g., molecular kinetic energy). In this way conservation of the mechanical energy of the particle is lost but conservation of energy of the larger system consisting of the particle and the molecules in the surface is retained. This is the general principle of the conservation of energy, concerning which more will be said in Chapter 6.

2·3. Motion in a Field Proportional to the First Power of the Distance. The next simplest type of rectilinear motion is perhaps that in which the force is directly proportional to the distance from some fixed point in the straight line in which the motion takes place; a state of affairs not uncommon in physical phenomena. In such a case the equation of motion has the general form

$$m\ddot{x} = cx, \tag{2·3–1}$$

where c is a constant. Two cases will arise, according as c is negative or positive. The former is by far the more important for our purpose and will be considered first. Let $c = -k$, where k is positive. Probably the simplest way[1] of solving the differential equation (2·3–1)

---

[1] This book is not primarily a mathematical treatise. We shall therefore attempt to develop and solve each problem by the simplest mathematical methods available. This explains why, in the present case, we do not enter into the more elegant mathematical methods for the solution of differential equations of the type of (2·2–1).

is to multiply both sides by $\dot{x}\, dt$.   Thus we have

$$m\dot{x}\ddot{x}\, dt = -kx\, dx.$$

But this is simply

$$\tfrac{1}{2}md(\dot{x})^2 = -\tfrac{1}{2}kd(x)^2. \tag{2·3-2}$$

Integrating once then yields

$$\tfrac{1}{2}m\dot{x}^2 = -\tfrac{1}{2}kx^2 + C_1, \tag{2·3-3}$$

where C_1 is a constant of integration.   This so-called first integral of the equation of motion is, of course, the energy equation already referred to in Chapter 1 and in Sec. 2·2.   This is more evident if we write it in the form

$$\tfrac{1}{2}mv^2 + \tfrac{1}{2}kx^2 = C_1 = U, \tag{2·3-4}$$

where $v = \dot{x}$ and the constant C_1 is put equal to the total energy of the particle. The quantity $kx^2/2$ thus appears as the potential energy of the particle.   It is clearly always positive and so is U.   The value of the total energy will depend on the initial conditions imposed on the motion.   It is only the assignment of such conditions that enables us to obtain *specific* physical results from our integration.   Let us assume, that when $x = R, v = 0$.   Then $C_1 = U = \tfrac{1}{2}kR^2$, or the total energy is the maximum potential energy.   Eq. (2·3-3) then can be written

$$\dot{x} = \pm\sqrt{\frac{k}{m}}\cdot\sqrt{R^2 - x^2}, \tag{2·3-5}$$

which yields the velocity of the particle for any distance x from the chosen origin, subject, of course, to the above condition, which is arbitrary in nature.   However, it should be noted from eq. (2·3-3) that the velocity must be zero for *some* value of x.   We have merely specified this value as R in our above assumption.   Separating variables in eq. (2·3-4) gives us

$$\frac{dx}{\pm\sqrt{R^2 - x^2}} = \sqrt{\frac{k}{m}}\, dt, \tag{2·3-6}$$

which on integration becomes

$$\text{arc}\left.\begin{matrix}\sin\\ \cos\end{matrix}\right\}\left(\frac{x}{R}\right) = \sqrt{\frac{k}{m}}\, t + C_2, \tag{2·3-7}$$

These will be found in any fairly comprehensive text on differential equations (e.g., Henry Margenau and G. M. Murphy, *The Mathematics of Physics and Chemistry*, 2d ed., Van Nostrand, Princeton, N.J., 1956, Chap. 2, and will of course be of great interest and ultimate use to the thoughtful student of theoretical physics.

where the notation of the left-hand side indicates that arc sin (x/R) or arc cos (x/R) results according as we choose the plus or minus sign in (2·3–6). C_2 is a second constant of integration, the value of which must be determined from a second initial condition giving the initial value of the displacement x. Thus if $x = R$ when $t = 0$, we have

$$C_2 = \text{arc} \left.\begin{matrix} \sin \\ \cos \end{matrix}\right\} \quad (1),$$ which equals either $\pi/2$ or zero, according as we use the sine or cosine function. On the other hand, if $x = 0$ for $t = 0$, $C_2 = 0$ or $\pi/2$, according as the sine or cosine is used.

The explicit expression for the displacement x in terms of the time is then

$$x = R \left.\begin{matrix} \sin \\ \cos \end{matrix}\right\} \left(\sqrt{\frac{k}{m}} \cdot t + C_2 \right). \qquad (2\cdot3\text{–}8)$$

The space-time graph of this case is the simple sine or cosine curve familiar to the student from elementary mathematics, and the motion is known by the term *simple harmonic*. If we choose $C_2 = 0$, the result is shown in Fig. 2·4, where curve I corresponds to the sine and II to

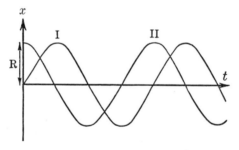

FIG. 2·4

the cosine. The two can, of course, be made to coincide by a relative displacement along the t axis. In *simple harmonic* motion there is thus a maximum displacement of the particle from the chosen origin and its value is R, defined as the *amplitude* of the motion. The motion repeats itself, i.e., is oscillatory or periodic, and the time for a complete oscillation, denoted by P and called the *period*, is given by

$$P = 2\pi \sqrt{\frac{m}{k}}. \qquad (2\cdot3\text{–}9)$$

This follows from an inspection of eq. (2·3–8). Thus to consider the sine term only, $x = R \sin C_2$ for $t = 0$. The *same* value of x will next recur at a time P for which $\sin (\sqrt{k/m}\, P + C_2) = \sin C_2$. But this will happen for $\sqrt{k/m}\, P = 2\pi$, whence (2·3–9) follows. The reciprocal of P is called the *frequency* and is represented by v.   It is the number of complete oscillations per second.   The displacement may then be written in the simplified form (using here the cosine only)

$$x = R \cos (2\pi vt + \epsilon),   (2\cdot3\text{–}10)$$

where C_2 has been replaced by ϵ.   The argument of the cosine, viz., $2\pi vt + \epsilon$, is called the *phase* of the simple harmonic motion and ϵ, its value for $t = 0$, is known as the *epoch*.

From the above discussion the reader will see at once that in simple harmonic motion the particle has its maximum velocity when $x = 0$ (i.e., while passing through the chosen origin) while its minimum velocity (viz. zero) occurs at $x = \pm R$, i.e., at the two ends of its path. On the other hand, the maximum acceleration or force corresponds to $x = R$, while the minimum (zero in value) occurs at $x = 0$.

The reader will have noted that the treatment of simple harmonic motion given immediately above is purely *analytic* in nature.   That is, we began with a *differential equation*, i.e., the equation of motion, and by two successive integrations obtained the expressions for the velocity and displacement which were rendered specific by the introduction of the initial or boundary conditions.   This is the straightforward method of discussing the problem.   Yet in many cases it is illuminating to start at the other end, i.e., to commence with a certain well-defined type of motion which appears to possess features of interest and then deduce its properties.   This method of approach to a dynamical problem is very often the simplest.   Let us now apply it to the case of simple harmonic motion.   We shall suppose that a particle Q moves with *uniform* angular velocity ω rad/sec about a circle with radius R and center at O (see Fig. 2·5).   Let us consider the motion of the projection of Q on *any* straight line in the plane of the circle.   For simplicity choose this straight line as the diameter AB and let P be the projection in question.   As the particle Q moves about the circle, P moves back and

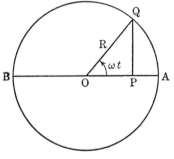

FIG. 2·5

forth on the line AB with a maximum excursion from O of magnitude R.   If the motion is assumed to begin at A when $t = 0$, the displacement of P from O at any subsequent instant t is, of course,

$$x = R \cos \omega t.   (2\cdot3\text{–}11)$$

Successive differentiations with respect to the time yield the instantaneous velocity and acceleration respectively, namely,

$$v = \dot{x} = -R\omega \sin \omega t$$

$$= \pm R\omega \sqrt{1 - \frac{x^2}{R^2}}$$

$$= \pm \omega \sqrt{R^2 - x^2}, \qquad (2\cdot3\text{–}12)$$

and

$$a = \ddot{x} = -R\omega^2 \cos \omega t$$

$$= -\omega^2 x. \qquad (2\cdot3\text{–}13)$$

If the number of revolutions per second of Q is $\nu = \omega/2\pi$, the frequency of the motion of P will likewise be ν. Comparison then shows that eq. (2·3–13) is equivalent to (2·3–1) with $k/m = \omega^2 = 4\pi^2\nu^2$. Likewise eq. (2·3–12) is identical with (2·3–5). In other words, the motion as defined above *kinematically* is precisely that which results when a particle moves in a straight line in a field of force varying directly as the distance from a fixed point on the line and everywhere opposite in direction to the displacement, and hence it is by definition simple harmonic motion. In the two treatments we have thus secured both a *dynamical* and a *kinematic* view of this important type of motion.

It is now in order to discuss an illustration. We shall consider the case of a *spring* (assumed here for simplicity as massless) one end of which is fastened to a rigid ceiling and to the other end of which there is attached a heavy particle of mass m (Fig. 2·6). At the moment when we first consider the system, it is assumed to be in equilibrium, i.e., the downward pull of gravity $m\mathbf{g}$ on the particle is balanced by the tension $\mathbf{F}_t = m\mathbf{g}$ with which the spring pulls upward on the mass. Now experiment shows that for *small* displacements from equilibrium (in general "small" will mean small compared with the length of the spring, though actually in this case the definition depends on the physical characteristics of the spring, a topic to which we shall recur later), the additional force $\mathbf{F}_d$ (generally in the form of a *weight*) required to stretch the spring in the direction of its length and thus

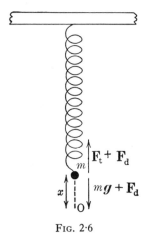

FIG. 2·6

displace the mass particle is approximately directly proportional to the displacement. This is, of course, an illustration of Hooke's law. From the third law of Newton the same statement is true for the additional tension with which the spring pulls back on the mass, the so-called elastic restoring force. We should therefore expect that when the displacing force is suddenly removed, leaving the mass particle subject to an unbalanced restoring force varying directly as the distance from the equilibrium point, the resulting motion of the particle will be approximately simple harmonic about this point as center. This is indeed verified by experiment and the resulting oscillations are called the *free* oscillations of the system consisting of the spring and attached mass particle. Their frequency, the spring being assumed to be massless, is

$$\nu = \frac{1}{2\pi}\sqrt{\frac{K}{m}}, \tag{2·3–14}$$

where K is the coefficient of proportionality between the displacing force and resultant displacement, i.e.,

$$F_d = Kx, \tag{2·3–15}$$

and the equation of motion is then

$$m\ddot{x} = -F_d = -Kx. \tag{2·3–16}$$

This has the same form as (2·3–1) with $c = -K$. The quantity K is often known as the *stiffness* of the spring. The formula (2·3–14) for the free oscillation frequency is worthy of special comment because we shall meet it again in our study of vibration problems. The significant thing to be noted is the presence of the elastic or stiffness factor in the numerator of the radical and the mass in the denominator. Thus, for given mass the stiffer the spring, the greater the frequency; on the other hand, for given stiffness, the larger the mass, the smaller the frequency.

In our treatment of the above illustration, we have neglected one important point. The theory implies that the simple harmonic motion of the mass particle attached to the spring never stops when once started. Experience, of course, rejects this result, for all such oscillations die down eventually when the system is left completely to itself. This indicates that our theory is of but approximate application and that to render it more complete we must assume a frictional or damping force acting on the mass in addition to the elastic restoring force. The solution of this problem will be postponed to Sec. 10·2.

It still remains our task to notice the case where the force though proportional to the displacement is always in the same direction as the displacement, that is, the constant c in eq. (2·3–1) is *positive*. The first integration then yields by the method used at the beginning of this section,

$$\tfrac{1}{2}m\dot{x}^2 = \tfrac{1}{2}cx^2 + C_1, \tag{2·3–17}$$

or

$$\tfrac{1}{2}mv^2 - \tfrac{1}{2}cx^2 = C_1 = U, \tag{2·3–18}$$

where the potential energy $-\tfrac{1}{2}cx^2$ is now negative. Hence as in (1·11–39) the total energy can be negative and must indeed necessarily be so if the velocity vanishes for some definite value of x, say $x = R$. Then

$$U = -\tfrac{1}{2}cR^2. \tag{2·3–19}$$

We must be careful not to think of the total mechanical energy as necessarily a positive quantity. Yet this immediately raises the question as to the physical significance of a negative energy, which somehow does not disturb us in the case of a positive total energy. If we examine (2·3–18) and (2·3–19) once more we see that if in some way we could contribute the energy $\tfrac{1}{2}cR^2$ to the particle (e.g., by performing work on it through the agency of an external force) we would increase U to zero and the particle would then obtain a kinetic energy at $x = R$ equal to $\tfrac{1}{2}cR^2$ or a velocity $v = R\sqrt{c/m}$. In fact any increase in the energy of the particle from its negative value $-\tfrac{1}{2}cR^2$ will insure that the particle gains kinetic energy at $x = R$ and will lose its kinetic energy at some smaller value of x. A contribution to the total energy is therefore necessary to drive the particle closer to the origin.

To revert to the general case, solution of (2·3–17) for v yields

$$v = \pm \sqrt{c/m} \sqrt{x^2 + \frac{2C_1}{c}}. \tag{2·3–20}$$

A second integration gives

$$\log\left(x + \sqrt{x^2 + \frac{2C_1}{c}}\right) = \pm \sqrt{\frac{c}{m}} \cdot t + C_2,$$

from which we may express x in explicit form as

$$x = \tfrac{1}{2}e^{C_2}e^{\pm\sqrt{c/m}\,t} - \frac{C_1}{c}e^{-C_2}e^{\mp\sqrt{c/m}\,t},$$

which may in turn be written in the more convenient form

$$x = Ae^{\sqrt{c/m}\,t} + Be^{-\sqrt{c/m}\,t}, \tag{2·3–21}$$

where the arbitrary constants A and B now replace C_1 and C_2. We shall recall without proof from the study of differential equations that the general solution of a second order linear differential equation

like (2·3–1) contains *two* arbitrary constants.   Indeed (2·3–21) satisfies
this requirement and the original differential equation, for c positive.
It remains only to express A and B in terms of the initial velocity and
displacement of the particle.   Taking the simple case in which $x = R$
and $v = 0$ when $t = 0$, we have the conditions

$$(1)\ A + B = R,$$

$$(2)\ A - B = 0,$$

whence $A = B = R/2$ and therefore

$$x = \frac{R}{2} \cdot [e^{\sqrt{c/m}\,t} + e^{-\sqrt{c/m}\,t}]. \qquad (2\text{·}3\text{–}22)$$

This may be more concisely expressed in terms of hyperbolic functions,
i.e., recalling that $e^x + e^{-x} = 2 \cosh x$, we may write

$$x = R \cosh \sqrt{\frac{c}{m}}\, t. \qquad (2\text{·}3\text{–}23)$$

The displacement increases rapidly with the time and there is no
oscillation.   The graph of (2·3–23) is shown in Fig. 2·7.   The curve
is known as the " catenary," and
we shall have occasion to use it
again in connection with problems
in statics.

The type of force leading to
(2·3–23) is a repulsion from a fixed
point.   Though repulsive forces
are encountered in physical phenomena, the one here considered is
uncommon, and it will not be profitable to discuss it further.   It has
served indeed the useful purpose
of stressing the method of handling initial conditions.

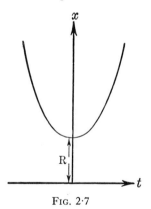

Fig. 2·7

It is instructive to consider this motion further from the standpoint
of negative total energy as discussed earlier in the section.   The reader
should plot v as a function of x for the special case corresponding to
eq. (2·3–23).

2·4. Motion in a Field Proportional to the Inverse Square of the Distance.

The equation of motion for a particle moving in a
straight line and acted on by a force inversely proportional to the

square of the distance from a given point of the line, taken as origin, is

$$m\ddot{x} = \frac{c}{x^2}. \qquad (2\cdot4\text{–}1)$$

If c is positive, the force is *repulsive*, while negative c corresponds to an *attractive* force. We shall here discuss only the latter case, as it is physically by far the more important. Thus as in Sec. 2·3, we put $c = -k$, where k is a positive constant. The eq. (2·4–1) then takes the form, multiplying both sides by $\dot{x}\,dt$,

$$\tfrac{1}{2}md(\dot{x})^2 = kd\left(\frac{1}{x}\right), \qquad (2\cdot4\text{–}2)$$

the result of the integration of which is

$$\tfrac{1}{2}m\dot{x}^2 = \frac{k}{x} + C_1, \qquad (2\cdot4\text{–}3)$$

This is precisely the energy equation for the particle and is indeed identical in form with eq. (1·11–39), developed for the straight-line radial motion of a particle with respect to the earth. The two equations become the same if we set $R + h = x$, $GmM = k$ and $C_1 = U$. All our results in Sec. 1·11 can therefore be applied at once.

However, if we wish to follow the temporal course of the motion, we must carry out a further integration of eq. (2·4–3). First solving for the velocity, we obtain

$$\dot{x} = \pm\sqrt{\frac{2k}{mx} + \frac{2C_1}{m}}. \qquad (2\cdot4\text{–}4)$$

Let us evaluate the constant C_1 by the boundary condition that the particle starts from rest at $x = R_0$. Then $C_1 = -k/R_0$, and eq. (2·4–4) becomes on separation of variables

$$\frac{dx}{\sqrt{1/x - 1/R_0}} = \pm\sqrt{\frac{2k}{m}}\,dt. \qquad (2\cdot4\text{–}5)$$

We must actually choose the minus sign before the radical on the right since positive dt will here correspond to negative dx. The result of a second integration may be expressed in the form

$$-\sqrt{R_0}\left(\sqrt{R_0 x - x^2} - R_0 \arcsin\sqrt{\frac{x}{R_0}}\right)$$

$$= -\sqrt{\frac{2k}{m}}\cdot t + C_2. \qquad (2\cdot4\text{–}6)$$

The boundary condition just assumed leads to $C_2 = \pi/2 \cdot R_0^{3/2}$. It follows that the time the particle takes to reach the origin if it starts from rest at $x = R_0$ is

$$t_1 = \sqrt{\frac{m}{2k}} \cdot \frac{\pi}{2} \cdot R_0^{3/2}. \qquad (2\cdot4\text{–}7)$$

According to Newton's law or hypothesis of universal gravitation every particle of matter in the universe attracts every other particle with a force, directed along the line joining the particles, directly proportional to the product of their masses and inversely proportional to the square of their distance apart, the coefficient of proportionality being known as the gravitation constant and generally denoted by G. The motion being discussed in this section is therefore linear motion in a *gravitational* field and of great importance in physics.

We discussed some aspects of it from the standpoint of energy in Sec. 1·11, where, indeed, we had to make the assumption that the earth exerts its gravitational effect on an external particle as if it were a single particle placed at the center of the earth with the whole mass of the earth concentrated there. We now desire to verify this assumption by calculating the resultant attraction between an aggregate of mass particles and another single particle. Let us consider the aggregate in the form of a homogeneous sphere and calculate its attraction for an external particle. The simplest procedure is to begin with a spherical shell with center at O (Fig. 2·8). The external mass particle, supposed

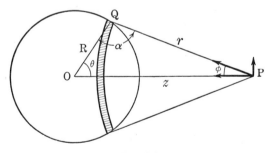

FIG. 2·8

for simplicity to be of unit mass, is located at P. Let $OP = z$ and the radius of the shell be R, while its mass is m, assumed to be uniformly distributed over its surface. Now let us draw about P as center two spheres of radii r and $r + dr$. These will cut the shell in a surface ring element of area $2\pi R^2 \sin \theta \, d\theta$. For the width of the ring is $R \, d\theta$, where $d\theta$ is the angle between the radii to the two edges of the ring. The circumference of the ring is $2\pi R \sin \theta$. The area is the product. All points of the ring are at approximately the same distance from P.

We may now conceive this zonal surface element to be subdivided into small sub-elements of unit area (e.g., the one at Q), each of mass $m/4\pi R^2$ and equidistant from P. The force of attraction between each sub-element and the unit mass at P has then the magnitude

$$\frac{m}{4\pi R^2} \cdot \frac{G}{r^2}, \qquad (2 \cdot 4{-}8)$$

and is directed from P to the sub-element in question. To find the resultant of these forces (i.e., the force between unit mass at P and the whole zonal surface element) we may most conveniently get their components normal and parallel to PO respectively. Examination at once discloses that the sum of the normal components is zero. Hence the required resultant is directed along PO. Its magnitude is obtained by multiplying the magnitude of each parallel component by the number of sub-elements. If the angle QPO is denoted by ϕ, the magnitude of each parallel component is

$$\frac{m}{4\pi R^2} \cdot \frac{G}{r^2} \cdot \cos \phi, \qquad (2 \cdot 4{-}9)$$

while the number of sub-elements is simply the area $2\pi R^2 \sin \theta \, d\theta$. Hence the magnitude of the resultant attraction is

$$\frac{Gm}{2r^2} \cdot \sin \theta \cos \phi \, d\theta. \qquad (2 \cdot 4{-}10)$$

In order to find the complete attraction for the whole shell, this must be integrated as θ goes from 0 to π. However, θ does not appear to be a desirable integration variable, hence we shall use r. From the law of cosines

$$r^2 = R^2 + z^2 - 2Rz \, \cos \, \theta,$$

so that

$$\sin \theta \, d\theta = \frac{r \, dr}{Rz}.$$

Moreover

$$\cos \phi = \frac{z^2 - R^2 + r^2}{2zr}.$$

Therefore on substitution the expression in $(2 \cdot 4{-}10)$ takes the form

$$\frac{Gm}{4Rz^2} \left[1 + \frac{z^2 - R^2}{r^2} \right] dr. \qquad (2 \cdot 4{-}11)$$

This must be integrated between the limits $r = z - R$ and $r = z + R$.

The total attraction of the spherical shell for the unit mass at P then has the magnitude

$$F = \frac{Gm}{4Rz^2} \left[r - \frac{z^2 - R^2}{r} \right]_{z-R}^{z+R}$$

$$= \frac{Gm}{z^2} . \tag{2·4-12}$$

This means that the spherical shell attracts the external point as if all its mass were concentrated at its center. Now any spherical mass may be thought of as made up of a series of concentric spherical shells of masses $m_1, m_2, m_3, \ldots$. From what we have just proved, the attraction for an external point of the totality of such shells has the magnitude

$$\frac{G(m_1 + m_2 + m_3 \cdots)}{z^2} = \frac{GM}{z^2} , \tag{2·4-13}$$

where M is the total mass of the sphere. It therefore follows that a solid sphere like a spherical shell attracts an external mass particle as if all its mass were concentrated at its center. For example, this will be very nearly true of the earth which is approximately spherical.

Thus we justify the assumption made in Sec. 1·11 and hence the results of that section with respect to the motion of a particle above the surface of the earth. Suppose a particle is dropped from rest at height h_0 above the earth's surface. From (1·11-39) we see that this entails

$$U = - \frac{GmM}{R + h_0} . \tag{2·4-14}$$

Hence the velocity v_0 with which the particle reaches the surface (neglecting air resistance) is

$$v_0 = \sqrt{\frac{2GMh_0}{(Rh_0 + R^2)}} . \tag{2·4-15}$$

When $h_0 \ll R$, this takes the familiar form

$$v_0 = \sqrt{2gh}. \tag{2·4-16}$$

The gravitation constant G which has entered so prominently into the discussion of the present section is one of the most important constants of physics. It is therefore of interest to note the most sensitive method for the determination of this quantity. This employs the so-called torsion balance in which two small metal spheres (usually of platinum or gold) are fixed to the ends of a light rod. This in turn is suspended at its mid-point by a fine vertical quartz fiber. In the schematic diagram (Fig. 2·9) *aPa* denotes the rod with the two metal balls at its extremities in its equilibrium position.   *P* is the point of suspension by the fiber which is, of course, perpendicular to the plane of the diagram.   Two heavy lead spherical balls are now placed at *A*, *A* and as a result the rod is deflected to *a'Pa'* as indicated by the dotted lines.   When the lead balls are moved to *A'*, *A'*, the deflection is in the opposite direction and the total deflection is measured by the angle δ.   From a knowledge of the elastic properties of the fiber (see Sec. 11·1) the magnitude of the force of attraction *F* between the small and large spheres can be computed and *G* calculated from the equation

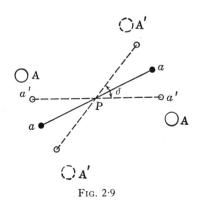

FIG. 2·9

$$F = \frac{GmM}{r^2},$$

where *m* and *M* are the masses of the small and large spheres respectively and *r* is the distance between their centers.   This method was devised in the late eighteenth century by Henry Cavendish and his name is usually attached to the experiment.   The most recent exact measurements by this method are due to P. R. Heyl of the United States Bureau of Standards.[1]   His apparatus is shown in the adjacent figure taken from the article indicated in the footnote (Fig. 2·10).   Heyl used small platinum spheres of mass about 50 gm each and large steel cylinders of mass 66 kg each.   For greater accuracy the torsion pendulum was placed in an evacuated region in which the pressure was usually about 1 or 2 mm of Hg.   Heyl allowed the rod to swing as a torsion pendulum instead of following the earlier static deflection method.   His value of *G*, which is now the accepted one, is (6.673 ± 0.003) × 10^{-8} $\frac{dyne\ cm^2}{gm^2}$.

The force of gravitation is not the only example of a force varying inversely as the square of the distance.   It will be recalled that electrically charged particles, like electrons, protons, nuclei of atoms, etc., attract or repel each other with forces of this kind.   Their mutual motions form an important part of the atomic theory of the structure of matter and in this book we shall frequently discuss applications of the

[1] P. R. Heyl and Peter Chrzanowski, *Journal of Research of the NBS*, **29**, 1, 1942.

principles of mechanics to their behavior.   We give here a simple example in the mutual motion of two charged particles which repel each
other with an inverse square force.   Let us suppose one is a nucleus of
mass m_N with positive charge Ne where e is the magnitude of the
charge on an electron and N is some integer (the so-called atomic
number), and let the other be an alpha particle which is the nucleus of
the helium atom, with positive charge $2e$ and mass m_α.

FIG. 2·10

We can at once use to advantage the energy considerations of Sec. 1·11.
In place of (1·11–31) we have Coulomb's law for the force of interaction
of two positively charged particles with charges $2e$ and Ne respectively.

$$F = \frac{2Ne^2}{r^2}, \qquad (2\cdot4\text{–}17)$$

where the minus sign has been changed to plus because the force is repulsive. The corresponding potential energy function becomes $V(r) = 2Ne^2/r$ and eq. (1·11–35) takes the form

$$\tfrac{1}{2}m_\alpha v_\alpha^2 + \tfrac{1}{2}m_N v_N^2 + \frac{2Ne^2}{r} = U, \qquad (2\cdot4\text{–}18)$$

where v_α and v_N are the velocities of the alpha particle and the nucleus respectively. We are entitled to apply the conservation of momentum relation (1·11–36, 37) and hence ultimately write the energy equation in the form

$$\tfrac{1}{2}m_\alpha(1 + m_\alpha/m_N)v_\alpha^2 = U - \frac{2Ne^2}{r}, \qquad (2\cdot4\text{–}19)$$

where we are tacitly assuming that $m_N > m_\alpha$, though we introduce no actual approximation as yet. Suppose the alpha particle is fired head on at the nucleus so that its velocity at a very great distance (effectively $r = \infty$) is $v_{\alpha 0}$. Substitution into (2·4–19) yields

$$U = \tfrac{1}{2}m_\alpha(1 + m_\alpha/m_N)v_{\alpha 0}^2. \qquad (2\cdot4\text{–}20)$$

It is clear that the repulsive force will bring the alpha particle to rest at a distance R from the center of the nucleus, where

$$R = \frac{2Ne^2}{\tfrac{1}{2}m_\alpha(1 + m_\alpha/m_N)v_{\alpha 0}^2}. \qquad (2\cdot4\text{–}21)$$

This distance provides an order of magnitude estimate of the size of the nucleus. If we suppose that $v_{\alpha 0}$ is the velocity of ejection of alpha particles from radium C, it comes out to be about 2×10^9 cm/sec. The mass of the alpha particle is $m_\alpha = 6.6 \times 10^{-24}$ gm. Let us choose copper (atomic number $N = 29$) as the nucleus, with $m_N = 63(1.67) \times 10^{-24}$ gm. The electron charge $e = 4.8 \times 10^{-10}$ e.s.u. Hence

$$R = 10^{-12} \text{ cm.}$$

This is a figure of considerable meaning in nuclear physics.

We shall discuss this problem in greater detail and without restricting the motion to straight-line form in Sec. 3·12.

2·5. Motion in a Field Proportional to the Inverse Cube of the Distance. This is a case of some physical interest because it arises when we have two force centers, very close together, the one attracting and the other repelling a distant particle with a force proportional to the inverse square of the distance. An example from magnetism will sufficiently illustrate this.   Imagine a very short magnet of length l and with north pole $+M$ and south pole $-M$ (Fig. 2·11), and inquire the

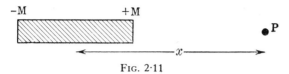

Fig. 2·11

resultant force on a unit north pole placed at P, distant x from the center of the magnet along the magnet extended, where $x \gg l$.   From Coulomb's law, according to which the force which a single isolated magnetic pole of strength M poles exerts on another of strength M' at a distance x is MM'/x^2, we have for the magnitude of the resultant force on the unit pole at P (in this case a force of repulsion)

$$\frac{-M}{(x + l/2)^2} + \frac{M}{(x - l/2)^2} = \frac{M \cdot 2xl}{(x^2 - l^2/4)^2}, \qquad (2\cdot5\text{--}1)$$

where the first term on the left denotes the force due to the south pole and the second that due to the north pole, and on the right we have reduced to a common denominator.   Now we further have

$$\frac{M \cdot 2xl}{(x^2 - l^2/4)^2} \doteq \frac{2Ml}{x^3},$$

if we utilize the assumption that $l \ll x$.   The direction of the force is away from and in the line containing the magnet.

In a force field of this nature, if the moving particle has mass m, the equation of rectilinear motion is

$$m\ddot{x} = \frac{K}{x^3}, \qquad (2\cdot5\text{--}2)$$

where K is a positive constant (e.g., $2Ml$ in the above illustration). Conducting a first integration, we have the energy equation

$$\tfrac{1}{2}m\dot{x}^2 = \frac{-K}{2x^2} + C_1. \qquad (2\cdot5\text{--}3)$$

Suppose that the particle starts from rest at a distance R from the force center.   Then $C_1 = K/2R^2$.   The velocity which the particle will have after traveling to infinity will then be

$$v = \frac{1}{R}\sqrt{\frac{K}{m}}, \qquad (2\cdot5\text{--}4)$$

or inversely proportional to the distance from which it started.   The student should also investigate the corresponding case in which K is a negative constant.   (Problem 15 at the end of the chapter.)

2·6. Force Dependent on the Time. Impulsive Force. The forces considered so far in this chapter have been either constant or dependent on the distance from some chosen origin. These are not the only forces leading to motions of interest in physics. Let us recall the type of force involved in the blow of a hammer. Here the force is definitely a function of time, rising from zero to a maximum and again falling to zero, more or less as in the accompanying figure (Fig. 2·12). If the time interval during which the force acts is sufficiently small we refer to the force as *impulsive*. Forces associated with the collisions of particles are usually of this character. The shape of the force curve is not always known, but a typical one might be of the form

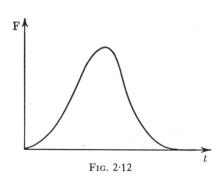

FIG. 2·12

$$F = Ate^{-Bt} \tag{2·6-1}$$

This is something like Fig. 2·12, except that F does not vanish for finite t but goes asymptotically to zero as t increases. If B is sufficiently large, however, F approaches zero fast after attaining its maximum, which occurs for $t = 1/B$. The equation of motion of a particle of mass m in this case is

$$m\ddot{x} = Ate^{-Bt}. \tag{2·6-2}$$

A first integration yields the velocity, viz.:

$$v = \dot{x} = \frac{A}{m}e^{-Bt}\left(-\frac{t}{B} - \frac{1}{B^2}\right) + C, \tag{2·6-3}$$

where C is the constant of integration. In terms of the initial velocity v_0 this becomes

$$v - v_0 = \frac{A}{m} - \frac{t}{B}\left[e^{-Bt} + \frac{1}{B^2}(1 - e^{-Bt})\right]. \tag{2·6-4}$$

In terms of the impulse-momentum theorem (1·10-2) the impulse of the force over the interval from 0 to t, which is also the change in momentum during the same interval, is

$$A\left[-\frac{t}{B}e^{-Bt} + \frac{1}{B^2}(1 - e^{-Bt})\right] \tag{2·6-5}$$

As t grows very great, this approaches the limiting value A/B^2. Hence there is a maximum finite change in momentum under the influence of this type of impulsive force. There is also a limiting velocity attained under the influence of the force, i.e., $A/B^2m + v_0$. This is also the maximum velocity, as may readily be shown by setting $\dot{v} = 0$ in (2·6–4). The determination of the distance traveled in time t is left as an exercise for the reader.

The action of most impulsive forces encountered in practice is more complicated than that considered above, the reason being that the motion produced by the impulsive force is commonly *resisted* by another force whose value changes during the motion and is generally dependent on the *velocity*. This leads to the considerations of the next section.

2·7. Rectilinear Motion in a Resisting Medium. It is found by experience that when a force produces acceleration through an actual material medium like the air (e.g., motion of a rain drop) or water (e.g., motion of a ship) or even a solid (as in the motion of a nail through a piece of wood) the medium always resists the motion with a force varying as some power of the velocity. The simplest case is that in which the resisting force varies directly as the velocity but is oppositely directed. This turns out to be a fair representation of the facts for motion in still air, for example, if the average velocity is small.

Let us consider the simple problem of a ball of mass m tossed straight up in the air. With the x axis vertical we have for the equation of motion

$$m\ddot{x} = -mg - R\dot{x}, \tag{2·7–1}$$

where R is a positive constant. Dividing through by m and putting $R/m = D$ for simplicity, we get the simpler form

$$\ddot{x} + D\dot{x} + g = 0. \tag{2·7–2}$$

We let $\dot{x} = v =$ instantaneous velocity, and have

$$\dot{v} + Dv + g = 0. \tag{2·7–3}$$

We separate the variables by writing this as follows:

$$\frac{dv}{v + g/D} = -D\,dt, \tag{2·7–4}$$

which has the solution

$$\log{(v + g/D)} = -Dt + K, \tag{2·7–5}$$

where K is the constant of integration. Let the initial velocity be v_0. Then (2·7–5) yields for the instantaneous velocity

$$v = (v_0 + g/D)e^{-Dt} - g/D. \tag{2·7–6}$$

The momentum-impulse theorem now takes the form

$$mv - mv_0 = \left(mv_0 + \frac{mg}{D}\right)(e^{-Dt} - 1). \tag{2·7–7}$$

As t increases indefinitely, the change in momentum approaches

$$\Delta mv \to -\left(mv_0 + \frac{mg}{D}\right). \tag{2·7–8}$$

This assumes of course that in the meantime the particle has not struck the earth. Under these conditions there is a limiting velocity given by

$$v_f = -\frac{g}{D}. \tag{2·7–9}$$

It is of interest to go back to (2·7–6) and note what the velocity v becomes for D very small, so that we can expand e^{-Dt} in the usual series

$$e^{-Dt} = 1 - Dt + D^2t^2/2! - D^3t^3/3! + \cdots \tag{2·7–10}$$

and keep only the first three terms. The result is

$$v = v_0 - gt - v_0Dt + (v_0 + g/D)D^2t^2/2! + \cdots. \tag{2·7–11}$$

As $D \to 0$, this takes on the familiar form

$$v = v_0 - gt \tag{2·7–12}$$

with the time of rising into the air equal to v_0/g. In the more general case in which D is non-vanishing the time to reach the highest point h is

$$t_h = \frac{1}{D} \log (1 + v_0D/g). \tag{2·7–13}$$

To compare this with v_0/g in the non-resistance case, we again expand in a series (treating D as small) and obtain

$$t_h = v_0/g - v_0^2D/2g^2 + \cdots. \tag{2·7–14}$$

It thus appears that $t_h < v_0/g$ or the time to reach the highest point is *less* in the resisting medium than in vacuo. This should be more carefully verified by the use of the inequality

$$\log (1 + x) < x,$$

which is true for all real, positive values of x. The result appears a trifle surprising until we reflect that the total height of rise will

probably turn out to be less than in the nonresistance case. To get
this we must solve (2·7–6) by putting $v = \dot{x}$ again, thus obtaining

$$dx = [(v_0 + g/D)e^{-Dt} - g/D]\, dt. \tag{2·7–15}$$

The integration yields (using the initial condition $x = 0$ for $t = 0$)

$$x = \left(\frac{v_0 + g/D}{D}\right)(1 - e^{-Dt}) - \frac{gt}{D}. \tag{2·7–16}$$

Once more, expansion in series gives the approximate result

$$x = v_0 t - gt^2/2 - v_0 Dt^2/2 + \cdots. \tag{2·7–17}$$

As $D \to 0$ this takes on the familiar form for upward flight in vacuo.
We obtain the maximum height h by substituting t_h for t in (2·7–16).
The result is

$$h = v_0/D - g/D^2 \cdot \log (1 + v_0 D/g). \tag{2·7–18}$$

Expansion of the logarithm again puts this in a form more readily
compared with the ordinary ideal case of motion in vacuo. Thus

$$h = v_0^2/2g - v_0^3 D/3g^2 + \cdots. \tag{2·7–19}$$

The second term on the right thus appears as a correction (for D small)
to the ideal maximum height given by the first term. The indication
is thus that the maximum height attained in a resisting medium for
given initial velocity v_0 is less than in the non-resisting medium.
This is verified by more careful examination of (2·7–18).

The use of series expansions in this section is recommended to
the reader as a useful device in many mechanical problems.

Our treatment of this problem of straight-line motion is a resisting
medium with the resisting force varying as the first power of the velocity
has neglected any mention of energy considerations. Indeed the usual
method of seeking a first integral of eq. (2·7–3), exemplified by the treatment of Chapter 1 and the earlier sections of this chapter, breaks down.
The best we can do is to multiply (2·7–3) through by v and write

$$v\dot{v} = -gv - Dv^2. \tag{2·7–20}$$

This may be rewritten

$$\frac{d}{dt}\left(\frac{mv^2}{2} + mgx\right) = -mDv^2. \tag{2·7–21}$$

This is interesting, since the term in the parenthesis on the left side is
(see eq. 2·2–3) the total energy of a particle of mass m in the uniform
force field $-mg$. This quantity is no longer constant in time. Consequently there is some question whether we have any right logically

to refer to it as the energy at all.   From the definition we have given for the term " energy," there strictly speaking is no energy in this motion.   To adopt this strictly logically attitude, however, seems an unnecessary sacrifice of a useful concept.   Hence we shall find it advantageous to continue to refer to the quantity $\frac{1}{2}mv^2 + mgx$ as U and write

$$\frac{dU}{dt} = -mDv^2, \qquad (2\cdot7\text{--}22)$$

taking this to mean that now the energy of the particle decreases with the time because of the resistance of the medium and indeed at the rate mDv^2.   This idea turns out to be very useful when we are considering the damped oscillations of a vibrator (see Sec. 9·3).   In the present case we can indeed express v^2 as a function of t and hence integrate (2·7–22) to find U as a function of t.   This is left as a task for the reader.

PROBLEMS

1. A monkey climbs a massless rope which passes over a massless and frictionless pulley P and has fastened on the other end a counter weight W of the same mass as the monkey.   Discuss the motion of the monkey and the weight.

2. In the accompanying figure particles of mass m_1 and m_2 respectively are connected by a perfectly flexible inextensible string and are constrained to move on the two inclined planes as indicated.   Obtain the expression for the acceleration of the system, as well as that for the tension in the string.   If the system starts from rest, what is the kinetic energy after each particle has moved a distance s along its respective plane?

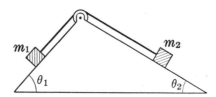

3. In the figure a particle of mass m starting from rest slides down a perfectly smooth inclined plane of angle θ and height h.   When it reaches P, it continues to move along the horizontal in the x direction but subject to a resisting force of the form kv, where v is the speed and k is a constant.   How far will it·go before coming to rest?   How long will it take to cover 99% of this distance?

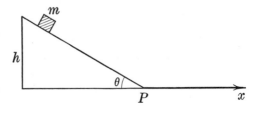

4. Prove that the time for a particle to descend a smooth inclined plane is to the time to descend vertically a distance equal to the height of the plane as $1 : \sin \theta$, where θ is the angle of the plane.

5. A metal ball of mass 100 grams falls from rest through a column of glycerine. It is ultimately observed to attain a practically constant velocity of 5 cm/sec. If the resisting force of the glycerine is assumed to vary as the first power of the velocity of the ball, find the magnitude of the force for any velocity v. Also find the distance traveled in the first second.

6. A particle of mass M is subject to two forces: (1) a constant force F; and (2) a resisting force varying as the square of the velocity. Find the expression for the distance traveled by the particle in time t and its velocity at the same time.

7. Prove that the motion of the projection of a fixed point located on the circumference of a circle on a uniformly rotating diameter of the circle is, relative to the diameter, simple harmonic motion.

8. A straight smooth tube is bored through the center of an otherwise homogeneous solid sphere of mass M and radius R. A particle of mass m falls from rest through the tube from the surface of the sphere. What will its motion be, assuming that the only force acting is the gravitational force between the particle and the sphere? How long will it take the particle to travel through the sphere?

9. One end of a vertical brass wire 10 meters long and 1 mm in radius is fastened to a rigid ceiling. The other end is loaded with a mass of 2 kilograms. If the mass is displaced 5 mm and released, show that its resulting motion is simple harmonic. If Young's modulus for brass is 9×10^{11} dynes/cm², find the frequency and the maximum kinetic energy of the load. What is the impulse of the force during a quarter period of the motion? How much average power is exerted during a quarter period?

10. A cylindrical disc of radius R and height h floats in water with half its volume immersed, and its flat side horizontal. If it is depressed a distance $x \ll h$ and released, show that the resulting motion is simple harmonic and find the frequency.

11. A body falls 2000 miles to the surface of the earth. Find the time it takes and also the time for the last 1000 miles.

12. An electron is attracted by a positive charge of magnitude Ne. Suppose that in addition to this there also acts a repulsive force on the electron varying inversely as the cube of the distance. Determine the coefficient of proportionality of this latter force so that the resultant force on the electron is zero at a distance of 10^{-11} cm from the positive charge. What velocity will it have at this point if it starts at rest from a distance of 10^{-8} cm?

13. Plot a space-time graph for the motion of the electron in Problem 12.

14. A free particle (i.e., one which is subject to no accelerating forces) possesses initial velocity v_0 in a straight line in a medium which exerts a resisting force proportional to the cube of the velocity. Show that the time it takes the particle to travel a given distance is a quadratic function of the distance.

15. A particle of mass m moves in a straight line subject to a force directed toward a fixed point on the line and varying inversely as the cube of the distance. Discuss the motion. In particular if the particle starts from rest at distance h from the fixed point, find the total time required to reach the latter point.

16. A particle of mass m is acted on by an attractive force directed along the x axis and varying inversely as the n-th power of the distance from the origin, where n is integral and different from 0 or 1. If the particle starts at rest at distance a from the origin, find the velocity it will attain at distance x.

17. In the rectilinear motion of a particle in a resisting medium (Sec. 2·7), find the dependence of the total energy U on the time by solving eq. (2·7–22).

18. Solve the problem of the Atwood machine (Sec. 2·1) by the use of the energy principle (Sec. 2·2).

19. A particle of mass m is constrained to move along the x axis subject not only to a restoring force $-kx$, where k is the stiffness and a positive quantity, but also to a constant force $\mathbf{F}$. Find x as a function of t. Also find the energy equation for the system.

20. Determine the expression for the distance traveled in time t by a particle subject to the impulsive force given in eq. (2·6–1) if it starts at x_0 with initial velocity v_0. Find the work done by the force during this time.

21. A particle of mass m moves subject to an impulsive force of the form given in eq. (2·6–1) and at the same time is subject to a resisting force varying as the first power of the velocity. Discuss the motion.

Chapter 3

CURVILINEAR MOTION IN A PLANE

3·1. Components of Motion in a Plane. After rectilinear motion the next stage of complexity is clearly motion in a plane. It follows from the discussion in Sec. 1·2 that the position of a particle in a plane may be represented either by the position vector **r** from some chosen origin to the point occupied by the particle or by the rectangular coördinates x, y in an appropriate reference system. In either case we have the relation

$$\mathbf{r} = \mathbf{i}x + \mathbf{j}y, \tag{3·1–1}$$

where **i** and **j** are the *unit* vectors along the x and y axes respectively.[1]

To consult the figure (Fig. 3·1), if AB denotes an infinitesimally small portion of the path of a particle, the vector from O to A which gives the position of A will be denoted by **r** and the corresponding vector to B is $\mathbf{r} + d\mathbf{r}$. Hence the displacement AB may be represented by the vector $d\mathbf{r}$. The velocity of the particle is $\mathbf{v} = \dot{\mathbf{r}}$ (Sec. 1·3), which from (3·1–1) becomes

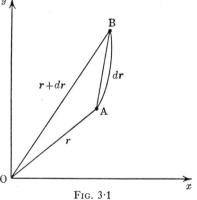

FIG. 3·1

$$\mathbf{v} = \dot{\mathbf{r}} = \mathbf{i}\dot{x} + \mathbf{j}\dot{y}. \tag{3·1–2}$$

It should be emphasized that in differentiating **r** in (3·1–1) with respect to the time the unit vectors **i** and **j** are treated as constants since the axes are assumed to remain fixed as time passes.

Similarly the acceleration of the particle is by definition

$$\mathbf{a} = \dot{\mathbf{v}} = \ddot{\mathbf{r}} = \mathbf{i}\ddot{x} + \mathbf{j}\ddot{y}, \tag{3·1–3}$$

whence $\ddot{x}$ and $\ddot{y}$ appear as the rectangular components of the vector acceleration. We may therefore write (cf. Sec. 1·5)

$$a_x = \ddot{x},$$
$$\tag{3·1–4}$$
$$a_y = \ddot{y}.$$

[1] Eq. (3·1–1) is thus a special case of (1·3–6).

We shall have occasion to use these acceleration components a great deal in the following sections.

3·2. Equations of Motion for a Particle in a Plane. The motion of a particle in a plane is a special case of motion in space and hence is described by the fundamental equation (1·7–4). It is important to recall that this equation, viz.,

$$\mathbf{F} = m\ddot{\mathbf{r}}, \tag{3·2–1}$$

is a vector equation. Its solution for each particular choice of $\mathbf{F}$ involves the integration of a second order ordinary differential equation. Methods are available in certain cases for the integration in vector form, but we shall prefer the more common alternative method of components. Thus we write (3·2–1) in the form (specialized to the xy plane)

$$\mathbf{i}F_x + \mathbf{j}F_y = m(\mathbf{i}a_x + \mathbf{j}a_y), \tag{3·2–2}$$

where F_x and F_y are the x and y component forces already mentioned, and a_x and a_y similarly the component accelerations. Since (3·2–2) holds in general, the coefficient of $\mathbf{i}$ on the left must be equal to that of $\mathbf{i}$ on the right, etc., with the result that (3·2–2) is actually equivalent to the two equations

$$F_x = ma_x = m\ddot{x},$$
$$F_y = ma_y = m\ddot{y}. \tag{3·2–3}$$

These are called the component equations of motion in the plane. Their independent solution provides the solution of the problem of plane motion. It is well to stress that our handling of them as independent simultaneous equations reflects our faith that a force F_x can act on the particle in the x direction independently of the action of F_y in the y direction. This is, of course, an illustration of the principle of superposition and is implicit in the vector form of the fundamental equation of motion.

We now proceed to a simple illustration of the integration of equations of the form (3·2–3).

3·3. Projectile Motion. Consider a particle of mass m projected into the air from a point on the ground with velocity of magnitude v_0 in a direction making an angle θ with the horizontal. We wish to determine its motion, neglecting the resistance of the air, which for small velocities will not affect the motion appreciably. We also neglect any effect of the wind. Since there are then no forces save gravity, the motion is confined to a plane which we shall take as the xy plane (cf. Fig. 3·2).   If we draw the x and y axes through O, the point of projection, the force components are then

$$F_x = 0, \quad F_y = -mg, \qquad (3 \cdot 3-1)$$

where we assume that the motion takes place so close to the surface of the earth that we are justified in taking the acceleration g as a constant. To be perfectly general we should have to take account of the fact that the particle is attracted to the earth by the Newtonian force of gravitation and hence should use the inverse square law. However, from the discussion in Sec. 2·4 it is clear that for elevations small compared with the radius of the earth, the error in assuming a constant g in (3·3–1) is negligible compared with that made in neglecting air resistance.

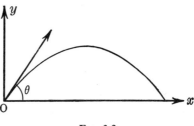

FIG. 3·2

The resulting equations of motion are (cf. 3·2–3)

$$\begin{aligned} m\ddot{x} &= 0, \\ m\ddot{y} &= -mg. \end{aligned} \right\} \qquad (3 \cdot 3-2)$$

Integrating, we have at once

$$x = \frac{c_1}{m}t + c_2, \qquad (3 \cdot 3-3)$$

$$y = -\tfrac{1}{2}gt^2 + c_3 t + c_4, \qquad (3 \cdot 3-4)$$

where c_1, c_2, c_3 and c_4 are the usual arbitrary constants of integration. To evaluate them, let us note that at $t = 0$, $x = y = 0$, and therefore $c_2 = c_4 = 0$.   Moreover

$$\frac{c_1}{m} = \dot{x}\Big|_{t=0} = v_0 \cos \theta, \qquad (3 \cdot 3-5)$$

and

$$c_3 = \dot{y}\,|_{t=0} = v_0 \sin \theta. \qquad (3 \cdot 3-6)$$

The component velocities at any instant are then

$$\dot{x} = v_0 \cos \theta, \quad \dot{y} = -gt + v_0 \sin \theta, \qquad (3 \cdot 3-7)$$

and the final parametric equations of the path of the particle are

$$x = v_0 \cos \theta \cdot t, \quad y = -\tfrac{1}{2}gt^2 + v_0 \sin \theta \cdot t. \qquad (3 \cdot 3-8)$$

Eliminating t between the two equations in (3·3–8) we get the equation of the path of the projectile in the form

$$y = -\tfrac{1}{2}g \frac{x^2}{v_0{}^2 \cos^2 \theta} + x \tan \theta, \qquad (3·3–9)$$

which is the equation of a parabola with axis parallel to the y axis and with vertex at the point with the coördinates

$$x = \frac{v_0{}^2 \sin 2\theta}{2g}, \quad y = \frac{v_0{}^2 \sin^2 \theta}{2g}.$$

This is the point at which the particle reaches its maximum height, as may be verified by applying the usual test of equating dy/dx to zero. The maximum height is therefore

$$h = \frac{v_0{}^2 \sin^2 \theta}{2g}, \qquad (3·3–10)$$

and the range, or total distance which the projectile travels along the x axis, is, from symmetry,

$$R = \frac{v_0{}^2 \sin 2\theta}{g}. \qquad (3·3–11)$$

For a given value of v_0, R is a maximum for $\theta = 45°$. The symmetry of the parabola about its axis indicates that the time spent on the upward part of the flight is equal to the time for the downward flight. From (3·3–8) the total time spent by the projectile in its flight is readily seen to be

$$t_R = \frac{2v_0 \sin \theta}{g}. \qquad (3·3–12)$$

In our discussion of the motion of a particle under gravity both in this section and Sec. 2·1, we have deliberately overlooked one point of small practical but considerable theoretical significance. It will be recalled from Sec. 1·12 that the equations of motion which we have used are applicable only in inertial systems, i.e., those which move with constant velocity (without rotation) with respect to the primary inertial system. In treating axes fixed in the rotating earth as an inertial system we are therefore committing a logical error and our results cannot then be completely correct. The thorough solution of the problem will be found in Sec. 8·12, where the correct equations of motion for such a case are set up and solved. As has been intimated, the modification in the results of the present section will be found to be very slight in practice.

For convenience, energy considerations applied to problems of the kind discussed here will be postponed to Chapter 4.

3·4. Projectile Motion in a Resisting Medium.   The general problem of the plane motion of a projectile through a medium that resists its flight is a highly involved one which it is the function of exterior ballistics to solve.   Nevertheless there is some value in considering here the rather simple special case in which the resisting force varies as the square of the resultant velocity magnitude and is directed at every point along the trajectory oppositely to the direction of motion.

Let us assume that the magnitude of the resisting force is of the form

$$kmv^2,$$

where m is the mass of the particle, and k is the specific resistance factor, i.e. the resisting force per unit mass per unit (velocity)^2.   The component equations of motion then become

$$\ddot{x} = -k\dot{x}\dot{s},$$
$$\ddot{y} = -k\dot{y}\dot{s} - g, \tag{3·4-1}$$

where

$$\dot{s}^2 = \dot{x}^2 + \dot{y}^2 \tag{3·4-2}$$

is the square of the magnitude of the resultant velocity.   We find it convenient to use as a variable, s, which denotes distance measured from the origin along the path of the projectile.   The reader should be able to show without difficulty from the first equation in (3·4-1) that

$$\dot{x} = v_0 \cos \theta \cdot e^{-ks}, \tag{3·4-3}$$

where v_0 and θ have the same meaning as in Sec. 3·3.   Note that when $s = 0$ (i.e. at the origin or point of projection) $\dot{x} = v_0 \cos \theta$, the initial horizontal velocity.   Combination of (3·4-3) with the second equation in (3·4-1) gives the differential equation of the orbit in the form

$$\frac{d^2y}{dx^2} = -\frac{g}{v_0^2 \cos^2 \theta} \cdot e^{2ks}. \tag{3·4-4}$$

Note that for $k = 0$, i.e. no resistance, this reduces to a differential equation which when integrated yields precisely the parabolic orbit (3·3-9) as it should.

If we now restrict the discussion to a rather flat trajectory, i.e. one in which $|dy/dx| \ll 1$ in all parts of the path, the first integral of (3·4-4) becomes

$$\frac{dy}{dx} = \tan \theta + \frac{g}{2kv_0^2 \cos^2 \theta} \cdot (1 - e^{2kx}), \tag{3·4-5}$$

yielding on a second integration the equation of the orbit in the form

$$y = x \left(\tan \theta + \frac{g}{2kv_0^2 \cos^2 \theta} \right) + \frac{g}{4k^2v_0^2 \cos^2 \theta} \cdot (1 - e^{2kx}) \quad (3 \cdot 4 - 6)$$

where the constant of integration has already been evaluated by the condition that, when $x = 0, y = 0$. If we expand e^{2kx} into the usual series and assume that kx is small so that no terms need be kept after the third power ones, the orbit becomes

$$y = x \tan \theta - \frac{gx^2}{2v_0^2 \cos^2 \theta} - \frac{gkx^3}{3v_0^2 \cos^2 \theta} \cdot \quad (3 \cdot 4 - 7)$$

The last term on the right represents the correction to the ideal parabola due to the presence of resistance. This might serve as an approximation to the path of a rifle bullet fired through air with a small elevation angle θ. Ballistically speaking the result should not be taken too seriously, however, since the resisting force does not vary with the square of the velocity for all speeds, and is not directed exactly opposite to the velocity of the bullet.

3·5. Composition of Simple Harmonic Motions in a Plane. Certain types of motion of interest in physics arise from the composition of simple harmonic motions along the coördinate axes. Confining our discussion as usual to motion in a plane, let us suppose that a mass particle at P (Fig. 3·3) moves in accordance with the following equations of motion

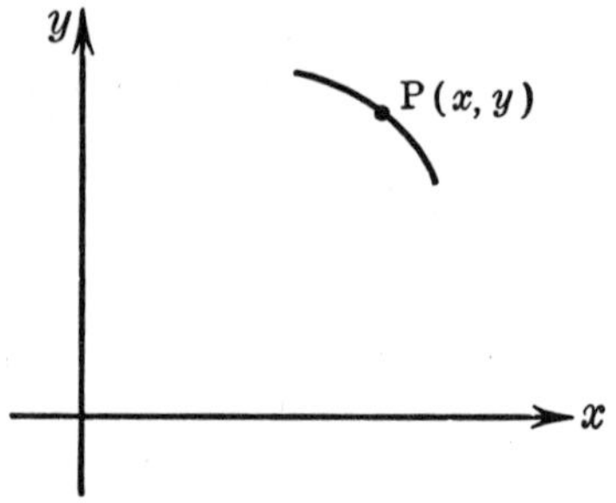

FIG. 3·3

$$\left. \begin{aligned} m\ddot{x} &= -c_1 x, \\ m\ddot{y} &= -c_2 y, \end{aligned} \right\} \quad (3 \cdot 5 - 1)$$

where c_1 and c_2 are *positive* constants. Consulting Sec. 2·3 we see that each of these can be integrated directly, yielding

$$\left. \begin{aligned} x &= A_1 \cos \left(\sqrt{\frac{c_1}{m}} t + \epsilon_1 \right), \\ y &= A_2 \cos \left(\sqrt{\frac{c_2}{m}} t + \epsilon_2 \right) \cdot \end{aligned} \right\} \quad (3 \cdot 5 - 2)$$

There are thus two simple harmonic motions along the x and y axes respectively having amplitudes A_1 and A_2 and frequencies

$$\nu_1 = \frac{1}{2\pi}\sqrt{\frac{c_1}{m}} \quad \text{and} \quad \nu_2 = \frac{1}{2\pi}\sqrt{\frac{c_2}{m}},$$

and differing in initial phase by $\epsilon_1 - \epsilon_2$. The equations (3·5–2) are the parametric equations of the path of the particle. We may obtain the geometric path by the elimination of the time between them.

Let us take first the special case where $c_1 = c_2 = c$, i.e., where the frequencies are the same along the two axes. Let $\sqrt{c/m} = \omega$ and for convenience choose the initial phase ϵ_1 to be zero by taking the initial x displacement equal to A_1. Then the total phase difference between the two motions will be ϵ_2, which we shall call ϵ for simplicity. The parametric equations become

$$\left.\begin{aligned} x &= A_1 \cos \omega t, \\ y &= A_2 \cos(\omega t + \epsilon) \end{aligned}\right\}. \qquad (3\cdot5\text{–}3)$$

By substitution from the first into the second, t is eliminated and we have

$$y = A_2\left[\frac{x \cos \epsilon}{A_1} - \sqrt{1 - \frac{x^2}{A_1^2}} \cdot \sin \epsilon\right].$$

By transposition, squaring and collecting terms, this equation takes the form

$$\frac{x^2}{A_1^2 \sin^2 \epsilon} - \frac{2xy}{A_1 A_2 \sin \epsilon \tan \epsilon} + \frac{y^2}{A_2^2 \sin^2 \epsilon} = 1. \qquad (3\cdot5\text{–}4)$$

Applying the usual test for a conic section, we find that this is the equation of an ellipse. Thus for an equation of the second degree in the form

$$Ax^2 + Bxy + Cy^2 + Dx + Ey + F = 0,$$

we have[1] a hyperbola, ellipse or parabola according as $B^2 - 4AC$ is greater than, less than or equal to zero respectively. In the present case this quantity is $-4/(A_1^2 A_2^2 \sin^2 \epsilon)$ and is less than zero. The student should show that the major axis of the ellipse lies along the line making with the x axis the angle θ such that

$$\tan 2\theta = \left\{\frac{2A_1 A_2 \cos \epsilon}{A_1^2 - A_2^2}\right\}. \qquad (3\cdot5\text{–}5)$$

---

[1] See, for example, any text on analytic geometry, e.g., P. R. Rider, *Analytic Geometry*, Macmillan, New York, 1947, pp. 152 f.

Let us note a few special cases. If $A_1 \neq A_2$ and $\epsilon = 90°$, $\theta = 0$ and the major axis of the ellipse lies in the x axis. Supposing further $A_1 = A_2 = A$ and $\cos \epsilon = 0$, i.e., $\epsilon = \pi/2$, the ellipse reduces to a circle of radius A about the origin as center. The student should work out other cases and show for example that if $\epsilon = 0$, the path is the straight line with equation

$$\frac{x}{A_1} = \frac{y}{A_2},\tag{3·5–6}$$

as is, of course, immediately evident from eq. (3·5–3).

It may be pointed out that the above motions are really special cases of a very important general kind of motion. For we see that if a particle is attracted toward the origin with a force proportional to the distance to the origin, i.e., if the force magnitude F is such that

$$F(r) = cr,\tag{3·5–7}$$

where $r = \sqrt{x^2 + y^2}$, the component equations of motion will be precisely the equations (3·5–1), with $c_1 = c_2 = c$. Such a motion is a special case of what is called *central motion* or motion in a *central field*. It will be discussed in detail in the next section (Sec. 3·6), where the truth of the statement immediately above will become perhaps more evident.

Let us now, however, consider the case of eqs. (3·5–1) with $c_1 \neq c_2$. This will correspond to the composition of two simple harmonic motions with different frequencies. For simplicity we shall call these $\sqrt{c_1/m} = \omega$ and $\sqrt{c_2/m} = \omega + \alpha$, where α appears as the difference between the two angular frequencies. Now assume that there is a time when the two motions are in phase and choose this as the time origin. Then in eqs. (3·5–2) we have $\epsilon_1 = \epsilon_2 = 0$ and the equations become, choosing $A_1 = A_2 = A$ for greater simplicity,

$$\left.\begin{array}{l} x = A \cos \omega t, \\ y = A \cos (\omega + \alpha)t. \end{array}\right\}\tag{3·5–8}$$

We first eliminate ωt and obtain

$$x^2 - 2xy \cos \alpha t + y^2 = A^2 \sin^2 \alpha t.\tag{3·5–9}$$

To get rid of the product term, change the coördinates to x', y', where

$$\left.\begin{array}{l} x = \dfrac{\sqrt{2}}{2}(x' - y'), \\[2mm] y = \dfrac{\sqrt{2}}{2}(x' + y'). \end{array}\right\}\tag{3·5–10}$$

This corresponds to a rotation of axes through the angle 45°.   In the new coördinates the equation (3·5–9) becomes

$$x'^2(1 - \cos \alpha t) + y'^2(1 + \cos \alpha t) = A^2 \sin^2 \alpha t,$$

or

$$\frac{x'^2}{2A^2 \cos^2 \alpha t/2} + \frac{y'^2}{2A^2 \sin^2 \alpha t/2} = 1, \qquad (3\cdot5\text{–}11)$$

where we have used the trigonometric identities

$$1 - \cos \alpha t = 2 \sin^2 \alpha t/2; \quad 1 + \cos \alpha t = 2 \cos^2 \alpha t/2;$$

$$\sin^2 \alpha t = 4 \sin^2 \alpha t/2 \cdot \cos^2 \alpha t/2.$$

Equation (3·5–11) is the equation of an ellipse with axes which change continuously with the time and with values running from 0 to $2\sqrt{2}A$.

As a matter of fact, of course, eq. (3·5–11) cannot be used alone to determine the actual path which is the composition of the two simple harmonic motions.   For this purpose the time must be eliminated between it and one of the equations (3·5–8).   To plot the path in special cases it is most simple to use eqs. (3·5–8) as parametric equations of the orbit.   As an illustration the case where $(\omega + \alpha)/\omega = 8/7$ or $\alpha = \omega/7$ is plotted in the accompanying figure (Fig. 3·4), the time origin being taken, of course, as that time when the motions are in phase.

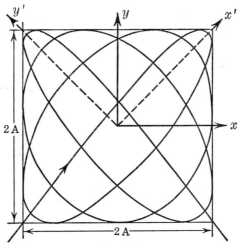

FIG. 3·4

Actually the figure does not plot precisely (3·5–8) but rather

$$x = -A \cos \omega t,$$

$$y = -A \cos (\omega + \alpha)t,$$

as is clear from the way the axes are chosen. This, however, is not significant.

A more important question is this: Is the resultant motion in this case periodic, i.e., does the path of the particle repeat itself after some period P? It is seen from (3·5–8) that if there is to be such a period P there must exist a pair of integers j and k such that

$$\omega P = 2\pi j,$$

$$(\omega + \alpha)P = 2\pi k.$$

But this means that the ratio of the two frequencies ω and $\omega + \alpha$ must be the ratio of two whole numbers, i.e. $(\omega + \alpha)/\omega$ must be a rational number or put in another way, $\omega + \alpha$ and ω must be commensurable. This is certainly true in the example illustrated in Fig. 3·4. If $\omega + \alpha$ and ω are not commensurable, it follows that the resulting motion is not periodic.

Curves for both commensurable and incommensurable cases have been widely studied and are known as Lissajous figures. A simple method of obtaining them experimentally is to allow a stiff rod with rectangular cross-section to oscillate perpendicular to its length when clamped in a vise. If a mirror is attached to the freely vibrating end and a ray of light is reflected from it, the figures can then be produced on a screen. These figures are also obtained in the cathode ray oscillograph. In this instrument, the cathode rays are permitted to pass through two perpendicular oscillating electric or magnetic fields, and the resulting path traced by the rays as they pass through these two fields may be observed on a fluorescent screen at the other end of the tube.[1]

The reader may find it of interest to express the horizontal and vertical harmonic motions in the form

$$x = A \cos \omega_1 t,$$

$$y = A \cos (\omega_2 t + \delta),$$

where the two angular frequencies ω_1 and ω_2 are different and the initial phase angle δ is not necessarily zero. As a matter of fact the Lissajous figure for $\delta = \pi/2$ is particularly useful since it turns out in this case that if ω_1 and ω_2 are commensurable, their ratio is equal to the ratio of the number of horizontal maxima to the number of vertical maxima in the figure. Electronic technicians make good use of this case.

3·6. Central Forces. Suppose that the force **F** on the particle is of such a nature that it is always directed toward or away from some fixed point, which we shall take as the origin, and is a function

---

[1] For an elaborate description of this instrument see Henry G. Booker, *An Approach to Electrical Science*, McGraw-Hill, New York, 1959, pp. 287 ff.

of the distance r from this point only.   Such a force is termed a *central force*, and it is no exaggeration to state that central forces are among the most important of all that arise in physical problems.   Geometrical reasoning shows that central field motion always takes place in a plane. Thus, the initial direction of motion of the particle and the initial line connecting it to the force center define a plane.   Since there is no force component normal to this plane, motion once started in it will continue in it.

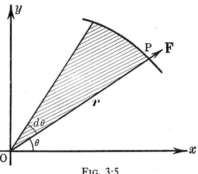

We shall call the line joining the particle P to the origin the *radius vector*.   It is strictly $\mathbf{r}$, the position vector of the point P with respect to O.   (Recall Sec. 1·2.)   Its magnitude is r, which will always be considered a positive quantity.   Consulting Fig. 3·5,

FIG. 3·5

let $F(r)$ denote the functional dependence of the force on the distance along the radius vector.   If $\mathbf{F}$ is assumed to be directed along $\mathbf{r}$, we have $\mathbf{F} = F(r)\mathbf{r}/r$, whence the components of the force along the x and y axes become

$$\left. \begin{aligned} F_x &= F(r) \cos \theta, \\ F_y &= F(r) \sin \theta, \end{aligned} \right\} \tag{3·6-1}$$

where θ is the angle which the radius vector makes with the x axis. But

$$\cos \theta = \frac{x}{r}, \quad \sin \theta = \frac{y}{r}, \tag{3·6-2}$$

whence the equations take the form

$$\left. \begin{aligned} m\ddot{x} &= F(r) \frac{x}{r}, \\ m\ddot{y} &= F(r) \frac{y}{r}. \end{aligned} \right\} \tag{3·6-3}$$

It is to be noted that if $F(r)$ is positive the central force is one of repulsion, while if $F(r)$ is negative, the force is attractive.   Before we integrate these equations for special cases, we can gain much information of a general nature about motion in a central force field.   Multiply the first equation in (3·6-3) by y and the second by x and subtract.

We then have

$$xÿ - yẍ = 0. \tag{3·6–4}$$

This can be integrated at once and yields

$$xẏ - yẋ = k, \tag{3·6–5}$$

where k is an arbitrary constant. The physical significance of eq. (3·6–5) will be better understood if we transform from rectangular to polar coördinates r and θ, as given by the defining equations (3·6–2). Thus

$$\left.\begin{aligned}
\dot{x} &= \dot{r} \cos \theta - r \sin \theta \cdot \dot{\theta}, \\
\dot{y} &= \dot{r} \sin \theta + r \cos \theta \cdot \dot{\theta},
\end{aligned}\right\} \tag{3·6–6}$$

whence (3·6–5) becomes at once

$$r^2 \dot{\theta} = k. \tag{3·6–7}$$

Referring again to Fig. 3·5, note that the area included between the path of the particle and the *radii vectores* r and $r + dr$ (enclosing the central angle $d\theta$) is equal to $\frac{1}{2}r^2 d\theta$. Therefore eq. (3·6–7) expresses the important fact that a particle in motion under the influence of a central force, irrespective of the exact form of $F(r)$, moves in such a way that the radius vector traces out equal areas in equal times. This is often called the *law of areas*. We shall have further occasion to note its significance when we come to the study of planetary motion. The constant k (the *area* constant) is numerically equal to twice the area swept out in unit time. Its value will depend on the initial circumstances of the motion.

To carry the discussion further it will be wise to employ polar coördinates exclusively. From (3·6–6) we have, differentiating again with respect to the time,

$$\left.\begin{aligned}
\ddot{x} &= (\ddot{r} - r\dot{\theta}^2) \cos \theta - (2\dot{r}\dot{\theta} + \underline{r}\ddot{\theta}) \sin \ddot{\theta}, \\
\ddot{y} &= (\ddot{r} - r\dot{\theta}^2) \sin \theta + (2\dot{r}\dot{\theta} + \underline{r}\ddot{\theta}) \cos \ddot{\theta}.
\end{aligned}\right\} \tag{3·6–8}$$

But from (3·6–7) it follows that

$$2\dot{r}\dot{\theta} + r\ddot{\theta} = 0. \tag{3·6–9}$$

Hence (3·6–8) reduce to

$$\left.\begin{aligned}
\ddot{x} &= (\ddot{r} - r\dot{\theta}^2) \cos \theta, \\
\ddot{y} &= (\ddot{r} - r\dot{\theta}^2) \sin \theta.
\end{aligned}\right\} \tag{3·6–10}$$

This means that the resultant acceleration in central field motion is directed along the radius vector **r** (a direct.result, of course, of the fact that the force is *central*) and has the magnitude

$$a_r = \ddot{r} - r\dot{\theta}^2. \tag{3·6–11}$$

We recognize the second term $r\dot\theta^2$ as the centripetal acceleration [cf. e.g. (1·5–12)]. The term $\ddot r$ is the second time rate of change of the length of the radius vector. From (3·6–4) it follows that we can write the equations of motion for a central field in the form of a single equation, viz.,

$$m\ddot r - mr\dot\theta^2 = F(r), \qquad (3\cdot6\text{–}12)$$

where $mr\dot\theta^2$ will be known as the *centripetal force*. Let us try to eliminate the time from (3·6–12) and obtain a differential equation connecting r and θ. From (3·6–7) we can write

$$r\dot\theta^2 = k^2/r^3. \qquad (3\cdot6\text{–}13)$$

It is now simpler to introduce the transformation

$$r = \frac{1}{u} \qquad (3\cdot6\text{–}14)$$

whence

$$\dot r = \frac{-\dot u}{u^2} = -\frac{du}{d\theta}\cdot\frac{\dot\theta}{u^2} = -k\frac{du}{d\theta},$$

and

$$\ddot r = -k^2u^2\frac{d^2u}{d\theta^2}.$$

Finally eq. (3·6–12) becomes by substitution of these results

$$\frac{d^2u}{d\theta^2} + u + \frac{f(u)}{mk^2u^2} = 0, \qquad (3\cdot6\text{–}15)$$

where $f(u) = F(r)$, i.e., when r is set equal to $1/u$ in $F(r)$ the result is $f(u)$. Eq. (3·6–15) connects u with θ and hence is the differential equation of the orbit of the particle in the central field. Its integration will yield the path directly. It will be noted that our procedure here is different from that pursued in Secs. 3·3 and 3·5 where we integrated the component equations of motion separately and obtained parametric equations for the path. Here we have followed essentially the method of Sec. 3·4 and have eliminated the time from the differential equation of motion before integrating. This course is indeed dictated by the fact that in general the component equations of motion (3·6–3) cannot be integrated separately.

The solution of eq. (3·6–15) will involve two arbitrary constants. A third is already represented by the area constant k. We need one more since in this problem we are really integrating *two* second order ordinary differential equations. The fourth appears in the integration of (3·6–7), after the result of integrating (3·6–15) (i.e., r in terms of θ)

has been substituted into (3·6–7). After this substitution, eq. (3·6–7) becomes the " time " equation of the motion, since it gives dr or $d\theta$ in terms of dt and, on integration, tells how r and θ depend on t. The four arbitrary constants are determined as usual by the initial conditions. We shall illustrate this by the special cases discussed in the remaining sections of this chapter.

It will have been noted that in handling the equation of motion in a central force field (3·6–12), we proceeded rather differently than we did in the linear case in Chapter 2. There we performed a first integration yielding the velocity and formed thereby the energy equation. This process has been bypassed in the treatment of this section. The setting up of the energy equation for curvilinear motion is a somewhat more elaborate process than in the linear case. However, we shall carry it out in Chapter 4, which will put special emphasis on the use of the energy concept in the motion of a particle.

3·7. Motion in a Central Force Field Varying Inversely as the Square of the Distance. We shall now discuss the most important illustration of a central force, namely that in which the force function

$$F(r) = -\frac{c}{r^2},\qquad (3\cdot7\text{–}1)$$

c being a *positive* constant, corresponding to *attraction* of the particle to the force center. The case of repulsion will be discussed later. The fundamental equation (3·6–15) now becomes

$$\frac{d^2u}{d\theta^2} + u - \frac{c}{mk^2} = 0,\qquad (3\cdot7\text{–}2)$$

which is most simply integrated by placing $w = u - c/mk^2$. Then (3·7–2) becomes

$$\frac{d^2w}{d\theta^2} + w = 0.\qquad (3\cdot7\text{–}3)$$

We have already encountered an equation of this mathematical form in Sec. 2·2 (with t as the independent variable). Hence the solution may be written at once

$$u = A\cos(\theta - \alpha) + C,\qquad (3\cdot7\text{–}4)$$

where $C = c/mk^2$ and A and α are the new arbitrary constants. Reverting to r we have

$$r = \frac{1}{A\cos(\theta - \alpha) + C}.\qquad (3\cdot7\text{–}5)$$

This is the polar equation of a conic section,[1] i.e., the locus of a point whose distances from a fixed point and a fixed line are in a constant ratio. Let us write (3·7–5) in the form

$$r = \frac{1/C}{1 + \dfrac{A}{C} \cos(\theta - \alpha)}. \tag{3·7–6}$$

Now referring to the figure (Fig. 3·6), let F be the given fixed point on the so-called polar axis OO, and let r be the distance from the particle P to F, with FP making the angle $\theta - \alpha$ with FO'', where the line $O'O''$ makes the angle α with the polar line. The angle θ is, of course, the angle the radius vector makes with the polar axis. Let $O'Q$, perpendicular to the line $O'O''$, be the given fixed line and $O'F = -1/A$. Then eq. (3·7–6) expresses the fact that the ratio of r to the distance $PQ = [O'F + r \cos(\theta - \alpha)]$ has the constant value $-A/C$.

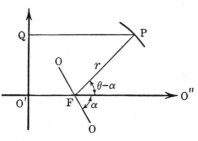

FIG. 3·6

This ratio is defined as the *eccentricity* ϵ of the conic, while the distance $O'F$ is usually written p. The point F is called the focus. In this notation the equation becomes

$$r = \frac{\epsilon p}{1 - \epsilon \cos(\theta - \alpha)}. \tag{3·7–7}$$

It is shown in texts on analytic geometry that for $\epsilon = 1$, the conic is a *parabola*; for $\epsilon < 1$, the conic is an *ellipse*; while for $\epsilon > 1$, the conic is a *hyperbola*. The exact shape of the orbit thus depends on the initial conditions, as we emphasized in the previous section. Since $\epsilon = -A/C$ and $C = c/mk^2$, we have

$$\epsilon = -mk^2 \frac{A}{c}, \tag{3·7–8}$$

where since c and ϵ are positive, A must be a *negative* constant. Thus according as

$$-A \lessgtr \frac{c}{mk^2} \tag{3·7–9}$$

there results an elliptic, parabolic or hyperbolic orbit. The physical considerations underlying the distinction between the various types of

---

[1] See, for example, Rider, *loc. cit.*, pp. 238 f., or F. D. Murnaghan, *Analytic Geometry*, Prentice-Hall, N.Y., 1946, p. 307.

orbits are more clearly brought out by a study of the initial conditions.

First let us notice from eq. (3·6–6) that the magnitude of the resultant velocity of the particle is

$$v^2 = \dot{x}^2 + \dot{y}^2 = \dot{r}^2 + r^2\dot{\theta}^2, \tag{3·7–10}$$

where $\dot{r}$ appears as the component of the velocity along the radius vector, and $r\theta$ the component of the velocity perpendicular to the radius vector. (Cf. eq. (1·4–3) for the latter for the special case of a circle. It is, however, true for any continuous plane motion.) From eq. (3·7–7) we obtain by time differentiation

$$\dot{r} = -\frac{\epsilon^2 p \sin(\theta - \alpha)\dot{\theta}}{[1 - \epsilon \cos(\theta - \alpha)]^2} = -\frac{k \sin(\theta - \alpha)}{p} \tag{3·7–11}$$

where we have also used (3·7–7) again as well as the law of areas (3·6–7). Finally

$$v^2 = \frac{k^2 \sin^2(\theta - \alpha)}{p^2} + \frac{k^2}{r^2}. \tag{3·7–12}$$

If now for r we substitute once more from (3·7–7) the result is, after a certain amount of algebraic manipulation,

$$\epsilon^2 - 1 = \frac{\epsilon^2 p^2}{k^2}\left(v^2 - \frac{2k^2}{\epsilon pr}\right). \tag{3·7–13}$$

But in eq. (3·7–7)

$$\epsilon p = -\frac{A}{C}\cdot\left(-\frac{1}{A}\right) = \frac{1}{C} = \frac{mk^2}{c}. \tag{3·7–14}$$

Hence we may rewrite (3·7–13) in the form

$$\epsilon^2 - 1 = \frac{m^2 k^2}{c^2}\left(v^2 - \frac{2c}{mr}\right). \tag{3·7–15}$$

Now suppose that the particle is initially projected with velocity v_0 from the initial position $r = r_0$. We still have

$$\epsilon^2 - 1 = \frac{m^2 k^2}{c^2}\left(v_0^2 - \frac{2c}{mr_0}\right). \tag{3·7–16}$$

If $v_0 = \sqrt{2c/mr_0}$, $\epsilon = 1$ and the orbit is a parabola. If $v_0 < \sqrt{2c/mr_0}$, $\epsilon < 1$ and the orbit is an ellipse. Finally if $v_0 > \sqrt{2c/mr_0}$, $\epsilon > 1$ and the orbit is a hyperbola.

The velocity $\sqrt{2c/mr_0}$ has an interesting physical significance. Returning to (3·7–15), we note that if the particle is considered to start at rest at an infinite distance from the force center, i.e., $v = 0$

for $r = \infty$, the left side of (3·7–15) must vanish identically. Hence $\epsilon = 1$, and the path is a degenerate parabola (the straight line joining the initial position to the force center). But this means that

$$v^2 = \frac{2c}{mr} \tag{3·7–17}$$

gives the velocity attained in the motion at the distance r. Hence at distance r_0 the velocity attained is

$$v = \sqrt{\frac{2c}{mr_0}}. \tag{3·7–18}$$

The results at the end of the preceding paragraph may then be restated: the orbit in an attractive inverse square force field is a parabola, ellipse, or hyperbola according as the velocity of projection at r_0 is equal to, less than, or greater than the velocity attained at r_0 by a particle falling freely in this field from infinity.

It is worthy of comment that, although the kind of conic represented by the orbit depends only on the speed v_0, the actual eccentricity ϵ for elliptic and hyperbolic orbits still depends on the area constant k and is therefore dependent on the direction of projection as well as the speed.

3·8. Ballistic Missiles. In Sec. 3·3 we treated projectile motion as if the earth were flat and the force of gravity were constant. Clearly a long-range ballistic missile demands more elaborate consideration, since it moves in the gravitational force field of the earth. We can, however, at once apply the results of Sec. 3·7 to this problem.

Suppose a projectile is fired from point Q (Fig. 3·7) on the earth's equator (we treat the earth as a perfect sphere with center at O and neglect its rotation) in a direction making angle ϕ with the vertical OV and in the meridian plane. Let its initial speed be v_0. It will then travel in a conic section about the center of the earth O as a focus. Let P be any position of the missile

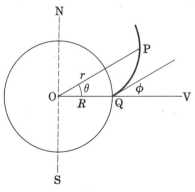

FIG. 3·7

with polar coördinates r, θ. The eccentricity of the orbit ϵ is given by (3·7–16), which we may rewrite as follows, noting from Sec. 2·4 that the force constant c is now GmM (m is the mass of the missile and

M is the mass of the earth), while the area constant k becomes (see eq. 3·6–7) $Rv_0 \sin \phi$,

$$\epsilon^2 - 1 = \frac{R^2 v_0^2 \sin^2 \phi}{G^2 M^2} \left(v_0^2 - \frac{2GM}{R} \right). \tag{3·8–1}$$

If

$$v_0 = \sqrt{\frac{2GM}{R}}, \tag{3·8–2}$$

which is just the escape velocity computed in Sec. 1·11, $\epsilon = 1$ and the ideal trajectory is a parabola. We know that if the missile is directed straight up, in this case it will never return (neglecting, of course, air and wind resistance). The question now arises what will happen when it is projected at the angle ϕ, different from zero. This can be answered by examining the equation of the conic (3·7–7), which we can write (recalling 3·7–14)

$$r = \frac{R^2 v_0^2 \sin^2 \phi}{GM(1 - \cos(\theta - \alpha))}. \tag{3·8–3}$$

Now it is clear that no matter what value of α corresponds to the initial condition, there will always be a value of $\theta \leqslant 2\pi$ for which r becomes infinite. Hence no matter how the missile is directed, if v_0 is the escape velocity, the trajectory will be open upwards and the projectile will never return.

Let us next examine the case in which

$$v_0^2 < 2GM/R$$

and

$$\epsilon < 1.$$

In this case the orbit is an ellipse. It will be convenient to let

$$v_0^2 = C(2GM/R), \tag{3·8–4}$$

where C is a positive number less than unity. Then (3·8–1) becomes

$$\epsilon^2 - 1 = 4C(C - 1) \sin^2 \phi \tag{3·8–5}$$

and (3·8–3)

$$r = \frac{2RC \sin^2 \phi}{1 - \epsilon \cos(\theta - \alpha)}. \tag{3·8–6}$$

When $\theta = 0$, $r = R$ by the initial conditions. Hence if we solve for α we get

$$\cos \alpha = \frac{1 - 2C \sin^2 \phi}{\sqrt{1 - 4C(1 - C) \sin^2 \phi}}. \tag{3·8–7}$$

Inspection shows that it is possible for us to find another value of θ ($\neq 0$) for which $r = R$ such that between 0 and this value r takes on values greater than R (i.e., the missile stays above the earth's surface) but does not become infinite.

As an example, consider $\phi = 30°$ and $C = 1/2$. Then

$$\cos \alpha = \sqrt{3}/2 \quad \text{or} \quad \alpha = 30°,$$

$$\epsilon = \sqrt{3/2},$$

and the equation of the orbit is

$$r = \frac{R/4}{1 - \sqrt{\tfrac{3}{2}} \cos (\theta - 30°)}.$$

For $\theta = 60°$, $r = R$ and the missile hits the earth again. For $60° > \theta > 0$, $r > R$. Hence the range of the missile on the earth's surface equals

$$\frac{\pi R}{3}.$$

The reader is urged to work out other cases for himself.

3·9. Planetary Motion. About the beginning of the seventeenth century the laws of planetary motion were enunciated by Kepler after many years of laborious calculation and reduction of observations of the positions of the planets. These laws are three in number, viz. (1) that the planets describe, relatively to the sun, ellipses of which the sun occupies a focus; (2) the radius vector of each planet traces out equal areas in equal times; (3) the squares of the periodic times (i.e., periods of revolution) of any two planets vary as the cubes of the major axes of their orbits. These laws do not imply that the sun must be stationary in the reference system being used. In this section we shall actually make this assumption, reserving the general case for later consideration.

We recall at once that the second law is satisfied by any particle moving in a central field of force [eq. (3·6–7)]. It remains to be shown, however, that *if* the second law is satisfied the force acting on the planet is directed toward the sun, i.e., it is a central force. But this follows at once from the result of differentiating eq. (3·6–5) (the expression of the second law in rectangular coördinates) with respect to the time. The result is, of course

$$\frac{\ddot{y}}{\ddot{x}} = \frac{y}{x}, \tag{3·9–1}$$

whence, since $m\ddot{y}$ and $m\ddot{x}$ are respectively the y and x components of the force, the latter must be directed through the origin and hence be a central force.

We can next show that the first law of Kepler implies an inverse square law of force. The polar equation of an ellipse referred to the focus as pole is (with $\alpha = 0$ for convenience)

$$\frac{1}{r} = u = \frac{1 - \epsilon \cos \theta}{\epsilon p}, \tag{3.9-2}$$

as given in eq. (3·7–7). We therefore have

$$\frac{d^2u}{d\theta^2} = \frac{\cos \theta}{p}. \tag{3.9-3}$$

Now for any central force we have shown that the function $f(u)$ [eq. (3·6–15)] obeys the equation

$$f(u) = -mk^2u^2 \left(u + \frac{d^2u}{d\theta^2} \right).$$

On substitution from (3·9–2) and (3·9–3) we therefore have

$$f(u) = -\frac{mk^2u^2}{\epsilon p}, \tag{3.9-4}$$

which shows that the force varies inversely as the square of the distance, the negative sign of course indicating attraction.

The third law of Kepler may also be shown to follow from the laws of motion in an inverse square central force field. For we have

$$r^2\dot{\theta} = 2\dot{S} = k, \tag{3.9-5}$$

where S is the area swept out in time t by the radius vector. In one period P of the motion the area traversed will be the area of the ellipse itself, or πab, where a is the semi-major axis and b is the semi-minor axis. (That this is the area may be verified by simple integration.) Noting the relation[1]

$$b = a\sqrt{1 - \epsilon^2}, \tag{3.9-6}$$

we have

$$P = \frac{2\pi a^2}{k} \sqrt{1 - \epsilon^2}. \tag{3.9-7}$$

From eq. (3·9–2) in connection with Fig. 3·8 we see that

$$r_{\max} = \frac{mk^2}{c(1 - \epsilon)}, \quad \text{and} \quad r_{\min} = \frac{mk^2}{c(1 + \epsilon)}, \tag{3.9-8}$$

[1] Rider, *loc. cit.*, p. 120.

corresponding respectively to the positions marked A and B. The former is termed *aphelion* while the latter is the *perihelion*. Clearly

$$2a = r_{max} + r_{min}$$

$$= \frac{mk^2}{c} \cdot \frac{2}{1 - \epsilon^2} \cdot \qquad (3\cdot9\text{--}9)$$

Therefore

$$\sqrt{1 - \epsilon^2} = \sqrt{\frac{mk^2}{ca}},$$

and (3·9–7) becomes

$$P^2 = \frac{4\pi^2 ma^3}{c}, \qquad (3\cdot9\text{--}10)$$

which is the mathematical statement of Kepler's third law.

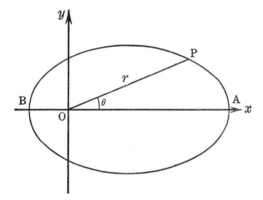

FIG. 3·8

It will be recalled that the connection between the laws of Kepler and motion in an inverse square central force field led Newton ultimately to propound his law of universal gravitation already stated and discussed in Sec. 2·3.

The quantity c, the coefficient in the central force expression used in this and the previous section, can be expressed in terms of the gravitational constant G (see Sec. 2·3) if the central force is due to a particle of mass M. Then $c = GmM$, and the equation (3·9–10) can be written in the form

$$P^2 = \frac{4\pi^2 a^3}{GM}. \qquad (3\cdot9\text{--}11)$$

From this it follows that if a planet has a satellite whose period of revolution P about the planet can be observed as well as the semi-major axis a of its orbit, the mass of the planet may thereby be obtained. The mass of the sun is, of course, obtainable by the use of the same equation.

It is interesting to note that the orbits of many comets (the non-returning kind) have been found to be parabolas, a special variety of central field motion, thus lending further support to Newton's law.

At the end of Sec. 3·6 we mentioned the " time " equation which expresses r or θ in terms of the time t. We obtain it in general by the use of eq. (3·6–7) and the equation of the orbit, (3·7–7). Thus from the latter we have

$$\theta - \alpha = \text{arc cos} \left(\frac{1}{\epsilon} - \frac{p}{r} \right) , \qquad (3\cdot9\text{--}12)$$

so that differentiating with respect to the time

$$\dot{\theta} = \frac{\pm p\dot{r}}{r^2 \sqrt{1 - \left(\frac{1}{\epsilon} - \frac{p}{r} \right)^2}} = \frac{k}{r^2} . \qquad (3\cdot9\text{--}13)$$

Hence we have for the determination of r in terms of t, the differential equation

$$\dot{r} = \pm \frac{k}{p} \sqrt{1 - \left(\frac{1}{\epsilon} - \frac{p}{r} \right)^2} . \qquad (3\cdot9\text{--}14)$$

We can now apply this to an elliptical planetary orbit. Separating variables by writing $\dot{r} = dr/dt$ and choosing the plus sign, we can write (3·9–14) in the form

$$\frac{dr}{\sqrt{1 - \left(\frac{1}{\epsilon} - \frac{p}{r} \right)^2}} = \frac{k}{p} dt. \qquad (3\cdot9\text{--}15)$$

If we recall that the quantity p is given by

$$p = \frac{mk^2}{c\epsilon} , \qquad (3\cdot9\text{--}16)$$

we have from (3·9–9) the relation

$$\epsilon p = a(1 - \epsilon^2). \qquad (3\cdot9\text{--}17)$$

Substituting for p in terms of a and ϵ in eq. (3·9–15), we are led to the form

$$\frac{r\,dr}{\sqrt{\epsilon^2 a^2 - (a - r)^2}} = \frac{k}{a\sqrt{1 - \epsilon^2}} dt. \qquad (3\cdot9\text{--}18)$$

Now it is of advantage to introduce the observable quantity P, the period of the planet's revolution. From eq. (3·9–10) we have

$$\frac{1}{P} = \frac{1}{2\pi} \sqrt{\frac{c}{ma^3}} .$$

But

$$\frac{c}{m} = \frac{k^2}{\epsilon p} = \frac{k^2}{a(1 - \epsilon^2)} , \qquad (3\cdot9\text{–}19)$$

from eq. (3·9–16) above.   Therefore

$$\frac{1}{P} = \frac{1}{2\pi} \cdot \frac{k}{a^2 \sqrt{1 - \epsilon^2}} , \qquad (3\cdot9\text{–}20)$$

and eq. (3·9–18) becomes

$$\frac{r}{a} \cdot \frac{dr}{\sqrt{\epsilon^2 a^2 - (a - r)^2}} = \frac{2\pi}{P} dt. \qquad (3\cdot9\text{–}21)$$

To integrate this equation conveniently it is customary to introduce a new variable E defined by the equation

$$a - r = a\epsilon \cos E, \qquad (3\cdot9\text{–}22)$$

so that

$$r = a(1 - \epsilon \cos E). \qquad (3\cdot9\text{–}23)$$

E is an angle and is called in texts on celestial mechanics the *eccentric anomaly*.   To understand the geometrical significance of the latter, let us refer to the following figure (Fig. 3·9).   This presents the elliptical orbit APB with the focus at O and center at C.   Let us draw the circle AQB of radius a about C as center.   This is termed the *auxiliary* circle.   Suppose the planet is at the position P with coördinates r and θ.   Through P construct PD, the perpendicular to the major axis AB, and let it intersect the circle at Q.   Then the angle $QCB = E$, the eccentric anomaly.

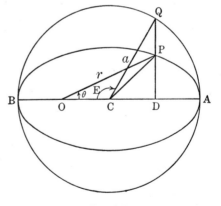

FIG. 3·9

That this satisfies the definition given in the relation (3·9–23) may be seen from the fact that from the figure we have

$$r \cos \theta + a \cos E = OC. \qquad (3\cdot9\text{–}24)$$

But $OC = a - r_{min} = a - \dfrac{mk^2}{c(1 + \epsilon)}$ from (3·9–8), and this reduces

to

$$OC = \frac{a + a\epsilon - \epsilon p}{1 + \epsilon} = \frac{a + a\epsilon - a + a\epsilon^2}{1 + \epsilon}$$

$$= a\epsilon.$$

Hence (3·9–24) becomes, using eq. (3·9–2),

$$\frac{r}{\epsilon} - p + a \cos E = a\epsilon,$$

or

$$r = \epsilon p + a\epsilon^2 - a\epsilon \cos E. \tag{3·9–25}$$

But $\epsilon p = a(1 - \epsilon^2)$ and hence (3·9–23) follows.

Now substituting into (3·9–16) the differential equation becomes

$$\frac{2\pi}{P} dt = (1 - \epsilon \cos E)\, dE, \tag{3·9–26}$$

and integrating we have

$$\frac{2\pi}{P} (t - t_0) = E - \epsilon \sin E, \tag{3·9–27}$$

where t_0 is the time for $E = 0$, i.e., the passage through perihelion (see the figure). Now $2\pi/P \cdot (t - t_0)$ represents the angle through which the radius vector would have moved at the uniform angular velocity $\omega = 2\pi/P$. This angle is called in celestial mechanics the *mean anomaly* and often denoted by M. The relation

$$M = E - \epsilon \sin E \tag{3·9–28}$$

is known as *Kepler's equation*, and as soon as M is known for any time, it can be solved for E, whence r and θ can be found for any instant. However, since the equation (3·9–28) is transcendental, its solution cannot be expressed in a closed form. Methods for its approximate solution in various cases will be found in texts on celestial mechanics.[1]

3·10. Artificial Satellites. The year 1957 will be forever memorable for the launching of the first artificial satellite of the earth by scientists of the U.S.S.R. This in a sense provided an *experimental* confirmation of the principle of gravitation. We can readily apply to this type of problem the considerations of the preceding sections. A simple special case will suffice.

[1] For example, see E. Finlay-Freundlich, *Celestial Mechanics*, Pergamon Press, New York, 1958, p. 22.

We assume that a rocket carries the artificial satellite up to a height h above the surface of the earth and then ejects the satellite horizontally and in the equatorial plane with an initial velocity of v_0. Neglecting air friction, we find for the eccentricity of the orbit from eq. (3·8–1)

$$\epsilon^2 = 1 + 4(v_0/v_\infty)^2 (1 + h/R)[(v_0/v_\infty)^2(1 + h/R) - 1], \quad (3\cdot10\text{–}1)$$

where $v_\infty = \sqrt{2GM/R}$, the escape velocity (see Secs. 1·11 and 3·8). Letting

$$(v_0/v_\infty)^2(1 + h/R) = C',$$

we have

$$\epsilon^2 = 1 + 4C'(C' - 1). \quad (3\cdot10\text{–}2)$$

For $C' = 0$, or $C' = 1$, $\epsilon^2 = 1$ and the orbit is parabolic. However for all values of C' such that $0 < C' < 1$ the orbit is elliptical. For $C' > 1$, the orbit is of course hyperbolic.

In the elliptical case we can evaluate the major axis $2a$ of the orbit from eq. (3·9–9). By use of (3·10–2) the former equation yields

$$2a = \frac{mk^2}{c} \cdot \frac{1}{2C'(1 - C')},$$

and if we employ the usual substitutions for k^2, c, and C', the result is

$$2a = \frac{R\left(1 + \dfrac{h}{R}\right)}{\left[1 - \left(\dfrac{v_0}{v_\infty}\right)^2\left(1 + \dfrac{h}{R}\right)\right]}. \quad (3\cdot10\text{–}3)$$

Since in general $h \ll R$, we can get an approximate estimate of $2a$ by writing

$$2a \doteq \frac{R}{1 - \left(\dfrac{v_0}{v_\infty}\right)^2}. \quad (3\cdot10\text{–}4)$$

It appears that for $2a$ to be greater than $2R$, so that the orbit of the satellite will not touch the earth's surface

$$v_0 > \frac{v_\infty}{\sqrt{2}} \quad (3\cdot10\text{–}5)$$

to the same approximation prevailing in (3·10–4).

3·11. Electron Motions in the Bohr Model of the Hydrogen Atom.

The Bohr-Rutherford atom model, which is still of great value in pictorial representations of atomic structure, pictures the hydrogen atom as formed of a heavy nucleus with a charge of positive electricity of magnitude $e = 4.80 \times 10^{-10}$ electrostatic units, and a negatively charged electron with charge $-e$. To a first approximation the electron is supposed to move about the nucleus in an orbit due to the central electrostatic attraction of magnitude $-e^2/r^2$, where r is the distance between the particles. The gravitational attraction can easily be shown to be negligible compared with the electrostatic, for the mass of the hydrogen nucleus is 1.66×10^{-24} gm while that of the electron is approximately 0.9×10^{-27} gm. As a matter of fact the investigation in a later chapter will show that the two particles both move about their common center of mass (see Sec. 6·3). However, the motion of the nucleus due to its much larger mass is so slight compared with that of the electron that for the present we may neglect it and consider that the electron moves in a central field about an approximately stationary nucleus. Since the orbit of the electron must be bounded in space as long as it remains in the atom, the path will then be an *ellipse* with the nucleus at one focus, as we learn from our study of the analogous case of planetary motion discussed in Sec. 3·9.

Now an outstanding feature of the Bohr theory is the postulate that not *all* elliptical orbits are possible for the electron, i.e., not all values of the semi-major axis a and eccentricity ϵ occur. The possible orbits are those for which the following extra-mechanical conditions are satisfied, viz.,

$$\left. \begin{aligned} \oint p_\theta \, d\theta &= n_1 h, \\ \oint p_r \, dr &= n_2 h. \end{aligned} \right\} \tag{3·11–1}$$

These relations are to be interpreted thus: p_θ is the so-called moment of *momentum* of the electron in its path, viz.,

$$p_\theta = mr^2\dot\theta = mrv_1, \tag{3·11–2}$$

where $v_1 = r\dot\theta = $ velocity component at any instant perpendicular to the radius vector [recall eq. (1·4–3)].[1] On the other hand p_r is the so-called radial momentum, i.e.,

$$p_r = m\dot r. \tag{3·11–3}$$

The form in which the integrals in (3·9–1) are written is to indicate that the integration is to extend over the whole region of variation of the variables in question. Thus the first integration will extend

---

[1] The moment of momentum is now commonly referred to as the *angular momentum*, though the latter term is more strictly applicable to rigid bodies than to single particles. Note that p_θ is also interpretable as the product of mass and area constant [cf. eq. (3·6–7)]. (See Sec. 6.4.)

from $\theta = 0$ to $\theta = 2\pi$ as limits, while the second is taken from r_{min} (i.e., perihelion) to r_{max} (aphelion) and back again to r_{min} along the elliptical path. The actual method of integration will be indicated below. The quantity h is the fundamental constant of the quantum theory, the so-called constant of Planck.[1] From (3·11–1) it is clear that this has the dimensions of momentum times distance. Its presently accepted value (see Chapter 14) is 6.62×10^{-27} erg sec. The quantities n_1 and n_2 are *integers*, and the conditions expressed in the equations (3·11–1) are known as the *quantum* conditions. We must emphasize that they are not deductions from previous theory but are outright postulates or assumptions. We cannot here be concerned with their true significance for it would take a considerable discussion of atomic structure theory to make this clear. What we *are* interested in is their influence on the possible motions of the electron.

Substituting the value of p_θ from (3·11–2) into the first condition and recalling that for a central field motion $r^2\dot\theta = k$ [eq. (3·6–7)] we have:

$$\int_0^{2\pi} mk \, d\theta = n_1 h,$$

or

$$mk = p_\theta = \text{const.} = \frac{n_1 h}{2\pi}. \qquad (3·11–4)$$

The carrying out of the integration in the second condition is somewhat more troublesome. Let us write the polar equation of the ellipse in the form

$$r = \frac{a(1 - \epsilon^2)}{1 - \epsilon \cos \theta}, \qquad (3·11–5)$$

which follows from eq. (3·9–2) if we note that

$$\epsilon p = \frac{mk^2}{c} = a(1 - \epsilon^2), \qquad (3·11–6)$$

from eqs. (3·7–14) and (3·9–9). Now the radial momentum can be transformed as follows

$$p_r = m\dot r = m \frac{dr}{d\theta} \dot\theta = \frac{mk}{r^2} \frac{dr}{d\theta}, \qquad (3·11–7)$$

---

[1] The student's attention at this point is directed to the good popular treatment of the classical quantum theory of atomic structure in Max Born, *The Restless Universe*, 2nd revised edition, Dover Publications, New York, 1957. Two good books which cover essentials of atomic physics as discussed in this and other sections of the present book are Max Born, *Atomic Physics*, 6th revised edition, Hafner, New York, 1957, and Henry Semat, *Introduction to Atomic and Nuclear Physics*, 3rd revised edition, Rinehart, New York, 1954. The more ambitious student may profitably consult F. K. Richtmyer, E. H. Kennard and T. Lauritsen, *Introduction to Modern Physics*, 5th revised edition, McGraw-Hill, New York, 1955.

while

$$dr = \frac{dr}{d\theta}\, d\theta = -\frac{a\epsilon(1 - \epsilon^2)\sin\theta\, d\theta}{(1 - \epsilon\cos\theta)^2}, \qquad (3\cdot11\text{--}8)$$

from eq. (3·11–5). Therefore on substitution the second condition becomes

$$mk\epsilon^2 \int_0^{2\pi} \frac{\sin^2\theta}{(1 - \epsilon\cos\theta)^2}\, d\theta = n_2 h. \qquad (3\cdot11\text{--}9)$$

We integrate this by parts, obtaining

$$n_2 h = mk\epsilon \left\{ -\left[\frac{\sin\theta}{1 - \epsilon\cos\theta}\right]_0^{2\pi} + \int_0^{2\pi} \frac{\cos\theta}{1 - \epsilon\cos\theta}\, d\theta \right\},$$

which reduces to

$$n_2 h = mk \int_0^{2\pi} \left(\frac{1}{1 - \epsilon\cos\theta} - 1\right) d\theta, \qquad (3\cdot11\text{--}10)$$

since the square bracket above vanishes on the introduction of the limits. The integral

$$\int_0^{2\pi} \frac{d\theta}{1 - \epsilon\cos\theta} = \frac{2\pi}{\sqrt{1 - \epsilon^2}}, \qquad (3\cdot11\text{--}11)$$

from No. 300 in Peirce's *Table of Integrals*. Therefore the second quantum condition becomes

$$\frac{1}{\sqrt{1 - \epsilon^2}} - 1 = \frac{n_2 h}{2\pi km}$$

$$= \frac{n_2}{n_1}, \qquad (3\cdot11\text{--}12)$$

utilizing the first condition [eq. (3·11–4)], whence

$$\epsilon^2 = 1 - \frac{n_1^2}{(n_1 + n_2)^2}. \qquad (3\cdot11\text{--}13)$$

But this means that the possible orbits of the electron are restricted to those for which the eccentricity ϵ takes the values allowed by (3·11–13), as n_1 and n_2 assume all possible positive integral values.[1] To each value of ϵ correspond also definite major and minor axes. Thus combining (3·11–4) and (3·11–6) we have

$$a = \frac{(n_1 + n_2)^2 h^2}{4\pi^2 me^2}, \qquad . \qquad (3\cdot11\text{--}14)$$

---

[1] It is customary to exclude the value $n_1 = 0$ since this corresponds to $\epsilon = 1$ and a straight line orbit through the nucleus, which is physically meaningless.

noting that $c = e^2$ in this special problem. The dimensions of the allowed orbits are thus fully fixed by the quantum conditions. A few sketches for certain selected small values of n_1 and n_2 will serve to illustrate the essential results we have obtained. (Fig. 3·10).

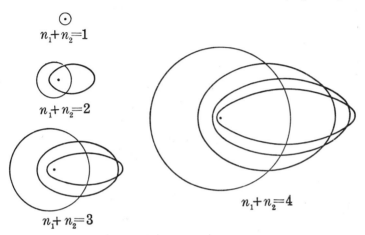

$n_1 + n_2 = 1$

$n_1 + n_2 = 2$

$n_1 + n_2 = 3$

$n_1 + n_2 = 4$

Fig. 3·10

The times of revolution in the allowed orbits are given at once from Kepler's third law, eq. (3·9–10). Thus substituting into (3·9–10) from (3·11–14) we have

$$P = \frac{(n_1 + n_2)^3 h^3}{4\pi^2 me^4},$$ (3·11–15)

the periodic times thus increasing with the cubes of the natural numbers.

It may also be remarked that under certain conditions an electron coming from outside the atom will move in a hyperbolic path about the nucleus. These conditions are, indeed, precisely those laid down in Sec. 3·7.

Further discussion of the application of the Bohr theory will be found in Sec. 4·3.

3·12. Motion in a Repulsive Inverse Square Force Field.   Alpha Particle Deflection.

In our discussion of the motion of a particle in an inverse square field we have dealt wholly with the case where the force is attractive. There is, however, an important significance to be attached to the case in which the force is repulsive. Consider a positively charged nucleus of an atom (Fig. 3·11) with charge Ne (N being an integer and e the fundamental unit of charge, 4.80×10^{-10} e.s. units). Next suppose that an alpha particle, a doubly charged helium atom, i.e., the nucleus of a helium atom with charge $2e$, is projected into the neighborhood of the nucleus *Ne* in such a way that at a very great distance where the repulsive action is very slight the alpha particle has a velocity v_0 in the direction QQ'. For convenience we shall describe the motion of the alpha particle in terms of polar co-ordinates r, θ, choosing the polar axis parallel to QQ' and placing *Ne*

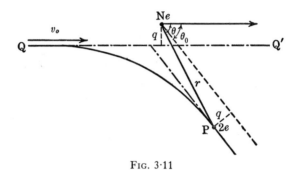

FIG. 3·11

at the pole. The perpendicular distance between QQ' and the axis is denoted by q. The force of *repulsion* between the alpha particle and the nucleus is of magnitude $2Ne^2/r^2$, and therefore the analysis of Sec. 3·7 will at once apply, with the quantity c of that section now assuming the value $-2Ne^2$, i.e., being *negative* instead of *positive*. The orbit of the alpha particle will therefore be a conic with equation [see eq. (3·7–7)]

$$r = \frac{\epsilon p}{1 - \epsilon \cos (\theta - \alpha)}. \tag{3·12–1}$$

From eq. (3·7–16) we see that since $v_0 > 0$ for $r_0 = \infty$, $\epsilon > 1$ and the orbit is a hyperbola. As Fig. 3·11 shows, r approaches ∞ for two values of θ, namely π and θ_0. Hence we have from (3·12–1) the conditions

$$\cos (\pi - \alpha) = \frac{1}{\epsilon} = - \cos \alpha, \tag{3·12–2}$$

and

$$\cos (\theta_0 - \alpha) = \frac{1}{\epsilon}. \tag{3·12–3}$$

Combining (3·12–2) and (3·12–3) yields (since $\sin \alpha = \sqrt{\epsilon^2 - 1}/\epsilon$)

$$\frac{1 + \cos \theta_0}{\sin \theta_0} = \sqrt{\epsilon^2 - 1}, \tag{3·12–4}$$

or in terms of $\theta_0/2$,

$$\cot \frac{\theta_0}{2} = \sqrt{\epsilon^2 - 1}. \tag{3·12–5}$$

Now if we examine Fig. 3·11 we see that as $\theta \to \pi$, we have to an increasingly good approximation

$$r \sin \theta \doteq q. \tag{3·12–6}$$

Hence in the neighborhood of $\theta = \pi$

$$\dot{r} \doteq -q \cos \theta \cdot \frac{\dot{\theta}}{\sin^2 \theta} \doteq -r\dot{\theta}\sqrt{\frac{r^2}{q^2} - 1}. \tag{3·12–7}$$

Applying (3·7–10) we are led at once to the simple but important result

$$k^2 = v_0^2 q^2. \tag{3·12–8}$$

Now return to (3·7–13) which becomes for $v = v_0$ at $r = \infty$

$$\epsilon^2 - 1 = \frac{\epsilon^2 p^2 v_0^2}{k^2}. \tag{3·12–9}$$

Employing (3·7–14) to substitute for ϵp, we get

$$\epsilon^2 - 1 = \frac{m^2 k^2 v_0^2}{c^2} = \frac{m^2 k^2 v_0^2}{4N^2 e^4}. \tag{3·12–10}$$

Using (3·12–8) we obtain finally

$$\sqrt{\epsilon^2 - 1} = \frac{m v_0^2 q}{2 N e^2}, \tag{3·12–11}$$

whence (3·12–5) becomes

$$\cot \frac{\theta_0}{2} = \frac{m v_0^2 q}{2 N e^2}. \tag{3·12–12}$$

This will give us the angular deviation of the alpha particle from its original path. Let us ascertain its order of magnitude in a special case. For an alpha particle we have approximately $m = 6.6 \times 10^{-24}$ grams,[1] and v_0 may be taken as approximately 2×10^9 cm/sec, which is very close to the actual value for the velocity of α-particles from Radium C. The velocities of these particles depend on the source.[2] The electronic charge e has already been given as 4.80×10^{-10} electrostatic units. Substitution then yields

$$\cot \frac{\theta_0}{2} = 5.83 \times 10^{13} \frac{q}{N}. \tag{3·12–13}$$

[1] These data are taken from Birge, " Values of the General Physical Constants," *Reviews of Modern Physics*, July 1929. For the methods of determining them and for other information on atomic theory the student is recommended to read the books referred to in Sec. 3·11.

[2] See J. B. Hoag and S. A. Korff, *Electron and Nuclear Physics*, 3rd ed., Van Nostrand, Princeton, N.J., 1948, p. 272 and Table 4 on p. 482.

Let us suppose that $N = 79$, i.e., that the nucleus is that of gold. In order to produce a deflection of 150°, such as has been experimentally observed in the case of gold, the α-particle must approach the nucleus within such a distance that $q = 3.66 \times 10^{-13}$ cm approximately. It is evident that experiments on the deflection of alpha particles are of great value in enabling us to estimate limits for the dimensions of the nucleus. As a matter of fact it should be noted that the whole nuclear theory of atomic structure rests on experiments of this nature (with the accompanying theory) carried out by Rutherford about 1911.[1]

PROBLEMS

1. A projectile is shot off with an initial velocity of 2500 ft/sec at an angle of 30° to the horizontal. Assuming no air resistance calculate the total time spent in the air, the range, and the total length of the path in the air.

2. A projectile travels in a medium which resists its motion with a force of the form $k\mathbf{v}$, where k is a coefficient of proportionality and $\mathbf{v}$ is the vector velocity in the orbit, with components $\dot{x}$ and $\dot{y}$ respectively. Calculate the range and time spent in air as a function of k and the projection velocity and angle.

3. A projectile is projected at angle α with velocity v_0. Find the time at which the angle which the direction of motion makes with the direction of projection is $\pi/2 - \alpha$.

4. Two simple harmonic motions take place along the x and y axes respectively with equal amplitudes but with frequencies in the ratio 4:3. Find the curve resulting from the composition of the two motions.

5. Calculate approximately the mass of the earth and the mass of the sun from Newton's law of gravitation. Data: radius of earth, 4000 miles; $g = 980$ cm/sec²; G, the constant of gravitation, $= 6.67 \times 10^{-8} \dfrac{\text{dyne cm}^2}{\text{gm}^2}$; $R = $ mean distance from earth to sun $= 93{,}000{,}000$ miles.

6. Calculate the orbit of a particle moving in a plane under the influence of a central force varying directly as the first power of the distance from the force center.

7. Find the way in which the central force must vary with the distance from the force center in order that the particle may describe the spiral $r = 1/c\theta$, where c is constant and r and θ are the usual polar coördinates.

8. Find the way in which the central force must vary with the distance from the force center in order that a particle may describe the lemniscate

$$r^2 = a^2 \cos 2\theta,$$

the force center being assumed to be at the pole. Use the law of areas to find the expression for the resultant velocity of the particle as a function of r.

[1] See Hoag and Korff, *loc. cit.*, Chap. 7.

9. The expression $2\dot{r}\dot{\theta}$ in central field motion is usually called the Coriolis acceleration. Show that it is equal to $-r\ddot{\theta}$. Hence find the expression for $\ddot{\theta}$ in an elliptical inverse square orbit as a function of θ.

10. The fourth satellite of Jupiter has a period of approximately 16.75 days and its semi-major axis is approximately 1.88×10^9 meters. Find an approximate value for the mass of the planet.

11. The eccentricity of the orbit of the planet Mercury is approximately 0.206. Its period of revolution is 0.24 year. If its semi-major axis is approximately 58×10^6 kilometers, at what rate does its radius vector sweep out area?

12. An electron moves in the xy plane under the influence of a uniform electric field directed along the y axis and a uniform magnetic field directed along the z axis (perpendicular to the xy plane). From the theory of electricity and magnetism the component equations of motion are:

$$m\ddot{x} = -e\dot{y}H/c$$
$$m\ddot{y} = -eE + e\dot{x}H/c,$$

where e is the charge on the electron, and E and H are the electric and magnetic field intensities respectively, and c is the conversion factor 3×10^{10}. Integrate to show that the orbit of the electron is a cycloid. Show that one gets different forms of cycloids depending on the choice of initial conditions.

13. Plot to scale the various types of orbits allowed to the electron in the hydrogen atom (discussed in the text) by the quantum conditions for the cases where the sum of the two quantum numbers $n_1 + n_2$ is equal to 1, 2, 3, 4 successively. Calculate in each case the perihelion and aphelion distances (i.e., minimum and maximum distances from the nucleus).

14. Prove that when a particle moves in any central field of force the velocity at any point is inversely proportional to the perpendicular from the force center to the tangent to the path at that point.

15. Under what central force will a particle describe a circle with the force center on the circumference of the circle?

16. The study of the motion of a projectile in a resisting medium is much facilitated by resolving the motion along the horizontal direction and along a direction perpendicular to the tangent to the orbit, respectively. Show that if the resisting force is R per unit mass and if the (variable) angle between the tangent to the path and the horizontal is denoted by ϕ, we can write the relation between ϕ and the instantaneous velocity v of the particle in the form

$$d(v \cos \phi) = Rv/g \cdot d\phi.$$

Hence show that if this equation can be solved, the path can be found by integrating the parametric equations

$$dx = -v^2/g \cdot d\phi,$$
$$dy = -v^2/g \cdot \tan \phi \, d\phi.$$

Solve the problem of the motion for the special cases in which $R = 0$ and $R = kv^3$, where k is constant.

17. Neglecting air resistance, with what velocity must a missile be ejected from the earth's surface at an angle of 45° to the vertical so as to have a range on the earth's surface of 5000 miles? What will be the maximum height of the path? Find the maximum velocity as well as the eccentricity of the orbit.

18. An artificial terrestrial satellite is ejected horizontally at a height of 50 miles. What must be the speed of ejection to insure that it enters an elliptical orbit about the earth with a minimum distance of approach to the earth's surface of 500 miles? What will be the eccentricity of the orbit and the maximum distance from the earth's surface?

CHAPTER 4

ENERGY IN PARTICLE DYNAMICS

4·1. Potential Energy and Conservative Forces. In Sec. 1·11 we introduced the concepts of work and energy and derived the work-kinetic energy theorem (eq. 1·11–17). We then defined the concept of potential energy and emphasized the significance of the total mechanical energy as an invariant in the motion of two particles subject only to their mutual interaction. This led us to a consideration of the principle of the conservation of mechanical energy as illustrated by the linear motion of two particles.

We now wish to generalize this important point of view to three-dimensional motion. Imagine that a particle of mass m is acted on by a resultant force $\mathbf{F}$, which may be written in terms of its components F_x, F_y, F_z along the x, y, z axes respectively as

$$\mathbf{F} = \mathbf{i}F_x + \mathbf{j}F_y + \mathbf{k}F_z,$$

where F_x, F_y and F_z are, in general, all functions of the three coördinates x, y, z. The displacement vector $d\mathbf{r}$ may also be written likewise

$$d\mathbf{r} = \mathbf{i}\,dx + \mathbf{j}\,dy + \mathbf{k}\,dz.$$

We then have from the definition (1·11–2)

$$\mathbf{F} \cdot d\mathbf{r} = F_x\,dx + F_y\,dy + F_z\,dz,$$

so that eq. (1·11–17) becomes, if the integration is conducted from the point P_0 to the point P_1,

$$\int_{P_0}^{P_1} (F_x\,dx + F_y\,dy + F_z\,dz) = \tfrac{1}{2}mv_1{}^2 - \tfrac{1}{2}mv_0{}^2. \qquad (4\cdot1\text{–}1)$$

Now if the expression $F_x\,dx + F_y\,dy + F_z\,dz$ is a perfect differential, i.e., if there exists a function $V(x, y, z)$ such that

$$F_x\,dx + F_y\,dy + F_z\,dz = -\frac{\partial V}{\partial x}\,dx - \frac{\partial V}{\partial y}\,dy - \frac{\partial V}{\partial z}\,dz = -dV,$$

$$(4\cdot1\text{–}2)$$

we have

$$K + V = U = \text{total energy} = \text{const}, \qquad (4\cdot1\text{–}3)$$

99

where K is the kinetic energy and V is the potential energy of the particle (see Sec. 1·11). We recall from calculus that dV is called the total differential of the function $V(x, y, z)$. It is the total change in V corresponding to the alterations dx, dy, dz in x, y, z respectively. F_x then appears as the negative rate of change of V with respect to x, viz., $F_x = -\partial V/\partial x$; similarly for F_y and F_z. We are now under the necessity of introducing partial derivative signs since V is a function of more than one variable.

It must be emphasized that the existence of the potential energy V to satisfy (4·1–2) demands a rather stringent condition. It will be recalled from calculus or can be seen without trouble from

$$F_x = -\frac{\partial V}{\partial x}, \quad F_y = -\frac{\partial V}{\partial y}, \quad F_z = -\frac{\partial V}{\partial z}$$

that we must have

$$\frac{\partial F_x}{\partial y} = \frac{\partial F_y}{\partial x}, \quad \frac{\partial F_x}{\partial z} = \frac{\partial F_z}{\partial x}, \quad \frac{\partial F_y}{\partial z} = \frac{\partial F_z}{\partial y}. \qquad (4\cdot1\text{–}4)$$

It will not need much experimentation to convince the reader that very few forces chosen at random will have components satisfying (4·1–4). Thus

$$F_x = ky, \quad F_y = kz, \quad F_z = kx,$$

where k is a positive constant, certainly will not yield a function V. On the other hand

$$F_x = -kx, \quad F_y = -ky, \quad F_z = -kz$$

does satisfy (4·1–4) and indeed leads at once to

$$V = \tfrac{1}{2}k(x^2 + y^2 + z^2) + C, \qquad (4\cdot1\text{–}5)$$

where C is any constant. Forces whose components satisfy (4·1–4) and for which the potential energy exists are called *conservative* forces, since for them it is possible to define a total mechanical energy U which remains constant during the motion or may be said to be *conserved*. Eq. (4·1–3) then becomes the celebrated principle of the *conservation of mechanical energy*. The particle in this case is said to constitute a *conservative* system. Since for a conservative system

$$\int_{r_0}^{r_1} \mathbf{F} \cdot d\mathbf{r} = -(V_1 - V_0), \qquad (4\cdot1\text{–}6)$$

where V_0 is the value of the potential energy at the beginning of the path, and V_1 the value at the end of the path, it follows that the *gain* in potential energy is the negative of the work done by the force during the motion. Or we can say that the gain in potential energy in any motion of a particle under a conservative force must be balanced by an equal loss in kinetic energy.

For another important consequence of the work–kinetic energy theorem, let us go back to eq. (4·1–1). The left-hand side is of course the work done as the particle moves from P_0 to P_1. The result of the integration depends in general on the path along which the particle moves. Thus if in Fig. 4·1 the particle moves along the path P_0AP_1 the value of the integral or the work done is usually different from that corresponding to the path P_0BP_1. For arbitrary forces the work depends on the path. However, for conservative forces, this is not so. For in this case

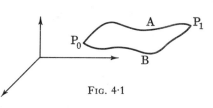

Fig. 4·1

$$\int_{P_0}^{P_1}(F_x\,dx + F_y\,dy + F_z\,dz) = -\int_{P_0}^{P_1}dV = V_0 - V_1.$$
(4·1–7)

Hence the work depends only on the values of the potential energy at the end points of the path and not on the path itself. The existence of the potential energy function V is thus a guarantee that the work done when the particle moves from one point to another is independent of the precise path followed.

Let us examine as an example the potential energy of the form (4·1–5). The expression for the conservation of mechanical energy in this case becomes

$$\tfrac{1}{2}mv^2 + \tfrac{1}{2}k(x^2 + y^2 + z^2) = U = \text{const},$$
(4·1–8)

where the constant C is absorbed in the total energy U. As in the simple linear case discussed in Sec. 2·2 this equation is a first integral of the three component equations of motion. In fact we can see this just as well in the general case. For let us write the equations of motion in component form

$$m\ddot{x} = F_x, \quad m\ddot{y} = F_y,$$
$$m\ddot{z} = F_z.$$
(4·1–9)

Multiplying these respectively by $\dot{x}\,dt$, $\dot{y}\,dt$, $\dot{z}\,dt$, and adding, we obtain

$$d[\tfrac{1}{2}m(\dot{x}^2 + \dot{y}^2 + \dot{z}^2)] = F_x\,dx + F_y\,dy + F_z\,dz,$$
(4·1–10)

and if the right-hand side is $-dV$, we have at once on integration

$$\tfrac{1}{2}mv^2 + V = U = \text{const}.$$
(4·1–11)

It is thus evident that whenever we are dealing with a conservative system the energy equation will be of considerable importance. Incidentally, examination of (4·1–11) reveals that at the place where V is a minimum, K (the kinetic energy) is a maximum and vice versa.

Inspection of eq. (4·1–11) shows that we can draw some conclusions from it concerning the variation in the speed of the particle from place to place. For if we solve for v we have

$$v = \sqrt{2(U - V)/m} \,. \qquad (4\cdot1\text{–}12)$$

Once the value of U has been assigned by the choice of v and V for one position, this equation enables us to calculate v at every point in space. In particular it says that the particle will have a real speed only if

$$U - V > 0.$$

This sets a limitation on the region in space in which the particle is permitted to move. If we plot $V(x, y, z) = C$ as a surface in three-dimensional space, for given U, the speed is high at the troughs or valleys in this surface and low at the peaks. This hardly tells us the whole story of the motion, of course, since it cannot give us the actual velocity, i.e., its direction as well as magnitude. This indicates a limitation of the energy equation as a complete description of the motion of a particle; it will be further emphasized in Chapter 6.

In Sec. 2·2 we have already discussed the simpler case of energy in a uniform field of force. We now undertake a problem of greater interest, namely that of the central force field from the standpoint of energy.

4·2. Energy Relations in a Central Force Field. The equations of motion for a particle in a central field of force have already been given (eqs. 3·6–3) as

$$\left. \begin{aligned} m\ddot{x} &= F(r)\frac{x}{r}, \\[2ex] m\ddot{y} &= F(r)\frac{y}{r}. \end{aligned} \right\} \qquad (4\cdot2\text{–}1)$$

Let us now vary the procedure of Sec. 3·6 by multiplying both sides of the first equation by $\dot{x}\, dt$ and both sides of the second by $\dot{y}\, dt$. We thus have

$$\left. \begin{aligned} d(\tfrac{1}{2}m\dot{x}^2) &= \frac{F(r)}{r} \cdot \tfrac{1}{2}d(x^2), \\[2ex] d(\tfrac{1}{2}m\dot{y}^2) &= \frac{F(r)}{r} \cdot \tfrac{1}{2}d(y^2). \end{aligned} \right\} \qquad (4\cdot2\text{–}2)$$

Adding, and recalling that

$$x^2 + y^2 = r^2, \qquad (4\cdot2\text{--}3)$$

and

$$\dot{x}^2 + \dot{y}^2 = v^2, \qquad (4\cdot2\text{--}4)$$

where v is the magnitude of the velocity of the particle, we obtain

$$d(\tfrac{1}{2}mv^2) = \frac{F(r)}{2r}\,d(r^2) = F(r)\,dr. \qquad (4\cdot2\text{--}5)$$

The indefinite integral yields

$$\tfrac{1}{2}mv^2 - \int F(r)\,dr = C. \qquad (4\cdot2\text{--}6)$$

We can now set $F(r)\,dr = -dV(r)$. Then

$$\tfrac{1}{2}mv^2 + V(r) = C = U, \qquad (4\cdot2\text{--}7)$$

where $V(r)$ is the *potential energy* of the particle in the central force field; the above expresses the fact that the field is *conservative*, i.e., the *total energy* U remains constant. Since the integral in $(4\cdot2\text{--}6)$ always exists, every central force field is conservative. Incidentally, $(4\cdot2\text{--}7)$ also expresses the important fact that in a central force field the magnitude of the *velocity* of the particle at any point depends only on its distance from the force center and is thus independent of the path or whether the particle is approaching or receding from the center of force.

Eq. $(4\cdot3\text{--}6)$ is the *energy integral*. Of course if the function $F(r)$ happened to be a function of the velocity or the time explicitly, eq. $(4\cdot3\text{--}7)$ would not exist and the system would not be *conservative*. But we should then, strictly speaking, not be dealing with a central field.

To go back to

$$F(r) = -\frac{dV}{dr}, \qquad (4\cdot2\text{--}8)$$

let us note that the component changes in V with respect to x and y are given by

$$\left.\begin{array}{l} \dfrac{\partial V}{\partial x} = \dfrac{dV}{dr}\dfrac{\partial r}{\partial x} = \dfrac{x}{r}\dfrac{dV}{dr}, \\[3ex] \dfrac{\partial V}{\partial y} = \dfrac{dV}{dr}\dfrac{\partial r}{\partial y} = \dfrac{y}{r}\dfrac{dV}{dr}. \end{array}\right\} \qquad (4\cdot2\text{--}9)$$

Substitution into $(4\cdot2\text{--}1)$ then yields

$$\left.\begin{array}{l} m\ddot{x} = -\dfrac{\partial V}{\partial x}, \\[3ex] m\ddot{y} = -\dfrac{\partial V}{\partial y}. \end{array}\right\} \qquad (4\cdot2\text{--}10)$$

But the right-hand members in (4·2–10) are the component forces F_x and F_y [eq. (3·6–1)].   Hence we have as in Sec. 4·1

$$F_x = -\frac{\partial V}{\partial x}, \quad F_y = -\frac{\partial V}{\partial y}, \qquad (4\cdot2\text{–}11)$$

and the potential energy V, considered as a function of x and y, is a function such that its negative partial derivatives with respect to x and y respectively are the component forces along the x and y axes.   From this point of view V has often been referred to as the *force function*.[1] We shall still continue to use the term potential energy when we take V to measure a property of the *particle*.   Often, however, it is extremely valuable to think of V as describing the *nature of the field* in which the particle is moving.   For this purpose we shall define V/m, i.e., the potential energy per unit mass for a particle at any particular point as the *potential* of the field at that point[2] and denote it by V_P.   This viewpoint may be made clearer as follows.   From the definition given in Sec. 1·11, it follows that

$$F(r)\, dr = dW \qquad (4\cdot2\text{–}12)$$

is the *work* done when the particle of mass m is displaced a distance dr in the direction of the force.   Then

$$\int_{r_0}^{r_1} \frac{F(r)}{m}\, dr = \frac{V_0}{m} - \frac{V_1}{m} = V_{P_0} - V_{P_1}$$

is called the *difference in potential* at the points distant r_1 and r_0 from the force center.   It is thus the work done in the motion of a particle of unit mass in the force field from the one place to the other, and it is interesting to see that this work is independent of the path followed by the particle, for it depends on the values of V_P at the two points only.

4·3. Inverse Square Field.   Electron Energies in the Bohr Theory.   In the case where the central field follows the inverse square law, $F(r) = -c/r^2$.   Hence

$$\int F(r)\, dr = \frac{c}{r} + \text{const.} \qquad (4\cdot3\text{–}1)$$

---

[1] More commonly the negative of V has been taken as the force function.   This accounts for the difference in sign often encountered in various texts in the corresponding potential formulas for gravitational attraction and electrostatic attraction respectively.

[2] This is the definition for the case of gravitational attraction.   We can also define the electrostatic potential as the potential energy per unit charge and the magnetostatic potential as the potential energy per unit magnetic pole in the case of electric and magnetic fields respectively.   In general then the potential at any point in a conservative field is the potential energy per unit " quantity " of a particle at that point.

The total energy in such a field is therefore

$$\tfrac{1}{2}mv^2 - \frac{c}{r} = U, \tag{4·3-2}$$

where the potential energy appears as

$$V(r) = -\frac{c}{r}. \tag{4·3-3}$$

We have already noted that the potential energy is not an *absolute* quantity for a given particle. In the integration (4·4–1) the constant is arbitrary and may have any value we choose to give it. It therefore follows that, in measuring potential energy, all we can really do is to give the difference in potential energy for a certain particle at two different places. If, however, in the special case of the inverse square motion, we agree to let the potential energy be *zero* at a very great distance from the force center, i.e., $r = \infty$, the value of the constant is zero and the potential energy is simply $V = -c/r$. The total energy U is thus equal to the kinetic energy at $r = \infty$. V divided by the mass of the particle also appears, as we have seen, as the *potential* of the field at any point distant r from the force center, i.e., the amount of work which is done on a particle of unit mass as it moves from the point in question to infinity (physically speaking a very great distance), or the work, equal to the former in amount, which is done by the particle in moving from an infinitely distant point to the point in question.

We have already seen in Sec. 3·7 that a particle in a central field of force varying inversely as the square of the distance to the force center moves in a conic section. In the particular case in which the motion is bounded the conic is an ellipse with the force center at one focus. We discussed in Secs. 3·8 to 3·11 important applications of this to planetary motion, ballistic missiles, artificial satellites, and the motion of an electron in the Bohr atomic model. It is now of interest to introduce energy considerations in this type of motion.

Let us get an expression for the total energy in elliptical motion in terms of a parameter connected with the elliptical orbit. It will pay indeed to get first a general expression for the total energy in any central field orbit in terms of the eccentricity. If we go back to eq. (3·7–15) we see that from (4·3–2) we can rewrite this equation in the form

$$U = \frac{c^2(\epsilon^2 - 1)}{2mk^2}. \tag{4·3-4}$$

This at once tells us that for an elliptical orbit in which $\epsilon < 1$, the total energy U is negative, whereas for a hyperbolic orbit for which $\epsilon > 1$, $U > 0$. Finally for a parabolic orbit for which $\epsilon = 0$, $U = 0$.

We had an illustration of the latter case in Sec. 1·11 in connection with the motion of a particle in a straight line with respect to the earth. What is the physical significance of a negative total energy? It may be interpreted to mean that on the average the potential energy outweighs the kinetic energy and hence the particle never gets indefinitely far away from the force center. In fact this is precisely the situation in the elliptical orbit. Hence we can look upon the equivalent positive total energy as a kind of *binding* energy which insures the localized character of the corresponding motion. It is the energy which must be given to the particle to remove it from the vicinity of the force center and reduce its velocity to zero at infinity. On the other hand the total energy in the case of a hyperbolic orbit is positive, which means that the particle has a nonvanishing velocity at infinity (cf. Sec. 3·12).

To come back to the special case of an elliptical orbit, we can use the relation (3·9–9) connecting the area constant k with the semimajor axis a of the ellipse. Solving this for k^2 and substituting into (4·3–4), we obtain

$$U = -\frac{c}{2a}, \tag{4·3–5}$$

an attractively simple result, which can be applied at once to calculate the allowed energy values for the electron orbits in the Bohr model of the hydrogen atom.

In (3·11–14) we found the allowed or quantized values of the semi-major axis of the electron orbit in hydrogen in the form

$$a = (n_1 + n_2)^2 h^2 / 4\pi^2 me^2.$$

Substitution into (4·3–5) immediately yields the allowed energy values (putting $c = e^2$ in this case)

$$U_n = -\frac{2\pi^2 me^4}{n^2 h^2}, \tag{4·3–6}$$

where we have set $n = n_1 + n_2$, the so-called principal quantum number. The smallest value of U corresponds to $n = 1$ and is called the energy of the ground state. Thus

$$U_1 = -\frac{2\pi^2 me^4}{h^2} = -\frac{e^2}{2a_0}, \tag{4·3–7}$$

where a_0 is the smallest possible value of a. Substitution of the relevant values of m, e, and h yields approximately

$$a_0 = 0.53 \times 10^{-8} \text{ cm.}$$

This provides an idea of the size of the hydrogen atom in the ground state.   Substitution yields

$$U_1 = 21.5 \times 10^{-12} \text{ erg.}$$

It is customary to use as the unit of energy in atomic problems the so-called electron volt, which is the energy gained by an electron in falling through a potential difference of 1 volt.   The charge on the electron is 4.8×10^{-10} electrostatic units and the volt is 1/300 e.s.u. of potential.   Hence the energy in question is 1.6×10^{-12} erg.   Therefore

$$U_1 = 13.5 \text{ electron volts.}$$

This is termed the ionization potential of hydrogen, since it is the energy which must be given to the hydrogen atom in its ground state in order to remove the electron completely, i.e., ionize the atom.

From what has been said above, it is also the binding energy of the hydrogen atom in its lowest or ground state.

Once the allowed energy values U_n (eq. 4·3–6) have been found for the hydrogen atom, the Bohr theory frequency postulate enables us to calculate the frequencies of the lines in the spectrum of radiation from excited and luminous hydrogen gas, as in a discharge tube. According to this postulate when a hydrogen atom makes a transition from the stationary state with energy U_{n1} to the state with energy U_{n2}, if $U_{n1} > U_{n2}$, radiation is emitted with frequency ν, where

$$\nu = \frac{U_{n1} - U_{n2}}{h}. \tag{4·3–8}$$

If $U_{n1} < U_{n2}$, the atom is said to move into an *excited* state.   It can then absorb radiation of the same frequency given in (4·3–8).   One of the conspicuous successes of the Bohr theory was its ability to predict the frequencies of the lines in the so-called Balmer series in the visible spectrum.   For this, $n_2 = 2$, while $n_1 = 3, 4, 5 \cdots$.   Thus

$$\nu = \frac{2\pi^2 m e^4}{h^3} \left(\frac{1}{4} - \frac{1}{n_1{}^2} \right) \tag{4·3–9}$$

gives the observed frequencies in question with very high accuracy when $n_1 = 3, 4, 5 \cdots$.   For further details on the Bohr theory the books referred to in Sec. 3·11 may be consulted.

4·4. Potential Calculations.   The calculation of the potential for a field of force is often an important problem.   Once it is accomplished we can write the energy equation for the motion of a particle in that field.   Hence much attention has been paid to this problem, particularly in the case where the force field is produced by collections of mass particles. We have already noted that, according to Newton's law of universal gravitation, every mass particle attracts every other one with a force which varies directly as the product of the masses and inversely as the square of the distance between them. For a single mass particle the force field is the simple one discussed in this section; for a collection of particles the field may be expected to be in general more complicated. We shall make here a few such calculations for special cases.

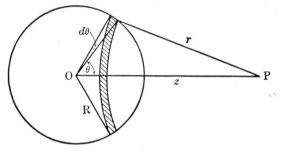

Fig. 4·2

Let us take first that of a thin homogeneous spherical shell of radius R. We have already computed the attractive force exerted by such a shell on an external mass particle in Sec. 2·4. At present we are more interested in the *potential* than the force. In Fig. 4·2 the shell is supposed to have its center at O. The external point is at P distant z from O. As in the previous calculation (Sec. 2·4), we consider as the element of mass of the shell the surface element of area

$$2\pi R \sin \theta \cdot R \, d\theta$$

obtained by drawing about P the two spheres with radii r and $r + dr$ respectively. If m is the total mass of the shell, the mass of the element will be

$$\frac{m}{4\pi R^2} 2\pi R^2 \sin \theta \, d\theta = \frac{m}{2} \sin \theta \, d\theta, \qquad (4\cdot4\text{--}1)$$

and the *potential* of the field produced by this element at P, which is by definition (Sec. 4·2) the potential energy of a unit mass particle placed at P, becomes,

$$V_P = -G \frac{m}{2} \frac{\sin \theta \, d\theta}{r}, \qquad (4\cdot4\text{--}2)$$

where G is the constant of gravitation (see Sec. 2·4). In writing this we are assuming a very important fact about the potential, namely that if we have a number of mass particles the potential produced by them collectively at any point is equal to the sum of the individual potentials.

We can prove this, quite generally, as follows. Suppose we have two mass particles of mass m_1 and m_2, and desire to calculate the potential of the field due to the two (there is no point in adding to the complexity by considering more) at the point (x, y, z) distant r_1 from mass m_1 and r_2 from mass m_2. The force on a unit mass distant r_1 from m_1 is $\mathbf{F}_1$ whose magnitude is Gm_1/r_1^2, and similarly the force on unit mass distant r_2 from m_2 is $\mathbf{F}_2$ with magnitude Gm_2/r_2^2. Now the work done in a small displacement $d\mathbf{r}$ by the resultant of the two forces is

$$(\mathbf{F}_1 + \mathbf{F}_2)\cdot d\mathbf{r} = \mathbf{F}_1\cdot d\mathbf{r} + \mathbf{F}_2\cdot d\mathbf{r},$$

since the distributive law holds for vectors. Therefore by definition the potential V_P at the point (x, y, z) is

$$V_P = \int_{(x,y,z)}^{\infty} (\mathbf{F}_1 + \mathbf{F}_2)\cdot d\mathbf{r}$$

$$= \int_{(x,y,z)}^{\infty} \mathbf{F}_1\cdot d\mathbf{r} + \int_{(x,y,z)}^{\infty} \mathbf{F}_2\cdot d\mathbf{r}$$

$$= (V_P)_1 + (V_P)_2.$$

Thus the additive property follows.

We may now return to eq. (4·4–2). To obtain the expression for the potential at the point P we have merely to carry out the integration

$$V_P = -\frac{Gm}{2}\int_0^{\pi} \frac{\sin\theta\, d\theta}{r}. \qquad (4\cdot4\text{–}3)$$

It will probably be most convenient to use r as the integration variable. Now

$$r^2 = R^2 + z^2 - 2Rz\cos\theta,$$

whence

$$r\, dr = Rz\sin\theta\, d\theta, \qquad (4\cdot4\text{–}4)$$

and therefore

$$V_P = -\frac{Gm}{2}\int_{z-R}^{z+R} \frac{dr}{Rz} = \frac{-Gm}{z}. \qquad (4\cdot4\text{–}5)$$

The conclusion to which we are led by this result is: the *potential* of the field due to a homogeneous spherical shell at a point outside the shell is that which would be obtained if all the mass of the shell were concentrated at the center. In Sec. 2·4 we had a similar result for the field intensity. Now as in that section we can consider a solid sphere as formed of concentric shells. Hence the result just obtained holds for the case of a solid sphere also.

It is important to find the potential due to a spherical shell at a point *inside* the shell. Consulting Fig. 4·3 and pursuing the same general plan as before, we note that the contribution to the potential at P (distant z from the center of the shell) due to the area element $2\pi R^2 \sin\theta \, d\theta$ is

$$- \frac{Gm}{2} \frac{dr}{zR},$$

recalling here eq. (4·4–4). We then have at once

$$V_P = - \frac{Gm}{2zR} \int_{R-z}^{R+z} dr = - \frac{Gm}{R}. \tag{4·4–6}$$

This result is interesting and significant in that V_P is shown to be independent of the position of P within the shell and dependent only on the mass and radius of the shell. It is therefore constant everywhere inside and equal to the value at the surface. Now since the force in the direction z is $-\partial V/\partial z$, it then develops that the force on any mass particle placed inside the shell is *zero*; or we may say that the intensity of the gravitational field (i.e., the force on a unit mass) inside a homogeneous shell vanishes. These results must be modified for the case of a *solid* sphere as far as internal points are concerned.

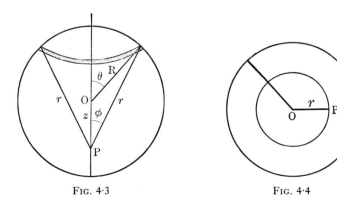

FIG. 4·3   FIG. 4·4

Suppose that we have a homogeneous solid sphere of radius a and mass M, and wish to calculate V at a point inside. Consulting Fig. 4·4, let P be the point in question (distant r from O, the center), and suppose that unit mass is placed there. Now draw the sphere through P with O as center. This divides the solid sphere into two parts. The part outside the sphere of radius r exerts no force on the mass particle at P, as we have just seen. The attractive force exerted on the particle by the inner sphere is G times the mass of the inner sphere divided by the square of the distance from O to P, namely r (see Sec. 2·4). Hence it is

$$-\frac{GM_i}{r^2} = -G\frac{4}{3}\pi r^3 \frac{\rho}{r^2}, \tag{4·4–7}$$

where ρ is the density of the material composing the sphere. But $\rho = M/\frac{4}{3}\pi a^3$ and hence the force on the unit mass at P is in magnitude

$$F = -\frac{GMr}{a^3}. \tag{4·4–8}$$

Its direction is, of course, radial and the minus sign indicates attraction toward the center. To get the potential at P we must calculate the work required to move the unit mass from P to infinity. This may be done by direct definite integration as in (4·4–5) and (4·4–6). However, since the integration is necessarily in two parts, a somewhat simpler scheme is provided by going back to (4·2–8) and writing

$$V_P = -\int F\,dr + C, \tag{4·4–9}$$

where C is a constant of integration to be evaluated from the known value of V_P at the surface of the sphere, namely $-GM/a$. We have (from 4·4–8)

$$V_P = \frac{GMr^2}{2a^3} + C. \tag{4·4–10}$$

But the application of the boundary condition at once yields $C = -3GM/2a$ and gives

$$V_P = \frac{GMr^2}{2a^3} - \frac{3GM}{2a}. \tag{4·4–11}$$

The calculation of the potential at points in gravitational fields due to other aggregates of mass particles will be indicated in the problems at the end of the chapter.

4·5. Further Considerations on the Potential. Gauss's Law and Laplace's Equation. The characterization of a conservative inverse square force field by means of the potential at any point, or what is the same thing (as we have seen), the *potential energy* for a unit mass at that point, is of such importance in mechanics that it will be well to consider it a little more fully.

The discussion of this section will relate to space of three dimensions and be quite general.   Consulting Fig. 4·5 suppose we have a closed

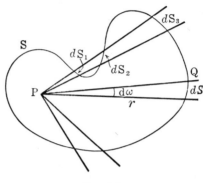

Fig. 4·5

surface S which may or may not enclose certain mass particles.   Let us consider one of these mass particles (of mass m_1) located at the point P.

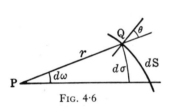

Fig. 4·6

Pick out an element of area dS distant r from P and draw the infinitesimal cone with dS as base and P as vertex. Examining the figure (Fig. 4·6) presenting an enlargement of Fig. 4·5, let the outward drawn normal to the surface element dS at Q make an angle θ with PQ.   Draw about P the sphere of radius $PQ = r$ and let the area cut off by the cone on this sphere be $d\sigma$.   We then have at once

$$d\sigma = dS \cos \theta. \qquad (4·5\text{--}1)$$

Now the force which the mass particle m_1 exerts on a unit mass particle at Q has the magnitude

$$-\frac{Gm_1}{r^2}, \qquad (4·5\text{--}2)$$

and is directed toward P.

The component of this along the outward drawn normal is

$$-\frac{Gm_1}{r^2} \cos \theta. \qquad (4·5\text{--}3)$$

Form the product of this by the area dS, whence by virtue of eq. (4·5–1) we have

$$F_N \, dS = \pm \frac{Gm_1}{r^2} \, d\sigma, \qquad (4·5\text{--}4)$$

where we have denoted the normal force component by F_N, and where the $-$ or $+$ sign is to be taken according as F_N is in the same direction as the normal or the contrary. Now if we construct about P as center the sphere of unit radius, and $d\omega$ is the area of the sphere cut out of the cone just mentioned, we shall have

$$d\omega = \frac{d\sigma}{r^2},$$

from the geometric properties of the cone. Hence (4·5–4) becomes

$$F_N \, dS = \pm Gm_1 \, d\omega. \tag{4·5–5}$$

Of course, $d\omega$ is an element of solid angle about the point P. Now if every straight line from P cuts the surface in question in but one point, we can at once integrate $F_N \, dS$ over the whole surface and have

$$\iint F_N \, dS = -Gm_1 \int d\omega = -4\pi Gm_1, \tag{4·5–6}$$

since the total solid angle about any point is 4π. This is an extremely important result, but in order to assure for it general validity and in particular justify the negative sign we must examine the case illustrated in Fig. 4·5, where some straight lines from P cut the surface in more than one point. It is to be noted, however, that the *number* of cuttings in this case (no matter how complicated the surface) must always be *odd* if P is within the surface. For example, let us take the case of *three* intersections. Here, if we pay due regard to the $+$ and $-$ signs in eq. (4·5–4), we have

$$F_{N1} \, dS_1 = -Gm_1 \, d\omega,$$
$$F_{N2} \, dS_2 = +Gm_1 \, d\omega,$$
$$F_{N3} \, dS_3 = -Gm_1 \, d\omega.$$

Hence the total contribution to the integral from these three will be simply $-Gm_1 \, d\omega$. Hence the theorem as stated mathematically in eq. (4·5–6) is generally valid. If now we proceed to apply it to the other mass particles enclosed in the surface, we have

$$\iint F_N \, dS = -4\pi G(m_1 + m_2 + \cdots)$$

$$= -4\pi GM, \tag{4·5–7}$$

where M is the total mass of all the particles inside the surface. We may now state in general form the theorem we have just proved. The surface integral of the normal component of the gravitational force on a particle of unit mass (i.e., the normal component of the intensity of the gravitational field) taken over any closed surface is equal to the negative of $4\pi G$ times the *total* mass enclosed by the surface. This is generally known as *Gauss's law of normal force*. The reader may prove that it holds also for surfaces which contain no mass particles, i.e., if there are mass particles *outside* a closed surface, the total surface integral of the gravitational force due to these particles is *zero*. This surface integral on the left-hand side of eq. (4·5–7) is sometimes called the *gravitational flux*.

Gauss's law is often of use in determining the gravitational intensity and potential of a field produced by a complicated aggregate of mass par-

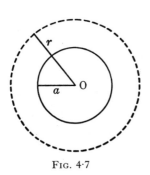

FIG. 4·7

ticles. Here we shall note merely as an illustration the case of the homogeneous sphere which has already been discussed by other methods in Secs. 2·4 and 4·4. Consider the sphere of radius a and mass M (Fig. 4·7). Draw about the center O a sphere of radius r. From symmetry it follows that the gravitational field of force at all points of this sphere will be the same, and will be directed normally to the spherical surface. Calling the intensity **F** and its normal component F_N, it follows from Gauss's law that

$$\iint F_N \, dS = F \iint dS = 4\pi r^2 F$$

$$= -4\pi G M. \qquad (4\cdot5\text{–}8)$$

Hence we have

$$F = \frac{-GM}{r^2}. \qquad (4\cdot5\text{–}9)$$

This agrees with the result of eq. (2·4–12), and from it follows, of course, that the potential at an external point distant r from the center of a solid sphere is

$$V = \frac{-GM}{r}, \qquad (4\cdot5\text{–}10)$$

in agreement with eq. (4·4–5).

It is interesting to note that the essential content of Gauss's law can also be expressed in the form of a differential equation — and indeed one of the most important in theoretical physics.   Let us suppose (Fig. 4·8) that we have an infinitesimal rectangular parallelepiped, i.e., a box of dimensions dx, dy, dz, placed for convenience at the origin of coördinates.   Let the average gravitational field intensity over the surface A (in the yz plane) in the x direction be F_x.   The value of this quantity over B will then be (neglecting differentials of order higher than the first)

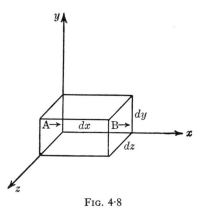

FIG. 4·8

$$F_x + \frac{\partial F_x}{\partial x} dx .$$

The outward gravitational flux through the surfaces A and B then is

$$\left(F_x + \frac{\partial F_x}{\partial x} dx\right) dy\, dz - F_x\, dy\, dz$$

$$= \frac{\partial F_x}{\partial x} dx\, dy\, dz. \tag{4·5–11}$$

In similar fashion we find that the flux through the pair of surfaces normal to the y direction is $\frac{\partial F_y}{\partial y} dx\, dy\, dz$, while that through the corresponding surfaces normal to the z direction is $\frac{\partial F_z}{\partial z} dx\, dy\, dz$. Hence the total normal flux out of the box is

$$\left(\frac{\partial F_x}{\partial x} + \frac{\partial F_y}{\partial y} + \frac{\partial F_z}{\partial z}\right) dx\, dy\, dz.$$

Now by Gauss's law this must be equal to $-4\pi G$ times the mass of the material in the box.   The latter can be expressed as the product of the density ρ (whether the distribution is continuous or discrete) and the volume $dx\, dy\, dz$.   We have, therefore:

$$\frac{\partial F_x}{\partial x} + \frac{\partial F_y}{\partial y} + \frac{\partial F_z}{\partial z} = -4\pi G\rho. \tag{4·5–12}$$

The partial differential equation of the first order (4·5–12) may be looked upon as Gauss's law in differential form.   The quantity on the left is called the *divergence* of the gravitational field intensity **F**.

In the terminology of the so-called vector operators, eq. (4·5–12) is more compactly written

$$\nabla \cdot \mathbf{F} = -4\pi G \rho \qquad (4\cdot5\text{--}13)$$

where $\nabla \cdot$ is called the divergence operator. Thus by definition

$$\nabla \equiv \mathbf{i}\frac{\partial}{\partial x} + \mathbf{j}\frac{\partial}{\partial y} + \mathbf{k}\frac{\partial}{\partial z} \qquad (4\cdot5\text{--}14)$$

where $\mathbf{i}$, $\mathbf{j}$, $\mathbf{k}$ are the unit vectors introduced in Sec. 1·3. If we use ∇ to operate dotwise on a vector like $\mathbf{F}$, we have

$$\left(\mathbf{i}\frac{\partial}{\partial x} + \mathbf{j}\frac{\partial}{\partial y} + \mathbf{k}\frac{\partial}{\partial z}\right) \cdot (\mathbf{i}\,F_x + \mathbf{j}\,F_y + \mathbf{k}\,F_z)$$

$$= \frac{\partial F_x}{\partial x} + \frac{\partial F_y}{\partial y} + \frac{\partial F_z}{\partial z}. \qquad (4\cdot5\text{--}15)$$

In carrying out the operations indicated in (4·5–15) we utilize the dot multiplication properties set forth in Sec. 1·10.

Another use of the ∇ operator (pronounced " del ") is provided by the relation between the force $\mathbf{F}$ and the potential V. Consulting Sec. 4·2 and in particular eq. (4·2–11) we have in general

$$F_x = -\frac{\partial V}{\partial x},\; F_y = -\frac{\partial V}{\partial y},\; F_z = -\frac{\partial V}{\partial z}. \qquad (4\cdot5\text{--}16)$$

Hence

$$\mathbf{F} = \mathbf{i}\,F_x + \mathbf{j}\,F_y + \mathbf{k}\,F_z$$

$$= -\left(\mathbf{i}\frac{\partial}{\partial x} + \mathbf{j}\frac{\partial}{\partial y} + \mathbf{k}\frac{\partial}{\partial z}\right) V = -\nabla V. \qquad (4\cdot5\text{--}17)$$

When ∇ operates on a scalar like the potential V the result is, of course, a vector, in this case the negative of the force $\mathbf{F}$ associated with the potential field V. We shall refer to ∇V as the *gradient* of V.

It follows that eq. (4·5–12) can be written equally well as a second-order equation, viz.,

$$\frac{\partial^2 V}{\partial x^2} + \frac{\partial^2 V}{\partial y^2} + \frac{\partial^2 V}{\partial z^2} = 4\pi G \rho \qquad (4\cdot5\text{--}18)$$

This in turn can be written more economically in vector notation

$$\nabla \cdot \nabla V = \nabla^2 V = 4\pi G \rho. \qquad (4\cdot5\text{--}19)$$

This is called *Poisson's equation* and is of great·significance throughout physics, finding application in hydrodynamics and electricity and magnetism as well as in mechanics proper. When it is integrated it gives the potential V due to any distribution of mass of density ρ in the neighborhood of that distribution. In *free* space, i.e., space unoccupied by material particles, we have $\rho = 0$, and the equation becomes

$$\nabla^2 V = 0 \qquad (4\cdot5\text{–}20)$$

which is known as *Laplace's equation*, and is also of great importance in theoretical physics. We shall not concern ourselves with the question of the solution of equations (4·5–13) and (4·5–14) at this place, except to ask the reader to verify the statement that the potential V due to a single mass particle satisfies Laplace's equation. We recall that in this case

$$V = \frac{-Gm}{r},$$

where $r = \sqrt{(x - x_1)^2 + (y - y_1)^2 + (z - z_1)^2}$, the point (x_1, y_1, z_1) being the position of the particle, while (x, y, z) is the place where V is to be computed.

It will be worth while to emphasize the importance of Laplace's equation by the following statement. If we can determine a solution of it for which the potential has a definitely assigned value at every point of the boundary of a given region, the potential is *uniquely* determined everywhere in space. For the proof of this the student should consult a more advanced treatise.[1] Incidentally, this is a very good illustration of the power of boundary conditions in physics. The solution of Laplace's equation to satisfy given boundary conditions is in general a mathematical problem of considerable difficulty. All that we wish to emphasize here is its perfectly definite physical significance.

The reader will probably have observed that the present section seems to contain more geometry than physics. What physics *is* involved comes in by virtue of the *inverse square* law of gravitational attraction. So important is this law, however, that, as has been pointed out, the results of this section are of enormous significance throughout the whole of physics. For it will be recalled that this is the law which describes the attraction and repulsion of electric charges and also the mutual actions of magnetic poles. Hence the mathematical analysis of this section can at once be applied with a few changes in notation to the mathematical theory of electricity and magnetism.

We shall meet Laplace's equation again in Chapter 11 in connection with the flow of fluids. This will provide another opportunity also to employ vector operator notation.

---

[1] See, for example, R. B. Lindsay, *Concepts and Methods of Theoretical Physics*, Van Nostrand, Princeton, N.J., 1951, pp. 288 f.

PROBLEMS

1. A particle of mass M is supported by a vertical spring of length l and linear density ρ attached to a rigid ceiling. Find the kinetic energy of the whole system consisting of the particle and spring when the particle is pulled down a short distance and released. Assume that the vertical displacement of any point of the spring is proportional to the distance below the point of suspension. If the stiffness of the spring is k, derive the expression for the frequency of vibration taking into account the mass of the spring.

2. A particle of mass m moves under gravity on the parabola $y^2 = 2px$ from the point $(a, \sqrt{2pa})$ to the origin. Use the space integral of the resultant force along the path to calculate the resultant kinetic energy attained at the origin and compare with that predicted by the conservation of mechanical energy.

3. A simple harmonic oscillator of mass 100 grams and stiffness 10^5 dynes/cm has a total energy of 2 joules. What is the maximum displacement of the oscillator and what is its maximum velocity? If we imagine a plane in which the coördinates of any point are the position x and velocity $\dot{x}$ respectively of a particle, what kind of curve will represent the motion of the oscillator? What physical significance can be associated with the area enclosed by the curve?

4. A particle of mass m is subject to both a restoring force $-kx$ $(k > 0)$ and a constant force $\mathbf{F}$ directed in the x direction. Find the expression for the total energy of the particle. If the latter has the value U, where will the kinetic energy of the particle vanish? Where will the potential energy vanish? Determine the displacement x of the particle as a function of the time.

5. Find the expressions for the kinetic energy of a particle moving in an inverse square central force field at perihelion and aphelion. Find the corresponding numerical values for the earth in its motion around the sun and for an electron moving about a nucleus with equal positive charge (hydrogen atom). (NB. Consult tables for necessary constants.)

6. The singly ionized helium atom consists of a single electron moving about a positively charged nucleus with mass four times that of the hydrogen nucleus and charge $= 2e$. Find the energy necessary to produce a doubly ionized helium atom. Between what energy states of ionized helium will a transition yield the same frequency as that of the longest wave length line in the Balmer series of hydrogen?

7. Compute the work required to raise a mass m from the surface of the earth to a point P, 1000 miles above the surface; also the work required to raise m from the center of the earth to the surface. What is the potential at P and at the center of the earth?

8. A sphere of radius a, mass M and density varying directly as the distance from the center is built up of matter brought from an infinite distance. Find the work W done throughout the process by the attraction of the matter which has already arrived on that which is brought up later, in terms of M, a, and the constant of gravitation G.

9. A particle moves in a central force field characterized by the potential energy $V(r) = -V_0re^{-\alpha r^2}$, where V_0 and α are positive constants. (a) Plot the function $V(r)$. (b) Find the magnitude of the force as a function of r.

(c) If the particle starts from rest at the point of inflection of $V(r)$, will it reach the origin and, if so, how much velocity will it acquire? (d) How much velocity must be given the particle at the origin to remove it to infinity with zero velocity? (e) If the particle starts from rest at a distance $\ll 1/\sqrt{2\alpha}$ from the minimum of the potential energy curve what sort of motion does it perform? Discuss the characteristics of the motion.

10. Find the potential due to an infinitely long cylinder, of mass M per unit length and radius a, at an external point whose distance from the axis of the cylinder is r.

11. A homogeneous hemispherical solid has density ρ_0 and radius a. Find the expression for the gravitational potential at the center of the corresponding sphere. Calculate the components of the intensity of the gravitational field at the same point.

12. Derive the equation for the family of equipotential surfaces in the neighborhood of two point charges $+e$ and $-e$ separated by distance a.

13. Prove that the following are solutions of Laplace's equation and hence suitable for potential functions:

$$V = \text{arc tan} \frac{y}{x},$$

$$V = \log \frac{r+z}{r-z},$$

$$V = \frac{1}{r} \text{arc tan} \frac{y}{x},$$

$$V = \frac{z}{r^3}.$$

(These are all called spherical harmonics. Note that $r^2 = x^2 + y^2 + z^2$.)

14. Show that if $V = V(r)$ where $r^2 = x^2 + y^2 + z^2$, Poisson's equation takes the form

$$\frac{1}{r^2} \frac{d}{dr} \left(r^2 \frac{dV}{dr} \right) = 4\pi G\rho.$$

Show that this is also equivalent to

$$\frac{1}{r} \frac{d^2}{dr^2} (rV) = 4\pi G\rho.$$

15. Integrate Poisson's equation to find $V(r)$ for the case of a homogeneous spherical distribution of mass, i.e., $\rho = $ constant in Problem 14. How may the constants of integration be evaluated?

16. Integrate Poisson's equation to find $V(r)$ for the case of a spherical distribution of mass in which $\rho = \rho_0 e^{-\alpha r}$, where α is a positive constant. What is the total mass of the distribution?

17. Find the gravitational potential at a point external to a sphere of radius a containing matter of mass m distributed so that its density is a function of r only, where r is the distance from the center of the sphere.

18. A particle moves in a central force field characterized by a potential energy function of the form

$$V(r) = \frac{C}{r}\,e^{-\alpha r},$$

where C is a constant.   Plot the function V and find the regions of space in which the particle can have a real velocity.   Find the force corresponding to this potential energy.

19. Find the binding energy of the single electron in the doubly ionized lithium atom and do the same for the trebly ionized beryllium atom.   Use these results to find the radii of these ionized atoms in their ground or lowest energy states.

20. The famous Lennard-Jones potential energy function for the interaction of two non-polar molecules has the form

$$V(r) = 4C[(\sigma/r)^{12} - (\sigma/r)^6]\,,$$

where C and σ are constants.   Plot the general shape of the function and find the value of r for which it is a minimum in terms of C and σ.   Find the expression for the force corresponding to this potential.   Find the value of r for which $V(r) = 0$ and comment on its physical significance.

CHAPTER 5

STATICS OF A PARTICLE

5·1. Equilibrium of a Particle. Simple Cases. In the previous chapters we have discussed the *motion* of a particle in an inertial system, and have seen that the accelerated motion of such a particle is closely associated with the idea of *force*. Now it often happens that a particle is at rest or moves in such a way that it suffers no acceleration, i.e., possesses constant velocity. The study of a particle in such a case, particularly that of rest, is usually called *statics*. It might at first be thought that the study of statics is a barren one, since the particle in this case is so restricted in its behavior. However, as soon as we are willing to admit that a particle may be subject to *two* or *more* accelerations simultaneously we see that the possibility exists for it to be at rest under those conditions, and this fact may be of great value in relating the various accelerations to which it is subject. In Chapter 1 we have already defined the force acting on a particle. Let us now consider a mass particle on which n forces $\mathbf{F}_1, \mathbf{F}_2, \mathbf{F}_3, \ldots, \mathbf{F}_n$ act. These may be replaced, in so far as their action on the particle is concerned, by one force $\mathbf{R}$, the vector sum of all the forces. We then have for the equation of motion of the particle

$$m\mathbf{a} = \mathbf{R} = \mathbf{F}_1 + \mathbf{F}_2 + \cdots + \mathbf{F}_n. \qquad (5\cdot1\text{-}1)$$

Now if the particle is at rest or, at most, moving with constant velocity, $\mathbf{a} = 0$, and we therefore have

$$\mathbf{R} = \sum_{i=1}^{n} \mathbf{F}_i = 0. \qquad (5\cdot1\text{-}2)$$

Fig. 5·1

$\mathbf{F}_1, \mathbf{F}_2, \ldots, \mathbf{F}_n$ are then said to form a system in equilibrium. We shall call forces of this character *static* forces. Let us illustrate this important idea with a few simple examples.

Consider first a particle of mass m suspended by a weightless cord as in Fig. 5·1. The particle is subjected to a gravitational force acting vertically downward and equal in magnitude to mg. But the particle

121

is at rest. Therefore it must be acted on by another force $\mathbf{F}_t$ directed upward, such that

$$\mathbf{F}_t + m\mathbf{g} = 0. \tag{5·1–3}$$

$\mathbf{F}_t$ is the so-called tension in the cord; a weightless spring balance or dynamometer inserted anywhere in this cord would record this force. We are not really introducing an entirely new concept of force, as might perhaps be supposed. We may still consider $\mathbf{F}_t$ to be measured by the acceleration it could produce in a given mass, but actually the equilibrium condition (5·1–2), of which (5·1–3) is a special case, enables us more easily to compare forces of this type.

Consider another illustration. Let a particle of mass m at P (Fig. 5·2) have two weightless strings attached to it, the other ends of the strings being fastened respectively to points A and B on the same horizontal level of a rigid ceiling. The strings being inextensible, the mass m is at

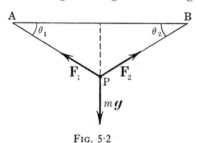

FIG. 5·2

rest and therefore in equilibrium. If we assume a force $\mathbf{F}_1$ in string PA and a force $\mathbf{F}_2$ in string PB, m will be in equilibrium provided that

$$\mathbf{F}_1 + \mathbf{F}_2 + \mathbf{F}_g = 0, \tag{5·1–4}$$

where $\mathbf{F}_g$ is the force of gravity, $m\mathbf{g}$. The magnitudes of $\mathbf{F}_1$ and $\mathbf{F}_2$ can be calculated by writing the equilibrium equation in scalar form. This is an important feature of the solution of problems in statics and hence we may note it particularly in connection with this simple illustration. We reason thus: the *resultant* $\mathbf{R}$ of the three forces must vanish. Hence its rectangular *component* along any line through P must likewise vanish. Let us therefore note the equation expressing the fact that the component along the line of action of $\mathbf{F}_g$ is zero. Now the component of the resultant of several forces along any line is the sum of the components of the individual forces along this line, for a force is a vector, and this statement is true of vectors in general. We therefore have

$$F_1 \sin \theta_1 + F_2 \sin \theta_2 = mg. \tag{5·1–5}$$

This equation alone is insufficient to determine F_1 and F_2 in terms of θ_1, θ_2 and mg. But we can express the same condition for the component of the resultant along the line perpendicular to the vertical. This yields

$$F_1 \cos \theta_1 - F_2 \cos \theta_2 = 0. \tag{5·1–6}$$

The two equations (5·1–5) and (5·1–6) are sufficient to determine F_1 and F_2 as follows,

$$F_1 = mg \cdot \frac{\cos \theta_2}{\sin (\theta_1 + \theta_2)},$$

$$F_2 = mg \cdot \frac{\cos \theta_1}{\sin (\theta_1 + \theta_2)}.$$

(5·1–7)

Of course, other equations may be obtained by writing the above condition for any other line through P, but they will not be independent of (5·1–5) and (5·1–6).

The equilibrium of a particle under the action of three forces lying

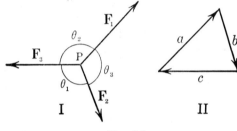

Fig. 5·3

in the same plane provides an interesting theorem. Suppose (Fig. 5·3, I) the three forces F_1, F_2 and F_3 acting on a mass particle at P are in equilibrium. Introduce the angles θ_1, θ_2 and θ_3. Now let us write the conditions that the components of the resultant shall be zero in directions normal to F_3, F_2, F_1 respectively. Examining the figure we see that these conditions are

$$F_1 \sin \theta_2 = F_2 \sin \theta_1,$$

$$F_1 \sin \theta_3 = F_3 \sin \theta_1,$$

$$F_2 \sin \theta_3 = F_3 \sin \theta_2.$$

These, however, may be combined at once into the two equations

$$\frac{F_1}{\sin \theta_1} = \frac{F_2}{\sin \theta_2} = \frac{F_3}{\sin \theta_3},$$

(5·1–8)

which thus serve as a useful algebraic criterion for the equilibrium of the particle under the action of the forces. A more suggestive geometrical condition is at once noted when we recall that the resultant of several vectors is formed (Sec. 1·3, Fig. 1·3) by laying off at the end

of the first vector a line equal in magnitude to and in the same direction
as the second vector, and repeating in turn with all the vectors.   The
resultant is the line joining the initial point of the first vector to the
end of the line last drawn.   For vectors whose sum is zero the line last
drawn will, of course, end at the inital point of the first vector and a
closed polygon will be formed.   In the case of three vectors this polygon
will be a triangle (Fig. 5·3, II).   Hence we have the theorem that when
three forces acting on a particle are in equilibrium the force vectors must
lie in a plane, and the triangle formed by drawing in the plane any three
lines (not intersecting in a single point) parallel respectively to the
force vectors will have the lengths of its sides proportional respectively
to the magnitudes of the forces acting.   This is known as the *triangle
of forces* and is often useful in the solution of problems in statics such
as the one indicated in Fig. 5·2 above.   The student should solve this
problem by this method, if necessary assuming definite numerical
values for mg, θ_1, and θ_2 to fix his ideas.

5·2. General Equations of Equilibrium of a Particle.   The
general analytical equations for the equilibrium of a particle under the
action of n coplanar forces can perhaps be most simply expressed in
terms of the components along
two mutually perpendicular axes.
Consulting Fig. 5·4, let the forces
$\mathbf{F}_1, \mathbf{F}_2, \ldots, \mathbf{F}_n$ act on a particle at
the point O.   Establish in the most
convenient way the rectangular
axes Ox and Oy and let the forces
make angles $\theta_1, \theta_2, \ldots, \theta_n$ respectively with the positive direction of
the x axis.   In each case by θ
we shall mean the smaller angle
between the positive x direction

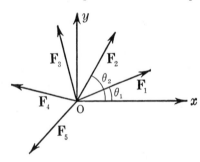

Fig. 5·4

and the direction of the force.   If we denote the resultant of the forces
by $\mathbf{R}$ and let R_x and R_y denote the components of $\mathbf{R}$ along the two axes
respectively, we have

$$R_x = F_1 \cos \theta_1 + F_2 \cos \theta_2 + \cdots + F_n \cos \theta_n = \sum_{i=1}^{i=n} F_i \cos \theta_i$$
$$R_y = F_1 \sin \theta_1 + F_2 \sin \theta_2 + \cdots + F_n \sin \theta_n = \sum_{i=1}^{i=n} F_i \sin \theta_i.$$
$$(5\cdot2\text{--}1)$$

If we denote the x component of $\mathbf{F}_1$ by X_1 and the y component by Y_1
we may also write

$$R_x = \sum X_i, \quad R_y = \sum Y_i. \qquad (5\cdot2\text{--}2)$$

The resultant is then given in magnitude by

$$R = \sqrt{(\sum X_i)^2 + (\sum Y_i)^2}, \qquad (5\cdot2\text{–}3)$$

and the direction it makes with the x axis is given by ϕ, where

$$\tan \phi = \frac{R_y}{R_x} = \frac{\sum Y_i}{\sum X_i}. \qquad (5\cdot2\text{–}4)$$

Now if the forces are in equilibrium, $\mathbf{R} = 0$ and therefore

$$\sum X_i = 0 = \sum Y_i. \qquad (5\cdot2\text{–}5)$$

Many illustrations of these conditions will be found in the problems at the end of this chapter.

Incidentally we may remark that results precisely similar to the above hold for a collection of non-coplanar forces. Here each force F_k may be considered to make angles α_k, β_k, γ_k with three mutually perpendicular coördinate axes. We then have analogously to $(5\cdot2\text{–}1)$

$$\left.\begin{aligned}
R_x &= \sum F_k \cos \alpha_k = \sum X_k, \\
R_y &= \sum F_k \cos \beta_k = \sum Y_k, \\
R_z &= \sum F_k \cos \gamma_k = \sum Z_k,
\end{aligned}\right\} \qquad (5\cdot2\text{–}6)$$

whence the resultant

$$R = \sqrt{R_x{}^2 + R_y{}^2 + R_z{}^2}$$
$$= \sqrt{(\sum X_k)^2 + (\sum Y_k)^2 + (\sum Z_k)^2}. \qquad (5\cdot2\text{–}7)$$

The condition for equilibrium is then $\mathbf{R} = 0$, whence we must have

$$\sum X_k = \sum Y_k = \sum Z_k = 0, \qquad (5\cdot2\text{–}8)$$

analogously to $(5\cdot2\text{–}5)$.

As a matter of fact we shall find that for most simple purposes in static problems coplanar forces are sufficient and hence we shall not press these three dimensional considerations.

5·3 A System of Particles. In the foregoing sections we have been concerned with forces acting on one particle only. We can extend our considerations to the equilibrium of several particles by the use of the following idea, sometimes referred to as the principle of *separate equilibrium*. Suppose we have a set of particles which are connected in some way by rods or strings or otherwise act on each other. Let us imagine that these particles are likewise acted on by *external* forces. We can then still examine the equilibrium of any one particle apart from all the others by considering all the forces which act on it, i.e., those due to the connections as well as the external forces.

We now discuss an illustration of the above. Let a string of negligible weight be suspended from two fixed points A and B. Knotted to the string at the points $P_1, P_2, \ldots, P_n$ are particles of equal mass m (Fig. 5·5). We are to find the angles of inclination $\theta_1, \theta_2, \ldots, \theta_n$

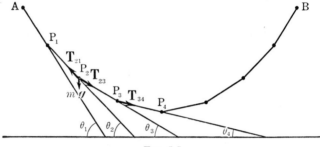

Fig. 5·5

which the portions of the string between successive mass particles make with the horizontal. Let us first consider the equilibrium of the mass particle at P_2. There are acting on it *three* forces, namely the weight mg and the two tensions $\mathbf{T}_{21}$ and $\mathbf{T}_{23}$ in the adjacent portions of the string.

The component equilibrium equations for the vertical and horizontal directions respectively are

$$\left.\begin{array}{l} T_{21} \sin \theta_2 - mg - T_{23} \sin \theta_3 = 0, \\ T_{21} \cos \theta_2 - T_{23} \cos \theta_3 = 0. \end{array}\right\} \qquad (5\cdot3\text{--}1)$$

Next consider P_3 and write the condition for horizontal equilibrium, namely

$$T_{34} \cos \theta_4 - T_{23} \cos \theta_3 = 0. \qquad (5\cdot3\text{--}2)$$

It therefore follows in general (noting that $T_{12} = T_{21}$, etc.) that

$$T_{12} \cos \theta_2 = T_{23} \cos \theta_3 = T_{34} \cos \theta_4 \cdots = T, \qquad (5\cdot3\text{--}3)$$

where T is some constant. Hence

$$T_{12} = \frac{T}{\cos \theta_2}, \quad T_{23} = \frac{T}{\cos \theta_3} \cdots$$

$$T_{ij} = \frac{T}{\cos \theta_j}.$$

Substitution into the first of the equations (5·3–1) yields

$$\tan \theta_2 = \tan \theta_3 + \frac{mg}{T},$$

and the similar equations

$$\left.\begin{array}{c} \tan \theta_3 = \tan \theta_4 + \dfrac{mg}{T}, \\[4pt] \cdot \quad \cdot \quad \cdot \quad \cdot \quad \cdot \quad \cdot \quad \cdot \\[4pt] \tan \theta_j = \tan \theta_{j+1} + \dfrac{mg}{T}. \end{array}\right\} \qquad (5\cdot3\text{--}4)$$

Let us now suppose that one of the pieces of string has a definite inclination, let us say, *zero*, for the sake of simplicity. That is, let $\tan \theta_{j+1} = 0$. Then

$$\tan \theta_j = \frac{mg}{T},$$

$$\tan \theta_{j-1} = \frac{2mg}{T},$$

$$\tan \theta_{j-2} = \frac{3mg}{T},$$

$$\cdot \quad \cdot \quad \cdot \quad \cdot \quad \cdot \quad \cdot$$

$$\tan \theta_1 = \frac{jmg}{T}. \qquad (5\cdot3\text{--}5)$$

It thus develops in this case that the tangents of the angles of inclination are the terms of an arithmetical progression. The string we have been discussing is often called a *funicular* polygon. It is of particular interest when the horizontal projections of the successive portions of the string are equal in length and one part is horizontal. Take the midpoint O (Fig. 5·6) of the horizontal portion Q_1P_1 as the origin of

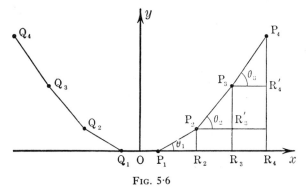

Fig. 5·6

rectangular coördinates. The positions of the various mass particles to the right of O will be denoted as before by $P_1, P_2, \ldots, P_j$. Let the projections of these points on the x axis be $R_2, R_3, \ldots, R_j$

respectively (note that R_1 and P_1 coincide). Let $P_2R_2 = a$, and let $Q_1P_1 = P_1R_2 = R_2R_3 = R_3R_4 = \ldots = b$. From our previous illustration we see that

$$\left.\begin{array}{c} \tan \theta_1 = \dfrac{a}{P_1R_2}, \\[2mm] \tan \theta_2 = 2 \tan \theta_1 = \dfrac{2a}{P_1R_2} = \dfrac{P_3R_3{}'}{P_2R_3{}'}. \end{array}\right\} \tag{5·3-6}$$

So we have, since $P_1R_2 = P_2R_3{}'$ etc.,

$$P_3R_3{}' = 2a, \tag{5·3-7}$$

$$P_4R_4{}' = 3a. \tag{5·3-8}$$

$$\cdot \quad \cdot \quad \cdot \quad \cdot \quad \cdot$$

It follows that in the system of axes chosen the coördinates of P_1, P_2, P_3, $\ldots$ are respectively $(\tfrac{1}{2}b, o)$, $(\tfrac{3}{2}b, a)$, $(\tfrac{5}{2}b, a + 2a)$ etc., so that the coördinates of P_n will be $\left((2n - 1)\dfrac{b}{2}, \dfrac{n(n - 1)}{2} a\right)$. If we eliminate n between the expressions

$$\left.\begin{array}{c} x = (2n - 1)\dfrac{b}{2}, \\[3mm] y = \dfrac{n(n - 1)}{2} a, \end{array}\right\} \tag{5·3-9}$$

the result will be the equation of the curve which passes through every vertex P_n. After a little reduction we find

$$2\frac{b^2y}{a} + \frac{b^2}{4} = x^2, \tag{5·3-10}$$

which is the equation of a *parabola* with Oy as its axis. The actual configuration of the string will approach more and more nearly the parabolic shape as the number of particles increases. The vertex of the parabola lies at a distance $a/8$ below the point O on Oy extended downwards.

The *suspension* bridge is an interesting illustration of equilibrium of this kind. In this case the string is replaced by a cable at intervals along which strands are placed cutting off equal intervals on the flooring of the bridge. The cable and sustaining strands may be supposed to have masses negligible compared with that of the flooring. If we assume that the masses suspended from each strand are equal to equal portions of the flooring, the conditions approximate those of the simple case just discussed. The curve of the cable will be approximately a parabola with vertex at the center of the bridge P.   Let the span of the bridge be $2l$ and the height above P be h (see Fig. 5·7).   The equation of this parabola with P as origin will be

$$y = \frac{x^2}{4m}, \tag{5·3–11}$$

where m is a constant.   Now the slope at any point is given by

$$\frac{dy}{dx} = \frac{x}{2m} = \frac{2y}{x}. \tag{5·3–12}$$

Hence the slope of the curve at B will be $\tan \theta_0 = 2h/l$, as we find by substituting the coördinates of B into the formula (5·3–12).   What is the *tension* of the cable on the support at B (which of course will be equal to that at A by symmetry)? If we recall eq. (5·3–3) and those immediately following we see that the tension at the end is equal in magnitude to

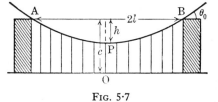

FIG. 5·7

$$\frac{T}{\cos \theta_0} = T \frac{\sqrt{4h^2 + l^2}}{l}, \tag{5·3–13}$$

where the constant T is given by noting from (5·3–5) that $\tan \theta_0 = \dfrac{jmg}{T} = \dfrac{W}{2T}$, if W is the total load suspended, i.e., the weight of the flooring of the bridge.   Therefore $T = \dfrac{Wl}{4h}$ and the terminal tension becomes

$$\frac{W}{4h} \sqrt{4h^2 + l^2}.$$

Its vertical component at both B and A is of course $W/2$.   The horizontal tension, which is everywhere the same, is, of course, T.

5·4. Equilibrium of a Flexible String.   This seems a rather appropriate place to introduce the discussion of a flexible string in equilibrium.   Such a string may be considered, of course, as a very large number of small particles tied together by small weightless strings or cords, as in the example of the previous section. In the present case, however, we consider the mass to be distributed continuously along the string and further assume that the latter is perfectly flexible, i.e., can be bent in any direction without the expenditure of work.

Let us suppose such a string is suspended by two points A and B (Fig. 5·8) and acted on by gravity only. This is the simplest case and will suffice for our illustration here as it is often encountered in nature. We desire to find the shape assumed by the string. In the first place we note that just as in the example of Sec. 5·3, the horizontal tension is the same everywhere. We shall represent distance along the string from an arbitrarily chosen origin by s. Consider an infinitesimal portion of the string of length ds at point P. Let ρ be the mass of the string per unit length. Then if the tension is denoted by $\mathbf{T}$, since the portion QP is in equilibrium the horizontal and vertical components are respectively

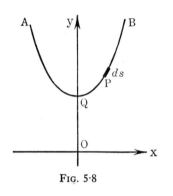

Fig. 5·8

$$T\frac{dx}{ds} = c_1, \qquad (5\text{·}4\text{–}1)$$

$$T\frac{dy}{ds} = \rho g s + c_2, \qquad (5\text{·}4\text{–}2)$$

where c_1 and c_2 are constants. Now if we choose our origin (i.e., $s = 0$) at the place where the curve is horizontal, we have $c_2 = 0$, and dividing (5·4–1) by (5·4–2), there results

$$dx = \frac{c_1\,dy}{\rho g s} = \sqrt{ds^2 - dy^2}, \qquad (5\text{·}4\text{–}3)$$

since $dx^2 + dy^2 = ds^2$. From this we have at once

$$dy = \frac{\rho g s\,ds}{\sqrt{c_1{}^2 + \rho^2 g^2 s^2}}, \qquad (5\text{·}4\text{–}4)$$

and the integration yields

$$y = \sqrt{s^2 + \left(\frac{c_1}{\rho g}\right)^2} + c_3. \qquad (5\text{·}4\text{–}5)$$

Proceeding as above, we find x in terms of s. Thus from (5·4–3) and (5·4–4)

$$dx = \frac{c_1}{\rho g} \cdot \frac{ds}{\sqrt{s^2 + \left(\dfrac{c_1}{\rho g}\right)^2}}. \qquad (5\text{·}4\text{–}6)$$

The result of the integration is

$$\frac{\rho g x}{c_1} = \log\left[s + \sqrt{s^2 + \left(\frac{c_1}{\rho g}\right)^2}\right] + c_4. \tag{5·4–7}$$

The boundary condition $x = 0, s = 0$, gives

$$c_4 = -\log\frac{c_1}{\rho g},$$

and therefore

$$\sqrt{s^2 + \left(\frac{c_1}{\rho g}\right)^2} = \frac{c_1}{\rho g}\,e^{\rho g x/c_1} - s. \tag{5·4–8}$$

Expanding and rearranging we have

$$s = \frac{c_1}{2\rho g}\cdot[e^{\rho g x/c_1} - e^{-\rho g x/c_1}]$$

$$= \frac{c_1}{\rho g}\sinh\frac{\rho g x}{c_1}. \tag{5·4–9}$$

Now from eq. (5·4–5), if we let $c_3 = 0$ by choosing $y = c_1/\rho g$ at $s = 0$, we get at once

$$y = \frac{c_1}{\rho g}\cosh\frac{\rho g x}{c_1}. \tag{5·4–10}$$

This is the equation of the famous catenary curve, as we have already noticed earlier (Sec. 2·3). The reader should plot the curve and note how it fulfills the various requirements of this section.

5·5. Equilibrium of a Particle on a Rough Surface. Static Friction. It will have been noted that the examples of equilibrium discussed in preceding sections involved the motion of a particle subject to a constraint, that is unable to move freely because of its attachment to other particles, etc. Another interesting case is provided by the equilibrium of a particle constrained to stay on a surface. In Sec. 2·1 we investigated the motion of a particle on a smooth inclined plane. The corresponding problem of equilibrium on such a plane is well known from elementary physics. We now look into the more general case in which the plane is rough and we must take into account the force of friction, i.e., a force *along* the surface resisting sliding.

It will be recalled from elementary physics that the force of friction is distinguished from the adhesion which bodies have for each other by the fact that while adhesion is independent of the force thrusting two surfaces together, friction is dependent on the normal force between them. This is usually referred to as the normal thrust. The statement just made is one of the so-called experimental laws of friction. The ratio of the force of friction to the total normal thrust for surfaces *just about to slip* over each other is a quantity which remains constant for considerable variations in the thrust. We are then led to define

$$\mu = \frac{F}{N} = \frac{\text{magnitude of maximum frictional force}}{\text{magnitude of normal thrust}}, \quad (5\cdot5\text{–}1)$$

as the *coefficient of friction*. It should be emphasized that the constancy of this quantity is only approximate, for μ varies greatly as N increases to a point where the surface is deformed under its action. The second law of friction states that for a given normal thrust the force of friction is approximately independent of the area of the surface of contact. Obviously this also has its limitations. One can hardly expect to apply it if the surface is a pin point, for example. The coefficient of friction depends, of course, on the nature of both surfaces in contact and varies greatly with variations in these. The following table gives some illustrations of the approximate values of μ for various cases.

COEFFICIENT OF FRICTION
(From Smithsonian Tables)

All values are approximate only

Materials	Coefficient of friction
Wood on wood, dry	.25–.50
Wood on wood, soapy	.20
Metals on oak, dry	.50–.60
Metals on oak, wet	.24–.26
Metals on oak, soapy	.20
Metals on elm, dry	.20–.25
Hemp on oak, dry	.53
Hemp on oak, wet	.33
Leather on oak	.27–.38
Leather on metals, dry	.56
Leather on metals, wet	.36
Leather on metals, greasy	.23
Leather on metals, oily	.15
Metals on metals, dry	.15–.20
Metals on metals, wet	.3
Smooth surfaces occasionally greased	.07–.08
Smooth surfaces, best results	.03–.036
Steel on agate, dry	.20
Steel on agate, oiled	.107
Iron on stone	.30–.70
Wood on stone	about .40
Earth on earth	.25–1.00
Earth on earth, damp clay	1.00
Earth on earth, wet clay	.31

As one might also expect, the coefficient μ depends on the character of the motion of one surface on the other. If the beginning motion is *rolling*, for example, rather than *sliding* we should not anticipate the same state of affairs in both cases. Moreover after motion has once been established, the coefficient of friction may be expected to be different. It is actually found that friction in sliding motion is less than *static* friction. It is the latter with which we are concerned in the present section.

Moreover we ought to emphasize the fact that the magnitude of the force of friction is variable. Thus if a heavy particle rests on a rough horizontal table and the only force acting on it is its weight, the force of friction is zero. If a horizontal force is applied to the particle, the force of friction will be equal to this force as long as no slipping takes place. It is *only* when slipping is about to take place that $F = \mu N$. Hence we may say in general that F can vary all the way from zero to μN.

We may now apply these ideas to the equilibrium of a particle on a rough inclined plane when gravity is the only applied force (cf. Fig. 5·9). The force of gravity mg has a component $mg \cos \theta$ perpendicular to the plane, which is the normal thrust, and hence by the third law of Newton the plane must react against the particle with a reaction force $\mathbf{R}_1$ whose magnitude is $mg \cos \theta$ and whose direction is normal to and away from the plane. The particle could not be in equilibrium under the action of these two forces alone but would tend to accelerate down the plane (Sec. 2·1). Since the plane is rough, the frictional force $\mathbf{F}$ acts parallel to the plane in such a direction as to oppose the acceler- ated motion (i.e., in this case, *up*). We may think of the forces $\mathbf{R}_1$ and

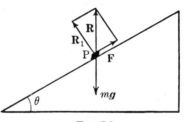

Fig. 5·9

$\mathbf{F}$ as combining to form a resultant reaction $\mathbf{R}$, which if equilibrium is to be maintained must be equal in magnitude to mg and be oppositely directed to the weight. For equilibrium $F = mg \sin \theta$ always, but it will not reach its maximum possible value $\mu R_1 = \mu mg \cos \theta$ until slipping is just about to take place. This will evidently happen when the angle θ reaches the value χ where

$$mg \sin \chi = \mu mg \cos \chi,$$

or

$$\tan \chi = \mu. \tag{5·5–2}$$

The angle χ is sometimes called the *angle of repose*. Its measurement provides a method for the determination of the coefficient of friction.

We may again emphasize the fact that frictional force is different in nature from the other forces so far discussed. Its essential nature is *resistance*; in fact we may call it passive resistance. It always acts in such a direction as to resist motion. Moreover, we may stress the fact that it is not a *conservative* force in the sense of Chapter 3. There is no potential associated with it. We shall encounter similar forces in hydrodynamics and elsewhere.

5·6. The Principle of Virtual Work. An interesting interpretation of equilibrium may be obtained by considering the idea of work (Chapter 1). Thus consider a particle at the point P (Fig. 5·10), and imagine that it is acted on by certain forces. Let one of these be the force **F**. We shall suppose that we do not know actually how the particle moves under the action of the forces; but imagine that an *arbitrary* possible small displacement of the particle be denoted by δ**r**. This displacement, it must be emphasized, need not be one that actually ever takes place. It is sufficient that we can imagine its taking place without violating any constraints to which the particle may be subjected. For this reason it is denoted by the term *virtual* displacement. We use the notation δ**r** to distinguish it from an actual displacement *d***r**.

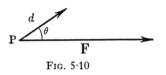

Fig. 5·10

The work that is done during this virtual displacement in the case considered is clearly

$$\mathbf{F} \cdot \delta\mathbf{r} = F\delta r \cos \theta. \tag{5·6–1}$$

This work is called the *virtual* work.

Suppose now we have a system of n particles $P_1, P_2, \ldots, P_n$ acted on respectively by the resultant forces $\mathbf{F}_1, \mathbf{F}_2, \ldots, \mathbf{F}_n$. We already know that these will be in equilibrium only if the resultant forces all vanish identically. In this case the total virtual work performed if the particles of the system receive the virtual displacements $\delta\mathbf{r}_1, \delta\mathbf{r}_2, \ldots, \delta\mathbf{r}_n$ respectively will certainly vanish, i.e.,

$$\sum_{i=1}^{n} \mathbf{F}_i \cdot \delta\mathbf{r}_i = 0. \tag{5·6–2}$$

Now it may be that the particles are not free to move but are subjected to certain *constraints*. They may, for example, be tied to each other by inextensible strings or forced to move on certain surfaces. In all such cases the resultant force on each particle may be resolved into a resultant external impressed force and a resultant internal constraint force. We may write

$$\mathbf{F}_i = \mathbf{F}_{ie} + \mathbf{F}_{ic}, \tag{5·6–3}$$

where $\mathbf{F}_{ie}$ denotes the resultant external impressed force on the i-th particle and $\mathbf{F}_{ic}$ the corresponding resultant constraint force. We shall define a *constraint force* as a force such that when the system is given the set of virtual displacements $\delta\mathbf{r}_1, \delta\mathbf{r}_2, \ldots, \delta\mathbf{r}_n$ the total work done by the constraint forces vanishes. Thus

$$\sum \mathbf{F}_{ic} \cdot \delta\mathbf{r}_i = 0. \tag{5·6–4}$$

It therefore follows that for a system in equilibrium when the particles undergo virtual displacements (i.e., displacements compatible with the constraints)

$$\sum \mathbf{F}_{ie} \cdot \delta\mathbf{r}_i = 0, \tag{5·6–5}$$

or the total virtual work done by the *impressed* external forces vanishes, even if these forces do not vanish individually. This is the content of the so-called principle of virtual work. It is probably the most im-

portant method of expressing the condition that a system of particles subject to constraints shall be in equilibrium under the influence of a set of impressed forces. In applying it the important thing is to be able to identify the impressed forces. A few illustrations are in order.

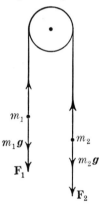

Let us consider the equilibrium of two mass particles m_1 and m_2 at the two ends of an inextensible string which slides freely over a smooth peg. We shall suppose that in addition to the impressed

Fig. 5·11

forces of gravity $m_1\mathbf{g}$ and $m_2\mathbf{g}$ there are also the extra impressed forces $\mathbf{F}_1$ and $\mathbf{F}_2$ as indicated in Fig. 5·11. Applying the virtual displacements $d\mathbf{r}_1$ and $d\mathbf{r}_2$, the general relation (5·6–5) becomes

$$(\mathbf{F}_1 + m_1\mathbf{g}) \cdot \delta\mathbf{r}_1 + (\mathbf{F}_2 + m_2\mathbf{g}) \cdot \delta\mathbf{r}_2 = 0. \tag{5·6–6}$$

The displacements may be taken in any way compatible with the constraints. We find it most convenient to take them vertically downward. Expanding the dot products then yields

$$(F_1 + m_1g)\, \delta r_1 + (F_2 + m_2g)\, \delta r_2 = 0. \tag{5·6–7}$$

But since the string is inextensible, δr_1 and δr_2 are not completely arbitrary. Rather

$$\delta r_1 + \delta r_2 = 0. \tag{5·6–8}$$

The combination of (5·6–7) and (5·6–8) then yields

$$F_1 + m_1 g = F_2 + m_2 g, \qquad (5·6–9)$$

which solves the problem. Note that, although the conventional equilibrium treatment of this problem is forced to introduce the tension in the string, the latter is not an impressed force and hence does not enter into the expression of the principle of virtual work.

Another illustration of similar nature is provided by two particles P_1 and P_2 of masses m_1 and m_2 respectively tied to the ends of an in-extensible string wrapped around a smooth peg S at the vertex of two perfectly smooth inclined planes of angles θ_1 and θ_2 respectively (Fig. 5·12). The impressed forces are the weights $m_1\mathbf{g}$ and $m_2\mathbf{g}$. It is unnecessary to consider the tension in the string or the reaction of the planes since they are constraining and not impressed forces. Taking virtual displacements $\delta\mathbf{r}_1$ and $\delta\mathbf{r}_2$ *down* the plane in each case, we write (5·6–5) in the form

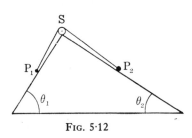

FIG. 5·12

$$m_1\mathbf{g}\cdot\delta\mathbf{r}_1 + m_2\mathbf{g}\cdot\delta\mathbf{r}_2 = 0. \qquad (5·6–10)$$

The expansion of the dot product gives us

$$m_1 g \sin\theta_1\, \delta r_1 + m_2 g \sin\theta_2\, \delta r_2 = 0, \qquad (5·6–11)$$

and the inextensibility of the string,

$$\delta r_1 + \delta r_2 = 0. \qquad (5·6–12)$$

Hence we are led ultimately to

$$m_1 g \sin\theta_1 = m_2 g \sin\theta_2. \qquad (5·6–13)$$

Reverting to eq. (5·6–5), let us express it in Cartesian form by writing for the i-th particle

$$\begin{aligned}
\delta\mathbf{r}_i &= \mathbf{i}\,\delta x_i + \mathbf{j}\,\delta y_i + \mathbf{k}\,\delta z_i \\
\mathbf{F}_{ie} &= \mathbf{i}\,F_{xie} + \mathbf{j}\,F_{yie} + \mathbf{k}\,F_{zie}.
\end{aligned} \qquad (5·6–14)$$

The principle of virtual work may now be expressed in the form (leaving off the subscript e for convenience)

$$\sum_{i=1}^{n} (F_{xi}\,\delta x_i + F_{yi}\,\delta y_i + F_{zi}\,\delta z_i) = 0. \qquad (5·6–15)$$

Let us suppose that the forces are conservative (Sec. 4·1) so that there exists a potential energy function $V_i(x_i, y_i, z_i)$ such that

$$\mathbf{F}_i = -\nabla V_i, \tag{5·6–16}$$

or

$$F_{ix} = -\frac{\partial V_i}{\partial x_i}, \quad \text{etc.} \tag{5·6–17}$$

Then

$$\sum_{i=1}^{n} V_i = V \tag{5·6–18}$$

may be considered the total potential energy of the collection of particles. The principle of virtual work then takes the form

$$\sum_{i=1}^{n} \delta V_i = 0 = \delta V. \tag{5·6–19}$$

For the virtual displacements considered the change in the total potential energy is zero. This signifies that for the equilibrium state the potential energy must be either a *maximum* or a *minimum*, for it is only in such a case that the variation due to a small displacement can vanish.[1] In the former case the equilibrium is said to be *unstable*, while in the latter case it is *stable*. Perhaps the simplest illustration is that of a single particle acted on by gravity and resting on a smooth surface. Taking the z axis vertical, the potential energy to an additive constant is

$$V = mgz, \tag{5·6–20}$$

where z is measured positively upward. Now suppose the particle is in equilibrium on a surface *concave* upward. The total force must act normally to the surface and hence z must be a minimum and therefore V also. This corresponds then to stable equilibrium (A in Fig. 5·13).

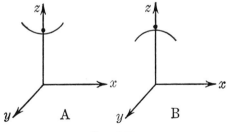

Fig. 5·13

[1] Mathematically this is an oversimplification. Strictly speaking, all we can say is that the potential energy has a stationary value. It might for example be a mini-max. Cf. W. V. Houston, *Principles of Mathematical Physics*, 2d ed., McGraw-Hill, New York, 1948, p. 89 ff. For most mechanical problems it is sufficient to confine our attention to maxima and minima.

Any *finite* displacement of the particle on the surface will increase the potential energy. On the other hand, if the particle is in equilibrium on a surface concave downward (B, Fig. 5·13), z must be a maximum and therefore V must be a maximum. The equilibrium is unstable. Any finite displacement of the particle leads to a *decrease* in potential energy.

This significant connection between equilibrium and potential energy affords another illustration of the utility of the principle of virtual work.

PROBLEMS

1. If a string of length l has a line density ρ and we consider its total weight concentrated at its central point, with how much tension must it be stretched between two fixed points in a horizontal line in order to make it assume a horizontal direction? Discuss the physical significance of the answer.

2. The magnitude of the resultant of two forces F_1 and F_2 is 14 lb wt. The force F_1 has a magnitude of 12 lb wt., and the direction of F_2 is inclined to the resultant at an angle of 30°. Find F_2 and the angle between F_1 and F_2.

3. A particle of mass m is attached to one end of a string and the other end is fixed. Find the force which must be applied to the particle perpendicular to the string in order to hold the string at an angle θ to the vertical. Find also the tension in the string.

4. A mass of 10 kilograms is supported at rest on a smooth inclined plane by a horizontal force of 4 kilograms wt. Find the inclination of the plane. If the plane was rough with coefficient of friction between body and plane of 0.2 and if the angle of inclination were that just determined, what horizontal force would be required to support the body at rest?

5. In the figure $m_1 = 1$ kg and $m_2 = 3$ kg and P is a smooth peg. The masses are connected by an inextensible string. The mass m_1 rests on a horizontal plane, with coefficient of friction between block and plane $= 0.2$. The mass m_2 rests on a plane making the angle 45° with the horizontal. What must the coefficient of friction be between m_2 and its plane in order to maintain equilibrium?

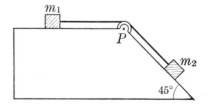

6. Two equal magnets of pole strength μ and length l are placed parallel to each other at distance a. If like poles are adjacent, calculate the position or positions where a single pole would be in equilibrium under the action of the

magnets (i.e., the so-called *neutral* point). Solve the same problem when the adjacent poles are unlike. (Hint: Recall Coulomb's law of force between poles, $F = \mu\mu'/r^2$.)

7. Given a magnet of length l and pole strength μ. Derive the equation of a line of force of the magnetic field surrounding the magnet, that is, a curve whose tangent at any point has the direction of the resultant force on a single pole placed at this point.

8. Derive the equation of a line of force in the field of two particles charged with equal amounts of positive electricity and separated by the distance a.

9. Two small metal spheres with a mass of 1 gram each are suspended from a single point by threads 20 cm long. The balls are equally charged with 20 electrostatic units of electricity. (The electrostatic unit is one such that it attracts an equal and opposite charge at a distance of one cm with a force of one dyne.) Find the distance to which the charged spheres will separate for equilibrium.

10. Two charged particles with charges $+10$ electrostatic units and -20 electrostatic units respectively interact with each other. What is the total potential energy of the system? Apply the principle of virtual work and find the conditions under which the system may be in equilibrium with each particle at rest.

11. If the small spheres in Problem 9 have masses 1 gram and 2 grams respectively, are charged with 10 and 20 electrostatic units respectively, and are suspended from a single point by threads 20 cm long, find the distance to which the spheres will separate for equilibrium. Also find the angles which the two threads make with the vertical and the tensions in them.

12. Given a double inclined perfectly smooth plane ABC with angles θ_1 and θ_2 as indicated in the accompanying figure. A smooth peg is placed vertically above C so that $CD = h$. An inextensible string with masses m_1 and m_2 at the two ends is passed over the peg and the masses are allowed to move on the planes. Find the position of equilibrium by the principle of virtual work.

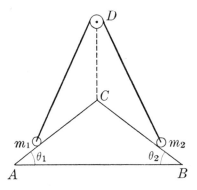

13. Given a circle of radius R in a vertical plane. A smooth peg is placed at point P directly above the center of the circle so that $OP = h$. (See figure.) A string of length l passes over the pulley and has at its extremities the two masses

m_1 and m_2. Assuming that the contact of the masses and the circle is smooth, calculate the position of the masses for equilibrium. Use the principle of virtual work.

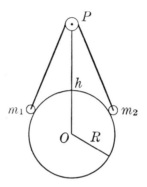

14. A flexible cord is suspended from two points on the same horizontal line. If the cord hangs in the form of a parabola, what must be the law of variation of the mass per unit length?

15. A flexible uniform cord of length l is suspended from two fixed points in the same horizontal line. Find the distance between the two fixed points so that each terminal tension is three times the tension at the lowest point.

16. The entire weight supported by a suspension bridge is 8 tons. The total length is 250 feet and the height is 20 feet. Find the tension on the points of support and the horizontal tension at the lowest point.

17. A telegraph line is constructed of copper wire weighing 0.079 pound per foot. The distance between the posts is 150 feet. If the tension at the posts is 200 lb wt., find the sag of the wire in the middle.

18. Discuss the stability of a particle in the field of a Lennard-Jones potential energy function (see Problem 20 in Chapter 4).

CHAPTER 6

MOTION OF A SYSTEM OF PARTICLES

6·1. Equations of Motion. Center of Mass. Conservation of Momentum. Except in our discussion of statics and virtual work in the preceding chapter, we have so far been concerned mainly with the behavior of a single particle or at most with two particles moving under their mutual influence. In the latter case we did show the existence of the important conservation principles of momentum and energy. Now actual bodies can be thought of as composed of a multitude of particles, and in order to understand their mechanical and other physical behavior it is desirable to study in some detail the equations governing the motion of a collection of particles. We shall approach the problem by endeavoring to generalize the momentum and energy principles to a system of arbitrary size.

Suppose we have a system of n particles of masses $m_1, m_2, \ldots\ldots m_n$, respectively, and acted on by the forces $\mathbf{F}_1, \mathbf{F}_2, \ldots, \mathbf{F}_n$, respectively. Each force will be the sum of an external force and all the interaction forces between the particle in question and all the other particles. Thus for the j-th particle

$$\mathbf{F}_j = \mathbf{F}_{je} + \sum_{k(\neq j)=1}^{n} \mathbf{F}_{jk}, \tag{6·1–1}$$

where $\mathbf{F}_{je}$ is the external force on the j-th particle, and $\mathbf{F}_{jk}$ is the force on the j-th particle due to the k-th particle. From eq. (1·7–4) the equation of motion of the j-th particle in vector form is then

$$m_j\ddot{\mathbf{r}}_j = \mathbf{F}_{je} + \sum_{k(\neq j)=1}^{n} \mathbf{F}_{jk}, \tag{6·1–2}$$

where $\mathbf{r}_j$ is the position vector of the j-th particle in the chosen reference system. The summation notation in (6·1–1) and (6·1–2) merely expresses the fact that, in the sum, as k goes from 1 to n the term corresponding to $k = j$ is omitted, as it is meaningless, since the j-th particle does not interact with itself. Let us now sum each equation over all the particles. We obtain formally

$$\sum_{j=1}^{n} m_j\ddot{\mathbf{r}}_j = \sum_{j=1}^{n} \mathbf{F}_{je} + \sum_{j=1}^{n} \sum_{k(\neq j)=1}^{n} \mathbf{F}_{jk}. \tag{6·1–3}$$

141

The double summation notation on the right appears a trifle complicated but should cause no difficulty. It means that after summing $\mathbf{F}_{jk}$ over k from 1 to n (leaving out $k = j$) we sum the resulting sum over j as the latter runs from 1 to n. Thus, writing it out in full,

$$\sum_{j=1}^{n} \sum_{k(\neq j)=1}^{n} \mathbf{F}_{jk} = \sum_{j=1}^{n} (\mathbf{F}_{j1} + \mathbf{F}_{j2} + \cdots + \mathbf{F}_{jn})$$

$$= \mathbf{F}_{12} + \mathbf{F}_{13} + \cdots + \mathbf{F}_{1n}$$

$$+ \mathbf{F}_{21} + \mathbf{F}_{23} + \cdots + \mathbf{F}_{2n}$$

$$+ \cdots\cdots\cdots\cdots\cdots\cdots$$

$$+ \mathbf{F}_{n1} + \mathbf{F}_{n2} + \cdots \mathbf{F}_{n,n-1}.$$

Now in the above expansion, for every term of the form $\mathbf{F}_{jk}$ there is a term of the form $\mathbf{F}_{kj}$. But $\mathbf{F}_{jk}$ is the force on the j-th particle due to the k-th particle, and $\mathbf{F}_{kj}$ is the force on the k-th particle due to the j-th particle. From Newton's third law (the law of action and reaction) we must have

$$\mathbf{F}_{jk} = -\mathbf{F}_{kj}. \tag{6·1–4}$$

It follows that the double sum in (6·1–3) vanishes identically, and the equation can be written in the following form

$$\sum m_j \ddot{\mathbf{r}}_j = \sum \mathbf{F}_{je}, \tag{6·1–5}$$

or alternatively

$$\frac{d^2}{dt^2} (\sum m_j \mathbf{r}_j) = \sum \mathbf{F}_{je}. \tag{6·1–6}$$

If we now follow the suggestion already made in Sec. 1·10 for the case of two particles, we find it worthwhile to introduce a point whose position vector $\mathbf{r}$ is given by

$$\bar{\mathbf{r}} = \frac{\sum m_j \mathbf{r}_j}{\sum m_j}. \tag{6·1–7}$$

The motion of this point will then be given by the equation

$$m\ddot{\bar{\mathbf{r}}} = \sum \mathbf{F}_{je}, \tag{6·1–8}$$

where $m = \sum m_j$ = the total mass of the collection. The point with position vector $\bar{\mathbf{r}}$ moves as if all the mass of the collection were concentrated there and all the external forces were acting there. In Sec. 1·10 where we introduced $\bar{\mathbf{r}}$ for the special case of two interacting particles we called the point with this position vector the center of mass. In the general case in which $\bar{\mathbf{r}}$ is given by (6·1–7) we shall use the same notation. The center of mass is an important property of the system, since if we can follow its motion we have at least some idea where in space the system is, even though we may be unable to follow the motion of every individual particle. Clearly (6·1–8) says that in the special case in which the sum of the external forces vanishes, the center of mass moves in a straight line with constant velocity (rest being, of course, a special case).

We can give another interpretation of eq. (6·1–6), since it may also be written in the form

$$\frac{d}{dt}\left(\sum m_j \dot{\mathbf{r}}_j\right) = \sum \mathbf{F}_{je}. \qquad (6\cdot1\text{–}9)$$

Now $\sum m_j \dot{\mathbf{r}}_j$ is the *resultant momentum* of the collection of particles, whose time rate of change is therefore equal to the resultant external force acting on the system. Once more note the important special case in which $\sum \mathbf{F}_{je} = 0$. Then the resultant momentum remains unchanged. This then becomes the theorem of the conservation of momentum for a system of particles subject to only their own mutual interaction forces. It is thus the generalization of eq. (1·10–4) developed earlier for the interaction of two particles. As a matter of fact, one of the best illustrations of (6·1–9) is still provided by the collision of two hard spheres or billiard balls and we shall devote the next section to this before passing on to more elaborate examples and further conservation theorems.

6·2. Conservation of Momentum in Collisions. We imagine two hard solid spheres of masses m_1 and m_2, respectively, moving originally with constant velocities $\mathbf{u}_1$ and $\mathbf{u}_2$ in the same straight line; we suppose that at some instant they collide squarely, with the result that after collision the spheres again separate and their velocities become $\mathbf{v}_1$ and $\mathbf{v}_2$, respectively. Though the spheres are themselves really aggregates of particles (i.e., approximately rigid bodies), since they collide squarely we may safely treat them as single particles. Since the collision involves only interaction forces, the principle of conservation of momentum applies and we can write

$$m_1\mathbf{u}_1 + m_2\mathbf{u}_2 = m_1\mathbf{v}_1 + m_2\mathbf{v}_2. \qquad (6\cdot2\text{–}1)$$

This equation does not enable us to predict the after-collision velocities from the original velocities. Consequently, the full solution of the problem demands further assumptions. Let us first write $\mathbf{u}_1 = u_1\boldsymbol{\delta}$, $\mathbf{u}_2 = u_2\boldsymbol{\delta}$, $\mathbf{v}_1 = v_1\boldsymbol{\delta}$, $\mathbf{v}_2 = v_2\boldsymbol{\delta}$, where $\boldsymbol{\delta}$ is the unit vector along the straight line in which the motion takes place. We can then replace the vector equation (6·2–1) by the scalar equation

$$m_1 u_1 + m_2 u_2 = m_1 v_1 + m_2 v_2. \qquad (6\cdot2\text{–}2)$$

Now Newton, who experimented with colliding spheres, found that their behavior satisfies the further equation

$$v_1 - v_2 = -e(u_1 - u_2),   (6\cdot2\text{--}3)$$

where e is a positive proper fraction, called the *coefficient* of *restitution*. Its value depends on the material composing the spheres. For highly elastic substances, i.e., those which, though deformed by the collision, regain their original size and shape immediately thereafter, e is very close to unity, while for plastic substances in which collision leads to a more or less permanent deformation, e may be close to zero.

Let us use (6·2–2) and (6·2–3) to calculate the after-collision velocity magnitudes v_1 and v_2 in terms of the original values u_1 and u_2. The algebra leads to

$$v_1 = \frac{(m_1 - m_2 e)u_1 + m_2(1 + e)u_2}{m_1 + m_2},$$

$$(6\cdot2\text{--}4)$$

$$v_2 = \frac{m_1(1 + e)u_1 + (m_2 - m_1 e)u_2}{m_1 + m_2}.$$

The special case $e = 1$ is of interest. For this

$$v_1 = \frac{(m_1 - m_2)u_1 + 2m_2 u_2}{m_1 + m_2},$$

$$(6\cdot2\text{--}5)$$

$$v_2 = \frac{2m_1 u_1 + (m_2 - m_1)u_2}{m_1 + m_2}.$$

If in addition $m_1 = m_2$, these equations become

$$v_1 = u_2, \quad v_2 = u_1,   (6\cdot2\text{--}6)$$

or the two spheres merely exchange their velocities on collision.

On the other hand, suppose $e = 0$ (plastic impact). In this case (6·2–4) yields

$$v_1 = \frac{m_1 u_1 + m_2 u_2}{m_1 + m_2} = v_2,   (6\cdot2\text{--}7)$$

which means that after collision the two spheres move off together. This is well illustrated in the impact of two putty balls.

Another important special case of collisions is that in which the mass of one particle is very much greater than that of the other. Let us suppose that $m_2 \gg m_1$ and that $u_2 = 0$. Then eqs. (6·2–4) yield effectively

$$v_1 = -eu_1, \quad v_2 = 0.   (6\cdot2\text{--}8)$$

A practical application is the rebound of a ball of mass m_1 from a horizontal table of mass very much larger than m_1. If the ball is dropped from height h_1, we have

$$v_1 = -e\sqrt{2gh_1}, \quad v_2 = 0.$$

The height of the rebound of m_1 is

$$h_2 = v_1^2/2g = h_1 e^2. \tag{6·2–9}$$

This provides a method of measuring the coefficient of restitution between two substances.

Further investigation of collision phenomena demands the introduction of energy considerations which we shall postpone to Sec. 6·5. For an application to nuclear physics see Sec. 6·6.

6·3. The Two-particle Problem with Gravitational Attraction.
The general results set forth in Sec. 6·1 receive another interesting illustration in the special case of a system of two particles. This has immediate practical application to celestial bodies which though large are very far apart and hence may be considered as particles attracting each other in accordance with the Newtonian law of gravitation. We therefore discuss the case in which two particles attract each other with a force varying inversely as the square of their distance apart and in which no other forces act. This is a generalization of the inverse square central force field problem treated in Sec. 3·7.

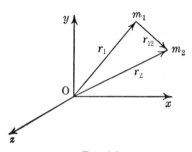

FIG. 6·1

If the masses of the particles are m_1 and m_2, respectively, and their position vectors in the chosen reference system are $\mathbf{r}_1$ and $\mathbf{r}_2$, respectively, the equations of motion of the particles are (cf. Fig. 6·1)

$$\left. \begin{aligned} m_1\ddot{\mathbf{r}}_1 &= \frac{Gm_1m_2\mathbf{r}_{12}}{r_{12}^3}, \\[2mm] m_2\ddot{\mathbf{r}}_2 &= \frac{Gm_1m_2\mathbf{r}_{21}}{r_{21}^3}. \end{aligned} \right\} \tag{6·3–1}$$

Here G is the constant of gravitation (Sec. 2·4) and

$$\mathbf{r}_{12} = \mathbf{r}_2 - \mathbf{r}_1 \tag{6·3–2}$$

is the vector joining m_1 and m_2, with direction as indicated in the figure. Note that $\mathbf{r}_{21} = -\mathbf{r}_{12}$. The direction of the force on m_1 is along the line joining it to m_2 and directed *toward* m_2, and similarly for m_2. We can now apply the general theorems of Sec. 6·1, but in this case it is simpler to proceed somewhat differently since by doing so we can actually solve the problem completely. We decide to treat the problem as one of motion of m_1 relative to m_2. Thus subtract the first equation in (6·3–1) from the second *after* dividing by m_1 and m_2, respectively. The result is

$$\ddot{\mathbf{r}}_{12} = \frac{-K}{r_{12}{}^3} \left(\frac{1}{m_1} + \frac{1}{m_2} \right) \mathbf{r}_{12}, \qquad (6\cdot3\text{–}3)$$

or

$$\mu \ddot{\mathbf{r}}_{12} = \frac{-K\mathbf{r}_{12}}{r_{12}{}^3}, \qquad (6\cdot3\text{–}3')$$

where

$$\mu = \frac{m_1 m_2}{m_1 + m_2}, \quad K = G m_1 m_2. \qquad (6\cdot3\text{–}4)$$

We see that eq. (6·3–3′) describes the motion of a single particle of mass μ in an inverse square central force field having the same force constant K as that prevailing in the interaction of the two particles. Effectively, we have reduced the *two*-particle problem to a *one*-particle problem, and all the equations developed in Sec. 3·7 for inverse square central field motion about a fixed center will apply to the present case if we merely replace the mass wherever it occurs by the quantity μ and replace the constant c (eq. 3·7–1) by K. It is customary to call μ the *reduced* mass for the system of two particles. Clearly if $m_2 \gg m_1$, as would be the case if m_2 represented the mass of the sum and m_1 that of a planet in the solar system, $\mu \doteq m_1$.

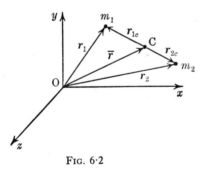

FIG. 6·2

It is often advantageous to refer the motion of the two particles m_1 and m_2 to neither mass but rather to the *center of mass* of the system. In Fig. 6·2 we denote the center of mass by C with position vector $\bar{\mathbf{r}}$. The position vector of m_1 relative to C as origin is

$$\mathbf{r}_{1c} = \mathbf{r}_1 - \bar{\mathbf{r}}, \qquad (6\cdot3\text{–}5)$$

and correspondingly that of m_2 is

$$\mathbf{r}_{2c} = \mathbf{r}_2 - \bar{\mathbf{r}}. \tag{6·3-6}$$

Hence we have

$$\left. \begin{aligned} \ddot{\mathbf{r}}_1 &= \ddot{\bar{\mathbf{r}}} + \ddot{\mathbf{r}}_{1c} = \ddot{\mathbf{r}}_{1c}, \\ \ddot{\mathbf{r}}_2 &= \ddot{\bar{\mathbf{r}}} + \ddot{\mathbf{r}}_{2c} = \ddot{\mathbf{r}}_{2c}, \end{aligned} \right\} \tag{6·3-7}$$

since $\ddot{\bar{\mathbf{r}}} = 0$, there being no force present save the gravitational interaction. Moreover by the use of (6·3–5) and (6·3–6) and the definition of center of mass,

$$\mathbf{r}_{1c} = \frac{-m_2 \mathbf{r}_{12}}{m_1 + m_2}, \quad \mathbf{r}_{2c} = \frac{-m_1 \mathbf{r}_{21}}{m_1 + m_2}. \tag{6·3-8}$$

Substitution into (6·3–3′) gives the equations of motion in terms of $\mathbf{r}_{1c}$ and $\mathbf{r}_{2c}$

$$\left. \begin{aligned} \mu \ddot{\mathbf{r}}_{1c} &= \frac{-m_2{}^3 K \mathbf{r}_{1c}}{(m_1 + m_2)^3 r_{1c}{}^3}, \\ \mu \ddot{\mathbf{r}}_{2c} &= \frac{-m_1{}^3 K \mathbf{r}_{2c}}{(m_1 + m_2)^3 r_{2c}{}^3}. \end{aligned} \right\} \tag{6·3-9}$$

These may obviously be presented in the alternative form

$$\left. \begin{aligned} m_1 \ddot{\mathbf{r}}_{1c} &= \frac{-m_2{}^2 K \mathbf{r}_{1c}}{(m_1 + m_2)^2 r_{1c}{}^3}, \\ m_2 \ddot{\mathbf{r}}_{2c} &= \frac{-m_1{}^2 K \mathbf{r}_{2c}}{(m_1 + m_2)^2 r_{2c}{}^3}. \end{aligned} \right\} \tag{6·3-10}$$

These differ from the original equations (6·3–1) only in the fact that the force constant is different for the two equations. We conclude that the path of each particle relative to the center of mass is of the same general geometrical form as that relative to the other particle. The center of mass itself, of course, either remains at rest or moves with constant speed in a straight line.

If $m_2 \gg m_1$, we have seen that $\mu \doteq m_1$ very nearly, while $r_{2c} \to 0$ and $r_{1c} \to r_{12}$. This means that when one mass is very much greater than the other, the motion of the heavier mass can be neglected compared with that of the other, and the problem reduces approximately to that of inverse square central field motion about a fixed center. The center of mass of the system in this case is very close to the heavier mass. Thus in the case of the motion of the two-particle system of the earth and the sun, the center of mass lies within the sun's surface and the approximation which considers merely the revolution of the earth about an effectively stationary sun is for many practical purposes a very good one.

In Sec. 3·11 we discussed the Bohr atomic model of hydrogen and assumed that the electron moves about a stationary nucleus. Since the mass of the nucleus is about 1840 times that of the electron, this is a rather good approximation. Nevertheless, the formula (3·11–14) for the semimajor axis of the orbits permitted by the quantum conditions can readily be corrected to take account of the actual motion of the nucleus. From what we have just learned in the present section it is only necessary to replace the mass of the electron by the reduced mass μ where now

$$\frac{1}{\mu} = \frac{1}{m_e} + \frac{1}{m_n},$$

in which m_e is the mass of the electron, and m_n that of the nucleus. The formula (3·11–14) then becomes

$$a = \frac{(n_1 + n_2)^2 h^2}{4\pi^2 \left(\dfrac{m_e m_n}{m_e + m_n}\right) e^2}. \tag{6·3–11}$$

Since

$$\mu \sim m_e \left(1 - \frac{1}{1840}\right),$$

the correction is a small one. Nevertheless the modification has been detected experimentally by precise spectroscopic measurements.[1]

6·4. Torque and Moment of Momentum.

Let us now revert to the equation of motion of a system of n particles, i.e. (6·1–2), which we repeat here for convenience

$$m_j \ddot{\mathbf{r}}_j = \mathbf{F}_{je} + \sum_{k(\neq j)=1}^{n} \mathbf{F}_{jk}.$$

We now multiply both sides of the equation by the position vector $\mathbf{r}_j$, but we shall not do it by the *dot* product defined earlier. Rather we define a new kind of vector called the *cross* product.

If we have two vectors $\mathbf{A}$ and $\mathbf{B}$, we shall define the *vector* or *cross product* as follows

$$\mathbf{A} \times \mathbf{B} = \boldsymbol{\epsilon} AB \sin \theta, \tag{6·4–1}$$

where A and B are as usual the magnitudes of the vectors $\mathbf{A}$ and $\mathbf{B}$ respectively. The angle θ is the smaller of the two angles between the positive directions of $\mathbf{A}$ and $\mathbf{B}$, and $\boldsymbol{\epsilon}$ is a *unit* vector (i.e. $|\boldsymbol{\epsilon}| = 1$) perpendicular to the plane of $\mathbf{A}$ and $\mathbf{B}$ and directed in such a way that as one looks along it a clockwise rotation will carry $\mathbf{A}$ into $\mathbf{B}$. The

[1] Cf. Ruark and Urey, *Atoms, Molecules and Quanta*, p. 126.

cross product is therefore a vector whose magnitude is the area of the parallelogram of which **A** and **B** are two adjacent sides. We note that the vector product does not satisfy the commutative law. Rather

$$\mathbf{A} \times \mathbf{B} = -\mathbf{B} \times \mathbf{A}. \tag{6·4-2}$$

However it can be shown that the distributive law holds, i.e.,

$$\mathbf{A} \times (\mathbf{B} + \mathbf{C}) = \mathbf{A} \times \mathbf{B} + \mathbf{A} \times \mathbf{C}. \tag{6·4-3}$$

If we apply the definition to the unit vectors **i, j, k** we get the interesting and often useful results

$$\mathbf{i} \times \mathbf{i} = \mathbf{j} \times \mathbf{j} = \mathbf{k} \times \mathbf{k} = 0,$$

$$\mathbf{i} \times \mathbf{j} = \mathbf{k}, \quad \mathbf{j} \times \mathbf{k} = \mathbf{i}, \quad \mathbf{k} \times \mathbf{i} = \mathbf{j}. \tag{6·4-4}$$

Moreover

$$\frac{d}{dt}(\mathbf{A} \times \mathbf{B}) = \dot{\mathbf{A}} \times \mathbf{B} + \mathbf{A} \times \dot{\mathbf{B}}, \tag{6·4-5}$$

which can be demonstrated by expanding **A** and **B** in terms of their components along the x, y, z axes and using (6·4-4).

We are now ready to apply the cross product to the present problem by forming

$$\mathbf{r}_j \times \ddot{\mathbf{r}}_j = \boldsymbol{\epsilon}_j r_j |\ddot{\mathbf{r}}_j| \sin (\mathbf{r}_j, \ddot{\mathbf{r}}_j). \tag{6·4-6}$$

Here $(\mathbf{r}_j, \ddot{\mathbf{r}}_j)$ is the smaller of the angles between the positive directions of the vectors $\mathbf{r}_j$ and $\ddot{\mathbf{r}}_j$ (cf. θ in Fig. 6·3), and $\boldsymbol{\epsilon}_j$ is the unit vector normal to the plane of $\mathbf{r}_j$ and $\ddot{\mathbf{r}}_j$ and in such a direction that, as one looks

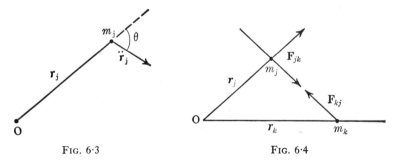

FIG. 6·3   FIG. 6·4

along it, a clockwise rotation will carry $\mathbf{r}_j$ into $\ddot{\mathbf{r}}_j$. The quantity $\mathbf{r}_j \times \ddot{\mathbf{r}}_j$ will be defined as the *moment* of the acceleration vector about the axis through O perpendicular to the plane of $\mathbf{r}_j$ and $\ddot{\mathbf{r}}_j$. Similarly

$$\mathbf{r}_j \times \mathbf{F}_{je}$$

will be defined as the *moment* of the force $\mathbf{F}_{je}$ about the axis through the origin perpendicular to the plane of $\mathbf{r}_j$ and $\mathbf{F}_{je}$. The moment of a force about an axis is also termed the *torque* due to the force about the axis in question. We shall often refer to it more simply as the torque about the point through which the axis passes. It is, of course, a vector and is usually designated by the symbol **L**. The result of taking the moments of both sides of the equation of motion then appears as

$$m_j \mathbf{r}_j \times \ddot{\mathbf{r}}_j = \mathbf{L}_{je} + \sum_{k(\neq j) = 1}^{n} \mathbf{L}_{jk}, \qquad (6\cdot4\text{--}7)$$

where $\mathbf{L}_{je}$ is the torque due to the external force on the mass m_j, while $\mathbf{L}_{jk}$ is the torque due to the interaction force between m_j and m_k. Let us assume that this interaction force is directed along the straight line joining m_j and m_k. It follows from Fig. that 6·4 the torque due to the force $\mathbf{F}_{jk}$ on m_j about the normal axis through O is equal and opposite in direction to that due to the force $\mathbf{F}_{kj}$ on m_k, about the same axis. Hence if we sum eq. (6·4–7) over all the particles of the system the double sum

$$\sum_{j=1}^{n} \sum_{k(\neq j) = 1}^{n} \mathbf{L}_{jk}$$

will vanish, and we shall have simply

$$\sum_{j=1}^{n} m_j \mathbf{r}_j \times \ddot{\mathbf{r}}_j = \sum_{j=1}^{n} \mathbf{L}_{je}. \qquad (6\cdot4\text{--}8)$$

To interpret this more conveniently, we use eq. (6·4–5) and finally get

$$\frac{d}{dt}[\mathbf{r}_j \times (m_j \dot{\mathbf{r}}_j)] = \mathbf{r}_j \times (m_j \ddot{\mathbf{r}}_j), \qquad (6\cdot4\text{--}9)$$

whence (6·4–8) becomes

$$\frac{d}{dt} \sum_{j=1}^{n} \mathbf{r}_j \times (m_j \dot{\mathbf{r}}_j) = \sum_{j=1}^{n} \mathbf{L}_{je}. \qquad (6\cdot4\text{--}10)$$

The quantity $\mathbf{r}_j \times (m_j \dot{\mathbf{r}}_j)$ from its method of construction is naturally termed the *moment of momentum* of the j-th particle about the origin. Eq. (6·4–10) then says that the time rate of change of the total moment of momentum of the collection of particles about the origin is equal to the total torque or force moment produced by the external forces about the same point. The reader will note its analogy with the force equation (6·1–9). Corresponding to the theorem of the conservation of momentum in Sec. 6·1 we now have the theorem of the conservation of moment of momentum: if the total external torque on a system of particles about a point vanishes, the total moment of momentum of the system about this point is constant. It must be remembered, of course, that the validity of this result depends on the internal interaction forces being directed along the lines joining the particles respectively. Otherwise the torques due to the internal forces will not cancel out. An illustration of the theorem is found in the solar system in so far as the whole system is not acted on by external forces. In this case it is interesting to note that about 98% of the total moment of momentum of the system resides in the planets.

Another example of the conservation of moment of momentum is provided by the electron motions in the planetary atom model already described in Chapter 3. Here, of course, it is only approximate since internal magnetic forces produce torques which do not entirely cancel out. Moreover, the electrons themselves are now assumed to have spins which must be taken into account.

The reader should show for his own satisfaction that eq. (6·4–10) when written in terms of rectangular coördinates becomes

$$\frac{d}{dt} \sum_{j=1}^{n} m_j(y_j \ddot{z}_j - z_j \ddot{y}_j) = \sum_{j=1}^{n} (y_j F_{jez} - z_j F_{jey}),$$

$$\frac{d}{dt} \sum_{j=1}^{n} m_j(z_j \ddot{x}_j - x_j \ddot{z}_j) = \sum_{j=1}^{n} (z_j F_{jex} - x_j F_{jez}), \qquad (6·4–11)$$

$$\frac{d}{dt} \sum_{j=1}^{n} m_j(x_j \ddot{y}_j - y_j \ddot{x}_j) = \sum_{j=1}^{n} (x_j F_{jey} - y_j F_{jex}).$$

Can we bring the center of mass into this picture? In line with the discussion of the motion of two particles let us refer the motion of the whole collection of n particles to the center of mass. Thus we write the position vector of the j-th particle in the form (analogous to the special case of eq. (6·3–5))

$$\mathbf{r}_j = \bar{\mathbf{r}} + \mathbf{r}_{jc}, \qquad (6·4–12)$$

where $\bar{\mathbf{r}}$ is the position vector of the center of mass, and $\mathbf{r}_{jc}$ is the position vector of m_j relative to the center of mass. The fundamental equation (6·1–9) becomes

$$\frac{d}{dt}(m\dot{\bar{\mathbf{r}}}) = \sum \mathbf{F}_{je}, \qquad (6·4–13)$$

since by definition $\sum_{j=1}^{n} m_j \mathbf{r}_{jc} = 0$. Eq. (6·4–13) is, of course, equivalent to eq. (6·1–8). This is nothing new, then. However, let us introduce the substitution (6·4–12) into (6·4–10). This gives

$$\frac{d}{dt} \sum_{j=1}^{n} m_j(\bar{\mathbf{r}} + \mathbf{r}_{jc}) \times (\dot{\bar{\mathbf{r}}} + \dot{\mathbf{r}}_{jc}) = \sum_{j=1}^{n} (\bar{\mathbf{r}} + \mathbf{r}_{jc}) \times \mathbf{F}_{je}.$$

After expansion and use of the definition of the center of mass and (6·4–13) the result is

$$\frac{d}{dt} \sum_{j=1}^{n} \mathbf{r}_{jc} \times (m_j \dot{\mathbf{r}}_{jc}) = \sum \mathbf{r}_{jc} \times \mathbf{F}_{je}. \qquad (6\cdot4\text{–}14)$$

This says that the time rate of change of the total moment of momentum about the center of mass is equal to the total torque about the center of mass. In other words we can completely describe the motion of the collection of particles by the motion of the center of mass (6·4–13) and the motion relative to the center of mass (6·4–14). This plan turns out to be particularly appropriate when the collection of particles forms a rigid body (Chapter 8). Another important application is met with in nuclear physics where in the theory of the deuteron (the nucleus of the hydrogen isotope of mass two), for example, it is convenient to separate the motion of the center of mass of the two particles (i.e., the neutron and the proton) from their relative motion.

6·5. Energy of a System of Particles. Let us revert once more to the equation of motion of the j-th particle and form the dot product of both sides by $\dot{\mathbf{r}}_j \, dt$ to find the work done by the forces in time dt. Thus

$$m_j \dot{\mathbf{r}}_j \cdot \ddot{\mathbf{r}}_j \, dt = \mathbf{F}_{je} \cdot \dot{\mathbf{r}}_j \, dt + \sum_{k(\neq j)=1}^{n} \mathbf{F}_{jk} \cdot \dot{\mathbf{r}}_j \, dt. \qquad (6\cdot5\text{–}1)$$

The left-hand side becomes

$$\tfrac{1}{2} m_j d(v_j^2),$$

where $v_j^2 = \dot{\mathbf{r}}_j \cdot \dot{\mathbf{r}}_j$ is the square of the resultant velocity of the j-th particle. Moreover, since we can write $\dot{\mathbf{r}}_j \, dt = d\mathbf{r}_j$, we have finally on summing over j

$$d \sum_{j=1}^{n} (\tfrac{1}{2} m_j v_j^2) = \sum_{j=1}^{n} \mathbf{F}_{je} \cdot d\mathbf{r}_j + \sum_{j=1}^{n} \sum_{k(\neq j)=1}^{n} \mathbf{F}_{jk} \cdot d\mathbf{r}_j. \qquad (6\cdot5\text{–}2)$$

Integrating over the path from $\mathbf{r}_j'$ to $\mathbf{r}_j''$ gives

$$K_1 - K_0 = \int_{\mathbf{r}_j'}^{\mathbf{r}_j''} \left[\sum \mathbf{F}_{je} \cdot d\mathbf{r}_j + \sum_{j=1}^{n} \sum_{k(\neq j)=1}^{n} \mathbf{F}_{jk} \cdot d\mathbf{r}_j \right]. \qquad (6\cdot5\text{–}3)$$

This is the generalization of the work-energy theorem to the case of a collection of particles: the total work done by the external and internal forces during the motion of the system is equal to the change in the total kinetic energy. The double sum on the right can be written in much simpler form if we assume that the force $\mathbf{F}_{jk}$ is directed along the line joining the j-th and k-th particles and is a function only of the distance between them and moreover the same function for all particles. Thus let us suppose that

$$\mathbf{F}_{jk} = f(r_{jk})\mathbf{r}_{jk}, \qquad (6\cdot5\text{--}4)$$

where

$$\mathbf{r}_{jk} = \mathbf{r}_k - \mathbf{r}_j.$$

Now the double sum consists of pairs of terms of the form

$$f(r_{jk})\mathbf{r}_{jk}\cdot d\mathbf{r}_j + f(r_{kj})\mathbf{r}_{kj}\cdot d\mathbf{r}_k$$

$$= -f(r_{jk})\mathbf{r}_{jk}\cdot d\mathbf{r}_{jk}. \qquad (6\cdot5\text{--}5)$$

From (1·11–26) it follows that we can write

$$f(r_{jk})\mathbf{r}_{jk}\cdot d\mathbf{r}_{jk} = f(r_{jk})r_{jk}\,dr_{jk},$$

and hence (6·5–3) becomes

$$K_1 - K_0 = \int_{\mathbf{r}_{j'}}^{\mathbf{r}_{j''}} \left[\sum_{j=1}^{n} \mathbf{F}_{je}\cdot d\mathbf{r}_j - \sum f(r_{jk})r_{jk}\,dr_{jk} \right], \qquad (6\cdot5\text{--}6)$$

where in the second sum we include all pairs of j and k with $j < k$ and k running from 1 to n. Now suppose there exists a potential energy function V_{je} such that

$$\sum_j \mathbf{F}_{je}\cdot d\mathbf{r}_j = -\sum \left(\frac{\partial V_{je}}{\partial x_j}\,dx_j + \frac{\partial V_{je}}{\partial y_j}\,dy_j + \frac{\partial V_{je}}{\partial z_j}\,dz_j \right) = -\sum_j dV_{je}. $$
$$(6\cdot5\text{--}7)$$

Since we have assumed that the forces of interaction are central forces and since we know that a central force is always conservative (Sec. 4·2), there exists a potential function $V(r_{jk})$ such that

$$\sum f(r_{jk})r_{jk}\,dr_{jk} = \sum dV(r_{jk}) \qquad (6\cdot5\text{--}8)$$

Eq. (6·5–6) then becomes

$$K_1 + \sum_j V_{je}'' + \sum_{k,j} V''(r_{jk}) = K_0 + \sum_j V_{je}' + \sum_{k,j} V'(r_{jk}). \qquad (6\cdot5\text{--}9)$$

We are then led to call $\sum_j V_{je}$ the total potential energy of the external forces, and $\sum V(r_{jk})$ the total potential energy of the internal forces. The total energy of the whole system remains constant: this is the theorem of the conservation of mechanical energy for a system of particles. Of course the external forces may not be conservative and in this case the theorem does not hold. On the other hand if the interaction forces are of the central type and there are no external forces, the total energy remains constant.

An important fact to note from (6·5–9) is that the internal forces make a contribution to the potential energy and hence appear in the energy conservation equation, whereas they cancel out in the momentum and moment of momentum conservation equations. This is well brought out in the energy equation for the two-particle problem discussed in Sec. 6·3. Let us consider this special case.

If we dot multiply the first equation in (6·3–1) by $\dot{\mathbf{r}}_1 \, dt = d\mathbf{r}_1$ and the second by $\dot{\mathbf{r}}_2 \, dt = d\mathbf{r}_2$, and add, by the arguments used in going from (6·5–1) to (6·5–2), we get

$$d(\tfrac{1}{2}m_1 v_1{}^2 + \tfrac{1}{2}m_2 v_2{}^2) = \frac{Gm_1 m_2}{r_{12}{}^3}\, \mathbf{r}_{12} \cdot (d\mathbf{r}_1 - d\mathbf{r}_2)$$

$$= -\frac{Gm_1 m_2}{r_{12}{}^3}\, \mathbf{r}_{12} \cdot d\mathbf{r}_{12}, \qquad (6\text{·}5\text{–}10)$$

where the last step comes from (6·3–2). Integration of both sides leads to

$$\tfrac{1}{2}m_1 v_1{}^2 + \tfrac{1}{2}m_2 v_2{}^2 = -\, Gm_1 m_2 \int \frac{\mathbf{r}_{12}}{r_{12}{}^3} \cdot d\mathbf{r}_{12}$$

$$= -Gm_1 m_2 \int \frac{dr_{12}}{r_{12}{}^2}, \qquad (6\text{·}5\text{–}11)$$

since

$$\mathbf{r}_{12} \cdot d\mathbf{r}_{12} = r_{12}\, dr_{12}. \qquad (6\text{·}5\text{–}12)$$

We therefore finally obtain as the energy equation

$$\tfrac{1}{2}m_1 v_1{}^2 + \tfrac{1}{2}m_2 v_2{}^2 - \frac{Gm_1 m_2}{r_{12}} = U, \qquad (6\text{·}5\text{–}13)$$

where U is the total energy. The potential energy of interaction of the two particles is

$$V_{12} = -\frac{Gm_1 m_2}{r_{12}}, \qquad (6\text{·}5\text{–}14)$$

as might have been expected from the discussion leading up to eq. (4·3–2). Here there is no external force and hence no external potential energy. In (6·5–13) the speeds v_1 and v_2 refer, of course, to the fixed origin. We can, if we please, express the energy equation in terms of the relative velocity $\dot{\mathbf{r}}_{12}$. In fact this is a simpler procedure. From eq. (6·3–3′) we have at once

$$\frac{\mu v_{12}{}^2}{2} - \frac{Gm_1 m_2}{r_{12}} = U, \qquad (6\text{·}5\text{–}15)$$

in which now the reduced mass once more appears. We can also express the energy equation in terms of the motion relative to the center of mass. By the use of (6·3–5) and (6·3–6) we can write for the left-hand side of (6·5–13)

$$\tfrac{1}{2}m_1v_1{}^2 + \tfrac{1}{2}m_2v_2{}^2 = \tfrac{1}{2}(m_1 + m_2)\dot{\mathbf{r}}\cdot\dot{\mathbf{r}} + \tfrac{1}{2}m_1\dot{\mathbf{r}}_{1c}\cdot\dot{\mathbf{r}}_{1c}$$
$$+ \tfrac{1}{2}m_2\dot{\mathbf{r}}_{2c}\cdot\dot{\mathbf{r}}_{2c}. \tag{6·5–16}$$

This says that the total kinetic energy in the fixed system of reference is equal to the kinetic energy of the center of mass (with the whole mass $m_1 + m_2$ concentrated there) plus the kinetic energy of the two particles relative to the center of mass. This scheme is often a useful one and of course may be generalized to apply to a collection of an arbitrary number of particles. We shall make good use of it in the study of rigid bodies in Chapter 8.

In the case of the collisions of spherical particles discussed in Sec. 6·2 it is extremely difficult if not practically impossible to express the interaction forces in terms of readily measurable quantities. Hence we cannot readily find an expression for the potential energy at every instant during the impact and therefore cannot write the energy equation for the interaction. However, if we are content to use the Newtonian coefficient of restitution, it is possible to examine the change in kinetic energy brought about by the collision.

The total kinetic energy of the system *before* collision is

$$K_u = \tfrac{1}{2}m_1u_1{}^2 + \tfrac{1}{2}m_2u_2{}^2, \tag{6·5–17}$$

whereas that *after* collision is

$$K_v = \tfrac{1}{2}m_1v_1{}^2 + \tfrac{1}{2}m_2v_2{}^2. \tag{6·5–18}$$

The change in kinetic energy is

$$\Delta K = K_v - K_u. \tag{6·5–19}$$

We can evaluate this by direct substitution for v_1 and v_2 from (6·2–4), so as to express ΔK in terms of u_1 and u_2 only. However, this turns out to be algebraically tedious, and we find it simpler to avail ourselves of the result demonstrated just above, namely, that the total kinetic energy is equal to that of the center of mass plus the kinetic energy relative to the center of mass. Since the velocity of the center of mass cannot be changed by the collision, the whole change in the kinetic energy of the system is the change in the kinetic energy *relative* to the center of mass. Now, using the notation of Sec. 6·3, we have

$$m_1u_{1c} + m_2u_{2c} = m_1v_{1c} + m_2v_{2c} = 0, \tag{6·5–20}$$

whence from (6·2–3) we conclude that

$$v_{1c} = -eu_{1c}, \quad v_{2c} = -eu_{2c}. \tag{6·5–21}$$

Therefore the change in kinetic energy becomes simply

$$\Delta K = \tfrac{1}{2}m_1v_{1c}^2 + \tfrac{1}{2}m_2v_{2c}^2 - \tfrac{1}{2}m_1u_{1c}^2 - \tfrac{1}{2}m_2u_{2c}^2$$
$$= \tfrac{1}{2}m_1(e^2 - 1)u_{1c}^2 + \tfrac{1}{2}m_2(e^2 - 1)u_{2c}^2. \qquad (6\cdot5\text{--}22)$$

From the fact that the coefficient of restitution e is a proper fraction (≤ 1) it follows that

$$\Delta K \leq 0. \qquad (6\cdot5\text{--}23)$$

Unless $e = 1$, the total kinetic energy of the system of spherical particles decreases on collision even though the total momentum remains constant. The kinetic energy thus lost reappears in the form of heat and sound, as is clearly shown by experiment.

6·6. Collisions of Nuclear Particles.   Attractive illustrations of collision problems are provided by the relative motion of atomic nuclei. In Sec. 3·12 we discussed the motion of an alpha particle in the repulsive field of a positively charged nucleus, and this is strictly speaking a collision phenomenon. With the use of the cloud chamber it has proved possible to make visible actual collisions of nuclear particles and the ensuing motions. Thus in Fig. 6·5, ON denotes the linear path of an alpha particle approaching a nucleus at N, approximately at

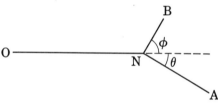

FIG. 6·5

rest in the inertial system to which the motion is referred. (Actually the nucleus in any practical case is moving, but only with a velocity much smaller than that of the alpha particle; so for practical purposes it can be considered at rest.)   After the collision the tracks in the cloud chamber show, for example, that the alpha particle moves off in the direction NA, whereas the nucleus moves along NB, the directions being given by the angles θ and ϕ respectively.

We have here a somewhat more general type of collision problem than any we have considered hitherto.   We can however solve it by the use of the principles of conservation of momentum and energy.   Let us suppose the mass of the alpha particle is m and that of the nucleus is M. Let the initial speed of the alpha particle be u and its speed after collision be v, while the corresponding values for the nucleus are 0 and V respectively.

We can at once write from the conservation of momentum the two equations

$$mu = mv \cos \theta + MV \cos \phi, \qquad (6·6{-}1)$$

$$mv \sin \theta = MV \sin \phi, \qquad (6·6{-}2)$$

the first of which expresses conservation of momentum in the original direction of motion and the second in the motion at right angles to the original direction. These two equations are of course insufficient for the evaluation of the four unknowns v, V, θ and ϕ. But we have one more equation at our disposal, namely, that expressing conservation of energy. This might indeed be considered a rather complicated equation to write, since it would appear to involve the potential energy of interaction between the alpha particle and the nucleus. However, we shall here make the simple assumption that the collision is analogous to a perfectly elastic collision in the case of billiard balls, so that effectively the equivalent Newtonian coefficient of restitution is unity. Hence we need concern ourselves only with conservation of kinetic energy, as was pointed out in the preceding section. This equation is

$$\tfrac{1}{2}mu^2 = \tfrac{1}{2}mv^2 + \tfrac{1}{2}MV^2. \qquad (6·6{-}3)$$

Before using the energy equation, let us see what we can extract from the two momentum equations. If we substitute for V in terms of v from (6·6–2) into (6·6–1) we can express v in terms of u as follows

$$v = \frac{u \sin \phi}{\sin(\theta + \phi)}. \qquad (6·6{-}4)$$

Similarly the elimination of v between (6·6–1) and (6·6–2) gives V in terms of u:

$$V = \frac{m}{M} \cdot \frac{u \sin \theta}{\sin(\theta + \phi)}. \qquad (6·6{-}5)$$

Finally by substituting these results into (6·6–3) we can eliminate the velocities entirely and obtain the following relation expressing the ratio of the masses m/M in terms of the angles θ and ϕ only:

$$\frac{m}{M} = \frac{\sin^2(\phi + \theta) - \sin^2 \phi}{\sin^2 \theta}. \qquad (6·6{-}6)$$

If we write

$$\sin^2(\phi + \theta) - \sin^2 \phi = [\sin(\phi + \theta) + \sin \phi][\sin(\phi + \theta) - \sin \phi]$$

and use the trigonometric identity

$$\sin(\phi + \theta) + \sin \phi = 2 \sin \tfrac{1}{2}(2\phi + \theta) \cos \tfrac{1}{2}\theta,$$

etc., we may reduce (6·6–6) to

$$\frac{m}{M} = \frac{\sin(2\phi + \theta)}{\sin \theta}. \tag{6·6–7}$$

This is an important result, since it enables us by simply measuring the angles θ and ϕ to estimate the ratio of the masses of the alpha particle and nucleus.

Certain conclusions from the above equations are of interest in connection with the examination of ray tracks in a cloud chamber. Suppose indeed that the struck nucleus is itself a helium nucleus, i.e., of the same mass as the alpha particle. Then $m = M$ and we have from (6·6–7)

$$\theta + \phi = \frac{\pi}{2}. \tag{6·6–8}$$

We therefore expect that whenever alpha particles are shot through helium gas and collisions result, the deflection angles must always add up to $\pi/2$. This expectation is borne out by experiment.

If $m \ll M$, i.e., the struck nucleus is a very massive one compared with the alpha particle, the maximum value of $\sin(2\phi + \theta)$ is very small, and hence $2\phi + \theta$ will differ only slightly from π. In this case we expect therefore that the track NB of the heavy nucleus when extended back will nearly bisect the angle ONA.

Other interesting conclusions can be drawn. For example, if $\phi = 0$, so that the struck nucleus moves along the line of collision (which can happen only if $m = M$), $v = 0$ and the alpha particle is brought to rest. Its whole kinetic energy is transferred to the struck particle. Other cases are left to the reader to investigate.

It must be emphasized that all the conclusions drawn here are based on the assumption that the collisions are elastic so that kinetic energy is conserved.

6·7. The Virial of Clausius. Closely related to the energy of a system of particles is the *virial* of Clausius. Consider the following scalar function of the position vectors of the n particles of the system

$$M = \sum_{j=1}^{n} \tfrac{1}{2} m_j \mathbf{r}_j \cdot \mathbf{r}_j. \tag{6·7–1}$$

Differentiating this twice with respect to the time gives

$$\dot{M} = \sum_{j=1}^{n} m_j \dot{\mathbf{r}}_j \cdot \dot{\mathbf{r}}_j + \sum_{j=1}^{n} m_j \mathbf{r}_j \cdot \ddot{\mathbf{r}}_j. \tag{6·7–2}$$

Now $\dot{M}$ is a function of the time. If we integrate it with respect to the time between the limits 0 and τ, where τ is an arbitrarily long time, and divide by τ, we shall obtain the *time average* of $\dot{M}$ over the time interval in question. Thus, if we use a bar to denote average with respect to time, we have

$$\overline{\dot{M}} = \frac{1}{\tau} \int_0^\tau \dot{M}\, dt = \frac{1}{\tau} (\dot{M}_\tau - \dot{M}_0), \qquad (6 \cdot 7\text{--}3)$$

where, of course, from $(6 \cdot 7\text{--}1)$

$$\dot{M} = \sum_{j=1}^n m_j \mathbf{r}_j \cdot \dot{\mathbf{r}}_j, \qquad (6 \cdot 7\text{--}4)$$

and $\dot{M}_\tau$ and $\dot{M}_0$ refer to the values of $\dot{M}$ at $t = \tau$ and $t = 0$, respectively. If the particles are assumed to move always in a closed space, the magnitude of $\mathbf{r}_j$ can never exceed a certain maximum value. We shall assume, moreover, that the velocities $\dot{\mathbf{r}}_j$ are likewise bounded, which is quite reasonable for a collection of particles for which the kinetic energy cannot become infinitely great. Hence $\dot{M}$ is bounded and as τ increases

$$\overline{\dot{M}} \to 0. \qquad (6 \cdot 7\text{--}5)$$

Therefore from $(6 \cdot 7\text{--}2)$

$$\tfrac{1}{2} \overline{\sum_{j=1}^n m_j \dot{\mathbf{r}}_j \cdot \dot{\mathbf{r}}_j} = -\tfrac{1}{2} \overline{\sum_{j=1}^n m_j \mathbf{r}_j \cdot \ddot{\mathbf{r}}_j}. \qquad (6 \cdot 7\text{--}6)$$

Now the left-hand side of $(6 \cdot 7\text{--}6)$ is the time average of the total kinetic energy of the system. The right-hand side may be rewritten by recalling that $m_j \ddot{\mathbf{r}}_j$ is the resultant force $\mathbf{F}_j$ acting on the j-th particle. We may then write it

$$\Omega = -\tfrac{1}{2} \overline{\sum_{j=1}^n \mathbf{r}_j \cdot \mathbf{F}_j}. \qquad (6 \cdot 7\text{--}7)$$

The quantity Ω was called by Clausius the *virial* of the system. Eq. $(6 \cdot 7\text{--}6)$ expresses the result that the *average kinetic energy of the system of particles moving subject to the imposed conditions is equal to its virial*. This is the virial theorem.

An interesting application of the virial theorem is the relation between the average kinetic energy and average potential energy of a system in which the only forces acting are central forces between the various particles. We shall illustrate this for the simple case of a single particle subject to a central attractive force varying as the n-th power of the distance to a force center. Then $(6 \cdot 7\text{--}6)$ reduces (with $\mathbf{F} = Cr^{n-1}\mathbf{r}$) to

$$\bar{K} = -\tfrac{1}{2} \overline{\mathbf{F} \cdot \mathbf{r}} = -\tfrac{1}{2} \overline{Cr^{n+1}}.$$

But from (4·2–8) the potential energy corresponding to this type of central field is

$$V(r) = -\frac{Cr^{n+1}}{n+1},$$

and consequently

$$\bar{K} = \frac{n+1}{2} \cdot \bar{V}. \tag{6·7–8}$$

In particular, for the inverse square field, where $n = -2$, the result becomes

$$\bar{K} = -\frac{\bar{V}}{2}. \tag{6·7–9}$$

From (6·7–9) the total energy becomes

$$E = \frac{\bar{V}}{2}, \tag{6·7–10}$$

which is, of course, negative, corresponding to the fact that the force is here a binding force. The generalization to a collection of particles is left as an exercise.

The material in this section has introduced for the first time in this book the application of time averages to mechanical problems. This is a very important development, as it enables us to apply the principles of mechanics to collections containing very large numbers of particles. We shall exploit this in Chapter 7 in connection with the kinetic theory of gases and elementary statistical mechanics.

PROBLEMS

1. An automobile of mass 2 tons traveling due south at 50 mi/hr collides at an intersection with a 5-ton truck traveling due east at 30 mi/hr. Assuming that the two cars lock together after impact, what is the velocity in magnitude and direction after collision? What is the velocity (magnitude and direction) of the center of mass of the two cars before and after collision? Calculate the total kinetic energy of the cars before and after collision and comment on the physical meaning of the result.

2. An alpha particle is projected from position x_1 in the positive x direction with speed v_1. At the same instant another alpha particle is projected from position x_2 ($x_2 > x_1$) in the negative x direction with speed v_2. Describe the subsequent motion of the two particles.

3. Two particles of masses m_1 and m_2 respectively move in arbitrary fashion. Prove that the total moment of momentum of the system about the center of mass is a vector at right angles to the plane containing the line joining the

instantaneous positions of the particles and the instantaneous *relative* velocity $\mathbf{v}_r$ of the two particles and has the magnitude

$$\left(\frac{m_1 m_2}{m_1 + m_2}\right) \cdot p v_r,$$

where p is the perpendicular distance from one of the particles to the line through the other particle having the direction of $\mathbf{v}_r$.

4. The two particles in an Atwood's machine have masses m_1 and m_2 grams respectively and the two strings are separated by a distance r. If the system is allowed to move from rest when the two masses are at the same height h from the floor, find the position of the center of mass after t seconds. Also find the kinetic energy and potential energy (with respect to the floor) of each particle at the end of the t seconds.

5. A shell is observed to explode when at the highest point of its path. It splits into two parts of equal mass of which one is observed to fall vertically. Find the path followed by the other with respect to the ground.

6. Two particles of masses m_1 and m_2 respectively move in arbitrary fashion. If $\mathbf{v}_c$ is the velocity of the center of mass and $\mathbf{v}$ the *relative* velocity of the two particles with respect to each other show that the total kinetic energy of the system is

$$\frac{1}{2}(m_1 + m_2)v_c^2 + \frac{1}{2}\left(\frac{m_1 m_2}{m_1 + m_2}\right)v^2.$$

7. Calculate the position of the center of mass of the system composed of the sun and the planet Jupiter. Compare the kinetic energy of the system at perihelion with that at aphelion.

8. Two particles of masses m_1 and m_2 respectively move about each other. Calculate the exact expression for the periodic time, i.e., the time for one complete period of the motion.

9. Two particles which move subject only to their mutual attraction are projected in any direction with any velocities. Show that the line joining the particles always remains parallel to a fixed plane.

10. A uniform chain 2 meters long hangs over a perfectly smooth peg with initially 110 cm on one side and 90 cm on the other. How long will it take the chain to slide off the peg and what velocity will it have at that instant?

11. In the Bohr model of a single electron atom (see 3.11) the electron is assumed to possess a quantized moment of momentum (also called angular momentum) given by

$$p_\theta = n_\theta h / 2\pi,$$

where n_θ is an integer. Suppose that the electron also possesses a spin about an axis through itself. Let this spin correspond to another quantized moment of momentum

$$p_s = n_s h / 2\pi,$$

where n_s is integral. Recalling that the moment of momentum is a vector quantity, find the magnitude of the resultant moment of momentum of a spinning electron revolving in a quantized orbit if the two moments make angle θ with each other. If the resultant moment of momentum is restricted in magnitude to $nh/2\pi$ where n is half-integral, show that θ may not take on all values. Find the allowed quantized values of θ and specialize to the case where $n_s = \pm\frac{1}{2}$, $n_\theta = 1$ and $n = \frac{3}{2}$.

12. A stationary nucleus of mass m is struck head on by a neutron of mass m_n moving with velocity v_0. If the collision is perfectly elastic, find the expression for the recoil velocity of the nucleus. How could this equation be used to determine the mass of the neutron, even if the velocity v_0 is not known?

13. In the figure, m_1 and m_2 are two balls of equal radius but different masses suspended vertically by equal cords of length 1 meter from the same horizontal plane. When hanging at rest the balls just touch. The mass m_1 is drawn aside so that its center is 20 cm above the center of m_2 and then released. The coefficient of restitution may be taken as 0.9. If $m_1 = 100$ grams and $m_2 = 200$ grams, find the motion of both balls subsequent to collision. Solve the problem also for $m_1 = 200$ grams and $m_2 = 100$ grams.

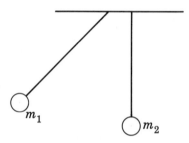

14. In the figure m_1, m_2, and m_3 are three balls of the same size but different masses suspended so as to satisfy the same conditions as in the previous problem. The length of the cords is again 1 meter. The mass m_1 is drawn aside so that its center is 20 cm above the centers of m_2 and m_3. It is then released. Taking the coefficient of restitution as 0.9, trace the motion of the three balls subsequent to collision if they are all of the same mass, i.e., 200 grams.

15. In the collision of alpha particles and nuclei, suppose the struck nuclei are protons (i.e., $m > M$; cf. Sec. 6·6). It is found experimentally that when alpha particles traverse hydrogen gas the maximum value of the deflection angle θ of the alpha particles is of the order of 15°. Show how this can be used to estimate the ratio of the mass of the alpha particle to that of the proton.

16. Alpha particles are shot through krypton gas. Find the approximate values of the angles θ and ϕ in the discussion in Sec. 6·6. If the initial velocity of the alpha particles is 2×10^9 cm/sec, find the values of the kinetic energy of the alpha particle and the krypton nucleus after collision.

17. Deduce the contribution to the virial of a collection of molecules due to interaction forces of the form (eq. 6·5–4.)

$$\mathbf{F}_{jk} = f(r_{jk}) \, \mathbf{r}_{jk}.$$

Hence show that the equation of state of the system has the form

$$pV = NkT + \frac{1}{3} \sum_{j,k=1}^{N} f(r_{jk}) \, r^2_{jk}.$$

If the pressure of the gas is interpreted as due primarily to the second term on the right rather than the first (i.e., to the interaction of the molecules rather than to their motion), show that Boyle's law could be satisfied only by assuming that the force of interaction varies inversely as the distance of separation of the molecules. Indicate why this is experimentally unreasonable.

If the interaction force is attractive, show that the second term on the right takes the form $-a/V$ where a is a positive constant. Comment on the connection with the van der Waals equation of state.

18. Derive the expression for the quantized energy of the two-particle system composed of an electron and a nucleus revolving about their common center of mass (cf. Sec. 4·3 for the equivalent one-particle problem).

CHAPTER 7

KINETIC THEORY OF GASES
AND STATISTICAL MECHANICS

7·1. Elementary Kinetic Theory of Gases. Equation of State of an Ideal Gas. One of the most important examples of a system of particles is provided by the kinetic theory, which considers a gas to be composed of a very large number of very small particles called molecules moving with varying velocities in every direction, colliding with each other and rebounding with undiminished speed from the walls of the vessel in which the gas is confined. In the so-called *ideal* gas the molecules are assumed to exert no forces on each other and consequently the only forces on them are due to the impact on the walls. Let us use Sec. 6·7 to calculate the virial for an ideal gas consisting of N molecules confined in a cubical box of side a. We suppose the gas to be in a state of equilibrium, i.e., assume that the spatial distribution of the molecules within the box is uniform so that the density is the same in all parts of the vessel and does not change with the time. It will be convenient to expand the scalar product in (6·7–7) and express the virial in terms of rectangular components. Thus

$$\Omega = -\tfrac{1}{2} \overline{\sum_{j=1}^{N} (x_j F_{jx} + y_j F_{jy} + z_j F_{jz})}. \tag{7·1–1}$$

Now the forces F_{jx}, etc., have non-vanishing values only for the values of x_j, y_j, z_j at the walls. These forces arise from the change in momentum experienced by the molecules in their reflection from the walls. It might seem, at first thought, difficult to compute them. However, when we recall that it is the time average which is involved in (7·1–1), we reflect that the average wall forces may be replaced by the integrated *pressure* p (force per unit area) which on the postulates of the kinetic theory is assumed to be due to the average effect of the continual bombardment of the walls by the molecules. We agree to establish coördinate axes as in Fig. 7·1. To form $\overline{\sum x_j F_{jx}}$ we must multiply the x coördinate of each molecule by the x component of the force acting on it, sum over all molecules, and then average. Now the only contribution to $\overline{\sum x_j F_{jx}}$ will come from the walls A and B. That at wall A must vanish since x is zero at all points of this wall.

At B we may assume that each single molecule is acted on by a surface element dS.   Hence $\overline{\sum x_j F_{jx}}$ becomes

$$-pa \int dS = -pa^3, \qquad (7\cdot1\text{-}2)$$

for at B, $x_j = a$ everywhere and the integration must be taken over the whole wall.   The negative sign results from the fact that the wall force acts *inward*.   The contribution of the pair of walls A and B to $\overline{\sum y_j F_{jy}}$ and $\overline{\sum z_j F_{jz}}$ will be zero since these walls are normal to the x axis and the force they exert is directed wholly along the x axis.   Proceeding similarly we find that the contribution to $\overline{\sum y_j F_{jy}}$ of the pair of walls E, F is $-pa^3$ and the same is true of the contribution of C, D to $\overline{\sum z_j F_{jz}}$.   Hence the total virial due to the forces exerted by the walls becomes

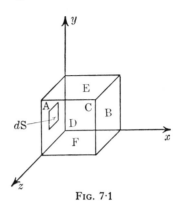

Fig. 7·1

$$\Omega = \tfrac{3}{2}pV_0, \qquad (7\cdot1\text{-}3)$$

where $V_0 = a^3$ is the volume of the cubical box.   The virial theorem $(6\cdot7\text{-}6)$ then gives

$$\tfrac{1}{2}\overline{\sum m_j v_j{}^2} = \tfrac{3}{2}pV_0, \qquad (7\cdot1\text{-}4)$$

where v_j is the resultant velocity of the j-th molecule.

The formula $(7\cdot1\text{-}4)$ at once gains fundamental importance for the thermal properties of gases if we assume that the temperature of an ideal gas is characterized entirely by the total average kinetic energy.   Then constant temperature implies constant average kinetic energy.   On this assumption $(7\cdot1\text{-}4)$ says that *the product of pressure and volume for an ideal gas at constant temperature is constant*.   This is *Boyle's law*.

It may be remarked that the foregoing derivation can be carried through much more generally using a vessel of any size or shape.   The reader may here refer to Lindsay, *Concepts and Methods of Theoretical Physics*, Van Nostrand, Princeton, N.J., 1951, pp. 185 ff. for the more general treatment.

Let us examine eq. $(7\cdot1\text{-}4)$ more closely.   Suppose that the molecules are all of equal mass and moreover suppose that $v_j{}^2$ is the same for all.   This is equivalent (for this special case) to the assumption that the mean kinetic energy is the same for all the molecules, i.e., that there is equipartition of energy among them.   This hypothesis or one closely connected with it has played a significant role in the development of the kinetic theory.   Eq. (7·1–4) now becomes (with $\overline{v_j{}^2} = \overline{v^2}$)

$$pV_0 = \tfrac{1}{3}mN\overline{v^2},\tag{7·1–5}$$

where N is the total number of molecules in the volume V_0, and m is the mass of each.   It should be carefully noted that $\overline{v^2}$ represents the time average of the square of the velocity, i.e., it has no connection with direction.   If we were to consider, for example, the average *velocity*, then we should have to admit that it must be zero, since for every molecule traveling at a given instant in a definite direction with a certain speed there will be to a very high degree of probability another one moving in the opposite direction with the same speed.   Now if we divide through eq. (7·1–5) by V_0, we have

$$p = \tfrac{1}{3}mn\overline{v^2},\tag{7·1–6}$$

where n is the number of molecules per unit of volume.   Hence $mn = \rho$, where ρ is the density of the gas, and we write finally

$$p = \tfrac{1}{3}\rho\overline{v^2}.\tag{7·1–7}$$

This provides at once a means of calculating the mean square velocity of the molecules and its square root, called the *root mean square* velocity. Thus

$$\sqrt{\overline{v^2}} = v_m = \sqrt{\frac{3p}{\rho}}.\tag{7·1–8}$$

For oxygen at standard pressure (76 cm of mercury) and at temperature $0°$ C., $\rho = 0.001429$ gram/cm³, and hence we calculate

$$v_m = 461.2 \text{ meters/sec},$$

approximately.   The reader should calculate for himself the corresponding values for other gases.   For example, he will find it of interest to work out the value for hydrogen and thus obtain a clue to the reason why there is so little hydrogen in the earth's atmosphere (cf. Sec. 1·11).   The foregoing is sufficient to indicate the order of magnitude of molecular velocities as calculated from kinetic theory.

Let us now introduce a more exact connection between the kinetic energy of the molecules and the temperature, and *assume*

$$mv_m{}^2 = 3kT,\tag{7·1–9}$$

where T is the absolute temperature.   It then develops from a study of the experimental data on many gases that k is a *universal* constant, depending only on the temperature scale used.   It is usually denoted as the Boltzmann gas constant or gas constant per molecule. If we knew the mass of the oxygen molecule, for example, we could calculate the value of k from (7·1–9). The most reliable data yield $k = (1.38041 \pm 0.00007) \times 10^{-16}$ ergs/degree C. Now substituting into (7·1–6) we have

$$p = nkT, \tag{7·1–10}$$

or multiplying through by a volume V_0,

$$pV_0 = NkT. \tag{7·1–11}$$

Eq. (7·1–11) is the *general gas equation* for an *ideal gas*, i.e., one in which the mutual forces of the molecules may be neglected compared with the forces of the walls on the molecules. It is also frequently called the *equation of state*.

7·2. Some Consequences of the Kinetic Theory. Specific Heats of Gases. Collisions of Molecules and Mean Free Path.

Several other results important for the theory of gases follow from the use of the virial theorem. We want to stress these here because they illustrate the very significant rôle that mechanical methods have played in the development of the theory of heat and the constitution of bodies.

In the first place note from eq. (7·1–11) that, since k is a universal constant, the number of molecules in volume V_0 of any ideal gas, given by

$$N = \frac{pV_0}{kT}, \tag{7·2–1}$$

is dependent only on the pressure, volume and temperature of the gas. It follows at once that if we have *two gases at the same temperature and pressure, equal volumes of the two will contain the same number of molecules*. This is the celebrated *hypothesis* of *Avogadro*, so important for chemistry. It here follows directly from kinetic theory considerations. Incidentally we note that if we were to assume Avogadro's hypothesis in *a priori* fashion and combine it with (7·1–6) the result would be that $\frac{1}{3}m\overline{v^2}$ must be the same for all gases at the same temperature. This at once suggests a kinetic theory definition of temperature like (7·1–9). The independent evidence in favor of Avogadro's hypothesis thus lends the greater weight to an assumption of the form (7·1–9). Of course, we cannot go here into the detail that a close inspection of this subject demands. Nevertheless the reader should see in it an illustration of the progressive interplay of hypotheses in constructing physical theories for various types of physical phenomena. Another conclusion closely allied to that just arrived at follows at once. Since $nm = \rho$, we have for two different ideal gases

$$n_1m_1 = \rho_1, \quad n_2m_2 = \rho_2. \tag{7·2–2}$$

But if the temperature and pressure are the same, $n_1 = n_2$, as we have just seen.   Hence under these conditions

$$\frac{m_1}{m_2} = \frac{\rho_1}{\rho_2},$$

(7·2–3)

that is, for constant temperature and pressure the ratio of the densities of two gases is equal to the ratio of the masses of their constituent molecules (i.e., chemically speaking the ratio of their *molecular weights*). This law was discovered originally by the chemist Gay-Lussac.

If we can suppose that when a gas is allowed to effuse through a very small opening in a vessel the outward velocity is proportional to the root mean square velocity v_m, it follows from eqs. (7·1–9) and (7·2–3) that

$$\frac{v_{m1}}{v_{m2}} = \sqrt{\frac{m_2}{m_1}} = \sqrt{\frac{\rho_2}{\rho_1}}$$

(7·2–4)

for two gases at the same temperature and pressure.   This, however, states in words that the effusion velocity (for gases at the same temperature and pressure) varies inversely as the square root of the gas density. This is actually satisfied experimentally to a considerable degree of approximation.

Some interesting results follow from the consideration of the energy of the molecules.   In an ideal gas the energy of the gas is the sum of the separate energies of motion of its molecules.   The latter energy for each molecule can be divided into two parts, viz., the kinetic energy of the molecule as a whole (i.e. the kinetic energy of the whole mass concentrated at the center of mass) and the kinetic energy of the separate parts of the molecule (supposing it has a structure) relative to the center of mass.   We shall assume that the latter energy, which we may call the internal kinetic energy of the molecule, is a constant fraction of the kinetic energy of translation.   So we shall write for the total energy of a single molecule

$$E = \tfrac{1}{2}\beta m \overline{v^2},$$

(7·2–5)

where β is a constant which should be the same for gases of the same constitution.   The energy for unit volume is then

$$E_V = \tfrac{1}{2}\beta n m \overline{v^2},$$

(7·2–6)

where n is the number of molecules per unit volume.   Now from eq. (7·1–6) we may write this in the form

$$E_V = \tfrac{3}{2}\beta p,$$

(7·2–7)

p being the pressure of the gas. The energy per unit mass of the gas is then

$$E_m = \frac{3}{2} \beta \frac{p}{\rho}, \tag{7·2–8}$$

where ρ is the density. Now the specific heat of a gas at constant volume c_V is measured by the increase in energy per unit mass per unit increase in absolute temperature while the volume remains the same. Hence we have

$$c_V = \left(\frac{dE_m}{dT}\right)_V = \frac{3}{2} \beta \left[\frac{d}{dT}\left(\frac{p}{\rho}\right)\right]_V. \tag{7·2–9}$$

This is expressed in mechanical units, i.e., ergs per degree. To change to calories per degree one must divide by the mechanical equivalent of heat, $\mathcal{J} = 4.2 \times 10^7$ ergs per calorie. What we are here interested in is, however, the fact that for an ideal gas (7·2–9) yields

$$c_V = \frac{3}{2} \frac{\beta k}{m}. \tag{7·2–10}$$

This shows that for a given gas the specific heat at constant volume should be independent of temperature and pressure. This is experimentally true over a wide range, but as one might expect breaks down at low temperatures, i.e., under the conditions such that the interaction forces can no longer be neglected. From (7·2–10) it is clear that c_V is inversely proportional to the mass of a molecule of the gas and directly proportional to β. If β were the same for a number of gases it would follow that the product of m by c_V or that which is proportional to this, the *product of c_V by the molecular weight, is constant*. This is the celebrated *law of Dulong and Petit* as applied to gases. It holds for a great many gases but, of course, is not valid for all gases under all conditions. It is also found to hold for most solid elements (the molecular weight being replaced by the atomic weight) if the temperature is high enough. The exact study of the specific heats of substances in general is very intricate. It has only yielded to successful treatment by the use of the quantum theory of the constitution of matter.[1]

If molecules have a structure and are made up of constituent parts, they clearly have nonvanishing size. Consequently one is entitled to expect effects associated with their collisions with each other as well as with the walls of the containing vessel. In view of the high average molecular velocities under standard conditions, we expect that the average number of collisions per second may be very considerable.

[1] For further discussion, cf. Lindsay, *Physical Statistics*, Wiley, New York, 1941, pp. 76 ff, 218, 234, 236.

Associated with it is the average distance traveled by a molecule between collisions, called the mean free path. For fixed average molecular velocity the mean free path λ will vary inversely with the average number of collisions per second Z_c. In fact if we use v_m for the mean molecular velocity, we have by definition the fundamental relation

$$\lambda = \frac{v_m}{Z_c}. \qquad (7 \cdot 2\text{--}11)$$

The calculation of λ thus depends on the evaluation of Z_c. This might be thought to be a very complicated affair in view of the widely varying speeds and directions of motion of the molecules. Fortunately we can make an approximate calculation in a rather simple way if we are willing to make some not unreasonable assumptions. We begin by postulating that the molecules are all solid spheres of diameter D and that they all move with the same speed v_m. We further assume that if we set up any three mutually perpendicular directions (such as a set of x, y, and z axes) one third will on the average move along each of the three directions. From symmetry we further agree that of those moving along the x axis, for example, half will move in the positive and half in the negative direction.

The average number of collisions per second suffered by any single molecule of diameter D will be equal to the average number of collisions suffered by a fictitious molecule of twice the diameter moving through a field of ideal point molecules. Hence Z_c will be the product of the cross section πD^2 with the average number of molecules per unit volume and the average relative velocity $\bar{v}_r$ of the molecules. Thus

$$Z_c = \pi D^2 n \bar{v}_r. \qquad (7 \cdot 2\text{--}12)$$

We must now evaluate $\bar{v}_r$. This is most simply done by considering a single molecule moving along the positive x axis and asking what its velocity is relative to all the other molecules moving as above assumed along the x, y, and z axes. Clearly the velocity relative to the other molecules moving along the positive x direction is zero; on the other hand, the velocity relative to the molecules moving along the negative x direction is $2v_m$. Similarly the velocity relative to the molecules moving along the positive and negative y and z directions respectively is $\sqrt{2}v_m$, as one can readily see by taking the difference between equal perpendicular vectors. Recalling the average numbers proceeding in each direction as noted above, we can break down $(7 \cdot 2\text{--}12)$ as follows

$$Z_c = \pi D^2 n \left(\frac{2v_m}{6} + \frac{4}{6} \sqrt{2}v_m \right) \doteq 1.276 \pi D^2 n v_m. \qquad (7 \cdot 2\text{--}13)$$

The mean free path then becomes

$$\lambda \doteq \frac{0.78}{\pi D^2 n} .$$ (7·2–14)

These values of Z_c and λ differ only slightly in the numerical factors from the expressions obtained by a more careful consideration of the varying directions and speeds of the molecules. For the ideal gas visualized in this section, the reader can show that Z_c in (7·2–13) is directly proportional to the pressure. Eq. (7·2–14) can be used to secure an estimate of the size of a molecule once λ is determined. The experimental evaluation of the mean free path can be made through its connection with the viscosity of the gas as discussed in the next section.

7·3. Elementary Kinetic Theory of the Viscosity of a Gas.   One of the most interesting applications of mechanics to kinetic theory is provided by the theory of gas viscosity. From elementary physics the reader will recall that in all real fluids in motion whether liquid or gaseous, there is always present a tendency for the fluid moving in one layer to retard the motion of the fluid in the immediately adjacent layers. This effect is attributed to a force of *viscosity* or viscous drag, which Newton assumed is directly proportional to the flow *velocity gradient* or rate of change of velocity with distance perpendicular to the direction of flow. It is moreover assumed that the viscous force is also proportional to the area of contiguous layers. If we denote the area in question by A, the flow velocity gradient by dV/ds, the viscous drag F_v may then be written

$$F_v = \eta A \frac{dV}{ds} ,$$ (7·3–1)

where η is the coefficient of viscosity or, more briefly, the *viscosity* of the fluid. It is the tangential viscous drag per unit area per unit flow velocity gradient. In absolute units its dimensions are dyne second per cm². This unit is called the poise. For example, the value for water in these units at 20° C is 0.01, while for hydrogen at 0° C η is 8.4×10^{-5}. It is of interest to note that the viscosity of liquids decreases as the temperature rises, whereas that of gases increases with the temperature.

The viscosity of liquids finds a plausible explanation in the cohesive forces between the constituent parts, but this is not available for an *ideal* gas in which such forces are assumed not to exist or are at any rate ignored. Maxwell was the first to give a kinetic theory explanation of gas viscosity in terms of the motion of the molecules and in particular by the transfer of momentum from one moving layer of gas to another by the random molecular motion.   Let us look into this matter in an elementary fashion.   Consider a gas which has a flow movement from left to right, let us say in the x direction.   Let the velocity in the plane AA' (Fig. 7·2) be denoted by V_1, while that in the lower plane BB' at a distance 2λ from AA' is $V_2 < V_1$, where λ, as in Sec. 7·2 is the mean free path.   Draw the imaginary plane PP' half way between AA' and BB'.   Now we may consider the molecules moving in the plane to be divided into three groups, namely, those traveling in the direction of the x, y and z axes respectively.   As in the preceding section we shall

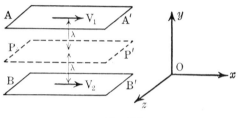

FIG. 7·2

suppose that if there are n molecules per unit volume, there will be on the average $n/3$ proceeding in each of the three directions.   Hence on the average the number of molecules that travel across *unit area* of the plane PP' in the positive y direction per second is $n/6 \cdot v_m$, where v_m is the root mean square molecular velocity, and we are making again the simplifying assumption that *all* the molecules may be considered as moving with this velocity.   The same number on the average cross unit area of the plane in the negative y direction per second. By virtue of the way in which the planes AA' and BB' are drawn, the above-mentioned molecules have each suffered their last collision (before striking PP') in either the plane AA' or BB'.   Now the velocity gradient of the gas in the neighborhood of PP' is approximately

$$\frac{dV}{ds} = \frac{V_1 - V_2}{2\lambda}. \qquad (7\cdot3\text{--}2)$$

It is, of course, assumed that the velocities V_1 and V_2 are very small compared with the molecular velocity v_m.   We shall next suppose that when a molecule passes through any plane it instantaneously acquires the velocity with which the gas as a whole is moving in that plane, the latter then being compounded with the molecular velocity.   Hence we can say that the $nv_m/6$ molecules which travel across unit area of the plane PP' per second coming from plane AA' carry with them or transfer a certain amount of momentum.   Each such molecule has acquired what may be called a " flow " momentum (to distinguish it from the momentum due to its velocity v_m) equal to mV_1. Hence in the passage of the molecules from AA' through PP' there is a transfer of momentum per second per unit area from the gas above PP' to the gas below PP' amounting to

$$\frac{nv_m}{6} \cdot mV_1. \tag{7·3–3}$$

But we know that a change in momentum implies a force which indeed is equal to the time rate of change of momentum. Hence we may look upon the expression (7·3–3) as representing a tangential force exerted by the gas *above* a unit area of the plane PP' on the gas *below* (tangential because the change in momentum is *in* the direction in which the gas flow is taking place). At the same time the passage of $nv_m/6$ molecules per second from the layer beneath PP' transfers in the *upward* direction tangential momentum per second per unit area to the amount of

$$\frac{nv_m}{6} \cdot mV_2. \tag{7·3–4}$$

This represents the tangential stress exerted by the gas below the plane PP' on the gas above. Now by Newton's third law (Sec. 1·7) the equal and opposite reaction on the gas below is $-nv_m/6 \cdot mV_2$. Hence the *resultant* tangential drag on unit area of the gas immediately below PP' is given by

$$\frac{nv_m}{6} \cdot m(V_1 - V_2). \tag{7·3–5}$$

By definition this is F_v/A in (7·3–1). From this and (7·3–2) the viscosity of the gas comes out to be

$$\eta = \frac{\rho v_m \lambda}{3}. \tag{7·3–6}$$

The deduction of this fundamental relationship given above is somewhat crude and the standard kinetic theory texts[1] should be consulted for a more elaborate treatment. Our purpose has been to bring out the fundamental rôle played by the transfer of momentum. If we employ (7·1–9) and (7·2–14) the relation (7·3–6) takes the form

$$\eta = \frac{0.26\sqrt{3kmT}}{\pi D^2}. \tag{7·3–7}$$

This indicates that the viscosity of an ideal gas is independent of the pressure and hence also of the density, a prediction first made by Maxwell

[1] See E. H. Kennard, *Kinetic Theory of Gases*, McGraw-Hill, New York, 1938, pp. 138 ff.

and experimentally verified by him over a wide range of values.[1]   The temperature dependence has also received ample verification.   It is of value to emphasize that the above result in no way depends on any assumed forces of interaction between molecules.

A number of striking numerical results can be readily obtained from the equations of this section and the preceding one.   Thus using the experimental value of η for hydrogen at $0°$ C as 8.41×10^{-5} poise we can calculate the mean free path of the hydrogen molecule at $0°$ C and atmospheric pressure.   We have

$$\lambda = \frac{3\eta}{\rho v_m} = \frac{3 \times 8.41 \times 10^{-5}}{8.99 \times 10^{-5} \times 1.83 \times 10^5} \text{ cm,}$$
$$= 1.53 \times 10^{-5} \text{ cm.}$$

This gives one a good idea of the order of magnitude of λ.   From this the average number of collisions experienced by a hydrogen molecule per second can at once be obtained.   Thus from (7·2–11)

$$Z_c = \frac{1.83 \times 10^5}{1.53 \times 10^{-5}} \text{ sec}^{-1} = 1.20 \times 10^{10} \text{ sec}^{-1}.$$

Lastly we may obtain some conception of the size of a molecule from eq. (7·2–14).   For

$$D = \left(\frac{0.78}{n\pi\lambda}\right)^{\frac{1}{2}}, \tag{7·3–8}$$

and taking $n = 2.705 \times 10^{19}$ as the number of molecules per cm³ (by Avogadro's hypothesis this is the same for all gases at the same temperature and pressure), and using the given value above of λ we have approximately

$$D = 2.4 \times 10^{-8} \text{ cm.}$$

There have been many estimates of the size of molecules on the kinetic theory, as the reader will find by an examination of texts on this subject. The interesting fact is that they all agree, so far as order of magnitude is concerned, with the foregoing result, which thus seems to have fundamental significance.   Of course, we must be careful not to think of this necessarily as the diameter of a solid sphere.   Modern physics has a great deal to say about the structure of molecules and the atoms which are their constituents.   We have already had occasion to note the Bohr-Rutherford theory of atomic structure.   On this point of view the atom and molecule have very *open* structures, so that the quantity represented by D will here presumably have some connection with the spatial separation of the component parts.

[1] At very high densities (e.g. 100 atmospheres) this result no longer follows and the viscosity increases more or less in proportion to the density.   A similar result obtains at very low densities.   (Cf. Kennard, *op. cit.*, p. 150).

7·4. Diffusion and Heat Conduction in a Gas.   In the preceding section we introduced the idea of the viscosity of a gas and obtained the interesting relation (7·3–6) between it and other quantities characteristic of the gas.   We did this by studying the transport of momentum from one layer of the gas to an adjacent one.   It is of interest to observe that we can secure similar relations by applying the same method to the transfer of mass (or more strictly the number of molecules per unit volume) and energy.   In the first case we learn something about diffusion in the gas and in the second case something about the conduction of heat.

It will indeed simplify the whole discussion if we think of the quantity being transferred as Q and then specialize Q after we have carried through the analysis in general terms.   Thus following the method in Sec. 7·3, we find that the *net* transfer or flux of Q per second per unit area in the positive y direction across the PP' plane is

$$\frac{v_m}{6}(Q_1 - Q_2) = \frac{\lambda v_m}{3}\cdot\frac{dQ}{dy}. \qquad (7\cdot4\text{–}1)$$

The three possibilities contemplated may be summarized as follows.
   (a) Total momentum per unit volume

$$Q = nmV. \qquad (7\cdot4\text{–}2)$$

   (b) Total molecular density

$$Q = n. \qquad (7\cdot4\text{–}3)$$

   (c) Total energy per unit volume

$$Q = E = nC_vT. \qquad (7\cdot4\text{–}4)$$

In (c), C_v denotes the specific heat *per molecule*.   (Cf. eq. 7·2–9 and note that c_v is in Sec. 7·2 the specific heat *per gram*.)

Phenomenologically the net transfer of total momentum is equal to the coefficient of viscosity η times the gradient of velocity in the y direction. The equation

$$\eta\,\frac{dV}{dy} = \frac{\lambda v_m}{3}\cdot nm\,\frac{dV}{dy} \qquad (7\cdot4\text{–}5)$$

of course yields eq. (7·3–6) directly, since $nm = \rho$.   In the case of diffusion the net transfer of Q is put equal to the so-called diffusion coefficient D times the gradient of molecular density in the y direction. Hence for case (b) we have

$$D\,\frac{dn}{dy} = \frac{\lambda v_m}{3}\frac{dn}{dy},$$

or

$$D = \frac{\lambda v_m}{3}. \qquad (7\cdot4\text{–}6)$$

In the case of heat conduction the net transfer of Q becomes equal by definition to the coefficient of thermal conductivity κ times the gradient of the temperature T in the y direction.   Hence for case (c) we have

$$\kappa \frac{dT}{dy} = \frac{\lambda v_m}{3} n C_v \frac{dT}{dy},$$

or

$$\kappa = \frac{n \lambda v_m C_v}{3}. \tag{7·4–7}$$

If we revert to the specific heat c_v per gram this becomes

$$\kappa = \frac{\rho \lambda v_m}{3} c_v = \eta c_v, \tag{7·4–8}$$

a relation of considerable interest in the kinetic theory of gases, since it connects three quantities which can be independently measured. Experiment indicates that the relation is verified as far as order of magnitude is concerned, though not precisely.   Thus for many nearly ideal gases $\kappa / \eta c_v$ is nearly 2 rather than unity.   The matter is discussed at length in E. H. Kennard, *Kinetic Theory of Gases*, McGraw-Hill, New York, 1938.

For reasons which should now be clear, the diffusion coefficient, viscosity, and thermal conductivity are termed *transport* properties of the gas.

7·5. The Statistical Method in Particle Mechanics.
In Chapter 6 we derived some very general theorems governing the motion of a system of particles subject to both external forces and forces of interaction. In particular we investigated the principles of conservation of momentum, moment of momentum, and energy.   These are very powerful tools for an understanding of the motion of the system as a whole, e.g., the motion of the center of mass; but they unfortunately shed little light on the motion of the individual particles.   In fact the equations of motion of a system of more than two particles have never been solved in general form, i.e., in such a way that given the forces acting and the initial values of position and velocity for every particle we could predict the position and velocity of every particle at any other time.   Approximate results are available for systems containing a relatively small number of particles, like the planets revolving about the sun, especially when some of the forces acting are very small compared with others.   In the special case in which all the particles are bound to each other so firmly that they suffer no mutual motion — i.e., the system forms a rigid body — very general results can be obtained.   Some of these are discussed in Chapter 8.

When we are dealing with a mechanical system composed of a very large number of particles, as in the kinetic theory of gases touched on in Secs. 7·1 and the following, we find we can make genuine progress by introducing *averages* of quantities characteristic of the system and then assigning operational significance to these averages. Thus in the virial theorem we assigned an operational significance, namely temperature, to the *average* kinetic energy of the whole system of particles making up a gas. This use of average behavior characterizes what is called the statistical method of handling the motion of large aggregates of particles and enables the principles of mechanics to be successfully applied to the understanding of the observed properties of gases. It introduces probability into mechanics, since the calculation of averages inevitably entails some assumptions about the comparative likelihood of the various values being averaged. In the next few sections we shall apply the statistical method to an ideal gas and extend the simple kinetic theory results already obtained. This will provide an introduction to statistical mechanics.

7·6. Statistical Distributions. To proceed as simply as possible without losing sight of the fundamental idea we visualize an ideal gas as an aggregate of a very large but finite number N of particles of the same mass confined to a vessel of finite size. The particles are assumed to have kinetic energy only, i.e., there are no forces of interaction save those resulting from collisions, and we shall suppose that all collisions are elastic, leading only to exchange of kinetic energy between particles. If the collisions with the walls are also elastic, it follows that the total energy of the aggregate remains constant as long as the vessel is isolated.

We further postulate that as a result of the collisions, which as we have seen from the simple kinetic theory of Secs. 7·2 and 7·3, are very numerous, the number of particles with kinetic energy lying in any given interval will settle down to a more or less constant value. As time passes, some particles will pass out of this energy interval, but others will come into it by collision. It seems reasonable to suppose that in this way a kind of equilibrium condition will ensue in which a definite fraction of the total number of particles will on the average lie in each of a series of energy intervals stretching from the very small to the very large. Such an assignment of particles is called a statistical distribution of the aggregate with respect to energy. The words " on the average " are important, since once we decide to indulge in the use of statistics we have no assurance that the number of particles having energy in any given interval will stay precisely the same from instant to instant. What we are assuming as reasonable is that if we average this number over a time long compared with the average time between collisions (the reciprocal of the quantity Z_c in Sec. 7·2) the fluctuations from this average in times over which we can observe the system experimentally will be very small and effectively negligible.

The question now arises: how can we find such a statistical distribution as has just been described? For convenience of visualization we replace the energy intervals by a set of imaginary boxes, to each of which we assign a definite energy, as in Fig. 7·3. To be specific we

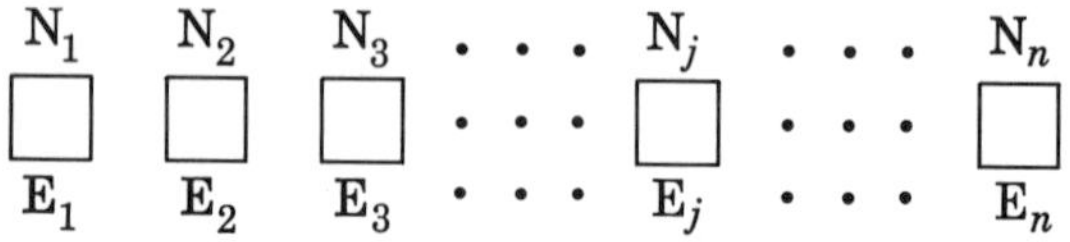

FIG. 7·3

shall suppose that there are n energy boxes into which the N particles can be placed. The distribution we are talking about is realized as soon as we have found N_j (the average number in the j-th box) as a function of E_j, the energy assigned to the j-th box. The use of discrete boxes is of course an approximation to continuous energy intervals, but by taking n sufficiently large we can come as close as we like to a continuous distribution. We can immediately write the following useful relations:

$$\sum_{j=1}^{n} N_j = N \tag{7·6-1}$$

$$\sum_{j=1}^{n} N_j E_j = E. \tag{7·6-2}$$

In (7·6-2), E represents the total kinetic energy of the system of particles, a constant. In writing this relation, we are of course assuming that every particle getting into the energy box E_j by collision at once assumes the corresponding energy value.

Suppose we have the distribution shown in Fig. 7·3. In how many ways can it be realized? That is, if we have N particles to distribute among n boxes, in how many different and independent ways can we place N_1 in the first box, N_2 in the second, and in general N_j in the j-th box? This is merely a matter of counting. We have N ways in which to place the first particle in the first box, since we can pick any one of the N particles for this purpose. Correspondingly there are $N - 1$ ways of putting the second particle in the first box, since we now have one less from which to make our choice. Proceeding in this way we see that we have $N - N_1 + 1$ ways of putting the N_1-th particle in the first box. Hence the total number of ways of placing the N_1 particles in the first box is

$$N(N - 1)(N - 2) \cdots (N - N_1 + 1).$$

But this takes for granted that the order in which the particles go into the box is important.   We do not wish to assume this.   For our purpose a rearrangement of the N_1 particles in the first box corresponds to the same distribution.   Hence to find the number of different and independent ways of placing any N_1 particles in the first box we must divide the number just found by the number of ways in which we can rearrange the order of the N_1 particles.   This is the number of permutations of N_1 things taken N_1 at a time or $N_1!$, which equals $1 \cdot 2 \cdot 3 \cdot 4 \cdots N_1$. The total number of ways we are seeking is then

$$\frac{N(N-1)\cdots(N-N_1+1)}{N_1!} = \frac{N!}{N_1!(N-N_1)!}. \qquad (7\cdot6\text{–}3)$$

We have rewritten the number somewhat more compactly on the right-hand side.

The process of assignment is now repeated for the second box.   Here we have to choose N_2 particles out of the $N - N_1$ remaining.   The number of ways then becomes

$$\frac{(N-N_1)!}{N_2!(N-N_1-N_2)!} \qquad (7\cdot6\text{–}4)$$

and we get corresponding expressions for the $N_3, N_4 \cdots N_j \cdots N_n$ particles in their appropriate boxes. The product of all these expressions is the total number of ways in which we may distribute the particles so that N_j land in the j-th box, in other words the total number of ways of achieving the desired distribution.   This number we shall call w. Hence we have

$$w = \frac{N!}{N_1!(N-N_1)!} \cdot \frac{(N-N_1)!}{N_2!(N-N_1-N_2)!}$$
$$\cdots \frac{(N-N_1-N_2\cdots-N_n)!}{N_n!}$$
$$= \frac{N!}{N_1!N_2!\cdots N_n!}. \qquad (7\cdot6\text{–}5)$$

It is customary to call w the statistical probability of the distribution. Its value will of course depend on the N_j values.   A few simple examples will serve to illustrate this.   Suppose all the particles have energy E_1, i.e., are in the first box.   Then $N_1 = N$ and all the other N's are zero.   This yields $w = 1$.   There is only one way to achieve this distribution.   This is a rather unlikely distribution and we suspect that w will be greater for others.   This suspicion is verified by examination of the case in which the particles are divided equally among the energy boxes, i.e., $N_j = N/n$ for all j. We can evaluate w for this situation approximately by the use of Stirling's formula, namely[1]

$$N! = (N/e)^N \sqrt{2\pi N}\ \{1 + 1/12N + (1/288)N^2 - (139/51840)N^3 \cdots\}.$$
$$(7\cdot6-6)$$

If $N \gg 1$, it is sufficiently accurate to take

$$N! = (N/e)^N \sqrt{2\pi N}, \qquad (7\cdot6-7)$$

particularly if the logarithm of N is to be used, as is customary in working with w. If we take log w in (7·6–5), use Stirling's formula and reconvert, we have for the case $N_j = N/n$

$$w = \sqrt{2\pi N}(n/N)^{n/2}n^N. \qquad (7\cdot6-8)$$

This assumes $N \gg n$. Suppose $N = 10^{20}$ and $n = 10^{10}$. Then w from (7·6–8) becomes approximately 4.6×10^{21}, which is certainly much larger than unity. We shall interpret this to mean that the distribution in question is very much more likely to occur than the one earlier considered in which all the particles were in one box. In general we are assuming that the more ways there are to achieve a given distribution the more likely it is to occur. We are also tacitly assuming here that it is just as likely for a given single particle to be in any one energy box as in any other. This assumption is of course not necessary for the general theory of statistical distributions and we shall modify it presently.

We now wish to find the distribution of N particles among n energy boxes which can be achieved in the largest number of ways consistent with the constancy of the total energy of the system. This means we wish to make w in (7·6–5) a maximum subject to the conditions that both N and E in (7·6–1) and (7·6–2) are constant. This distribution will be called the *canonical* distribution.

As has already been suggested it is more convenient to solve this problem by working with log w, which becomes

$$\log w = \log N! - \sum_{j=1}^{n} \log N_j!. \qquad (7\cdot6-9)$$

With the use of Stirling's formula this can be written to a good approximation for N large

$$\log w = N \log N - \sum N_j \log N_j. \qquad (7\cdot6-10)$$

[1] E. T. Whittaker and G. N. Watson, *Modern Analysis*, 4th ed., Cambridge University Press, 1940, p. 253.

Suppose we have a distribution and imagine that it is disturbed so that each N_j is altered by a small amount which we shall denote by δN_j. The corresponding change in log w is

$$\delta \log w = - \sum_{j=1}^{n} \delta N_j \log N_j, \qquad (7\cdot6\text{--}11)$$

where we have utilized the fact that $\sum \delta N_j = 0$ since the total number of particles must remain constant in any redistribution.

Now the distribution we are seeking is that for which log w is a maximum consistent with $(7\cdot6\text{--}1)$ and $(7\cdot6\text{--}2)$ with N and E constant. From calculus we know that if we change the independent variable in a function in the neighborhood of a maximum value of the function by a first order quantity, the change in the function to the first order must vanish. Hence to find the canonical distribution we must make $\delta \log w = 0$ subject to $(7\cdot6\text{--}1)$ and $(7\cdot6\text{--}2)$. The latter say that the δN_j are not perfectly arbitrary. Rather there are two equations connecting them, namely,

$$\sum_{j=1}^{n} \delta N_j = 0, \qquad (7\cdot6\text{--}12)$$

$$\sum_{}^{n} E_j \delta N_j = 0. \qquad (7\cdot6\text{--}13)$$

These equations really say that we can solve any two of the δN_j, let us say for convenience δN_1 and δN_2 in terms of all the rest which can then be perfectly arbitrary. Let us pick two constant parameters a and b. No matter what their values are, we can replace $(7\cdot6\text{--}11)$ (because of the existence of $(7\cdot6\text{--}12)$ and $(7\cdot6\text{--}13)$) by

$$\log w = -\sum \delta N_j(-\log N_j + a + bE_j). \qquad (7\cdot6\text{--}14)$$

Let us now make a and b definite by choosing them so as to satisfy the linear equations

$$-\log N_1 + a + bE_1 = 0,$$
$$-\log N_2 + a + bE_2 = 0. \qquad (7\cdot6\text{--}15)$$

It then follows that the condition $\delta \log w = 0$ takes the form

$$\sum_{j=3}^{n} \delta N_j(-\log N_j + a + bE_j) = 0, \qquad (7\cdot6\text{--}16)$$

and this must be true no matter what values the δN_j have, since δN_3, $\delta N_4, \ldots, \delta N_n$ are now perfectly arbitrary. But from algebra we know that the only way in which $(7\cdot6\text{--}16)$ can hold identically for arbitrary δN_j is to have the coefficient of δN_j vanish for every j from 3 to n. Hence, recalling $(7\cdot6\text{--}15)$, we have for *all j*

$$N_j = e^{a+bE_j}. \qquad (7\cdot6\text{--}17)$$

This is the canonical distribution we have sought. To understand it better, it is necessary to provide some physical meaning for the constants a and b. We shall find it convenient to replace them by two others denoted by ψ and Θ, defined as follows:

$$a = \psi/\Theta + \log N_n,$$
$$b = -1/\Theta. \tag{7.6-18}$$

Then (7.6–17) becomes

$$N_j = Nne^{\psi/\Theta}\, e^{-E_j/\Theta}. \tag{7.6-19}$$

It has here been assumed that Θ is positive. This is necessary (recall that E_j is always positive) to insure that N_j will not become indefinitely large with the increase in E_j. Moreover, positive Θ means that the extreme value of $\log w$ in (7.6–10) is a maximum and not a minimum. We recall that the condition $\delta \log w = 0$ does not distinguish between the two. It is customary to call ψ and Θ distribution moduli since they affect the numerical magnitudes of N_j for given E_j. We can of course solve (7.6–19) for ψ and Θ, if we use (7.6–1) and (7.6–2). From the first we get

$$\psi = -\Theta \log \sum ne^{-E_j/\Theta} \tag{7.6-20}$$

while the second yields

$$E = Nne^{\psi/\Theta}\sum E_j e^{-E_j/\Theta}. \tag{7.6-21}$$

These equations may be combined to eliminate ψ, viz.,

$$\bar{E} = E/N = \frac{\sum\limits_{j=1}^{n} E_j e^{-E_j/\Theta}}{\sum\limits_{j=1}^{n} e^{-E_j/\Theta}}. \tag{7.6-22}$$

This expresses the arithmetical average energy per particle in terms of Θ, and hence by the solution of the relation as a transcendental equation we can in principle solve for Θ. However, this is really an unnecessary step. We shall shortly identify Θ and ψ with physically measurable properties of the aggregate considered as a gas and shall find indeed that Θ will represent something connected with the temperature of the gas and ψ its free energy.

7.7. General Canonical Distribution. The considerations of the preceding section, though adequate for the introduction of the notion of statistical distribution in the case of a many-particle system, suffer from a certain drawback. We made the assumption that it was equally likely that a particle would locate in any energy box. This is too restrictive a postulate, as we can see if we consider the example of the distribution of the aggregate of particles among a set of actual boxes with different volumes V_j such that

$$\sum_{j=1}^{n} V_j = V, \tag{7·7-1}$$

where V is the physical volume of the vessel in which the particles are confined. It does not seem reasonable to suppose that it is equally likely that a particle will be found in a small box and a large box. Rather it is much more plausible to assume that other things being equal a particle will more frequently be found in a large box than a small one. In fact the relative frequencies of occurrence would appear to be V_j/V and experiments have confirmed this to a sufficiently high degree, though it must be confessed that no experiment is adequate to provide complete verification of an assumption of this kind which involves the notion of probability. However, we do not think it does violence to common sense and common experience to assume that there is an *a priori* probability g_j attached to each of the n boxes and that in the example being discussed, this is

$$g_j = V_j/V. \tag{7·7-2}$$

In any given case it is necessary to assign the g_j by an inspection of the situation and the best possible assumption based on this. Naturally there will always be a certain arbitrariness in the choice of the g_j. This is part of the price one has to pay for indulging in statistical considerations. No matter what choice is made, we must clearly always have

$$\sum_{j=1}^{n} g_j = 1. \tag{7·7-3}$$

Note that the g_j are genuine probabilities, i.e., proper fractions, unlike the so-called statistical probability w, which is an integer.

From elementary probability theory[1] the probability of a distribution in which there are N_1 particles in the first box, etc., when the *a priori* probabilities are $g_1 g_2 \cdots g_n$ is

$$g_1^{N_1} g_2^{N_2} \cdots g_n^{N_n} = \prod_{j=1}^{n} g_j^{N_j} . \tag{7·7-4}$$

This presumes that there is only one way for the given distribution to be realized. Actually the number of ways is w (eq. 7·6–5) and hence the total probability (a genuine mathematical probability this time) for the distribution is

$$P = w \prod_{j=1}^{n} g_j^{N_j} . \tag{7·7-5}$$

[1] Cf. A. C. Aitkin, *Statistical Mathematics*, Interscience Publishers, New York, 1942, pp. 12 ff.

To secure the general canonical distribution it is only necessary to make $\log P$ a maximum subject to the usual conditions (7·6–1) and (7·6–2).   The method is precisely that of Sec. 7·6 and yields

$$N_j = g_j N n e^{\psi/\Theta}\, e^{-E_j/\Theta}, \qquad (7\cdot7\text{–}6)$$

where now (7·6–20) and (7·6–21) are replaced respectively by

$$\psi = -\Theta \log \sum_{j=1}^{n} n g_j e^{-E_j/\Theta}, \qquad (7\cdot7\text{–}7)$$

and

$$E = N \frac{\displaystyle\sum_{j=1}^{n} n g_j E_j e^{-E_j/\Theta}}{\displaystyle\sum_{j=1}^{n} n g_j e^{-E_j/\Theta}}. \qquad (7\cdot7\text{–}8)$$

The expression in the denominator of (7·7–8) is called the *partition function* and is denoted by Z.   Thus

$$Z = \sum_{j=1}^{n} n g_j e^{-E_j/\Theta}. \qquad (7\cdot7\text{–}9)$$

In terms of it the general canonical distribution can be written

$$N_j = \frac{n g_j N e^{-E_j/\Theta}}{Z}. \qquad (7\cdot7\text{–}10)$$

Some rather important consequences ensue from these equations. Let us evaluate from it the expression for $\log P_c$, where P_c denotes the value of the probability P (7·7–5) for the canonical distribution.   Thus from

$$\log P = N \log N - \sum N_j \log \frac{N_j}{g_j} \qquad (7\cdot7\text{–}11)$$

we get from (7·7–10)

$$\log P_c = N \log N + \frac{nN}{\Theta} \sum \frac{g_j E_j e^{-E_j/\Theta}}{Z} - nN \log \frac{nN}{Z} \sum \frac{g_j e^{-E_j/\Theta}}{Z}. \qquad (7\cdot7\text{–}12)$$

By the use of (7·7–7) and (7·7–8) we see by multiplication by $\log n^N$ that

$$\log n^N P_c = \frac{E - N\psi}{\Theta}. \qquad (7\cdot7\text{–}13)$$

If we denote $n^N P_c$ as the canonical statistical probability and write it as w_c, we can rewrite (7·7–13) as

$$\log w_c = E/\Theta + N \log Z, \qquad (7\cdot7\text{–}14)$$

a relation which we stress again holds only when the system is canonically distributed. Suppose now we wish to change the environment of the system while still keeping it canonically distributed. Let us find the corresponding change in $\log w_c$, recognizing that in the process the individual energies E_j will change as well as the total energy E. The modulus Θ and of course the partition function will also be affected. Such an environmental alteration might, for example, be a change in volume. Taking the differentials, we get

$$d \log w_c = dE/\Theta - E/\Theta^2 \cdot d\Theta$$

$$+ N \frac{\partial \log Z}{\partial \Theta} d\Theta$$

$$+ N \sum d_1 \log Z, \qquad (7\cdot7\text{--}15)$$

where $d_1 \log Z$ is the change in $\log Z$ due to all changes except that of Θ. By differentiating $\log Z$ as given in $(7\cdot7\text{--}9)$ with respect to Θ, we can show that

$$N \frac{\log Z}{\partial \Theta} - E/\Theta^2 = 0, \qquad (7\cdot7\text{--}16)$$

so that

$$d \log w_c = dE/\Theta + N \sum d_1 \log Z. \qquad (7\cdot7\text{--}17)$$

Now

$$d_1 \log Z = \frac{d_1 Z}{Z}$$

$$= - \frac{\sum n g_j/\Theta \cdot e^{-Ej/\Theta}}{Z} dE_j. \qquad (7\cdot7\text{--}18)$$

Consequently

$$N\Theta \, d_1 \log Z = -\sum N_j dE_j. \qquad (7\cdot7\text{--}19)$$

Now the only way in which the energy E_j of a particle in the j-th box can change at constant Θ is either by having work done on the system by the external environment (dE_j positive) or by having the system do work on the environment (dE_j negative). Since N_j is the number of particles in the j-th box in the canonical distribution, $-\sum N_j dE_j$ therefore corresponds to the work done *by* the system on the environment while it remains canonically distributed. We denote it by dW and can then write $(7\cdot7\text{--}17)$ in the form

$$\Theta \, d \log w_c = dE + dW. \qquad (7\cdot7\text{--}20)$$

In words this says that when a canonically distributed system is altered slightly by changes in the external environment but still remains canonically distributed throughout the process, the distribution modulus multiplied by the change in the logarithm of the canonical statistical probability is equal to the change in the total internal energy of the system plus the work done by the system on the surroundings. Let us rewrite (7·7–20) in the form

$$dE = \Theta \, d \log w_c - dW, \qquad (7\text{·}7\text{–}21)$$

where $-dW$ is the work done *on* the system by the changes in the external environment. This equation has important consequences, since it expresses the fact that in general the change in the total internal energy E of the system is not equal to the work done on the system by the surroundings. There is an additional contribution $\Theta \, d \log w_c$ connected with the statistical distribution. We seem to have run into a contradiction to the principle of the conservation of mechanical energy. We obviously need to account physically for the extra term $\Theta \, d \log w_c$.

Reflection reminds us that there are many simple situations in mechanics in which the work done on a system is not equal to the change in the energy, i.e., conservation of mechanical energy breaks down. This is of course the case where friction enters the problem as in Chapter 5. When we do work on a block moving on a rough plane, for example, the gain in energy is always less than the work done: we say that some of the work goes to overcome friction. Experience indicates that in all such cases the system grows warm, or we say heat is produced. It appears therefore that we have at hand a plausible interpretation of the extra term in eq. (7·7–21) which results theoretically from our statistical considerations. We shall assume that $\Theta \, d \log w_c$ is the *quantity of heat dQ* communicated to the system by the external environment and indeed write

$$dQ = \Theta \, d \log w_c. \qquad (7\text{·}7\text{–}22)$$

In this way we have defined a new physical concept in terms of quantities connected with the notion of statistical distribution of particles subject to the principles of mechanics. The meaningfulness of this concept becomes apparent when we rewrite (7·7–20) as

$$dQ = dE + dW. \qquad (7\text{·}7\text{–}23)$$

With the interpretation just introduced, this becomes the first principle of thermodynamics as ordinarily written for a system like the gas we have been considering. We thus see the possibility of establishing what appears to be an independent branch of physics on the basis of statistical ideas applied to the mechanics of a collection of particles.

7·8. Thermodynamics from the Statistical Point of View.

Thermodynamics may be defined as the study of the properties of large-scale matter in states of equilibrium and in their changes from one equilibrium state to another, especially but not necessarily when changes of temperature are involved and work is done.   A state of equilibrium is one in which the system if left entirely to itself, will stay forever.   The theory of thermodynamics as classically presented specifies such states in terms of operationally defined concepts like pressure, volume, and temperature relating to macroscopic objects.   It operates from two fundamental assumptions or principles called generally the first and second " laws " of thermodynamics.   Of these the first postulates that in all thermodynamic processes or changes between equilibrium states, there is no change in the total energy of a system and its environment.   All that can happen is a change from one form of energy to another, e.g., mechanical work into heat or vice versa.   In the special case of a gas in which no chemical reactions are assumed to take place, the first principle says that when a quantity of heat is communicated to the gas, in general part of it enables the gas to do work on the surroundings while the rest goes to increase what is called the internal energy of the gas, usually manifested by a rise in temperature.   In analytical form the principle appears as eq. (7·7–23).   But from the classical thermodynamical point of view the interpretation of dQ is calorimetric, i.e., strictly operational; whereas we have just seen in the preceding section that there dQ has a statistical significance.   Moreover, while in classical thermodynamics the change in internal energy is strictly speaking defined in terms of the first law itself, in the statistical interpretation dE refers to the actual change in the aggregate energy of the particles making up the system.   In other words the statistical point of view provides a microscopic interpretation or if we like a deduction of the first principle of thermodynamics, giving it the character of an actual physical law.

But thermodynamics also deals with the direction of thermodynamic processes, e.g., the natural flow of heat from hot to cold bodies, and the first law or principle sheds no light on this.   Another principle is necessary, the famous second law.   This also receives a statistical interpretation.   To understand this we must say something more about processes and state variables.

A state variable in thermodynamics is a quantity descriptive of the system under discussion which depends only on the state and not on the process by which the system got into that state.   It therefore always returns to its original value when the system undergoes a process which takes it back to its original state, i.e., a so-called cyclic process.   As we have already remarked, temperature, pressure and volume are thermodynamic state variables.   The total internal energy E is also a state variable.   This is readily understood on the statistical interpretation, since each equilibrium state is characterized by a definite canonical distribution function N_j (7·7–10) and with each E_j fixed, the total energy $E = \sum N_j E_j$ is completely determined for each state. On the other hand the work done on or by the system in a thermodynamic process is not a state variable in the same sense. It is possible for quite different amounts of work to be done in the transition between two specified states, depending on the change in temperature and other characteristics of the environment. Suppose, for example, the system is an ideal gas which is heated at constant volume from temperature T_1 to temperature T_2 and then allowed to expand, keeping the temperature constant at T_2, to double its volume. The work done in this process is not the same as that which would be done if the gas were first permitted to double its volume at constant temperature T_1 and then have the temperature increased from T_1 to T_2 at constant volume. The work done by or on a thermodynamic system depends on the nature of the process it undergoes.

From eq. (7·7–23) it therefore follows that Q is not a state variable, for if it were, in any cyclic process both dQ and dE would have to vanish and hence dW would have to become zero also. But we have just seen that dW does not in general vanish in a cyclic process. Hence dQ will not vanish in a cyclic process and hence Q can not be a state variable. Of course we can visualize processes in which dQ does vanish. These are termed adiabatic.

In eq. (7·7–23) all quantities are expressed in terms of energy units. Since in practical experiments dQ is measured calorimetrically, an energy equivalent of heat is necessary in the use of the equation. This is the celebrated mechanical equivalent of heat, usually represented by $\mathcal{J}$ and equal to 4.2 joules per calorie.

From what has just been said $\Theta\, d \log w_c$ if it is to correspond to dQ cannot be the change in a state variable. However, $\log w_c$ itself must be a state variable, since w_c depends solely on the equilibrium state of the system and indeed on the statistical point of view defines this state by its own maximum value subject to the constancy of the total number of particles in the system and the total energy. It has nothing to do with the process through which the system got into this state. It must be emphasized again that the change $d \log w_c$ refers to a change from one equilibrium state to another, i.e., both states must correspond to canonical distributions.

It follows that

$$\frac{dQ}{\Theta} = d \log w_{\hat{c}} \qquad (7\cdot8\text{–}1)$$

is the change in a state variable. In order to give a thermodynamic interpretation of this it is necessary to identify the statistical modulus with some thermodynamic quantity. Let us recall that in classical thermodynamics the quantity

$$\frac{dQ}{T},$$

where T is the so-called absolute temperature of the system, is the change in a state variable if dQ means the heat gained or lost by the system when it changes from one equilibrium state to another, i.e., by what is called a reversible process. In other words, when summed around a cyclic reversible process, dQ/T is zero. But dQ/Θ in (7·8–1) possesses precisely the same property. Hence it is tempting to identify Θ with T or some constant multiplied by T.

We shall set

$$\Theta = KT, \tag{7·8–2}$$

where K is a universal constant, and define the new thermodynamic state variable S, the so-called entropy, as

$$S = K \log w_c + C, \tag{7·8–3}$$

where C is a disposable constant which we may choose so as to make S defined statistically in (7·8–3) agree best with the known thermodynamic properties of the entropy. It is found to be convenient to take $C = -K \log N!$ and write

$$S = K \log \left(\frac{w_c}{N!}\right). \tag{7·8–4}$$

We shall presently investigate the significance of S from the statistical point of view, but first we desire to establish the meaning of the constant K in terms of classical thermodynamics. For this purpose we examine the quantity A, known as the Helmholtz free energy of the system and defined as

$$A = E - TS. \tag{7·8–5}$$

If we substitute for S from (7·8–4) and utilize (7·7–14) we get

$$A = -NKT \log Z + KT \log N!,$$

and if we employ Stirling's theorem, this reduces further to

$$A = -NKT \log \left(\frac{Z}{N}\right) - NKT. \tag{7·8–6}$$

Let us continue to discuss the case of an ideal gas, whose statistical representation is an aggregate of free mass particles, having kinetic energy only. We take the differential of both sides of (7·8–6) and have

$$dA = dE - TdS - SdT. \tag{7·8–7}$$

But the first law of thermodynamics (7·7–23) for a gas has the form

$$TdS = dE + pdV, \tag{7·8–8}$$

where pdV is the work done by the gas when it expands against its surroundings[1] by an increase in volume dV at pressure p. The combination of (7·8–7) and (7·8–8) yields

$$dA = -SdT - pdV, \tag{7·8–9}$$

whence

$$p = -\left(\frac{\partial A}{\partial V}\right)_T. \tag{7·8–10}$$

But if we know the free energy A as a function of volume and temperature, (7·8–10) is the equation of state of the gas, since it will give the relation connecting pressure, volume, and temperature. We know (eq. 7·1–11) that this equation for an ideal gas has the form

$$pV = NkT, \tag{7·8–11}$$

where N is the number of molecules and k is the gas constant per molecule or Boltzmann's constant, a universal constant having the value 1.38×10^{-16} erg/°C. Obviously if we can find A for the statistical model of the ideal gas and evaluate p in (7·8–10), comparison with (7·8–11) will indicate the proper choice of the constant K. This involves the evaluation of the partition function Z for an ideal gas. Actually it follows from (7·8–6) that we do not need the complete expression for Z, but only its dependence on the volume V. Fortunately it is easy to see that Z will be directly proportional to the volume, since the *a priori* probabilities g_j in the expression for Z each contain a multiplicative term equal to the size of a spatial volume element, and since the $e^{-E_j/\Theta}$ does not contain any reference to space (the E_j being kinetic energies only), in the sum the volume elements sum up to the total volume of the gas. A complete evaluation[2] actually yields

$$Z = \frac{nV}{C} \cdot (2\pi m KT)^{3/2}, \tag{7·8–12}$$

where C is a constant we do not need to concern ourselves with here. It follows from (7·8–6) that

$$\left(\frac{\partial A}{\partial V}\right)_T = -\frac{NKT}{V}. \tag{7·8–13}$$

---

[1] Cf. R. B. Lindsay, *General Physics*, Wiley, New York, 1940, p. 206.
[2] Cf. R. B. Lindsay, *Concepts and Methods of Theoretical Physics*, Van Nostrand, Princeton, N.J., 1951, p. 197.

Hence the equation of state (7·8–10) yields

$$pV = NKT. \qquad (7\cdot8\text{–}14)$$

If this is to be the same equation as (7·8–11) it is clear we must choose $K = k$, the Boltzmann constant. The statistical modulus will therefore be chosen as

$$\Theta = kT, \qquad (7\cdot8\text{–}15)$$

and the entropy S as defined statistically becomes

$$S = k \log \left(\frac{w_c}{N!}\right). \qquad (7\cdot8\text{–}16)$$

We are now ready to draw some conclusions about the behavior of S from its statistical definition. If we visualize a system isolated from its surroundings, the entropy as defined in (7·8–16) cannot be expected to decrease since w_c is already the largest statistical probability subject to the given conditions (constancy of number of particles and total energy) and if the entropy were to decrease it would mean a transition to a less probable state. This by virtue of the meaning of probability is very unlikely, though of course not impossible. Moreover the definition emphasizes the essentially irreversible character of the approach to equilibrium in naturally occurring thermodynamic processes, since a system not in equilibrium will have a statistical probability w less than w_c and will hence tend to move so as to increase w. This is a process which tends to go in only one direction, unless interfered with by external influences.

The statement that the entropy of an isolated system does not decrease is one form of the second principle of thermodynamics. In classical thermodynamics it is a postulate suggested by the observed behavior of actual systems. In the present point of view it is a deduction from the statistical interpretation of thermodynamic processes and the statistical definition of entropy as a special thermodynamic state function. Of course, the price we pay for the statistical deduction is that we are no longer permitted to say that the entropy in question never decreases; we may say only that it *hardly ever* decreases. The statistical interpretation being based on probability considerations necessarily must allow for fluctuations, but we can actually calculate the probability of such fluctuations as would correspond to violations of the second law and show that it is extremely small in practical cases.

It will pay to look a little more closely at this matter since it is vital to an appreciation of the statistical interpretation of thermodynamics. Assume we have a thermodynamic system in a state given by the statistical probability w. We do not here assume that the system is in equilibrium and hence w is not the canonical statistical probability w_c.

Now assume that in a second state which can be reached by the system the statistical probability is $w + \Delta w$, where Δw is positive. This corresponds to a gain in statistical probability of Δw in going from the first to the second state. A plausible measure of the tendency for the system to go from the first to the second states is the ratio

$$\frac{w + \Delta w}{w},$$

which we may call z. Then

$$\log z = \Delta \log w,$$

or

$$z = e^{\Delta \log w}. \qquad (7 \cdot 8 - 17)$$

$\Delta \log w$ is in general difficult to calculate. However, there are special cases in which the two states are equilibrium states and $\Delta \log w$ becomes $\Delta \log w_c$. Then we can at once use $(7 \cdot 8 - 1)$ for the calculation, since

$$\Delta \log w_c = \frac{\Delta Q}{kT}. \qquad (7 \cdot 8 - 18)$$

We shall illustrate by a simple example. Suppose a gas is confined to a volume V_1 (Fig. 7·4) which is part of a vessel of larger volume V_2. The rest of the vessel is devoid of matter, i.e., is ideally a vacuum. We imagine that the gas in V_1 is in a state of equilibrium which can, however, be upset by making a hole in the wall which separates V_1 from the rest of the vessel. We know from experience that the gas rushes out of the hole and does not stop until the whole volume V_2 has been filled. It then settles down to another state of equilibrium. This is a " natural " process in that it is the one commonly observed: we do not observe the reverse process whereby the gas in the whole volume V_2 rushes back through the hole and boxes itself into V_1 all by itself.

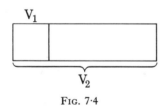

V_1

V_2

FIG. 7·4

We can of course make it do so by appropriate means but the point is it does not occur naturally. Observation further indicates that if the gas is ideal and the region into which the expansion takes place is a true vacuum there is no change in temperature in the process, which then may be thought of as taking the gas at temperature T and volume V_1 and changing its state to one of the same temperature T and volume V_2.

We should like to calculate the change in entropy in this process in order to obtain $\Delta \log w_c$ in eq. $(7 \cdot 8 - 18)$. Now in the naturally occurring process, $\Delta Q = 0$ and hence we might conclude that there is no change in entropy. But this would be jumping to a wrong conclusion; we recall that (7·8–18) holds only for processes in which the various states passed through are all equilibrium states in which the distribution is canonical. This is certainly not true for the natural expansion just considered. However, the entropy is a state function and hence the change in entropy in the process of going from one equilibrium state to another is independent of the nature of the process. If we could find a process which takes the gas from state T, V_1 to state T, V_2 through a succession of equilibrium states and could calculate ΔQ for such a process, we would then have a way of obtaining the change in entropy and consequently $\Delta \log w_c$. There is such a way: we need only imagine the wall replaced by a piston which slides freely in the vessel and allow the difference in pressure inside the gas at volume V_1 to push the piston along until the volume becomes V_2. In order that the gas shall remain in equilibrium during the expansion it is necessary that it proceed very slowly, in fact ideally with infinite slowness: we must not permit the piston to accelerate, for then the result would be too much like the natural expansion over which we have no theoretical control. This very slow motion of the piston corresponds to what is termed in thermodynamics a *reversible* process, since the slightest change in the pressure at any instant can turn the expansion into a compression and reverse the process. There is no such possibility in the natural expansion earlier referred to and hence we call the latter *irreversible*.

Now in the reversible expansion, the gas in expanding does work on the piston. In fact as in eq. (7·8–8) when the volume increases by dV with the pressure in the gas equal to p, the work $dW = pdV$. Since the temperature of the gas remains constant, $dE = 0$ and in order to enable the gas to expand and do this work, heat $dQ = pdV$ must be provided. If we can calculate the work, we obviously have also obtained the heat. Now

$$\Delta W = \int_{V_1}^{V_2} pdV. \qquad (7\cdot8\text{--}19)$$

But if the gas is ideal, the equation of state is

$$pV = RT \qquad (7\cdot8\text{--}20)$$

and therefore

$$\Delta Q = \Delta W = RT \int_{V_1}^{V_2} \frac{dV}{V} = RT \log \frac{V_2}{V_1}. \qquad (7\cdot8\text{--}21)$$

Hence

$$\log w_c = N \log \frac{V_2}{V_1}, \qquad (7\cdot8\text{--}22)$$

since $R = Nk$, where N is the number of gas molecules.   The quantity z in eq. (7·8–17) then becomes

$$z = e^{N \log \frac{V_2}{V_1}} .$$ (7·8–23)

Let us suppose that we are dealing with 1 mole of gas so that $N =$ Avogadro's number $= 6.03 \times 10^{23}$.   Further suppose, for example, that $V_2 = 2V_1$.   Then

$$z = e^{6.03 \times 10^{23} \log 2},$$ (7·8–24)

which is a monstrously large number compared with unity.   It measures the extent to which the probability of the final state is greater than the initial state and hence provides a measure of the irreversibility of the natural process by which the gas moves from the one state to the other. Increase in probability is definitely associated with gain in entropy as well as the direction in which the system changes its state.

It is of course important to note that by making the volume change from V_1 to V_2 appropriately small we can make z correspondingly small and hence come out with a small probability for the change. Very small changes are thus increasingly difficult to predict with any assurance.   Fortunately in the types of changes contemplated in most of thermodynamics such embarrassments rarely occur.

The discussion in this section has indicated how the use of statistical reasoning can lead to a logical basis for thermodynamics and establish the principles of this subject as veritable laws.   The deductions from these laws constitute the appropriate subject matter for texts in thermodynamics.   We shall not go further into this subject matter here.   It has been our aim merely to indicate how readily one can proceed from the mechanics of systems of many particles to another branch of physics as sophisticated as thermodynamics.

PROBLEMS

1. A sphere of radius R contains an ideal gas.   Derive the expression for the virial due to the impact of the molecules on the surface of the sphere.

2. Compare the root mean square velocity of hydrogen molecules at temperature 300° K with that at liquid air temperature and at the temperature of the sun.   Carry out similar calculations for a number of other gases.   Indicate the reason why there is little or no hydrogen in the earth's atmosphere.

3. Determine the dependence of the mean free path of an ideal gas on the pressure and temperature.   Calculate the mean free path in hydrogen at 100° C and a pressure of 10^{-6} atmosphere.

4. The mass of an electron is 9×10^{-28} gram.   Assuming a gas composed entirely of electrons, calculate their root mean square velocity at $T = 300°$ K. Compare the pressure they would exert on the walls of a container with the

pressure that hydrogen molecules at this temperature would exert on the walls of an identical container, if the concentration of particles is the same in both cases.

5. Calculate the value of R, the gas constant per gram molecule. Use this to compute the specific heat at constant volume for a number of monatomic gases (e.g., rare gases).

6. Use experimental data from a handbook to test the validity of eq. (7·4–8) connecting the thermal conductivity, viscosity and specific heat of a gas. Discuss both monatomic and polyatomic gases.

7. Use eq. (7·4–6) to evaluate the coefficient of self-diffusion D of the monatomic rare gases. Investigate qualitatively the relation between D and the molecular weight and give a physical explanation of the result.

8. In a canonical distribution of N free particles, find the expression for the number of particles with kinetic energy in the range from E to $E + dE$. Evaluate this number for the special cases in which $E = \bar{E} = 3\Theta/2$ and $E = (1.01)\,\bar{E}$ respectively. Take the ratio of the two results and interpret it physically.

9. Derive eq. (7·6–11), i.e.,

$$\delta \log w = -\sum \delta N_j \cdot \log N_j$$

without the explicit use of Stirling's theorem. Thus from (7·6–9) obtain directly

$$\delta \log w = -\sum \delta \log N_j!$$

and write the right-hand side as

$$\sum \delta \log N_j! = \sum [\log (N_j + \delta N_j)! - \log N_j!].$$

Evaluate the latter by direct expansion.

10. Apply the general canonical distribution (7·7–10) to an ideal gas consisting of molecules of equal mass and having kinetic energy only. Thus

$$E_j = \tfrac{1}{2} m \, (v_{jx}^2 + v_{jy}^2 + v_{jz}^2),$$

where v_{jx}, v_{jy}, v_{jz} are the components of the molecular velocity in the j-th energy state. The molecules may be thought of as distributed in a kind of coordinate–velocity " space " in which the element of volume is

$$dx_j \, dy_j \, dz_j \, dv_{jx} \, dv_{jy} \, dv_{jz}.$$

Hence the a priori weight is

$$g_j = K \, dx_j \, dy_j \, dz_j \, dv_{jx} \, dv_{jy} \, dv_{jz},$$

where K is a constant. Show that if one integrates over the physical volume V containing the molecules one can express (7·7–10) in the form

$$dN = C \, N \, E^{-m(v_x^2 + v_y^2 + v_z^2)/2\Theta} dv_x \, dv_y \, dv_z,$$

where C is a constant involving the partition function Z. This is the famous Maxwell distribution, where dN/N is the average fractional number of molecules having velocities in the velocity interval $dv_x \, dv_y \, dv_z$ in the neighborhood of velocity components v_x, v_y, v_z.

More elaborate investigation by methods of statistical mechanics shows that for this case

$$C = \left(\frac{m}{2\pi\Theta}\right)^{3/2}.$$

Use the above result to show that the average molecular velocity components v_x, v_y, v_z are all zero, and discuss the physical meaning of this.

11. Show from the previous problem that the average number of molecules having speeds in the interval v, $v + dv$ (without regard to sign) is given by

$$dN = 4\pi v^2 N (m/2\pi \Theta)^{3/2} e^{-mv^2/2\Theta} dv.$$

Plot the coefficient of dv on the right as a function of v.   Calculate the average speed v as well as the root-mean-square speed $\sqrt{\overline{v^2}}$.

CHAPTER 8

MECHANICS OF A RIGID BODY

8·1. Definition of a Rigid Body. Types of Motion. An important special case of the motion of an aggregate of particles is that in which the forces of interaction of the particles are such that the distance between any two particles remains constant in time. The aggregate is then called a *rigid body*. Since the interaction forces in actual solids, though strong, are finite and all such solids can be deformed by sufficiently strong external forces, it is clear that there exist no really rigid bodies (see Chapter 11). Nevertheless, many bodies act sufficiently like the ideal rigid body just defined to make the study of their motions and general behavior a significant branch of mechanics.

The general theorems established in Chapter 6 may be applied at once to rigid bodies. But certain simplifications are apparent since the possible types of motion are restricted. If one point of the body is fixed with respect to the primary inertial system, the only possible motion is that in which every other point moves on the surface of a sphere whose radius is the invariable distance from the moving point to the fixed point. If two points of the body are fixed, the only possible motion is that in which all points save those on the line joining the two fixed points (extended, of course) move in circles about centers located on the line. Finally if three points of the body not in the same straight line are fixed, it is unable to move at all, and its position is completely determined.

Motion of a rigid body in which one point is kept fixed or two points are kept fixed is known as motion of *rotation*. This is simpler than the general motion of the body when no point is kept fixed. Nevertheless, there is a special case of the latter which is elementary, namely, that in which all points of the body move in the same direction at any instant with the same velocity and acceleration. This is called motion of *translation*. The reader is advised to take a meter stick or similar object and exemplify to himself these two types of motion. They are the most important types of motion of a rigid body, since it can be shown that every displacement of a rigid body can be considered as a combination of translations and rotations. Consider Fig. 8·1 and suppose the problem is to get the rigid body shown schematically there from position I to position III in which three points of the body which were originally at positions A, B, C now appear at A', B', C'.   First translate

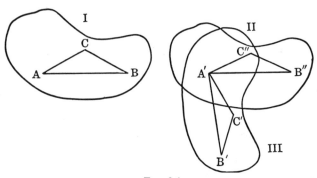

FIG. 8·1

the body so that A moves to A', its new desired position.   Then from the definition of translation, AB will become $A'B''$, where $A'B''$ is parallel to AB, and likewise $A'C''$ is parallel to AC, and $B''C''$ is parallel to BC.   Now holding A' fixed, rotate the body so that B'' coincides with B', the desired final position of B.   Without moving A' or B' it will now be possible to make C'' coincide with C', the desired final position of C, since the triangle $A'B'C'$ is congruent to the triangle $A'B''C''$.   Hence it has been possible to go from the original to the final position by a translation followed by a motion in which one point remains fixed, i.e. a rotation.

The translation of a rigid body will be given by the translation of any point in it, e.g., the center of mass (Sec. 6·1).   Hence the mechanics of particle motion will take care of this, and we need not consider it further.   In what follows we shall concentrate on rotation.

8·2. Rotation and Angular Velocity.   Let us consider an axis OA fixed in space (cf. Fig. 8·2) either in the rigid body or outside it. From the definition given in the preceding section, if the body rotates about OA, it means that any point of the body such as P moves in a circle with center B on the line OA (extended if necessary), where B is the normal projection of P on OA.   Let $\mathbf{r}$ be the position vector of P relative to O as origin.   Then the circle of motion of P lies in a plane perpendicular to the plane of

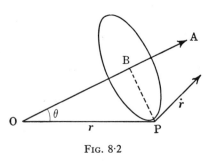

FIG. 8·2

r and the axis OA.   The velocity of P, namely $\dot{\mathbf{r}}$, always lies in the plane of the circle and hence is perpendicular to the plane AOP.   In time dt, P moves through the arc $|\dot{\mathbf{r}}|\, dt$.   But this equals the radius $BP (= r \sin \theta)$ multiplied by the angle through which BP moves.   Call the latter $d\phi$. We then have

$$|\dot{\mathbf{r}}|\, dt = r \sin \theta \, d\phi, \qquad (8\text{·}2\text{--}1)$$

or

$$|\dot{\mathbf{r}}| = r \sin \theta \, \frac{d\phi}{dt} = r\omega \sin \theta, \qquad (8\text{·}2\text{--}2)$$

where we have written ω for $d\phi/dt$.   If we revert to Sec. 6·4 (eq. 6·4–1) we see that it is reasonable to interpret $r\omega \sin \theta$ in eq. (8·2–2) as the magnitude of the cross product of the position vector **r** with a new vector of magnitude ω whose direction makes the angle θ with **r**, in such a way that $\dot{\mathbf{r}}$ is perpendicular to the plane of the new vector and **r**. If the new vector lies along OA and is directed from O to A, it will fulfill these requirements precisely.   We shall call it the instantaneous angular velocity of the rigid body (it is the same for every particle by virtue of the definition of rigid body) and represent it by **ω**.   The vector formulation corresponding to (8·2–2) then becomes

$$\dot{\mathbf{r}} = \boldsymbol{\omega} \times \mathbf{r}. \qquad (8\text{·}2\text{--}3)$$

The connection between the definition of angular velocity **ω** for a rigid body as given here and the definition of angular speed of a particle moving in a circle as given in Sec. 1·4 should be carefully noted.

It can be shown that **ω** as defined above possesses the usual properties of vectors (cf. Sec. 1·3).   In particular the resultant of two angular velocities passing through the same point is found by using the customary parallelogram rule.   Hence we can always resolve any angular velocity **ω** into rectangular components ω_x, ω_y, ω_z such that

$$\boldsymbol{\omega} = \mathbf{i}\omega_x + \mathbf{j}\omega_y + \mathbf{k}\omega_z. \qquad (8\text{·}2\text{--}4)$$

It is well to emphasize that the vector property of angular velocity is not shared by a finite rotation, even though the latter can be given a direction and a magnitude.   It is not therefore customary to consider a finite rotation as representable by a vector.

The time rate of change of angular velocity is termed the angular acceleration.   Thus

$$\boldsymbol{\alpha} = \frac{d\boldsymbol{\omega}}{dt}. \qquad (8\text{·}2\text{--}5)$$

8·3. Rotation about a Fixed Axis. The simplest case of rotation of a rigid body is that of rotation about an axis fixed in space. We suppose the axis chosen as the z axis of an appropriate system of coördinates and indicate the trace of the rigid body in the xy plane in Fig. 8·3. Consider the mass particle m_i in this plane with coördinates x_i, y_i (such that $r_i^2 = x_i^2 + y_i^2$). Suppose the force F_i acts on the particle in the xy plane and let its x and y components respectively be F_{ix} and F_{iy}. These produce a force moment or torque (cf. Sec. 6·4) about the z axis with magnitude equal to

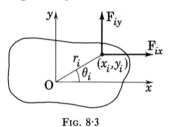

Fig. 8·3

$$L_i = x_i F_{iy} - y_i F_{ix} = m_i x_i \ddot{y}_i - m_i y_i \ddot{x}_i = \frac{d}{dt}[m_i(x_i \dot{y}_i - y_i \dot{x}_i)].$$

(8·3–1)

Now from the figure we have

$$x_i = r_i \cos \theta_i, \quad y_i = r_i \sin \theta_i,$$

(8·3–2)

whence

$$\dot{x}_i = -r_i \omega \sin \theta_i = -\omega y_i, \quad \dot{y}_i = r_i \omega \cos \theta_i = \omega x_i.$$ (8·3–3)

Note that $\omega = \dot{\theta}_i$ is independent of i because of the rigidity. If we substitute from (8·3–3) into (8·3–1) we get

$$L_i = \frac{d}{dt}[\omega m_i(x_i^2 + y_i^2)] = \frac{d}{dt}[\omega m_i r_i^2].$$

(8·3–4)

Let us now sum over *all* the particles of the body and arrive at the magnitude of total torque about the z axis. We have a right to sum because all the individual torques are vectors directed along the z axis. Thus

$$L = \sum L_i = \frac{d}{dt}[\omega \sum_i m_i r_i^2].$$

(8·3–5)

Note the quantity $\sum_i m_i r_i^2$, which is formed by multiplying the mass of each particle by the square of its distance to the z axis or axis of rotation. We call this the *moment of inertia* of the rigid body about the z axis and denote it here simply by I. Eq. (8·3–5) then becomes

$$L = \frac{d}{dt}(I\omega).$$

(8·3–6)

The formal analogy between this and Newton's second law (1·7–5) is very striking, and it is not surprising that $I\omega$ is known as the *angular momentum* about the fixed axis. As presented here for the special case of rotation about a fixed axis it is a scalar quantity. We shall generalize the definition somewhat later.

If the body is really rigid, I is independent of time and (8·3–6) becomes

$$L = I\alpha, \tag{8·3-7}$$

whose analogy with $\mathbf{F} = m\mathbf{a}$ is worthy of notice.

Still restricting ourselves to the fixed axis, let us calculate the work done by the forces $\mathbf{F}_i$ on the rigid body. If the particle at (x_i, y_i) makes a displacement with components dx_i and dy_i, respectively, the work done is clearly

$$dW_i = F_{ix}\,dx_i + F_{iy}\,dy_i. \tag{8·3-8}$$

But we have from (8·3–2)

$$\left. \begin{array}{l} dx_i = -r_i \sin\theta_i\,d\theta = -y_i\,d\theta, \\[2mm] dy_i = r_i \cos\theta_i\,d\theta = x_i\,d\theta. \end{array} \right\} \tag{8·3-9}$$

Here we replace $d\theta_i$ by $d\theta$ since, when the rigid body rotates about the fixed axis, all particles move through the same angle for a given displacement. Substituting into (8·3–8) yields

$$dW_i = (x_i F_{iy} - y_i F_{ix})\,d\theta = L_i\,d\theta. \tag{8·3-10}$$

Hence the work done on the whole body during a rotation from θ_0 to θ_1 becomes

$$W = \int_{\theta_0}^{\theta_1} \sum L_i\,d\theta = \int_{\theta_0}^{\theta_1} \frac{d}{dt}(I\omega)\,d\theta. \tag{8·3-11}$$

If I is constant, this results in

$$W = \int_{\omega_0}^{\omega_1} I\omega\,d\omega = \tfrac{1}{2}I\omega_1^2 - \tfrac{1}{2}I\omega_0^2, \tag{8·3-12}$$

where ω_0 is the initial angular velocity magnitude, i.e., that corresponding to the initial angle θ_0 and ω_1 is the final angular velocity component. The analogy between (8·3–12) and the work-kinetic energy theorem for the motion of a particle (eq. 1·11–17) is clear. We naturally refer to $I\omega^2/2$ as the kinetic energy of rotation, and eq. (8·3–12) is called the work-kinetic energy theorem for rotation. The units of $I\omega^2/2$ are the same as those of $mv^2/2$.

8·4. Moment of Inertia Calculations. Since the moment of inertia is such an important quantity in the motion of rigid bodies we ought to devote some attention to its calculation in special cases. As we have already seen, if we consider the body in question to be a collection of *discrete* particles of masses $m_1, m_2, \ldots, m_n$, rigidly connected, the moment of inertia about the given axis of rotation is

$$I = \sum_{i=1}^{n} m_i r_i^2, \qquad (8\cdot4\text{–}1)$$

where r_i is the perpendicular distance from the mass m_i to the axis. In most cases arising in practice, however, the body is a continuous distribution of mass and for the actual calculation of I the summation in (8·4–1) must be replaced by the corresponding integral extended over the whole body, viz.:

$$I = \int r^2 \, dm = \int \rho r^2 \, dV, \qquad (8\cdot4\text{–}2)$$

where dV is an appropriately chosen volume element, ρ is the value of the density of the substance composing the body at the element, and r is the perpendicular distance from the element to the axis. The determination of I then reduces to the mathematical problem of evaluating a definite volume integral. The ease with which this is accomplished in a given case depends largely on the appropriate choice of dm or dV.

Let us take first a very simple illustration. Find the moment of inertia of a *homogeneous* solid rod of constant linear density ρ_l (grams/cm, say) and of length l about an axis perpendicular to the rod through one end (Fig. 8·4). In the figure, OL represents the rod and

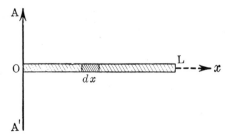

FIG. 8·4

AOA' the axis. We choose the x axis of a rectangular system along OL extended with the origin at O. The mass element here is clearly

$$dm = \rho_l \, dx,$$

and hence

$$I = \int_0^l \rho_l x^2 \, dx = m_l \frac{l^2}{3}, \qquad (8\cdot4\text{–}3)$$

where $\rho_l \, l$ has been replaced by m_l, the mass of the rod.

There is a simple but important interpretation of the result embodied in (8·4–3). We note at once that the behavior of the rod, in so far as its rotation about the axis AOA' is concerned, may be studied by replacing the rod by a *particle* of mass $m_l/3$ whose distance from the axis is l, or by a particle of mass m_l whose distance from the axis is $l/\sqrt{3}$. Ordinarily greater significance is attributed to the latter type of replacement. The distance $l/\sqrt{3}$ is called the *radius of gyration* of the rod with respect to the axis of rotation. We may immediately generalize this definition by setting in all cases

$$k = \sqrt{\frac{I}{m}}, \qquad (8·4–4)$$

where k is the radius of gyration of the rigid body of mass m, whose moment of inertia about the axis in question is I.

Coming back to the solid rod, if we were to calculate the value of I about a perpendicular axis through the center of the rod (i.e., in this case the center of mass), we should have

$$I_C = \int_{-l/2}^{+l/2} \rho_l x^2 \, dx = m_l \frac{l^2}{12}. \qquad (8·4–5)$$

It is seen that we have the relation

$$I = I_C + m_l \left(\frac{l}{2}\right)^2. \qquad (8·4–6)$$

This is a special case of a general law called the theorem of parallel axes. We may state it as follows: *The moment of inertia of a rigid body about any axis is equal to the moment of inertia about a parallel axis through the center of mass plus the product of the mass of the body and the square of the perpendicular distance between the two axes.* Let us prove the theorem for the general case. Consulting Fig. 8·5, we shall take the z axis as the axis of rotation and let C with coördinates $\bar{x}, \bar{y}, \bar{z}$ be the center of mass. Treating the body as a set of mass particles, let us suppose that a particle m_i

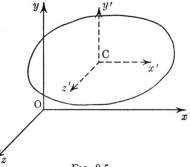

FIG. 8·5

with coördinates x_i, y_i, z_i in the original system has the coördinates x_i', y_i', z_i' when referred to a set of parallel axes through C. Now since $\bar{x}' = \bar{y}' = \bar{z}' = 0$, we must have

$$\sum m_i x_i' = \sum m_i y_i' = \sum m_i z_i' = 0, \qquad (8·4–7)$$

from the definition of center of mass (Sec. 6·1). By definition the moment of inertia about the z axis is

$$I = \sum m_i(x_i^2 + y_i^2). \qquad (8\cdot4\text{–}8)$$

But

$$x_i = x_i' + \bar{x}, \quad y_i = y_i' + \bar{y},$$

and hence

$$I = \sum m_i(x_i'^2 + y_i'^2) + (\bar{x}^2 + \bar{y}^2)\sum m_i + 2\bar{x}\sum m_i x_i' + 2\bar{y}\sum m_i y_i'. \qquad (8\cdot4\text{–}9)$$

Now the last two terms in (8·4–9) vanish by virtue of (8·4–7). Then $\sum m_i$ is the total mass of the body, while $\bar{x}^2 + \bar{y}^2 = l^2$, where l is the perpendicular distance between the z and z' axes. $\sum m_i(x_i'^2 + y_i'^2)$ is the moment of inertia with respect to the z' axis (i.e., axis through center of mass parallel to the z axis). Hence in general

$$I = I_C + ml^2. \qquad (8\cdot4\text{–}10)$$

To continue our brief discussion of the calculation of I in special cases, let us compute the moment of inertia of a homogeneous elliptical disk of mass m, superficial density σ, and semi-axes a and b, about the two axes respectively (Fig. 8·6).

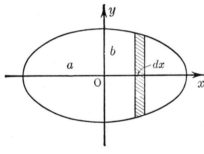

FIG. 8·6

If the x and y axes are chosen along the major and minor axes respectively the equation of the ellipse is

$$\frac{x^2}{a^2} + \frac{y^2}{b^2} = 1. \qquad (8\cdot4\text{–}11)$$

First let us calculate I about the minor axis. Taking a strip of width dx at distance x from the origin, we find its mass is $2\sigma y\,dx$ and its moment of inertia about the y axis

$$2\sigma y x^2\,dx.$$

Hence the total moment for the whole disk is, because of symmetry,

$$I_y = 4\sigma \int_0^a x^2 y\,dx = \frac{4\sigma b}{a} \int_0^a x^2\sqrt{a^2 - x^2}\,dx, \qquad (8\cdot4\text{–}12)$$

utilizing eq. (8·4–11). From Peirce's tables (No. 145) the integration is readily carried out, yielding

$$I_y = \pi\sigma b\frac{a^3}{4} = m\frac{a^2}{4}, \qquad (8\cdot4\text{–}13)$$

where we have placed $m = \sigma\pi ab$, the area of the ellipse being πab. Similarly the moment of inertia about the major axis is

$$I_x = m\frac{b^2}{4}. \qquad (8\text{·}4\text{--}14)$$

As a final illustration let us take a solid body, say a sphere of radius a and calculate the moment of inertia about a diameter. The equation of the sphere with center at the origin is $x^2 + y^2 + z^2 = a^2$. Consider the octant shown in Fig. 8·7 and cut out the slice of thickness dx at distance x from the yz plane. If now we can find the moment of inertia of this slice or rather the whole circular disk of which this is one quadrant, about the x axis (i.e., perpendicular axis through the center), we can calculate the total moment by integration with respect to x with limits $-a$ and $+a$.

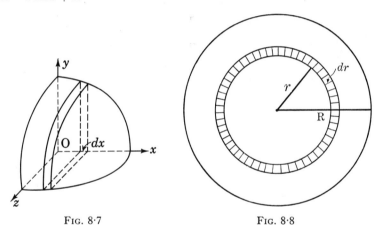

FIG. 8·7   FIG. 8·8

Let us consider then the case of the circular disk of radius R and calculate I about the perpendicular axis through the center. As mass element (Fig. 8·8) take the ring of radius r and thickness dr. The superficial density being σ, we have

$$I = 2\pi\sigma \int_0^R r^3 \, dr = 2\pi\sigma \frac{R^4}{4} = \tfrac{1}{2}mR^2, \qquad (8\text{·}4\text{--}15)$$

if m is here the mass of the disk.

We now utilize the foregoing result in the problem of the sphere. The radius of the disk in question is $\sqrt{a^2 - x^2}$ and its mass is $\rho dx \cdot \pi(a^2 - x^2)$, so that the moment about the x axis is from (8·4–15)

$$\tfrac{1}{2}\cdot\pi\rho(a^2 - x^2)^2 \, dx.$$

MOMENT OF INERTIA OF VARIOUS BODIES

m = mass of the body

Body	Axis	Moment of Inertia
Thin rectangular sheet of sides a and b	Through the center parallel to b	$m \dfrac{a^2}{12}$
Thin rectangular sheet of sides a and b	Through the center perpendicular to the sheet	$m \dfrac{a^2 + b^2}{12}$
Thin circular sheet of radius r	Normal to the plate through the center	$m \dfrac{r^2}{2}$
Thin circular sheet of radius r	Along any diameter	$m \dfrac{r^2}{4}$
Thin circular ring. Radii r_1 and r_2	Through center normal to plane of ring	$m \dfrac{r_1^2 + r_2^2}{2}$
Thin circular ring. Radii r_1 and r_2	A diameter	$m \dfrac{r_1^2 + r_2^2}{4}$
Spherical shell, very thin, mean radius, r	A diameter	$m \dfrac{2r^2}{3}$
Thin cylindrical shell, radius r, length l	Longitudinal axis	mr^2
Right circular cylinder of radius r, length l	Longitudinal axis	$m \dfrac{r^2}{2}$
Right cone, altitude h, radius of base r	Axis of the figure	$m \dfrac{3}{10} r^2$
Spheroid of revolution, equatorial radius r	Polar axis	$m \dfrac{2r^2}{5}$
Ellipsoid, axes $2a$, $2b$, $2c$	Axis $2a$	$m \dfrac{(b^2 + c^2)}{5}$
Uniform thin rod	Normal to the length, at one end	$m \dfrac{l^2}{3}$
Uniform thin rod	Normal to the length, at the center	$m \dfrac{l^2}{12}$
Rectangular prism, dimensions $2a$, $2b$, $2c$	Axis $2a$	$m \dfrac{(b^2 + c^2)}{3}$
Sphere, radius r	A diameter	$m \dfrac{2}{5} r^2$
Rectangular parallelepiped, edges a, b, and c	Through center perpendicular to face ab (parallel to edge c)	$m \dfrac{a^2 + b^2}{12}$
Right circular cylinder of radius r, length l	Through center perpendicular to the axis of the figure	$m \left(\dfrac{r^2}{4} + \dfrac{l^2}{12} \right)$
Spherical shell, external radius r_1, internal radius r_2	A diameter	$m \dfrac{2}{5} \dfrac{(r_1^5 - r_2^5)}{(r_1^3 - r_2^3)}$
Hollow circular cylinder, length l, external radius r_1, internal radius r_2	Longitudinal axis	$m \dfrac{(r_1^2 + r_2^2)}{2}$
Hollow circular cylinder, length l, radii r_1 and r_2	Transverse diameter	$m \left[\dfrac{r_1^2 + r_2^2}{4} + \dfrac{l^2}{12} \right]$
Hollow circular cylinder, length l, very thin, mean radius r	Transverse diameter	$m \left(\dfrac{r^2}{2} + \dfrac{l^2}{12} \right)$

Hence the total moment is

$$I = \pi\rho \int_0^a (a^2 - x^2)^2 \, dx$$

$$= \pi\rho \frac{8a^5}{15} .$$ (8·4–16)

Now the mass of the sphere is

$$m = \tfrac{4}{3}\pi a^3\rho,$$

and hence we may write

$$I = \tfrac{2}{5}ma^2.$$ (8·4–17)

The table on page 206 includes the values of the moment of inertia for a number of special cases which are likely to prove useful to the student.

8·5. The Physical Pendulum. An interesting practical illustration of the motion of a rigid body about a fixed axis is provided by the oscillations due to gravity of a body suspended from a fixed horizontal axis. This is the so-called physical or compound pendulum (Fig. 8·9). In order to apply the analysis of Sec. 8·3 to this problem, it is necessary to calculate the total torque about the axis of suspension through O. In Sec. 6·1 we learned that the center of mass of a collection of particles is the point which moves as if all the mass were concentrated there and as if all the external forces acted there. In the present problem the external force acting is the force of gravity on every particle of the body. To think of all these forces acting at the center of mass is to suppose that the whole weight of the body mg acts at the center of mass. This enables us at once to calculate the resultant torque about O. Assume that the center of mass (cf. Sec. 8·8 for calculations of the position of the center of mass of continuous aggregates) is at C, distant l from the axis of suspension.

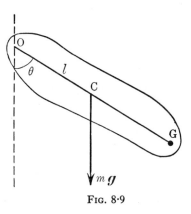

FIG. 8·9

The resultant torque about the axis for any displacement θ has therefore the magnitude

$$L = mgl \sin \theta.$$ (8·5–1)

If we denote the radius of gyration about the center of mass by k, the moment of inertia about the axis of suspension by the parallel axis theorem is $I = m(k^2 + l^2)$. Hence the fundamental eq. (8·3–6) takes the form

$$-mgl \sin \theta = m(k^2 + l^2)\ddot{\theta},$$

or

$$\ddot{\theta} = -\frac{gl \sin \theta}{k^2 + l^2}. \tag{8·5–2}$$

Now for small displacements $\sin \theta \doteq \theta$, and hence if we confine ourselves to such, we have

$$\ddot{\theta} = -\frac{gl\theta}{k^2 + l^2}. \tag{8·5–3}$$

We have met this equation before (cf. Sec. 2·3). It is indeed the equation of simple harmonic angular motion and the solution is

$$\theta = A \left.\begin{matrix} \sin \\ \cos \end{matrix}\right\} \left(\sqrt{\frac{gl}{k^2 + l^2}}\, t + B\right), \tag{8·5–4}$$

so that the frequency of the motion is

$$\nu = \frac{1}{2\pi} \sqrt{\frac{gl}{k^2 + l^2}}, \tag{8·5–5}$$

or expressed directly in terms of the moment of inertia I

$$\nu = \frac{1}{2\pi} \sqrt{\frac{mgl}{I}}. \tag{8·5–6}$$

The amplitude A is arbitrary within the limits of the assumption of small displacements. The arbitrary constant B is the initial phase. Both A and B must be determined by the initial conditions of the motion.

A special case of significance is that in which the whole mass of the body is concentrated at the point C, and the rest of the body is replaced by a theoretically massless cord of length l_1 connecting C to the point of suspension. Then $I = ml_1^2$ at once, and we have

$$\ddot{\theta} = -\frac{g \sin \theta}{l_1}, \tag{8·5–7}$$

which under the same approximation as before yields

$$\theta = A \left.\begin{matrix} \sin \\ \cos \end{matrix}\right\} \left(\sqrt{\frac{g}{l_1}}\, t + B\right), \tag{8·5–8}$$

where the frequency and period of the motion are respectively

$$\left.\begin{aligned} \nu &= \frac{1}{2\pi}\sqrt{\frac{g}{l_1}}, \\ P &= 2\pi\sqrt{\frac{l_1}{g}}. \end{aligned}\right\} \qquad (8\cdot5\text{-}9)$$

and

Such a pendulum is called a *simple pendulum*. From (8·5–5) and (8·5–9) we see that the period of the *physical* pendulum with moment of inertia I and distance from the center of mass to the point of suspension l, is equal to the period of a *simple* pendulum of length l_1, where

$$l_1 = \frac{I}{ml} = \frac{k^2 + l^2}{l}. \qquad (8\cdot5\text{-}10)$$

The length l_1 satisfying this condition is called the length of the equivalent simple pendulum. This means that if we extend the line OC in Fig. 8·9 to a point G on the other side of C such that $OG = l_1$, then a simple pendulum with length l_1 will have the same period as the actual physical pendulum. The point G has long been known as the *center of oscillation*. We note that since $k \neq 0$, G lies on the opposite side of C from O. Moreover, suppose we were to suspend the body by the point G; the new moment of inertia about the axis of suspension would be

$$\begin{aligned} I' &= mk^2 + m(l_1 - l)^2 \\ &= mk^2 + ml_1^2 + ml^2 - 2ml_1l. \end{aligned}$$

But since $ll_1 = k^2 + l^2$, the above reduces to

$$\begin{aligned} I' &= ml_1^2 - m(k^2 + l^2) \\ &= \frac{mk^2}{l^2}(k^2 + l^2), \end{aligned} \qquad (8\cdot5\text{-}11)$$

so that the frequency of the resulting motion is

$$\nu_1 = \frac{1}{2\pi}\sqrt{\frac{mg(l_1 - l)}{\dfrac{mk^2}{l^2}(k^2 + l^2)}} = \frac{1}{2\pi}\sqrt{\frac{gl}{k^2 + l^2}}, \qquad (8\cdot5\text{-}12)$$

which, however, is precisely equal to ν from eq. (8·5–5); in other words the frequency is the same whether the body is suspended from axes passing through O or G, the *center of suspension* or *center of oscillation*. These points are thus interchangeable. It is not difficult to show that a blow transverse to the line OG at G transfers no momentum to the axis of suspension at O.   Hence G is also called the center of percussion.

To revert to eq. (8·5–10), if the frequency is given, the length of the equivalent simple pendulum is fixed and hence (8·5–10) is a quadratic equation in l.   Solving we have

$$l = \frac{l_1 \pm \sqrt{l_1^2 - 4k^2}}{2};\qquad(8\cdot5\text{–}13)$$

there are then two values of l corresponding to each frequency, viz., $l' = \dfrac{l_1 + \sqrt{l_1^2 - 4k^2}}{2}$ and $l'' = \dfrac{l_1 - \sqrt{l_1^2 - 4k^2}}{2}$.   Consequently for any body there are *two* possible distances from the center of mass such that suspension at points at these distances yields the *same* frequency. It is a fact of considerable importance that the period and frequency of the simple pendulum are *independent* of the *mass* of the pendulum bob and of the substance of which the latter is made.   This recalls a historical matter of some interest, namely the experiments of Newton using the pendulum to show that gravity gives the same acceleration to all rigid bodies independently of shape, constitution or mass.   We must remember, however, that in any actual experiment the observed frequency will be influenced by a number of factors not accounted for in the simple theory presented in the previous section.   Thus the air will provide a certain resistance to the motion (cf. Sec. 2·7).   Moreover, changes in temperature will affect l, and the finite size of the amplitude necessitates corrections to the simple assumption involved in $\sin \theta \doteq \theta$ (see Sec. 9·1).

One of the most interesting physical uses of the pendulum is the evaluation of g, the acceleration of gravity.   Consulting eq. (8·5–10) and combining it with (7·5–9) we have

$$k^2 + l^2 = \frac{lP^2 g}{4\pi^2},$$

whence

$$g = \frac{4\pi^2(k^2 + l^2)}{P^2 l},\qquad(8\cdot5\text{–}14)$$

in terms of experimentally observable quantities.   Of course the implication is that k^2 can be calculated from a geometrical knowledge of the body concerned.   Since this is often difficult to carry out exactly, it is perhaps better to use two different axes of suspension, corresponding to the two values of l, viz., l_A and l_B, with corresponding periods,

P_A and P_B respectively. Then in place of (8·5–14) we have the two equations

$$k^2 + l_A{}^2 = \frac{l_{Ag}P_A{}^2}{4\pi^2},$$

(8·5–15)

$$k^2 + l_B{}^2 = \frac{l_{Bg}P_B{}^2}{4\pi^2},$$

(8·5–16)

whence elimination of k gives finally

$$g = \frac{4\pi^2[l_A{}^2 - l_B{}^2]}{l_A P_A{}^2 - l_B P_B{}^2}.$$

(8·5–17)

A pendulum used in the above fashion is called a *reversible* pendulum. It was used by Kater in a careful determination of g.

8·6. Plane Motion of a Rigid Body. Next to rotation about a fixed axis the most simple case of motion of a rigid body is that in which all its particles move in planes parallel to a fixed plane. This will in general involve both translation and rotation. As a special case consider the rolling under gravity of a homogeneous right circular cylinder down a perfectly rough plane, on which no slipping can take place. The situation is schematically depicted in Fig. 8·10, which shows the cylinder of mass m and radius a in contact with the plane at A. The inclination of the plane to the horizontal is θ. The forces acting on the cylinder are the weight $m\mathbf{g}$ acting at the center of mass O, the reaction $\mathbf{R}$ of the plane acting normally to the plane at A, and the force of friction $\mathbf{F}$, acting up the plane if the cylinder rolls down.

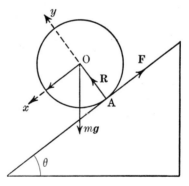

FIG. 8·10

When the cylinder rolls the center of mass O *translates*, while the particles composing the cylinder *rotate* about O. The motion therefore is a combination of translation and rotation which, as we have already seen (Sec. 8·1), is true in general for rigid bodies. We are therefore led to suppose that we can legitimately treat the two motions separately (cf. Secs. 6·3 and 8·7).

If we denote the displacement of the center of mass parallel to the plane by x, its equation of motion becomes

$$m\ddot{x} = mg \sin \theta - F.$$

(8·6–1)

Now the resultant torque about O is due wholly to $\mathbf{F}$, and we have therefore for the rotational motion about O,

$$Fa = I\alpha, \qquad (8 \cdot 6\text{--}2)$$

where I is the moment of inertia about the axis of the cylinder, and α is the angular acceleration about this axis.

Next we note the purely kinematic relation

$$\ddot{x} = a\alpha. \qquad (8 \cdot 6\text{--}3)$$

The combination of $(8 \cdot 6\text{--}1)$, $(8 \cdot 6\text{--}2)$, and $(8 \cdot 6\text{--}3)$ yields at once

$$\ddot{x} = \frac{mg \sin \theta}{m + I/a^2}. \qquad (8 \cdot 6\text{--}4)$$

But from Sec. $8 \cdot 4$ we know that the moment of inertia of a homogeneous right circular cylinder about its axis is $ma^2/2$. Hence the acceleration of the center of mass becomes

$$\ddot{x} = \tfrac{2}{3}g \sin \theta, \qquad (8 \cdot 6\text{--}5)$$

whose relation with the acceleration of a sliding object of an inclined plane should be carefully noted, as well as the fact that the dimensions or constitution of the cylinder nowhere appear in the formula.

It is interesting to observe that the problem of the rolling cylinder can also be solved by energy considerations. Conservation of energy dictates that the gain in kinetic energy of the rolling cylinder shall be equal to the loss in potential energy. Here we must, however, remember that the kinetic energy consists of two parts, i.e., kinetic energy of translation of the center of mass and kinetic energy of rotation about the center of mass. If, for simplicity, we suppose the cylinder starts from rest and rolls a distance x through a vertical drop $h = x \sin \theta$, the energy equation takes the form

$$\tfrac{1}{2}mv^2 + \tfrac{1}{2}I\omega^2 = mgx \sin \theta. \qquad (8 \cdot 6\text{--}6)$$

Once again we have the kinematic relation between v and ω, viz.,

$$v = \omega a. \qquad (8 \cdot 6\text{--}7)$$

Hence

$$v^2 = \frac{2mgx \sin \theta}{m + I/a^2} = 2x \cdot \tfrac{2}{3}g \sin \theta. \qquad (8 \cdot 6\text{--}8)$$

If we recall Sec. $2 \cdot 1$, it is clear that the constant acceleration of the center of mass is once more

$$\ddot{x} = \tfrac{2}{3}g \sin \theta.$$

8·7. General Equations of Motion of a Rigid Body. Having so far studied the nature of the motion of a rigid body and examined some special illustrations of a simple character, we now find it advisable to set up the equations of motion in general form. Actually these are included in the general equations for a collection of particles as treated in Chapter 6, but we shall repeat as much of the former analysis as seems necessary to give a complete account.

We shall agree that the translation of the rigid body is given by the motion of some point in it and take this as our origin. We are therefore here principally interested in the rotation of the body about this point. As we have seen in Sec. 6·4, the instantaneous moment of momentum about this origin of the j-th particle in the body is given by

$$\mathbf{r}_j \times m_j \dot{\mathbf{r}}_j.$$

But since the motion is that of a rigid body about the origin, we can at once replace $\dot{\mathbf{r}}_j$ by $\boldsymbol{\omega} \times \mathbf{r}_j$ from (8·2–3) and write for the total moment of momentum of the rigid body about the origin the vector

$$\mathbf{M} = \sum_{j=1}^{n} m_j \mathbf{r}_j \times (\boldsymbol{\omega} \times \mathbf{r}_j), \tag{8·7–1}$$

it being supposed that there are n particles in the body. The fundamental equation (6·4–10) still applies and hence we may write

$$\dot{\mathbf{M}} = \mathbf{L}, \tag{8·7–2}$$

which says that the time rate of change of the total moment of momentum, now to be renamed the *angular momentum* of the rigid body, about the chosen origin is equal to the resultant torque of all the forces acting on the body about the chosen origin. This is the fundamental equation of rotational motion of the rigid body.

Let us look a bit more carefully at $\mathbf{M}$. From (8·2–4) and the fact that $\mathbf{r}_j = \mathbf{i}x_j + \mathbf{j}y_j + \mathbf{k}z_j$, we can expand $\boldsymbol{\omega} \times \mathbf{r}_j$ and get (cf. 6·4–4)

$$\boldsymbol{\omega} \times \mathbf{r}_j = (\mathbf{i}\omega_x + \mathbf{j}\omega_y + \mathbf{k}\omega_z) \times (\mathbf{i}x_j + \mathbf{j}y_j + \mathbf{k}z_j)$$

$$= \mathbf{i}(\omega_y z_j - \omega_z y_j) + \mathbf{j}(\omega_z x_j - \omega_x z_j) + \mathbf{k}(\omega_x y_j - \omega_y x_j).$$

Therefore

$$\mathbf{r}_j \times (\boldsymbol{\omega} \times \mathbf{r}_j) = \mathbf{i}[y_j(\omega_x y_j - \omega_y x_j) - z_j(\omega_z x_j - \omega_x z_j)]$$

$$+ \mathbf{j}[z_j(\omega_y z_j - \omega_z y_j) - x_j(\omega_x y_j - \omega_y x_j)]$$

$$+ \mathbf{k}[x_j(\omega_z x_j - \omega_x z_j) - y_j(\omega_y z_j - \omega_z y_j)]. \tag{8·7–3}$$

This leads to the following expanded expression for the angular momentum

$$\mathbf{M} = \mathbf{i}[\omega_x \sum m_j(y_j^2 + z_j^2) - \omega_y \sum m_j x_j y_j - \omega_z \sum m_j x_j z_j]$$

$$+ \mathbf{j}[-\omega_x \sum m_j x_j y_j + \omega_y \sum m_j(x_j^2 + z_j^2) - \omega_z \sum m_j y_j z_j]$$

$$+ \mathbf{k}[-\omega_x \sum m_j x_j z_j - \omega_y \sum m_j y_j z_j + \omega_z \sum m_j(x_j^2 + y_j^2)]. \tag{8·7–4}$$

By the introduction of simplifying notation we may write this in the form

$$\mathbf{M} = \mathbf{i}(\omega_x I_{xx} - \omega_y I_{xy} - \omega_z I_{xz})$$
$$+ \mathbf{j}(-\omega_x I_{yx} + \omega_y I_{yy} - \omega_z I_{yz})$$
$$+ \mathbf{k}(-\omega_x I_{zx} - \omega_y I_{zy} + \omega_z I_{zz}), \tag{8.7-5}$$

where evidently I_{xx}, I_{yy}, I_{zz} from their makeup are the *moments of inertia* of the rigid body with respect to the x, y, z axes respectively. The quantities I_{xy}, I_{yz}, etc., are less familiar and we have not had to mention them in our earlier analysis. I_{xy} is termed the *product of inertia* with respect to the x and y axes, etc. Clearly we have $I_{xy} = I_{yx}$, etc.

Eq. (8.7-2) reduces to component equations of which the one corresponding to the x axis is

$$\dot{\omega}_x I_{xx} - \dot{\omega}_y I_{xy} - \dot{\omega}_z I_{xz} + \omega_x \dot{I}_{xx} - \omega_y \dot{I}_{xy} - \omega_z \dot{I}_{xz} = L_x, \tag{8.7-6}$$

where L_x is the component of the resultant torque about the x axis. Note that the moments and products of inertia being calculated with respect to axes fixed in space will in general change with the time. Hence the general component equations of rotational motion are complicated. Obviously if the motion of the rigid body is restricted to rotation about the fixed x axis so that $\omega_y = \omega_z = 0$ at all times, eq. (8.7-6) reduces to

$$\frac{d}{dt}(I_{xx}\omega_x) = L_x,$$

i.e., of the same form as (8.3-6).

We have already shown in Secs. 6.1 and 6.4 that the motion of a general collection of particles subject to arbitrary external and internal forces can be reduced to the motion of the center of mass, given by eq. (6.4-13) and the motion *relative to* the center of mass, given by eq. (6.4-14). This result holds, of course, for a rigid body as a special collection of particles. In the case of a rigid body, however, motion relative to the center of mass means rotational motion about the center of mass. Hence we can now state without further demonstration that the motion of a rigid body can be completely described by : (1), the translational motion of the center of mass, given by the equation

$$m\ddot{\mathbf{r}} = \mathbf{F}, \tag{8.7-7}$$

where $\mathbf{F}$ denotes the vector sum of all the forces applied to the body, m is the mass of the body, and $\bar{\mathbf{r}}$ the position vector of the center of mass, and (2), the rotational motion about the center of mass, given by

$$\dot{\mathbf{M}}_c = \mathbf{L}_c, \tag{8.7-8}$$

where $\mathbf{M}_c$ is the angular momentum measured with respect to the center of mass as origin, and $\mathbf{L}_c$ is the resultant torque due to the applied forces about the center of mass.   In other words we can apply (8·7–8) to the center of mass just as if it were *fixed*.   This may be called the principle of the independence of translational and rotational motions of a rigid body already illustrated in the treatment of plane motion in Sec. 8·6.   It focusses attention on the great importance of the center of mass of a rigid body and hence makes the determination of the latter point of considerable significance.   Before we go on to discuss examples of eq. (8·7–8) it will therefore be well to give some attention to the center of mass.

8·8. Center of Mass of a Rigid Body.   The center of mass of a discrete collection of particles has already been defined as the point with the position vector [eq. (6·1–7)]

$$\bar{\mathbf{r}} = \frac{\sum m_i \mathbf{r}_i}{m}, \qquad (8\text{·}8\text{–}1)$$

where $\mathbf{r}_i$ is the position vector of the i-th particle, and m_i is its mass. The mass of the whole collection is $m = \sum m_i$.   We have discussed an illustration of (8·8–1) in the two-particle problem of Sec. 6·3.   Most rigid bodies, however, have to be considered as essentially *continuous* collections of particles and therefore (8·8–1) must be generalized as far as its mathematical calculation is concerned, though its physical meaning remains the same.   From integral calculus we know that we can replace the limit of a sum such as that in (8·8–1) as the number of particles grows very large and the mass of each grows very small by a definite integral taken over the whole body.   Thus, to go over to the rectangular coördinates, we must now replace (8·8–1) by

$$\bar{x} = \int x \, dm \Big/ \int dm,$$

$$\bar{y} = \int y \, dm \Big/ \int dm, \qquad (8\text{·}8\text{–}2)$$

$$\bar{z} = \int z \, dm \Big/ \int dm.$$

Here dm denotes the mass of the element of volume of the body whose rectangular coördinates are x, y, z.   Though no limits are indicated, it is understood that the integration is to be conducted over the whole volume of the body.   We denote the mass m by $\int dm$.

A simple illustration of (8·8–2) is provided by a homogeneous infinitely thin rod of line density ρ, extending along the x axis a distance l from the origin. We at once have $\bar{y} = \bar{z} = 0$, whereas x is calculated by taking $dm = \rho\, dx$, where dx is the element of length at distance x from the origin. We then have

$$\bar{x} = \int_0^l \rho x\, dx \Big/ \int_0^l \rho\, dx = l/2. \qquad (8\cdot8\text{–}3)$$

The center of mass is at the geometrical center of the rod, which is indeed intuitively clear from symmetry considerations.

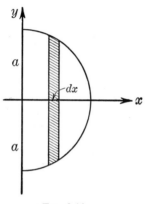

FIG. 8.11

We are often guided by symmetry in determining the center of mass of a rigid body without evaluating integrals. A simple example is a homogeneous sphere for which the center of mass is evidently at the center. We can make the general statement that the center of mass of any homogeneous rigid body lies at its geometrical center or center of symmetry.

As another example of the general formulas (8·8–2) let us calculate the center of mass of a semicircular, homogeneous flat plate of radius a. We take the axes as in Fig. 8·11. From symmetry the center of mass must lie on the x axis, i.e., as we have chosen our axes

$$\bar{y} = 0,$$

$$\bar{x} = \frac{\displaystyle\int x\, dm}{\displaystyle\int dm} \left.\right\} \qquad (8\cdot8\text{–}4)$$

Now $dm = \rho\, dA$, where dA is an area element and ρ is the superficial density which is constant here. Then $\bar{x}$ reduces to the center of area (or *centroid*, as it is often called), viz.,

$$\bar{x} = \frac{\displaystyle\int x\, dA}{A}, \qquad (8\cdot8\text{–}5)$$

where A is the area of the plate. The problem now is essentially mathematical in nature: the appropriate choice of the area element

dA and the carrying out of the integration. For example, if we choose as our element the strip of width dx as illustrated in the figure,

$$dA = 2\sqrt{a^2 - x^2}\, dx.$$

Therefore

$$\bar{x} = \frac{2 \int_0^a x\sqrt{a^2 - x^2}\, dx}{\pi a^2/2} = \frac{4a}{3\pi} . \tag{8·8-6}$$

For z we have, of course, by symmetry $h/2$, where h is the thickness of the plate.

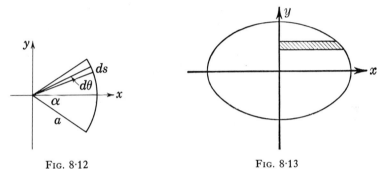

FIG. 8·12   FIG. 8·13

As a second illustration, let us consider the center of mass of a circular arc subtending the angle 2α at the center (see Fig. 8·12). If ds is the element of arc of the circle and ρ is the line density, then $dm = \rho\, ds$. From the figure $ds = a\, d\theta$ and $x = a \cos \theta$. Hence

$$\bar{x} = \frac{\int_{-\alpha}^{+\alpha} a \cos \theta \cdot a\, d\theta}{\int_{-\alpha}^{+\alpha} a\, d\theta} = a\, \frac{\sin \alpha}{\alpha} . \tag{8·8-7}$$

For $\alpha = \pi/2$, this yields $\bar{x} = 2a/\pi$. From symmetry, of course $\bar{y} = 0$.

Cases where the body considered is non-homogeneous (i.e., of variable density) are sometimes important. For example, let us find the center of mass of the quadrant of an elliptical plate of constant thickness enclosed by the two semi-axes (Fig. 8·13). The density is supposed to vary in such a way that at any point it is directly proportional to the distance from the point to the major axis. Symbolically, $\rho = ky$. Hence

$$\bar{x} = \frac{\int \rho x\, dA}{\int \rho\, dA} = \frac{\int yx\, dA}{\int y\, dA} , \tag{8·8-8}$$

while

$$\bar{y} = \frac{\int y^2 \, dA}{\int y \, dA} \, . \tag{8·8–9}$$

To get $\bar{y}$, choose $dA = x \, dy = a/b \cdot \sqrt{b^2 - y^2} \, dy$ (the equation of the ellipse being $x^2/a^2 + y^2/b^2 = 1$). Then

$$\bar{y} = \frac{\dfrac{a}{b} \displaystyle\int_0^b y^2 \sqrt{b^2 - y^2} \, dy}{\dfrac{a}{b} \displaystyle\int_0^b y \sqrt{b^2 - y^2} \, dy} = \frac{3\pi b}{16} \, . \tag{8·8–10}$$

To get $\bar{x}$, let us note that the center of mass of each of the horizontal strips, one of which is indicated in the figure, is $x/2$ which equals $a/2b \cdot \sqrt{b^2 - y^2}$. Thus the whole mass of each strip $(ky \cdot dy \cdot a/b \cdot \sqrt{b^2 - y^2})$ may be considered to be located at the distance $a/2b \cdot \sqrt{b^2 - y^2}$ from the y axis. Therefore

$$\bar{x} = \frac{\dfrac{1}{2} \displaystyle\int_0^b \dfrac{a}{b} \cdot \sqrt{b^2 - y^2} \cdot \dfrac{a}{b} \cdot \sqrt{b^2 - y^2} \cdot y \, dy}{\dfrac{a}{b} \cdot \dfrac{1}{3} \cdot b^3}$$

$$= \frac{3}{8} a. \tag{8·8–11}$$

The center of mass of the quadrant is then the point $\left(\dfrac{3}{8} a, \dfrac{3\pi}{16} b\right)$.

So far we have confined our attention to the center of mass of plane plates or lamina. It remains to consider surfaces in general and volumes. The center of mass of any surface will be given by

$$\bar{x} = \frac{\int \sigma x \, dS}{\int \sigma \, dS}, \quad \bar{y} = \frac{\int \sigma y \, dS}{\int \sigma \, dS}, \quad \bar{z} = \frac{\int \sigma z \, dS}{\int \sigma \, dS}, \tag{8·8–12}$$

where dS is the element of area and σ is the mass per unit area (surface density). Perhaps the most important case of this kind is that of a surface of revolution. Let the x axis be the axis of symmetry. Then $\bar{y} = \bar{z} = 0$, and we have for the area element

$$dS = 2\pi y \sqrt{1 + \left(\frac{dy}{dx}\right)^2} \, dx, \tag{8·8–13}$$

where $y = f(x)$ is the equation of the generating curve. We can use this formula to obtain, for example, the center of mass of the curved surface of a right circular cone. Letting the vertex be at the origin we have

$$y = f(x) = bx, \tag{8·8–14}$$

where b is the slope of the generator. For constant surface density there results

$$\bar{x} = \frac{\displaystyle\int 2\pi yx \sqrt{1 + \left(\frac{dy}{dx}\right)^2}\, dx}{\displaystyle\int 2\pi y \sqrt{1 + \left(\frac{dy}{dx}\right)^2}\, dx}, \tag{8·8–15}$$

from which on substitution we obtain

$$\bar{x} = \frac{\displaystyle\int_0^h x^2\sqrt{1 + b^2}\, dx}{\displaystyle\int_0^h x\sqrt{1 + b^2}\, dx} = \frac{2}{3}h, \tag{8·8–16}$$

where h is the height of the cone.

For the *volume* enclosed by a surface we have

$$\bar{x} = \frac{\displaystyle\int \rho x\, dV}{\displaystyle\int \rho\, dV}, \quad \text{etc.,} \tag{8·8–17}$$

where ρ is the volume density and dV the volume element. Thus for the special case of the volume of the right circular cone above considered,

$$dV = \pi y^2\, dx = \pi b^2 x^2\, dx, \tag{8·8–18}$$

and

$$\bar{x} = \frac{\displaystyle\int_0^h \pi b^2 x^3\, dx}{\displaystyle\int_0^h \pi b^2 x^2\, dx} = \frac{3}{4}h. \tag{8·8–19}$$

The difference between (8·8–19) and (8·8–16) should be noted.

The more general problem of finding the center of mass for any solid introduces the general volume element. In rectangular coordinates

$$dV = dx\, dy\, dz, \tag{8·8–20}$$

and the calculation involves a triple integration. As a type problem let us consider the center of mass of that portion of the ellipsoid with equation

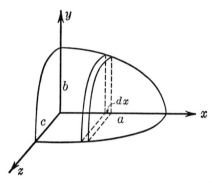

FIG. 8·14

$$\frac{x^2}{a^2} + \frac{y^2}{b^2} + \frac{z^2}{c^2} = 1, \quad (8\cdot8\text{--}21)$$

which is included in one octant, as is indicated in Fig. 8.14. We must choose the limits of integration of x, y, z. At x draw a thin slice dx parallel to the yz plane. Its volume is dx times one-quarter of the area of the ellipse cut out by a plane parallel to the yz plane at this point. Since the area of an ellipse is π times the product of the semi-major and semiminor axes, the volume in question is $\dfrac{\pi}{4}\, yz\, dx$, where, however,

$$y = b\sqrt{1 - \frac{x^2}{a^2}}, \quad z = c\sqrt{1 - \frac{x^2}{a^2}}. \quad (8\cdot8\text{--}22)$$

Therefore

$$\bar{x} = \frac{\displaystyle\int_0^a \frac{\pi}{4} bcx \left(1 - \frac{x^2}{a^2}\right) dx}{\displaystyle\int_0^a \frac{\pi bc}{4} \left(1 - \frac{x^2}{a^2}\right) dx}$$

$$= \frac{3}{8}\, a. \quad (8\cdot8\text{--}23)$$

Similarly

$$\bar{y} = \frac{3}{8}\, b, \quad \bar{z} = \frac{3}{8}\, c. \quad (8\cdot8\text{--}24)$$

The reader should carry out the problem for the case where the density is variable.

8·9. Equilibrium of a Rigid Body. Center of Gravity. In Chapter 5 we agreed to say that a particle is in equilibrium under the action of a set of forces if its acceleration with respect to the primary inertial system vanishes. We have now to decide what we shall mean by the equilibrium of a rigid body. Clearly if the center of mass of the body remains at rest or moves with constant velocity in a straight

line it will be appropriate to say that the body is in translational equilibrium. In this condition, however, it still might suffer rotational
acceleration *about* the center of mass and in this case we should not wish
to say it is in equilibrium with respect to rotation. The natural
definition of the latter is the absence of rotational acceleration about
any axis through the center of mass or indeed any other point; this will
ensue (from eq. (8·7–8)) if the resultant torque of the applied forces
about the center of mass vanishes. In this case it may readily be shown
that the torque will also vanish about any axis whatever, provided the
forces also satisfy the condition of translational equilibrium. There
are thus two conditions of equilibrium of a rigid body.[1]

A simple case of a rigid body in translational equilibrium but not
necessarily in rotational equilibrium is provided by a homogeneous
rod of length l supported by a fulcrum at its center of mass. This is
shown schematically in Fig. 8·15. We imagine that forces $\mathbf{F}_1$ and $\mathbf{F}_2$
act in the same plane at the left and right ends of the rod, respectively.

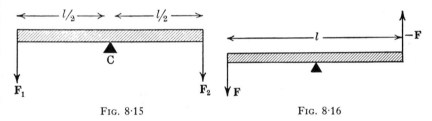

FIG. 8·15   FIG. 8·16

Clearly, as long as the fulcrum can exert an upward reaction force on
the rod equal in magnitude to $|\mathbf{F}_1 + \mathbf{F}_2|$ the center of mass will remain
at rest. However, the resultant torque about the center of mass has
the magnitude (in the clockwise direction)

$$F_2\,l/2 - F_1\,l/2,$$

and this will in general produce a rotational acceleration about C
(clockwise if $F_2 > F_1$ and counterclockwise if $F_2 < F_1$). To assure
rotational equilibrium it is necessary to have

$$F_1 = F_2. \tag{8·9–1}$$

[1] More careful consideration into which we shall not enter here (but cf. eq. (8·11–15)
and accompanying discussion) discloses that this definition has defects. Actually it
turns out that it *is* possible to have a rigid body rotate with angular acceleration about
a certain axis if the resultant torque is zero, provided it already has an angular velocity
to begin with. It is also possible to envisage a situation in which a resultant torque
will accompany constant angular velocity about some axis. To avoid these difficulties
we shall actually confine our association of the term rotational equilibrium with a rigid
body to the case of *rest*.

Note that if $\mathbf{F}_2$ is directed *upward* and $\mathbf{F}_1$ directed *downward*, (8·9–1) could not produce equilibrium unless both forces have zero magnitude. The particular case

$$\mathbf{F}_1 = -\mathbf{F}_2 \qquad (8\cdot9\text{–}2)$$

is interesting. Here $\mathbf{F}_1$ and $\mathbf{F}_2$ are said to form a *couple*. A rigid body acted on by a couple will be in translational equilibrium so far as the forces of the couple are concerned but cannot be in rotational equilibrium.

From Fig. 8·16 it is clear that the torque produced by the couple about the center of mass C (strictly the torque about an axis through C perpendicular to the plane of the forces) has the magnitude

$$Fl.$$

This is often termed the *moment* of the couple. The perpendicular distance (in this case l) between the lines of action of the forces of the couple is termed the *arm* of the couple. The reader may show that the moment of the couple has the same value about *any* axis perpendicular to the plane. It is also simple to prove that, so far as its rotational action on a rigid body is concerned, a couple may be replaced by any other couple with the same moment in the same plane.

Since a couple involves parallel forces in a plane, it will be well to consider the general problem of the composition of coplanar parallel forces acting on a rigid body. Consulting Fig. 8·17 let us assume that the coplanar forces $\mathbf{F}_1$, $\mathbf{F}_2$ and $\mathbf{F}_3$ act at points O_1, O_2 and O_3, respectively, of the body schematically indicated. Now the resultant of the forces is the vector $\mathbf{F}_1 + \mathbf{F}_2 + \mathbf{F}_3$ with magnitude $F_1 + F_2 + F_3$. Unfortunately the method of vector summation does not prescribe the line of action of the resultant and hence in this case we must settle this by arbitrary definition. Here it is appropriate to agree that the resultant force must produce the same *translational* and *rotational* effects as the forces individually.

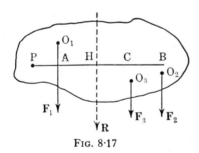

Fig. 8·17

The former effect is, of course, independent of the resultant line of action. The latter, however, demands that the moment or torque of the resultant about any axis perpendicular to the plane shall be equal to the sum of the moments of the individual forces about the same axis. Consider any point P and draw the line $PACB$ perpendicular to the three forces and intersecting their lines of action at A, B, C, respectively, with $PA = a$, $PB = b$ and $PC = c$. We now must suppose the resultant $\mathbf{R}$ to be drawn parallel to the individual forces and at distance $PH = h$ from P such that

$$h = \frac{aF_1 + bF_2 + cF_3}{F_1 + F_2 + F_3}. \qquad (8\cdot9\text{–}3)$$

This fixes the line of action of $\mathbf{R}$, although it does not determine its point of application.

The most important case of parallel, but not necessarily coplanar, forces acting on a rigid body is provided by the force of gravity. In Fig. 8·18 we imagine a rigid body referred to the set of axes indicated.

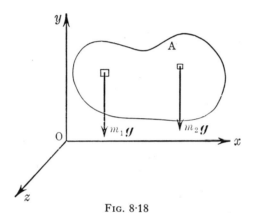

FIG. 8·18

We think of it as composed of the collection of mass particles m_1, m_2, m_3, ... possessing weights m_1g, m_2g, m_3g, ... which are all *parallel* forces in so far as we can consider $\mathbf{g}$ to have the same direction for all the particles of the body. If the body is *very* large, this is not strictly true, but is sufficiently so if the body is not too extended. Clearly,

$$\mathbf{W} = \sum m_i \mathbf{g} \qquad (8\cdot9\text{–}4)$$

is the weight of the body if the sum is extended over all its particles. Along what line now does the weight act? Let us denote the co-ordinates of the i-th particle by x_i, y_i, z_i. If we apply the criterion of the previous paragraph, it follows that the resultant $\mathbf{W}$ will lie in a plane parallel to the yz plane with perpendicular distance from the latter given by

$$\bar{x} = \sum m_i x_i g / mg, \qquad (8\cdot9\text{–}5)$$

where

$$m = \sum m_i \qquad (8\cdot9\text{–}6)$$

is the total mass of the body.   This results from the requirement that
the moment of $\mathbf{W}$ about the z axis must be the sum of the separate
moments about the z axis of all the individual particle weights.   Taking
moments in similar fashion about the x axis, we find that the resultant
must also lie in a plane parallel to the xy plane and distant from the
latter by

$$\bar{z} = \sum m_i z_i g / mg. \qquad (8\cdot9\text{--}7)$$

Finally if we turn the whole body around through an angle of 90°
about the z axis, so that the gravity forces act parallel to the x axis, we
find, taking moments once more about the z axis that the resultant must
lie in a plane parallel to the zx plane and at distance from it

$$\bar{y} = \sum m_i y_i g / mg. \qquad (8\cdot9\text{--}8)$$

The three planes thus determined meet in the point $(\bar{x}, \bar{y}, \bar{z})$, which
is thus the *center* of the rigid body as far as the action of the parallel
gravity forces is concerned.   It is the point through which the resultant
force of gravity always acts no matter how the body is placed and is
termed therefore the *center of gravity*.   The formulas (8·9–5), (8·9–7)
and (8·9–8) suffice to determine its position with respect to any set of
axes for a body made up of discrete parts.   For a continuous body,
however, the summations must be replaced by integrations.   In this
case we have for $\bar{x}, \bar{y}, \bar{z}$, precisely the equations (8·8–2) from which the
g, being constant, has disappeared.   What we have actually shown then
is that the center of gravity for a body of extent small compared with the
earth coincides approximately with the center of mass.   For a rigid body
of *large* extent the center of gravity can not be obtained by eqs. (8·8–2)
since the weight forces on the various portions of the body will then
no longer be parallel, since $\mathbf{g}$ is no longer to be considered constant
either in magnitude or direction over the whole body.   In this case the
center of gravity and the center of mass do *not* coincide.   The coincidence, however, will naturally be almost exactly true for any body used,
for example, for engineering purposes on the earth's surface.   Since
the mass concept is independent of gravitation in classical mechanics
and since the mass of any particle remains constant everywhere at all
times, the *center of mass* of a rigid body is a more fundamental quantity
than the center of gravity.

We may appropriately point out here that the center of gravity and
center of mass are but two illustrations of the general concept of center
of mean position with respect to any set of effects.   For example, in a
given country we can ascertain the center of *population* with coördinates
x_p and y_p, where

$$x_p = \frac{\sum N_i x_i}{N}, \quad y_p = \frac{\sum N_i y_i}{N},$$

where N_i is the number of people in an arbitrarily chosen area element of the country with coördinates x_i and y_i with respect to some chosen origin, and N is the total number of people in the country.   Other more physical illustrations are center of pressure (see Chapter 11), center of area and center of volume.   In each case the problem is one of finding the *mean position* with respect to some property of the body or some outside influence on the body.

An interesting and important illustration of the concept of center of gravity, particularly with reference to parallel forces, is to be found in the common balance used for the measurement of mass.   Consulting Fig. 8·19, imagine AB to represent schematically a rigid rod with center

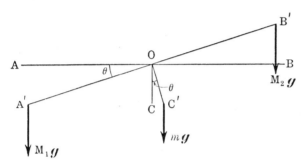

Fig. 8·19

of gravity at C, a distance $OC = a$ below the point O which is half-way between A and B, with $AO = OB = l$.   Let the mass of the rod be m. Assume that the rod is supported at O and that at A and B there are suspended masses M_1 and M_2 respectively.   Then the rod will assume for equilibrium a position $A'B'$ making the angle θ with AB.   If the rod is not too long the equilibrium may be considered as due to the *parallel* forces $M_1\mathbf{g}$, $m\mathbf{g}$ and $M_2\mathbf{g}$.   (*Strictly speaking* these forces are never exactly parallel nor is the value of $\mathbf{g}$ exactly the same for each mass.   But since the rod is small compared with the earth, the approximation is an extraodinarily good one for all practical purposes.)   Taking moments about O we have

$$g(M_1 - M_2)l \cos \theta - gma \sin \theta = 0$$

or

$$M_1 - M_2 = \frac{ma}{l} \tan \theta. \qquad (8\cdot9\text{–}9)$$

In this way the two masses M_1 and M_2 may be compared, and we have then a method of measuring mass which is of greater practical value than the ideal scheme on which the definition of mass used in this text has been based (Sec. 1·6). The reader will, however, easily convince himself that while the balance affords an accurate practical method of mass measurement, it does not provide a satisfactory method for *defining* mass.

There are several ways of using a balance for the attainment of maximum accuracy. The method of waiting for the attainment of the equilibrium indicated in eq. (8·9–9) is usually a slow process, for the balance will oscillate about the equilibrium position before coming to rest. A pointer is usually attached to the balance beam at O and is arranged to move over a fixed scale. Equality of the masses M_1 and M_2 is then assumed when the amplitudes of the pointer movements to the right and left of a point vertically under O are equal. This of course assumes that the arms (i.e., AO and OB) are really of the same length l. To avoid errors due to a possible difference here, Gauss suggested that the body whose mass is being measured be weighed first on one side and then on the other. If the two results are denoted by M' and M'', the reader may show that the actual mass is given by

$$M = \sqrt{M'M''}. \tag{8·9–10}$$

8·10. Equilibrium under Coplanar Forces. Illustrations. The conditions of equilibrium of a rigid body can be most readily visualized when the forces acting on it lie in a plane. To proceed with this let

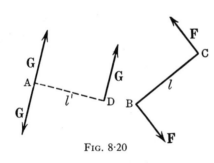

us note an important result about couples: a coplanar force and couple acting on a rigid body are equivalent in their action to a single force. Thus consider the couple consisting of the pair of forces **F** with the arm l, and the additional force **G** acting at A (cf. Fig. 8·20). Now the couple may be replaced by any other couple in the same plane with a moment equal in

Fig. 8·20

magnitude and direction without changing its effect on the body. Let us then replace the original couple by another with the extremities of its arm at A and D and with moment of magnitude

$$Gl' = Fl.$$

From the way the new but equivalent couple has been chosen, one of its forces is equal and opposite to **G** so that the two *cancel* each other in their action on the rigid body, and there remains effectively the force

G acting in a line parallel to the original force but at a perpendicular distance $l' = Fl/G$ from the line of application of the latter. This proves the result stated above.

We can now appreciate the important fact that if a *force* and a *couple* act in a single plane they can not produce *equilibrium*. We can also use the above proposition to prove at once that a given force **F** acting at a point A of a rigid body can be replaced by an *equal force* acting at any other point B of the body, together with a couple with moment equal to the moment of **F** about an axis through B perpendicular to the plane of the forces. Suppose now we have acting on a rigid body the coplanar forces $\mathbf{F}_1, \mathbf{F}_2, \ldots, \mathbf{F}_n$. We proceed in the usual way to find a resultant (cf. Sec. 1·3), i.e., we translate the line of action of $\mathbf{F}_2$ so that its origin is at the end of $\mathbf{F}_1$, and find the resultant of $\mathbf{F}_1$ and $\mathbf{F}_2$ which we may call $\mathbf{R}_{12}$. We then compound this with $\mathbf{F}_3$ to get $\mathbf{R}_{123}$, etc., until we finally have $\mathbf{R}_{123 \ldots n}$, the *sum* of all the forces, viz.,

$$\mathbf{R}_{12 \ldots n} = \mathbf{F}_1 + \mathbf{F}_2 + \cdots + \mathbf{F}_n. \qquad (8 \cdot 10\text{--}1)$$

However we must be careful to note the possibility that $\mathbf{R}_{12 \ldots n-1}$ and $\mathbf{F}_n$ may form a *couple*, and hence can not be reduced to a single force whose effect on the rigid body is the same as that of all the n forces acting together. Consider for example the special case of a rigid rod AB of length l, and assume that the coplanar forces $\mathbf{F}_1, \mathbf{F}_2$, and $\mathbf{F}_3$ act at A, B and C respectively, where, to be specific, $\theta_1 = \theta_2 = 45°$ and $AC = l/4$; also $F_1 \sin \theta_1 + F_2 \sin \theta_2 = F_3$ and $F_1 \cos \theta_1 = F_2 \cos \theta_2$, i.e., the forces are in equilibrium with respect to translations (cf. Fig. 8·21). That is,

$$\sum \mathbf{F} = 0. \qquad (8 \cdot 10\text{--}2)$$

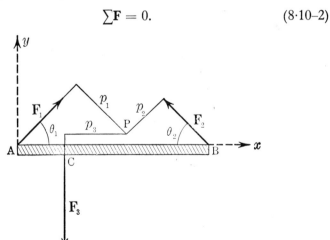

FIG. 8·21

Let us take any point P in the plane of the rod and forces, and calculate the moment of the forces or torque about a perpendicular axis through this point keeping θ_1 and θ_2 perfectly general. Let the perpendicular distances from P to the lines of action of the forces be p_1, p_2 and p_3 respectively. Then the resultant counterclockwise torque has the magnitude

$$-p_1 F_1 + p_2 F_2 + p_3 F_3. \tag{8·10-3}$$

Suppose the coördinates of P with respect to A as origin are x_1, y_1, taking the x axis along the rod. The equation of the line of action of $\mathbf{F}_1$ is

$$y = x \tan \theta_1. \tag{8·10-4}$$

That of the line of action of $\mathbf{F}_2$ is

$$y = -(x - l) \tan \theta_2, \tag{8·10-5}$$

and finally that of the line of action of $\mathbf{F}_3$ is here equivalent to

$$x = \frac{l}{4}. \tag{8·10-6}$$

Now the perpendicular distance from the point (x_1, y_1) to the line whose equation is

$$Ax + By + C = 0, \tag{8·10-7}$$

is from analytic geometry given by

$$p = \frac{Ax_1 + By_1 + C}{\sqrt{A^2 + B^2}}. \tag{8·10-8}$$

On substitution we finally have in our special case

$$\left.\begin{aligned} p_1 &= \frac{y_1 - x_1 \tan \theta_1}{\sec \theta_1}, \\ p_2 &= \frac{x_1 \tan \theta_2 + y_1 - l \tan \theta_2}{\sec \theta_2}, \\ p_3 &= -x_1 + \frac{l}{4}. \end{aligned}\right\} \tag{8·10-9}$$

The expression for the resultant moment then becomes

$$-p_1 F_1 + p_2 F_2 + p_3 F_3 = F_3 \frac{l}{4} - F_2 l \sin \theta_2, \tag{8·10-10}$$

i.e., a constant independent of the position of P. Moreover it is different from zero unless

$$F_3 = 4F_2 \sin \theta_2, \tag{8·10-11}$$

which in turn is incompatible with the assumed relation (8·10–2), unless we have the relation between the angles

$$3 \tan \theta_2 = \tan \theta_1. \qquad (8\cdot10\text{–}12)$$

The latter is the condition that, in addition to translational equilibrium, *rotational* equilibrium shall also be maintained.   In general, however, as in the present case, this condition will not be satisfied and there will be a resultant moment so that the three forces will be equivalent to a *couple* with this moment.   The arm of this couple may be chosen anywhere in the plane of the forces.

To summarize: If we have a system of forces in a plane they may either have a single force as a resultant or reduce to a *couple*.   Suppose now that the forces actually have a resultant.   Consulting Fig. 8·22, where the three parallel forces $\mathbf{F}_1$, $\mathbf{F}_2$ and $\mathbf{F}_3$ are represented as acting on a rigid body at the three points A, B and C respectively, we proceed to find the resultant $\mathbf{R}$ passing through the line PP'.   Now it is some-

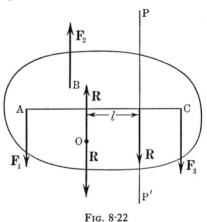

FIG. 8·22

times convenient to consider this resultant $\mathbf{R}$ as acting at some other point, such as O in the figure.   In order to do this we must, however, introduce at O another force $\mathbf{R}$ equal in magnitude and opposite in direction.   This will then not alter the situation.   But the new force will form with the original force a couple of moment $= Rl$ in magnitude, where l is the perpendicular distance from O to PP'.   Hence we have replaced the single resultant force by a force of equal magnitude acting at the point O *and* a couple of moment Rl, which in the example used is clockwise. By simple analysis it can be shown that the moment Rl is the sum of the moments of the original forces $\mathbf{F}_1$, $\mathbf{F}_2$ and $\mathbf{F}_3$ about the point O.   Hence the system reduces to the force $\mathbf{R}$ and couple of moment $\mathbf{M}$ where

$$\mathbf{R} = \sum \mathbf{F}_i,$$

and

$$M = \sum F_i l_i, \qquad (8\cdot10\text{–}13)$$

l_i being the perpendicular distance from the line of action of the i-th force to O.   The reader should carry out the analysis proving the similar result for a system of coplanar, *non*-parallel forces.

Finally it can be shown[1] that any system of forces (not necessarily parallel or coplanar) acting on a rigid body can be replaced by a force acting at any particular chosen point and a couple.

It can further be proved that any system of forces acting on a rigid body can be replaced by a force and a couple whose axis is parallel to the line of action of the force.

It being now clear that any system of forces acting on a rigid body can be replaced by a single force acting at any arbitrarily chosen point and a couple, under what conditions will the body be in equilibrium? We have already noted that a single non-vanishing force and a couple in the same plane can not produce equilibrium. The same result follows even if the force and the couple are not coplanar. For we may always transfer the couple in its plane so that one of its forces, say **F**, intersects the line of action of the given force **R**. The resultant of the two forces **F** and **R** can not equilibrate the other force of the couple, and hence the general statement follows. It therefore results that for the rigid body to be in equilibrium the single force must be equal to zero and the moment of the couple must likewise vanish. If the former (i.e., the force) is denoted by **R** and the latter (i.e., the moment of the couple) by **L**, the conditions of equilibrium may be written in the form

$$\mathbf{R} = 0, \qquad (8\cdot10\text{--}14)$$

$$\mathbf{L} = 0. \qquad (8\cdot10\text{--}15)$$

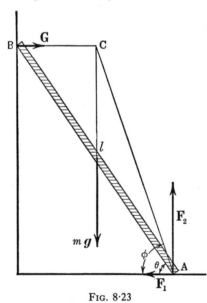

FIG. 8·23

As an illustration of the application of the principles of equilibrium to a rigid body, consider the simple case of a ladder *AB* resting with one end against a smooth wall, and the other on the ground. We suppose that the ladder is of uniform density. Hence by symmetry the center of mass is at the geometrical center. Its length is *l*, and it rests so that it makes an angle θ with the ground (see Fig. 8·23). The various forces acting on the ladder may then be tabulated as follows: (1) the reaction **G** of the wall, which, since the surface is smooth, is normal to the surface; (2) the reaction of the ground **F** which, on the other hand, will not be normal to the ground,

[1] Cf. Jeans, *Theoretical Mechanics*, Ginn & Co., Boston, 1907, pp. 106 ff.

for it is a rough reaction; (3) the weight $\mathbf{W}$ acting at the center of mass. Since the direction of $\mathbf{F}$ is unknown, we find it most simple to consider the horizontal and vertical components F_1 and F_2 as our two unknowns (though of course we could take $\mathbf{F}$ and the angle ϕ it makes with the ground). We then proceed to write the conditions of equilibrium. First the condition for *translational* equilibrium, viz.,

$$\sum F_x = 0,$$
$$\sum F_y = 0.$$

These give respectively

$$\left. \begin{aligned} W = mg &= F_2, \\ F_1 &= G. \end{aligned} \right\} \tag{8·10–16}$$

The condition for rotational equilibrium we may write in a variety of ways, for the total moment of all the forces about any point in the plane is zero. We shall preferably choose the point in such a way as to render as small as possible the number of forces having a moment different from zero. In the present case we shall thus naturally choose the point A. Then

$$Gl \sin \theta - mg \frac{l}{2} \cos \theta = 0,$$

or

$$G = \frac{mg}{2} \cot \theta = F_1. \tag{8·10–17}$$

The magnitude of $\mathbf{F}$ may be found at once. For

$$F = \sqrt{m^2g^2 + m^2g^2 \frac{\cot^2 \theta}{4}} = mg \sqrt{1 + \frac{\cot^2 \theta}{4}}, \tag{8·10–18}$$

and the angle ϕ is given by

$$\phi = \arctan\left(\frac{2}{\cot \theta}\right) = \arctan(2 \tan \theta). \tag{8·10–19}$$

We may note an interesting thing about this problem. There are effectively three forces acting on the ladder, $\mathbf{G}$, $\mathbf{W}$ and $\mathbf{F}$. If we extend the lines of action of these forces sufficiently they will meet in a point. This will be true of any three coplanar non-parallel forces in equilibrium. We can prove the theorem very simply. Let the lines of action of the forces $\mathbf{G}$ and $\mathbf{F}$ meet at the point C. Now let us take moments about an axis through C normal to the plane of the forces. The moments of $\mathbf{G}$ and $\mathbf{F}$ will of course be zero since the moment arms vanish. But since the total moment of all the forces must be zero about

C, that of $\mathbf{W}$ must be also. Hence the line of action of $\mathbf{W}$ must pass through C, and the theorem is proved. It is worth noting that we can use the latter to solve other problems involving the equilibrium of three non-parallel coplanar forces. For if we represent the angles made at the point C by the lines of action of the three forces with each other as $\alpha_1, \alpha_2, \alpha_3$ respectively (Fig. 8·24), we have from the law of sines

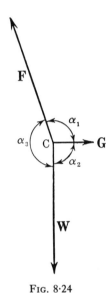

FIG. 8·24

$$\frac{W}{\sin \alpha_1} = \frac{F}{\sin \alpha_2} = \frac{G}{\sin \alpha_3}, \qquad (8\cdot10\text{--}20)$$

as we have already noted in the previous chapter in the case of three forces acting at a point.

However, in most practical cases the reader will probably find the method used in eq. (8·10–16) (the so-called method of *components*) the most advantageous one for problems involving coplanar forces. It is of course not restricted to the case of three forces only, but always yields *three* independent equations from which *three unknowns* may be evaluated. The student should convince himself by trial that instead of the two equations $\sum F_x = 0$, $\sum F_y = 0$, we could use two other equations obtained by setting equal to zero the torque about two different axes (each different from the one chosen already for the eq. $\sum \mathbf{L} = 0$).

8·11. Moving Axes. We now return to the problem of the motion of a rigid body, the general equations for which were set up in Sec. 8·7, and indeed expressed in most general form in eqs. (8·7–7) and (8·7–8). It will be recalled that these equations refer to axes fixed in space, i.e., the primary inertial system. We commented on the fact that as the body rotates about the center of mass (or any other point for that matter) the moments and products of inertia entering into the angular momentum $\mathbf{M}$ (eq. 8·7–5) will change, and that consequently the rotational equation of motion (8·7–8) will, in general, be very complicated. Much of this complexity can be removed by a rather simple expedient, namely, referring the rotational motion to axes which are *fixed* in the body and hence move with the body. We refer to these as *moving axes* and now wish to give some attention to them. With respect to these axes the products and moments of inertia remain invariant, so that, in $\dot{\mathbf{M}}$, terms like $\dot{I}_{xx}$ and $\dot{I}_{xy}$ vanish. It must be pointed out, to be sure, that there is the usual compensation for this gain in simplification: we can now no longer look upon the unit vectors $\mathbf{i}, \mathbf{j}, \mathbf{k}$ as constant in time. As the body moves they will change, and this change will be reflected in $\dot{\mathbf{M}}$. Thus, denoting the components of $\mathbf{M}$ along the new axes (fixed in the body) as M_x, M_y, M_z, we must now write

$$\dot{\mathbf{M}} = \mathbf{i}\dot{M}_x + \mathbf{j}\dot{M}_y + \mathbf{k}\dot{M}_z + M_x \frac{d\mathbf{i}}{dt} + M_y \frac{d\mathbf{j}}{dt} + M_z \frac{d\mathbf{k}}{dt} \cdot \quad (8\cdot11\text{--}1)$$

Here the last three terms represent the contribution to $\dot{\mathbf{M}}$ due to the rotation of the axes. We proceed to evaluate $d\mathbf{i}/dt$, etc., on the assumption that the origin of the moving axes is fixed in space, so that the only possible motion of the axes is one of rotation about a fixed point.

Since $\mathbf{i}$ is a unit vector, $d\mathbf{i}/dt$ must be perpendicular to $\mathbf{i}$ and hence must lie in the plane of $\mathbf{j}$ and $\mathbf{k}$. Therefore we can write

$$\frac{d\mathbf{i}}{dt} = A_3\mathbf{j} - A_2\mathbf{k}, \quad (8\cdot11\text{--}2)$$

where A_3 and A_2 are coefficients which are initially undetermined. Similarly

$$\frac{d\mathbf{j}}{dt} = A_1\mathbf{k} - B_3\mathbf{i}; \quad \frac{d\mathbf{k}}{dt} = B_2\mathbf{i} - B_1\mathbf{j}. \quad (8\cdot11\text{--}3)$$

But we recall from (6·4–4) that

$$\mathbf{i} = \mathbf{j} \times \mathbf{k}; \quad \mathbf{j} = \mathbf{k} \times \mathbf{i}; \quad \mathbf{k} = \mathbf{i} \times \mathbf{j}.$$

Hence

$$\frac{d\mathbf{i}}{dt} = \frac{d\mathbf{j}}{dt} \times \mathbf{k} + \mathbf{j} \times \frac{d\mathbf{k}}{dt}, \quad (8\cdot11\text{--}4)$$

and therefore from (8·11–2) and (8·11–3)

$$A_3\mathbf{j} - A_2\mathbf{k} = (A_1\mathbf{k} - B_3\mathbf{i}) \times \mathbf{k} + \mathbf{j} \times (B_2\mathbf{i} - B_1\mathbf{j}). \quad (8\cdot11\text{--}5)$$

From this it follows by comparing coefficients of identical unit vectors that

$$A_3 = B_3 \quad \text{and} \quad A_2 = B_2. \quad (8\cdot11\text{--}6)$$

Similarly we can show that $A_1 = B_1$ so that the six coefficients are reduced to three independent ones. Hence finally

$$\frac{d\mathbf{i}}{dt} = A_3\mathbf{j} - A_2\mathbf{k}; \quad \frac{d\mathbf{j}}{dt} = A_1\mathbf{k} - A_3\mathbf{i}; \quad \frac{d\mathbf{k}}{dt} = A_2\mathbf{i} - A_1\mathbf{j}.$$

$$(8\cdot11\text{--}7)$$

To see the significance of the coefficients A_1, A_2, A_3, dot multiply di/dt with $\mathbf{j}$ etc., and get (recalling $\mathbf{k} \cdot \mathbf{j} = 0$, etc.)

$$\mathbf{j} \cdot \frac{di}{dt} = A_3; \quad \mathbf{k} \cdot \frac{d\mathbf{j}}{dt} = A_1; \quad \mathbf{i} \cdot \frac{d\mathbf{k}}{dt} = A_2. \qquad (8\cdot11\text{--}8)$$

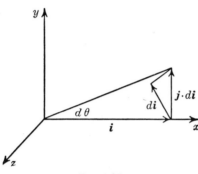

FIG. 8·25

This means, for example, that A_3 is the component of di/dt along the y axis and that $\mathbf{j} \cdot di = A_3 dt$ is the component of di along the y axis. We represent this in Fig. 8·25 in which $\mathbf{j} \cdot di$ clearly is the angle $d\theta$ through which the x axis rotates about the z axis due to the change di during the time dt. But $d\theta$ is $\omega_z \, dt$ by definition (cf. 8·2–4) and hence we have

$$A_3 = \omega_z. \qquad (8\cdot11\text{--}9)$$

Similarly it can be shown that

$$A_1 = \omega_x; \quad A_2 = \omega_y. \qquad (8\cdot11\text{--}10)$$

We can now go back to (8·11–1) and write

$$\mathbf{\dot{M}} = \mathbf{i}\dot{M}_x + \mathbf{j}\dot{M}_y + \mathbf{k}\dot{M}_z$$
$$+ \mathbf{i}(M_z\omega_y - M_y\omega_z) + \mathbf{j}(M_x\omega_z - M_z\omega_x)$$
$$+ \mathbf{k}(M_y\omega_x - M_x\omega_y)$$
$$= \mathbf{i}\dot{M}_x + \mathbf{j}\dot{M}_y + \mathbf{k}\dot{M}_z + \boldsymbol{\omega} \times \mathbf{M}, \qquad (8\cdot11\text{--}11)$$

utilizing the fact that

$$\boldsymbol{\omega} \times \mathbf{M} = (\mathbf{i}\omega_x + \mathbf{j}\omega_y + \mathbf{k}\omega_z) \times (\mathbf{i}M_x + \mathbf{j}M_y + \mathbf{k}M_z)$$
$$= \mathbf{i}(M_z\omega_y - M_y\omega_z) + \mathbf{j}(M_x\omega_z - M_z\omega_x)$$
$$+ \mathbf{k}(M_y\omega_x - M_x\omega_y) \qquad (8\cdot11\text{--}12)$$

by the use of the distributive rule and the relations (6·4–4).[1] It is often valuable to express the cross product in determinant form to facilitate its expansion into components. Thus

$$\boldsymbol{\omega} \times \mathbf{M} = \begin{vmatrix} \mathbf{i} & \mathbf{j} & \mathbf{k} \\ \omega_x & \omega_y & \omega_z \\ M_x & M_y & M_z \end{vmatrix}. \qquad (8\cdot11\text{--}13)$$

[1] It should perhaps be emphasized that the method of expressing $\mathbf{\dot{M}}$ in terms of moving axes leading to (8·11–11) can be applied to *any* vector. This fact will be utilized in the following section.

Equation (8·11–11) is a general equation whose physical meaning will become clearer if we consider some special cases. First suppose that instead of a single point being fixed, there is a fixed line of points or axis and take this as the z axis. The x and y axes rotate then with the body about the z axis, and we have $\omega_x = \omega_y = 0$ and $\omega_z = \omega$. Consequently from (8·7–5)

$$\mathbf{M} = \omega(-\mathbf{i}I_{xz} - \mathbf{j}I_{yz} + \mathbf{k}I_{zz}), \qquad (8\cdot11\text{–}14)$$

and the equation of motion (8·7–2) (or (8·7–8) if the fixed axis passes through the center of mass) becomes[1]

$$\mathbf{L} = \mathbf{i}(-I_{xz}\dot\omega + I_{yz}\omega^2) + \mathbf{j}(-I_{yz}\dot\omega - I_{xz}\omega^2) + \mathbf{k}I_{zz}\dot\omega. \qquad (8\cdot11\text{–}15)$$

If we specialize still further and suppose that the body is symmetrical about a plane perpendicular to the axis of rotation, $I_{yz} = I_{xz} = 0$ and (7·11–15) reduces to

$$\mathbf{L} = \mathbf{k}I_{zz}\dot\omega, \qquad (8\cdot11\text{–}16)$$

which is recognized as equivalent to the equation (8·3–7) for rotational acceleration about a fixed axis.

8·12. More About Moving Axes. Motion of a Particle on the Earth's Surface. The use of moving axes is of sufficient importance to warrant further consideration from a somewhat more general point of view, which is indeed not restricted to rigid bodies but may refer equally well to particles in general. In Fig. 8·26 we represent a set of rectangular axes, fixed with respect to the primary inertial system, in which the position of the point P is given by the coordinates x_f, y_f, z_f, with origin at O_f. Similarly we introduce a set of moving rectangular axes x_m, y_m, z_m with center at O_m, whose position vector in the fixed system

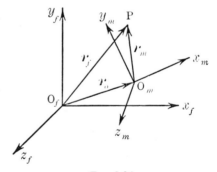

Fig. 8·26

is $\mathbf{r}_0$. This, of course, can change with the time. The position vector of a particle at P in the moving system is $\mathbf{r}_m$ while in the fixed system it is $\mathbf{r}_f$. From the figure we have

$$\mathbf{r}_m = \mathbf{r}_f - \mathbf{r}_0, \qquad (8\cdot12\text{–}1)$$

[1] We note from (8·11–15) the interesting fact that, if the body has at any instant an angular velocity $\boldsymbol{\omega}$, there will also exist an angular acceleration $\dot{\boldsymbol{\omega}}$ even if $\mathbf{L} = 0$. This has a bearing on the difficulty of defining the rotational equilibrium of a rigid body already mentioned in Sec. 8·9. Of course, the difficulty vanishes if the rotation takes place about an axis of symmetry.

and likewise for the corresponding velocities

$$\dot{\mathbf{r}}_m = \dot{\mathbf{r}}_f - \dot{\mathbf{r}}_0. \tag{8·12–2}$$

Let the unit vectors in the fixed system be $\mathbf{i}_f$, $\mathbf{j}_f$, $\mathbf{k}_f$, and those in the moving system be $\mathbf{i}_m$, $\mathbf{j}_m$, $\mathbf{k}_m$. The former remain unchanged in time, whereas the latter change with the time, since the directions of the moving axes vary with time with respect to the fixed axes. Hence we can write in analogy with (8·11–1)

$$\dot{\mathbf{r}}_m = \mathbf{i}_m \dot{x}_m + \mathbf{j}_m \dot{y}_m + \mathbf{k}_m \dot{z}_m + x_m \frac{d\mathbf{i}_m}{dt} + y_m \frac{d\mathbf{j}_m}{dt} + z_m \frac{d\mathbf{k}_m}{dt}.$$

$$\tag{8·12–3}$$

The first three terms yield the *apparent velocity* of P relative to the moving axes, whereas the last three terms represent the contribution to the velocity of P due to the rotation of the moving axes. We have already worked out the expressions for $d\mathbf{i}_m/dt$, etc., in Sec. 8·11 and hence can replace (8·12–3) by

$$\dot{\mathbf{r}}_m = \dot{\mathbf{r}}_{ma} + \boldsymbol{\omega} \times \mathbf{r}_m, \tag{8·12–4}$$

where $\dot{\mathbf{r}}_{ma}$ is the apparent velocity of P in the moving system. We need, however, to make sure of the meaning of $\boldsymbol{\omega}$. Actually it is the angular velocity of the moving axes about the instantaneous axis of rotation through O_m. We shall show first that $\boldsymbol{\omega}$ has the direction of the instantaneous axis of rotation through O_m. Since this axis is the locus of points which have at the instant in question *zero* linear velocity as far as rotation is concerned, if P lies on the axis through O_m so that $\mathbf{r}_m$ is the axis, we must have from (8·12–3)

$$x_m \frac{d\mathbf{i}_m}{dt} + y_m \frac{d\mathbf{j}_m}{dt} + z_m \frac{d\mathbf{k}_m}{dt} = 0. \tag{8·12–5}$$

But this means

$$\boldsymbol{\omega} \times \mathbf{r}_m = 0, \tag{8·12–6}$$

whence $\boldsymbol{\omega}$ and $\mathbf{r}_m$ are parallel. Hence $\boldsymbol{\omega}$ has the same direction as the axis of rotation through O_m. We can next show that the magnitude of $\boldsymbol{\omega}$ is equal to that of the angular velocity of the axes about the instantaneous axis through O_m. Consider a point P not on the axis of rotation. Its translational velocity due to the rotation of the axes has the magnitude $\omega r_m \sin \theta$, where θ is the angle between $\mathbf{r}_m$ and $\boldsymbol{\omega}$. Moreover, the direction of the translational velocity is at right angles to the plane of $\boldsymbol{\omega}$ and $\mathbf{r}_m$. This velocity is therefore precisely that of a point moving in a circle of radius $r_m \sin \theta$ with angular speed ω about the center, which in this case lies on the axis of rotation. Finally, the sign of $\boldsymbol{\omega}$ agrees with that of the rotation of the axes as is clear from (8·12–4).

We can now go back to (8·12–2) and write for the general relation between velocity in the fixed system and that in the moving system

$$\dot{\mathbf{r}}_f = \dot{\mathbf{r}}_0 + \dot{\mathbf{r}}_{ma} + \boldsymbol{\omega} \times \mathbf{r}_m. \qquad (8·12–7)$$

Before using (8·12–7) for further discussion of the motion of a rigid body it will be of interest to apply it to the motion of a single particle. An obvious case of great significance in which the motion of a particle is referred to moving axes is that of a particle on the surface of the earth related to axes fixed in the earth and therefore rotating with the earth. To express the motion of such a particle with respect to a fixed system having the same origin, viz., the center of the earth, we must use eq. (8·12–7), noting that $\dot{\mathbf{r}}_0 \doteq 0$ in this case.

To write the equation of motion, we must differentiate (8·12–7) with respect to the time. Thus the acceleration of the particle in the *fixed* system becomes

$$\ddot{\mathbf{r}}_f = \ddot{\mathbf{r}}_{ma} + \boldsymbol{\omega} \times \dot{\mathbf{r}}_m, \qquad (8·12–8)$$

since $\dot{\boldsymbol{\omega}} = 0$, if we treat the angular velocity of the earth as approximately constant. We now use (8·12–4) in (8·12–8) and get

$$\ddot{\mathbf{r}}_f = \ddot{\mathbf{r}}_{ma} + \boldsymbol{\omega} \times \dot{\mathbf{r}}_{ma} + \boldsymbol{\omega} \times (\boldsymbol{\omega} \times \mathbf{r}_m). \qquad (8·12–9)$$

But we must look into $\dot{\mathbf{r}}_{ma}$ more closely. From (8·12–3)

$$\dot{\mathbf{r}}_{ma} = \mathbf{i}_m \dot{x}_m + \mathbf{j}_m \dot{y}_m + \mathbf{k}_m \dot{z}_m. \qquad (8·12–10)$$

Therefore

$$\ddot{\mathbf{r}}_{ma} = \mathbf{i}_m \ddot{x}_m + \mathbf{j}_m \ddot{y}_m + \mathbf{k}_m \ddot{z}_m$$
$$+ \dot{x}_m \frac{d\mathbf{i}_m}{dt} + \dot{y}_m \frac{d\mathbf{j}_m}{dt} + \dot{z}_m \frac{d\mathbf{k}_m}{dt}. \qquad (8·12–11)$$

But from (8·11–11) (which is perfectly general and not restricted to **M**) this can be written

$$\ddot{\mathbf{r}}_{ma} = \mathbf{a}_m + \boldsymbol{\omega} \times \dot{\mathbf{r}}_{ma}, \qquad (8·12–12)$$

where $\mathbf{a}_m$ is the *apparent* acceleration of the particle in the moving system, neglecting the rotation of the axes. Then (8·12–9) becomes

$$\ddot{\mathbf{r}}_f = \mathbf{a}_m + 2\boldsymbol{\omega} \times \dot{\mathbf{r}}_{ma} + \boldsymbol{\omega} \times (\boldsymbol{\omega} \times \mathbf{r}_m), \qquad (8·12–13)$$

and the corresponding resultant force on the particle of mass m in the fixed system becomes

$$\mathbf{F} = m\ddot{\mathbf{r}}_f = m\mathbf{a}_m + 2m\boldsymbol{\omega} \times \dot{\mathbf{r}}_{ma} + m\boldsymbol{\omega} \times (\boldsymbol{\omega} \times \mathbf{r}_m). \qquad (8·12–14)$$

We may rewrite this in terms of the apparent acceleration relative to the moving axes (i.e., those fixed in the earth) thus

$$\mathbf{a}_m = \mathbf{F}/m - 2\boldsymbol{\omega} \times \dot{\mathbf{r}}_{ma} - \boldsymbol{\omega} \times (\boldsymbol{\omega} \times \mathbf{r}_m). \qquad (8·12–15)$$

From its form it seems clear that the term $\boldsymbol{\omega} \times (\boldsymbol{\omega} \times \mathbf{r}_m)$ corresponds to the well-known centripetal acceleration. On the other hand the term $2\boldsymbol{\omega} \times \dot{\mathbf{r}}_{ma}$ is relatively unfamiliar, though if we go back to eq. (3·6–9) we shall see that we have actually encountered it in connection with central field motion. There it is completely balanced by the acceleration due to angular acceleration. The acceleration $2\boldsymbol{\omega} \times \dot{\mathbf{r}}_{ma}$ is called the Coriolis acceleration. Its importance will be appreciated in a moment.

If the particle is subject only to the attraction of the earth we must write[1]

$$\mathbf{F} = m\mathbf{g} + m\boldsymbol{\omega} \times (\boldsymbol{\omega} \times \mathbf{r}_m). \qquad (8\cdot12\text{–}16)$$

This combined with (8·12–15) yields

$$\mathbf{a}_m = \mathbf{g} - 2\boldsymbol{\omega} \times \dot{\mathbf{r}}_{ma} \qquad (8\cdot12\text{–}17)$$

for the actual *apparent* acceleration relative to the earth. This is the quantity which is actually measured when we observe a falling body on the surface of the earth. If we write (8·12–17) in terms of the rectangular components we get

$$\ddot{x}_m = g_x + 2\omega\dot{y}_{ma},$$
$$\ddot{y}_m = g_y - 2\omega\dot{x}_{ma}, \qquad (8\cdot12\text{–}18)$$
$$\ddot{z}_m = g_z,$$

recalling that $\omega_x = \omega_y = 0$, and $\omega_z = \omega$ in this special case. In Fig. 8·27 let us consider rectangular axes set up at the center of the earth O as indicated and let APB be one quarter of the trace of the earth's surface on the yz plane. Unit vectors $\mathbf{i}, \mathbf{j}, \mathbf{k}$ are set up at P, and the horizon plane is indicated by WPN with N indicating the north, etc. PU is the zenith direction. The direction of the earth's axis is given by $\mathbf{k}$ which makes angle λ with PN. Suppose a particle is dropped from rest at P in latitude λ. We then have $g_x = 0$, $g_y = -g \cos \lambda$, $g_z = -g \sin \lambda$. Let v be the observed speed of fall at any instant. Eqs. (8·12–18) then become

$$\ddot{x}_m = -2\omega v \cos \lambda,$$
$$\ddot{y}_m = -g \cos \lambda, \qquad (8\cdot12\text{–}19)$$
$$\ddot{z}_m = -g \sin \lambda.$$

[1] It should be emphasized that in (8·12–16) $\mathbf{g}$ is really defined in such a way as to agree with Newton's law of gravitation, i.e., $m\mathbf{g} = -\dfrac{GmM}{R^2}\mathbf{r}_{01}$, where M = mass of earth, R = radius of earth, and $\mathbf{r}_{01}$ = unit vector. Moreover the particle is assumed to have no initial velocity.

The first equation shows that in addition to the acceleration due to gravity the falling particle also experiences an additional acceleration directed at right angles to the meridian plane in which it starts to fall. This acceleration has the magnitude $2\omega v \cos \lambda$, is entirely a Coriolis effect, and is always directed toward the east as should be clear from the diagram.

Since $v = gt$, approximately, the magnitude of the easterly acceleration becomes

$$|\ddot{x}_m| = 2\omega gt \cos \lambda, \qquad (8\cdot12–20)$$

and hence the total easterly deflection after time t from rest is approximately

$$x_m = \frac{\omega gt^3}{3} \cos \lambda = \frac{2}{3} \omega \sqrt{\frac{2h^3}{g}} \cos \lambda, \qquad (8\cdot12–21)$$

if we use $h = \frac{1}{2}gt^2$ as the height from which the fall has taken place.

The Coriolis acceleration gives rise to cyclonic wind movements on the earth's surface.[1]

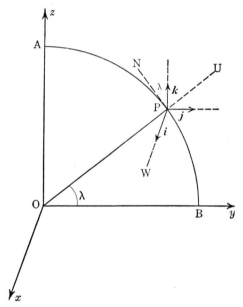

Fig. 8·27

8·13. Kinetic Energy of a Rigid Body. Let us revert to eq. $(8\cdot12–7)$ for the velocity of any point of a rigid body in the fixed set of axes,

[1] Cf. Page, *Introduction to Theoretical Physics*, 2nd ed., Van Nostrand, Princeton, N.J., pp. 107 ff.

i.e., the axes fixed in space, and assume that *one point* of the body is fixed. The body then performs rotation about this point. It follows that both $\dot{\mathbf{r}}_0 = 0$ and $\dot{\mathbf{r}}_{ma} = 0$, the latter being true since the moving axes are fixed *in* the body. Hence (8·12–7) reduces to

$$\dot{\mathbf{r}}_f = \boldsymbol{\omega} \times \mathbf{r}_m \qquad (8\cdot13\text{–}1)$$

where $\mathbf{r}_m$ is the position vector of the point P with respect to axes fixed in the body, and $\dot{\mathbf{r}}_f$ is the velocity of the corresponding point with respect to the axes fixed in space.

Let us now form the expression for the kinetic energy of the rigid body relative to the axes fixed in space. We have

$$K = \sum \frac{m_i}{2} \dot{\mathbf{r}}_{fi} \cdot \dot{\mathbf{r}}_{fi} = \sum \frac{m_i}{2} (\boldsymbol{\omega} \times \mathbf{r}_{mi}) \cdot (\boldsymbol{\omega} \times \mathbf{r}_{mi}), \qquad (8\cdot13\text{–}2)$$

wherein the sums are extended over all the particles of the body and the subscript i refers to any one particle. Now if we carry out the multiplication indicated in the right-hand term in (8·13–2) we can readily verify that

$$(\boldsymbol{\omega} \times \mathbf{r}_{mi}) \cdot (\boldsymbol{\omega} \times \mathbf{r}_{mi}) = \boldsymbol{\omega} \cdot [\mathbf{r}_{mi} \times (\boldsymbol{\omega} \times \mathbf{r}_{mi})]. \qquad (8\cdot13\text{–}3)$$

This is an important vector identity. In the present case it enables us to write (8·13–2) in the form

$$K = \tfrac{1}{2} \boldsymbol{\omega} \cdot \mathbf{M}, \qquad (8\cdot13\text{–}4)$$

where, of course, we are introducing again the angular momentum $\mathbf{M}$ from (8·7–1). We should expect a connection between K in (8·13–4) and the work done by the resultant *torque* during the rotation of the rigid body, similar to that connecting the kinetic energy of translation of a particle and the work done by the resultant *force* during the translation [cf. eqs. (1·11–16, 17)]. From (8·13–1) it follows that during time dt, the work done is

$$dW = \sum \mathbf{F}_i \cdot \dot{\mathbf{r}}_{fi} \, dt = \sum (\boldsymbol{\omega} \times \mathbf{r}_{mi}) \cdot \mathbf{F}_i \, dt. \qquad (8\cdot13\text{–}5)$$

But inspection shows that we can write $(\boldsymbol{\omega} \times \mathbf{r}_{mi}) \cdot \mathbf{F}_i = \boldsymbol{\omega} \cdot (\mathbf{r}_{mi} \times \mathbf{F}_i)$ and hence have in place of (8·13–5)

$$dW = \sum \mathbf{L}_i \cdot \boldsymbol{\omega} \, dt = \mathbf{L} \cdot \boldsymbol{\omega} \, dt, \qquad (8\cdot13\text{–}6)$$

where $\mathbf{L}$ is the resultant torque about the fixed point measured with respect to axes fixed in the body. Now we revert to (8·7–5) and form the change in $\mathbf{M}$, namely, $d\mathbf{M}$, remembering that since the axes are fixed in the body the I_{xx}, etc., do not change. Thus we have

$$\begin{aligned} d\mathbf{M} = \; &\mathbf{i}(I_{xx} \, d\omega_x - I_{xy} \, d\omega_y - I_{xz} \, d\omega_z) \\ &+ \mathbf{j}(-I_{yx} \, d\omega_x + I_{yy} \, d\omega_y - I_{yz} \, d\omega_z) \\ &+ \mathbf{k}(-I_{zx} \, d\omega_x - I_{zy} \, d\omega_y + I_{zz} \, d\omega_z). \qquad (8\cdot13\text{–}7) \end{aligned}$$

Let us form $\boldsymbol{\omega} \cdot d\mathbf{M}$ with the result

$$\boldsymbol{\omega} \cdot d\mathbf{M} = \omega_x(I_{xx}\, d\omega_x - I_{xy}\, d\omega_y - I_{xz}\, d\omega_z)$$
$$+ \omega_y(-I_{yx}\, d\omega_x + I_{yy}\, d\omega_y - I_{yz}\, d\omega_z)$$
$$+ \omega_z(-I_{zx}\, d\omega_x - I_{zy}\, d\omega_y + I_{zz}\, d\omega_z).$$

$$(8\cdot13\text{–}8)$$

Next we write out the kinetic energy (8·13–4) as follows:

$$\tfrac{1}{2}\boldsymbol{\omega} \cdot \mathbf{M} = \tfrac{1}{2}[\omega_x(I_{xx}\omega_x - I_{xy}\omega_y - I_{xz}\omega_z)$$
$$+ \omega_y(-I_{yx}\omega_x + I_{yy}\omega_y - I_{yz}\omega_z)$$
$$+ \omega_z(-I_{zx}\omega_x - I_{zy}\omega_y + I_{zz}\omega_z)]. \quad (8\cdot13\text{–}9)$$

Finally form the differential of $\tfrac{1}{2}\boldsymbol{\omega} \cdot \mathbf{M}$. Thus

$$d(\tfrac{1}{2}\boldsymbol{\omega} \cdot \mathbf{M}) = \omega_x(I_{xx}\, d\omega_x - I_{xy}\, d\omega_y - I_{xz}\, d\omega_z)$$
$$+ \omega_y(-I_{yx}\, d\omega_x + I_{yy}\, d\omega_y - I_{yz}\, d\omega_z)$$
$$+ \omega_z(-I_{zx}\, d\omega_x - I_{zy}\, d\omega_y + I_{zz}\, d\omega_z)$$
$$= \boldsymbol{\omega} \cdot d\mathbf{M}, \quad (8\cdot13\text{–}10)$$

where we have, of course, utilized the fact that $I_{yx} = I_{xy}$, etc. The upshot is that

$$\boldsymbol{\omega} \cdot d\mathbf{M} = \mathbf{L} \cdot \boldsymbol{\omega}\, dt = dW = dK, \quad (8\cdot13\text{–}11)$$

and therefore

$$W = K_1 - K_0 \quad (8\cdot13\text{–}12)$$

on integration between any two configurations of the body. This is the general work-kinetic energy relation for rotation of a rigid body with one point fixed.

The special case of zero resultant torque is of particular interest. From (8·7–2) there follows here

$$\mathbf{M} = \textbf{const.}, \quad (8\cdot13\text{–}13)$$

and hence from (8·13–10) we also have

$$2K = \boldsymbol{\omega} \cdot \mathbf{M} = \text{const.} \quad (8\cdot13\text{–}14)$$

Consider now an angular velocity " space " in which every point corresponds to a set of values of ω_x, ω_y, ω_z. Since from (8·13–9) twice the kinetic energy becomes

$$\boldsymbol{\omega} \cdot \mathbf{M} = I_{xx}\omega_x{}^2 + I_{yy}\omega_y{}^2 + I_{zz}\omega_z{}^2$$
$$- 2I_{xy}\omega_x\omega_y - 2I_{yz}\omega_y\omega_z - 2I_{zx}\omega_z\omega_x, \quad (8\cdot13\text{–}15)$$

it follows that (8·13–14) is the equation of a quadric surface in this space. By proper choice of the axes fixed in the body the products of inertia may be made to vanish[1] and the equation of the quadric surface becomes

$$I_{xx}\omega_x{}^2 + I_{yy}\omega_y{}^2 + I_{zz}\omega_z{}^2 = 2K. \qquad (8\cdot13-16)$$

This is the equation of an ellipsoid in the angular velocity space with its center at the origin. The magnitude of the vector from the origin of coördinates in the ω space to any point on the ellipsoid (8·13–16) represents a possible value of the angular speed consistent with the given kinetic energy. The ellipsoid has been called the *momental ellipsoid* or *ellipsoid of Poinsot*. It is clear that in the direction corresponding to the minor axis of the ellipsoid (the principal axis corresponding to maximum moment of inertia) the angular speed is least, whereas in the direction of the major axis the angular speed is greatest.

The change in $\boldsymbol{\omega}$ in passing from one point of the momental ellipsoid to another is given by

$$d\boldsymbol{\omega} \cdot \mathbf{M} = 0. \qquad (8\cdot13-17)$$

Now $d\boldsymbol{\omega}$ must lie in the plane tangent to the ellipsoid at the point in question. Hence the tangent plane is perpendicular to $\mathbf{M}$. But $\mathbf{M}$ is a constant vector since we are still considering the resultant torque to be zero. Therefore in this case the tangent plane remains fixed in position relative to a set of fixed axes. If we set

$$\mathbf{p} = \mathbf{M}/2K, \qquad (8\cdot13-18)$$

the vector $\mathbf{p}$ is normal to the tangent plane, and eq. (8·13–14) becomes

$$\boldsymbol{\omega} \cdot \mathbf{p} = 1. \qquad (8\cdot13-19)$$

But $\boldsymbol{\omega} \cdot \mathbf{p}$ is p times the projection of $\boldsymbol{\omega}$ along the normal to the tangent plane. It follows that the tangent plane remains at a constant distance from the origin as the motion goes on. The motion of the rigid body then can be represented by a rolling (without slipping) of the momental ellipsoid on the fixed tangent plane. During the rolling the vector $\boldsymbol{\omega}$ traces out a cone relative to the axes fixed in the body with vertex at the fixed point. This cone intersects the momental ellipsoid in a curve called by Poinsot the *polhode*. It intersects the invariable tangent plane in a curve called the *herpolhode*. For illustrations of these curves, A. G. Webster's *Dynamics* may be consulted.[2]

---

[1] Cf., for example, Paul R. Rider, *Analytic Geometry*, Macmillan, New York, 1947, pp. 149 ff.

[2] A. G. Webster, *The Dynamics of Particles and of Rigid, Elastic and Fluid Bodies*, Dover Publications, New York, 1959, pp. 263 ff.

8·14. Euler's Equations of Motion.   We have not yet exhausted the utility of axes fixed in the rigid body.   We shall continue to restrict our attention to the case in which one point is fixed and take this as the origin of rectangular coördinates fixed in the body.   However, we shall now insist that the axes are so chosen that the products of inertia I_{xy}, etc., all vanish, leaving only the moments of inertia I_{xx}, etc., in the expression for M in (8·7–5).   Axes for which this is true are termed the principal axes and there exist mathematical methods for finding them in each case.   If the body is symmetrical about the fixed point, the three mutually perpendicular axes of symmetry through this point will be principal axes.   We have then

$$\mathbf{M} = \mathbf{i}\omega_x I_{xx} + \mathbf{j}\omega_y I_{yy} + \mathbf{k}\omega_z I_{zz}. \tag{8·14–1}$$

Now from (8·11–11) we have

$$\dot{\mathbf{M}} = \mathbf{i}I_{xx}\dot{\omega}_x + \mathbf{j}I_{yy}\dot{\omega}_y + \mathbf{k}I_{zz}\dot{\omega}_z$$
$$+ \boldsymbol{\omega} \times \mathbf{M}$$
$$= \mathbf{i}[I_{xx}\dot{\omega}_x + (I_{zz} - I_{yy})\omega_y\omega_z]$$
$$+ \mathbf{j}[I_{yy}\dot{\omega}_y + (I_{xx} - I_{zz})\omega_z\omega_x]$$
$$+ \mathbf{k}[I_{zz}\dot{\omega}_z + (I_{yy} - I_{xx})\omega_x\omega_y]. \tag{8·14–2}$$

The fundamental equation of rotational motion (8·7–2) then takes a particularly simple form and in terms of rectangular components becomes the three equations

$$I_{xx}\dot{\omega}_x + (I_{zz} - I_{yy})\omega_y\omega_z = L_x,$$
$$I_{yy}\dot{\omega}_y + (I_{xx} - I_{zz})\omega_z\omega_x = L_y, \tag{8·14–3}$$
$$I_{zz}\dot{\omega}_z + (I_{yy} - I_{xx})\omega_x\omega_y = L_z.$$

These are known as Euler's equations of motion of the rigid body with one point fixed.

Let us specialize to the case in which the resultant torque vanishes, i.e., $L_x = L_y = L_z = 0$.   Then multiply through the resulting equations by ω_x, ω_y, ω_z, respectively, and add.   The algebra gives

$$\frac{d}{dt}[I_{xx}\omega_x^2 + I_{yy}\omega_y^2 + I_{zz}\omega_z^2] = 0,$$

or

$$I_{xx}\omega_x^2 + I_{yy}\omega_y^2 + I_{zz}\omega_z^2 = const. \tag{8·14–4}$$

From (8·13–15) the expression on the left is simply twice the kinetic energy of the body (recalling that the products of inertia are now zero) and we have again the fact that the kinetic energy remains constant under the action of zero resultant torque. It is appropriate to point out at this place that the constancy of the kinetic energy does not necessarily imply that there is no angular acceleration, since in (8·14–1) ω_x, ω_y, and ω_z may change with the time without invalidating the equation.

8·15. The Motion of a Top. This is probably the most interesting elementary application of Euler's equations. The top is assumed to be a solid of revolution with one end of the axis of symmetry (i.e., the peg) fixed in space. This axis is also taken as the spin axis. The fixed point (cf. Fig. 8·28) is taken as the origin O of a set of axes fixed in space x_f, y_f, z_f. With O as origin we also set up another set of axes x_m, y_m, z_m in which z_m is fixed to the body along its axis of symmetry.

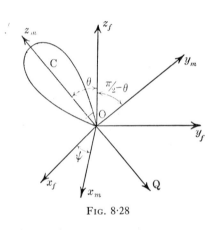

FIG. 8·28

Ordinarily we should also expect to fix the axes x_m and y_m to the body, but it now proves more convenient to let x_m and y_m rotate with angular velocity ω which is different from that of spin, which we denote by **s**. This will not affect the application of our previous reasoning since the moments of inertia about all axes perpendicular to the axis of spin are the same (i.e., $I_{xx} = I_{yy}$) and do not change with the time as the axes x_m and y_m rotate. We choose as the x_m axis the line of intersection of the plane through O perpendicular to the z_m axis and the x_f y_f plane. Let the angle between x_m and x_f be ψ and that between z_m and z_f be θ. These are usually known as the *Eulerian* angles. There is a third, namely, ϕ, which a line OQ in the $x_m y_m$ plane rotating with the top makes with the x_m axis. The components ω_x, ω_y, ω_z about the x_m, y_m, and z_m axes can be expressed in terms of $\dot\theta$ and $\dot\psi$ as follows:

$$\omega_x = \dot\theta,$$
$$\omega_y = \dot\psi \sin\theta, \qquad\qquad (8\cdot15\text{–}1)$$
$$\omega_z = \dot\psi \cos\theta.$$

Note that the x_m axis always lies in the x_f y_f plane. This accounts for the expression for ω_x. Note also that z_f, z_m, and y_m are all in the same plane. As the figure indicates, $\dot\psi$ is the angular velocity of the rotating axes about the z_f axis. It is known as the *precessional* velocity of the top.

The resultant torque on the top is due to gravity. If we denote the mass as m and locate it as usual at the center of mass C (with $OC = l$) the component torque about the x_m axis is $mgl \sin \theta$. The components about the y_m and z_m axes vanish. Before we can write Euler's equations we must rewrite M to take account of the spin velocity $\mathbf{s}$. Thus we now write (recalling that $I_{xx} = I_{yy}$)

$$\mathbf{M} = \mathbf{i} I_{xx} \omega_x + \mathbf{j} I_{xx} \omega_y + \mathbf{k} I_{zz}(\omega_z + s), \qquad (8\cdot15\text{--}2)$$

whence

$$\begin{aligned}
\dot{\mathbf{M}} = {} & \mathbf{i} I_{xx} \dot{\omega}_x + \mathbf{j} I_{xx} \dot{\omega}_y + \mathbf{k} I_{zz}(\dot{\omega}_z + \dot{s}) \\
& + \mathbf{i}[\omega_y I_{zz}(\omega_z + s) - \omega_z I_{xx} \omega_y] \\
& + \mathbf{j}[\omega_z I_{xx} \omega_x - \omega_x I_{zz}(\omega_z + s)] \\
& + \mathbf{k}[\omega_x I_{xx} \omega_y - \omega_y I_{xx} \omega_x]. \qquad (8\cdot15\text{--}3)
\end{aligned}$$

Hence Euler's equations (8·14–3) now take the form

$$\begin{aligned}
I_{xx} \dot{\omega}_x + (I_{zz} - I_{xx})\omega_y \omega_z + I_{zz}\omega_y s &= mgl \sin \theta, \\
I_{xx} \dot{\omega}_y + (I_{xx} - I_{zz})\omega_x \omega_z - I_{zz}\omega_x s &= 0, \qquad (8\cdot15\text{--}4) \\
I_{zz}(\dot{\omega}_z + \dot{s}) &= 0.
\end{aligned}$$

These can be somewhat simplified by writing $s + \omega_z = S$, so that

$$\begin{aligned}
I_{xx} \dot{\omega}_x - I_{xx}\omega_y \omega_z + S I_{zz}\omega_y &= mgl \sin \theta, \\
I_{xx} \dot{\omega}_y + I_{xx}\omega_x \omega_z - S I_{zz}\omega_x &= 0, \qquad (8\cdot15\text{--}5) \\
I_{zz}\dot{S} &= 0.
\end{aligned}$$

The last equation says that the resultant angular speed about the z_m axis is constant. If we multiply the first equation by ω_x, the second by ω_y, and the third by S and add, we obtain, after integrating,

$$\tfrac{1}{2}I_{xx}(\omega_x^2 + \omega_y^2) + \tfrac{1}{2}I_{zz}S^2 + mgl \cos \theta = E, \qquad (8\cdot15\text{--}6)$$

where E is the total energy of the motion, $mgl \cos \theta$ is the potential energy with respect to the horizontal plane, and the rest of the left-hand side is the resultant kinetic energy. Eq. (8·15–6) is then the energy equation of the top.

A special case of the first equation in (8·15–5) is not without interest. Suppose that the spin speed s is so large that the term $S I_{zz}\omega_y$ dominates the right-hand side. Then $I_{xx}\dot{\omega}_x - I_{xx}\omega_y \omega_z$ may be neglected and the equation becomes

$$S I_{zz}\dot{\psi} = mgl, \qquad (8\cdot15\text{--}7)$$

which says that the precessional velocity is inversely proportional to the spin velocity and the moment of inertia about the spin axis.

This is the familiar result of the elementary theory of the simple gyroscope.

To treat the problem more generally we note that the torque about the z_f axis is zero and hence the angular momentum about this axis is constant. But the latter is the sum of the components of **M** along z_f. We therefore have

$$I_{zz}S \cos \theta + I_{xx}\omega_y \sin \theta = A = \text{constant}. \qquad (8\cdot15\text{–}8)$$

Written in terms of the precessional velocity $\dot{\psi}$, this yields

$$\dot{\psi} = \frac{A - I_{zz} S \cos \theta}{I_{xx} \sin^2 \theta}. \qquad (8\cdot15\text{–}9)$$

Moreover the energy equation $(8\cdot15\text{–}6)$ can be written

$$\dot{\theta}^2 + \dot{\psi}^2 \sin^2 \theta = \frac{2E - 2mgl \cos \theta - I_{zz}S^2}{I_{xx}}. \qquad (8\cdot15\text{–}10)$$

With the introduction of the new quantities

$$\alpha = A/I_{xx}, \quad \beta = I_{zz}S/I_{xx},$$

$$a = \frac{2E - I_{zz}S^2}{I_{xx}}, \quad b = 2mgl/I_{xx}, \qquad (8\cdot15\text{–}11)$$

eqs. $(8\cdot15\text{–}9)$ and $(8\cdot15\text{–}10)$ take on the simpler form

$$\dot{\psi} = \frac{\alpha - \beta \cos \theta}{\sin^2 \theta}, \qquad (8\cdot15\text{–}12)$$

$$\dot{\theta}^2 + \dot{\psi}^2 \sin^2 \theta = a - b \cos \theta.$$

The elimination of $\dot{\psi}$ between these equations yields

$$\dot{\theta}^2 = -\frac{(\alpha - \beta \cos \theta)^2}{\sin^2 \theta} + a - b \cos \theta. \qquad (8\cdot15\text{–}13)$$

Letting $u = \cos \theta$, we get

$$\dot{u}^2 = (a - bu)(1 - u^2) - (\alpha - \beta u)^2 = f(u). \qquad (8\cdot15\text{–}14)$$

Evidently the variation of θ with time depends on the quadrature

$$t = \int \frac{du}{\sqrt{f(u)}} + \text{constant}, \qquad (8\cdot15\text{–}15)$$

which in turn can be expressed only in terms of elliptic functions. However, we can learn something about the top's behavior without carrying out the integration in $(8\cdot15\text{–}15)$. Clearly $f(u)$ must be positive to insure the reality of u, and, further, u must lie between 0 and $+1$. The function $f(u)$ is a cubic with three roots of which two must lie between 0 and $+1$. The situation is depicted in Fig. 8·29. We shall call the roots of $f(u)$ lying in the allowed interval u_1 and u_2. It follows that the inclination of the top's axis to the vertical is restricted to lie within the limiting angles $\theta_1 = \arccos u_1$ and $\theta_2 = \arccos u_2$. More elaborate consideration of the problem shows that θ varies periodically between these limits. This motion is known as *nutation*. In general the spinning of a top or gyroscope is accompanied by

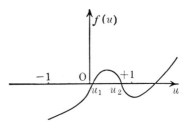

FIG. 8·29

both precession and nutation. Under certain conditions the nutation vanishes: this demands, of course, that $\theta_1 = \theta_2$ always. Hence $u_1 = u_2$ must be a double root of $f(u)$, and for vanishing nutation we must be able to write this function in the form

$$f(u) = B(u - u_3)(u - u_1)^2, \qquad (8·15–16)$$

where B is constant. It is clear that $u = u_1$ must satisfy both $f(u) = 0$ and $df/du = 0$. This will suffice to fix u_1, and the precessional velocity $\dot{\psi}$, given by the first equation in (8·15–12), becomes in terms of u_1

$$\dot{\psi} = \frac{\beta}{2u_1}[1 \pm \sqrt{1 - 2bu_1/\beta^2}]. \qquad (8·15–17)$$

For each u_1 there are then two possible precessional velocities.

If the spin velocity is so great that $\beta^2 \gg 2bu_1$ the two values of $\dot{\psi}$ are

$$\dot{\psi}_1 = mgl/I_{zz}S, \qquad (8·15–18)$$

$$\dot{\psi}_2 = \frac{I_{zz}S}{u_1 I_{xx}}\left[1 - \frac{mglu_1 I_{xx}}{I_{zz}^2 S^2}\right]. \qquad (8·15–19)$$

Evidently $\dot{\psi}_1 \ll \dot{\psi}_2$. The slower precession is usually the one observed.

Suppose the top is started with axis vertical and $S = s$, i.e., with spin velocity only. This leads at once to $\alpha = \beta$ and $a = b$. The roots of $f(u)$ then become

$$u_1 = +1, \quad u_2 = +1, \quad u_3 = \alpha^2/a - 1.$$

As long as $S^2 > 4mglI_{xx}/I_{zz}^2$, $u_3 > 1$, and the motion of the top is confined to simple rotation about the vertical axis with no precession or nutation, i.e., the top sleeps. As a result of friction at the point of support, energy may be lost until $S^2 < 4mglI_{xx}/I_{zz}^2$ when u_3 becomes less than unity, and precession sets in with nutation between the angles $\theta = 0$ and $\theta = \theta_2$, where

$$\cos \theta_2 = I_{zz}{}^2 S^2 / 2mgl I_{xx} - 1. \qquad (8 \cdot 15 – 20)$$

This means the top begins to wobble. With the continued decrease of S, θ_2 increases until the top falls down.

PROBLEMS

1. A rigid body possesses velocity of translation $\mathbf{v}$ and rotational velocity $\boldsymbol{\omega}$. What is the velocity of a point P of the rigid body with position vector $\mathbf{r}$ with respect to a fixed origin? If $\mathbf{v}$ and $\boldsymbol{\omega}$ are constant in time, what is the path of the point P and what is its equation?

2. A flat cylindrical disc of brass 10 cm in diameter and 2 cm in thickness has coiled about its edge a light flexible and inextensible string. If the free end of the string is attached to a fixed point and the disc is allowed to fall, what will be its total kinetic energy at the end of 2 seconds?

3. A steel ring in the form of a torus with inside diameter 50 cm and outside diameter 52 cm is allowed to perform small oscillations in a vertical plane about a rod on which the ring is hung. (See figure). Calculate the frequency of the vibrations. How much torque is needed to displace the ring through an angle of 5° from its equilibrium position?

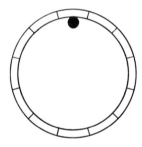

4. An elliptical disc of brass of major and minor axes 20 cm and 10 cm respectively and 2 cm thick may rotate about an axis through one focus and perpendicular to the disc. If the disc is displaced so that its major axis is horizontal and let go, find the angular velocity of the disc at the instant when the major axis is vertical.

5. Consider two particles of mass m joined by a weightless rod of length l. The system is assumed to rotate about an axis through the center of the rod and perpendicular to it. The quantum theory requires that only those rotational motions are possible for which the angular integral of the angular momentum over the period from 0 to 2π (viz. $\int_{0}^{2\pi} M \, d\theta$) is equal to some multiple of Planck's constant h. Find the expression for the allowed values of the energy of rotation and compare with the similar expressions for the quantized energy states of a hydrogen atom (Sec. 4·3).

6. A non-homogeneous circular rod has line density varying with distance x along it of the form $\rho = \rho_0 + kx$. The length of the rod is l. The rod falls from rest in a vertical position to a horizontal floor. If the bottom in contact with the floor does not slip, with what kinetic energy will it strike? What will be the velocity of the top end?

7. Calculate the translational acceleration of a sphere rolling down an inclined plane of angle θ. First solve the problem by the torque equation and then by energy considerations.

8. The ring of Problem 3 rolls down a 30° incline. How much velocity does it gain in 1 second?

9. Find the period of the small oscillations of a cube of side a about one edge and show that the length of the equivalent simple pendulum is $\dfrac{2\sqrt{2}}{3}\, a$. Also find the center of oscillation.

10. Show that the moment of inertia of a thin rectangular sheet with sides a and b about an axis through the center and parallel to the side b is $ma^2/12$, where m is the mass of the sheet.

11. Prove that the moment of inertia of a homogeneous spherical shell with internal and external radii r_1 and r_2 respectively about any diameter is $\dfrac{2}{5}\, m\, \dfrac{r_2^5 - r_1^5}{r_2^3 - r_1^3}$.

12. Prove that the moment of inertia of a solid homogeneous sphere about an axis tangent to the sphere is $\frac{7}{5} \cdot ma^2$, where m is the mass and a the radius of the sphere.

13. Prove that the moment of inertia of a homogeneous plane triangular plate about any axis in its plane is equal to the moment of inertia about the same axis of three masses each placed at a midpoint of a side of the triangle and each equal to one third the mass of the plate.

14. Consider a non-homogeneous ellipsoid with semi-axes a, b, c respectively and with density varying directly as the distance from the center along the longest axis (the layers of equal density being concentric elliptical sheets perpendicular to the longest axis). Show that the moment of inertia of the ellipsoid with respect to its longest axis is $\frac{1}{6}\, m\, (b^2 + c^2)$.

15. Prove that the product of inertia of a rigid body with respect to any two mutually perpendicular rectangular coördinate axes is equal to the product of inertia with respect to two parallel axes through the center of mass plus the product of inertia of the whole mass of the body located at the center of mass with respect to the original axes.

16. A uniform wire is bent into the form of a triangle. Find the position of the center of mass.

17. Out of a uniform circular disc of radius a, one quadrant is cut. Find the center of mass of the remainder.

18. A uniform flexible cord is suspended between two points in the same horizontal line. Calculate the position of the center of mass of the cord.

19. In a hemisphere of radius a the density varies inversely as the distance from the center. Determine the position of the center of mass.

20. Find the center of mass of one octant of a homogeneous sphere.

21. Determine the coördinates of the center of mass of one octant of the ellipsoid $x^2/a^2 + y^2/b^2 + z^2/c^2 = 1$, in which the density is a linear function of the distance along the x axis.

22. Prove that the moment of a couple has the same value about *any* axis perpendicular to the plane of the couple.

23. Show that a couple may be replaced by any other couple with the same moment in the same plane.

24. A uniform rod of mass m and length l rests on two inclined planes AB and BC (see figure), with their line of intersection lying in a horizontal plane. The rod lies in a vertical plane perpendicular to the line of intersection. The angles of the planes are θ_1 and θ_2 respectively. Find the position of equilibrium of the rod if its contact with both planes is smooth. Calculate the normal thrusts. What would be the effect on the foregoing result if one plane only is smooth and the other rough?

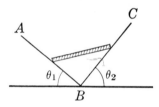

25. A uniform ladder rests with one end against a rough horizontal plane and the other end against an equally rough vertical plane. What is the smallest coefficient of friction that will allow the ladder to rest in all positions?

26. A uniform rod of length l and mass m rests against the horizontal rim of a hemispherical bowl of radius a, its lower end touching the inside of the bowl. Find the position it will assume for equilibrium.

27. Given a circular table with three legs vertically below the rim and forming an equilateral triangle. Find the smallest weight which when placed on the table is able to upset it.

28. Write the equation of motion of a general rigid body which rotates about the fixed x axis and show that in general in addition to the torque component about the x axis (due to gravity, for example) there must be torque components about the y and z axes as well. What is the nature of the forces producing the latter torques?

29. Calculate the magnitude of the easterly deflection from the plumb line experienced by a particle dropped from rest at a height of 500 feet in latitude 45° N.

30. A railroad train of mass 100 tons moves due east in latitude 45° N with constant velocity of 60 mi/hr. Find the magnitude of the force at right angles to the direction of motion. How is it directed?

31. A particle is thrown vertically upward in a vacuum with velocity **v**. Prove that on its return it hits the ground a distance $\dfrac{4\omega v^3}{3g^2}$. cos λ west of the place from which it was thrown.   (The latitude is λ and ω is the angular velocity of the earth.)

32. A simple pendulum has its point of suspension directly over the center of a horizontal turntable rotating with angular velocity **ω**.   If the bob is pulled aside and let go, what sort of curve will it trace out on the turntable?

33. A bullet is fired horizontally with a velocity of 1000 meters/sec in latitude 45° N.   What is the deflection from the plane of projection in direction and magnitude after 1 second of flight?

34. Find the equation of the momental ellipsoid of a homogeneous elliptical plate in the xy plane with semi-major and semi-minor axes a and b respectively.

35. Prove that the momental ellipsoid of any regular polyhedron with its center at the origin of rectangular coördinates is a sphere.   Specialize to the case of a cube and find the radius of the corresponding sphere.

36. An airplane motor and propeller has a moment of inertia about the axis of spin of 25 kilogram meters^2.   If it is moving instantaneously in a curved path with a radius of curvature of 150 meters with a velocity of 300 km/hr, what is the torque (direction and magnitude) tending to make the plane move vertically?   Where does the counter torque come from?

37. A simple top may be formed by piercing the center of a uniform disc of radius a and mass m.   We may assume that the mass of the pin is negligible compared with the mass of the disc.   Calculate the moment of inertia about the mutually perpendicular axes passing through O, the point of contact of the pin with the floor, the pin itself being taken as the z axis.   Compute the minimum spin velocity at which the top will "sleep."   At what spin velocity will the top begin to roll on the ground?

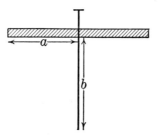

38. The equation of motion for an electron of mass m and charge e moving in an electric field **F** and magnetic field **H** is in vector form

$$m\mathbf{a} = e\mathbf{F} + \frac{e}{c}\,\mathbf{v} \times \mathbf{H}$$

where **v** is the velocity of the electron and c is numerically equal to the velocity of light.   The first term on the right is the force due to the electric field, whereas the second is that due to the magnetic field.   (See, for example, Page and Adams, *Principles of Electricity*, D. Van Nostrand Co., N.Y., 1931, Chap. VIII.) Find the form assumed by this equation when the motion of the electron is referred to a system of axes rotating about the direction of the magnetic field with constant angular velocity $\omega = -\dfrac{e}{2mc}H$. In particular show that if terms proportional to H^2 are neglected the equation of motion in the moving system reduces to the form

$$m\mathbf{a}_m = e\mathbf{F}.$$

This is known as Larmor's theorem, and the angular velocity of the rotating axes is called the Larmor precession. It is of vital importance in the study of the effect of a magnetic field on an atom.

39. Using the appropriate values for e, m, and c, calculate the value of the Larmor precession in the preceding problem for a magnetic field of 10,000 gauss. Consider an electron moving in the circular orbit of smallest quantum number (viz., $n_1 + n_2 = 1$) in the Bohr model of the hydrogen atom (see Sec. 3·11 and Fig. 3·10). Calculate the numerical magnitudes of the Coriolis force, viz., $2m\omega \times \mathbf{v}_a$ and the centripetal force, $m\omega \times (\omega \times \mathbf{r}_m)$, acting on the electron in the axes rotating with the above precessional velocity ω. Compare the latter with the actual centripetal force on the electron in its circular orbit about the nucleus, unaffected by the field.

Chapter 9

CONSTRAINED MOTION

9·1. Simple Types of Constraints. The Simple Pendulum.
There are many important cases of motion of a particle in which the latter is compelled by the geometry of its environment to move on some specified curve or surface. We have already encountered in Chapter 2 a simple illustration in motion on an inclined plane. Another example is furnished by the simple pendulum, where the motion of the bob must take place along the arc of a circle due to the invariable length of the string. We have indeed taken up already the approximate case of small motions in connection with the physical pendulum. This will be a good place to investigate the more general case where the swing may be of arbitrary amplitude. Consider Fig. 9·1 where the bob P,

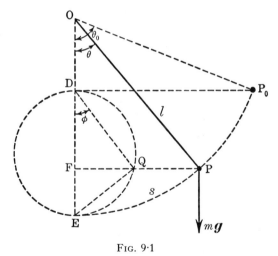

Fig. 9·1

which for our purposes here is to be considered a single particle, is suspended by a string of length l from the fixed point O. The bob is in equilibrium under gravity when OP is vertical, i.e., coincides with OE. We wish to determine the motion resulting when the bob is pulled aside through any arbitrary arc (less than $\pi/2$ for our convenience) and then let go.

The force on the bob in the direction of the motion is of magnitude $mg \sin \theta$. If we denote the displacement along the arc by s, the equation of motion is

$$m\ddot{s} = -mg \sin \theta. \tag{9·1–1}$$

Now $s = l\theta$ and hence (9·1–1) becomes

$$\ddot{\theta} = -\frac{g}{l} \sin \theta. \tag{9·1–2}$$

A first integration may be carried out by multiplying both sides by $\dot{\theta} \, dt$, whence

$$\frac{1}{2} \dot{\theta}^2 = \frac{g}{l} \cos \theta + C_1. \tag{9·1–3}$$

The constant C_1 may be evaluated by the initial condition that $\dot{\theta} = $ zero for a value of $\theta = \theta_0$, the *amplitude* angle. Then there results

$$\frac{1}{2} \dot{\theta}^2 = \frac{g}{l} (\cos \theta - \cos \theta_0). \tag{9·1–4}$$

Now if the initial angle θ_0 is small (say $< 10°$) we may write

$$\cos \theta = 1 - \frac{\theta^2}{2}, \tag{9·1–5}$$

and on substitution and rearrangement

$$\frac{d\theta}{\sqrt{\theta_0^2 - \theta^2}} = \sqrt{\frac{g}{l}} \, dt. \tag{9·1–6}$$

Integration yields

$$\arcsin \frac{\theta}{\theta_0} = \sqrt{\frac{g}{l}} \, t + C_2,$$

or

$$\theta = \theta_0 \sin \left(\sqrt{\frac{g}{l}} t + C_2 \right). \tag{9·1–7}$$

In this case the motion is simple harmonic with frequency

$$\nu = \frac{1}{2\pi} \sqrt{\frac{g}{l}}. \tag{9·1–8}$$

Look now at the motion in the case of *arbitrary* amplitude; we have the general integral

$$\frac{d\theta}{\sqrt{\cos \theta - \cos \theta_0}} = \sqrt{\frac{2g}{l}} \, dt. \tag{9·1–9}$$

From elementary trigonometry

$$\cos \theta = 1 - 2 \sin^2 \left(\frac{\theta}{2}\right).$$

On substitution into (9·1–9) we have therefore

$$\frac{d\left(\frac{\theta}{2}\right)}{\sqrt{\sin^2\left(\frac{\theta_0}{2}\right) - \sin^2\left(\frac{\theta}{2}\right)}} = \sqrt{\frac{g}{l}}\, dt. \qquad (9\cdot1\text{--}10)$$

We shall now introduce a new angle ϕ defined by the relation

$$\sin\left(\frac{\theta}{2}\right) = \sin\left(\frac{\theta_0}{2}\right)\cdot\sin\phi = k\sin\phi,$$

whence

$$\frac{\theta}{2} = \text{arc sin } (k \sin \phi),$$

so that

$$d\left(\frac{\theta}{2}\right) = \frac{k\cos\phi\, d\phi}{\sqrt{1 - k^2\sin^2\phi}}.$$

We can see the physical meaning of the angle ϕ by letting the initial position of P be P_0 (Fig. 9·1), so that $\angle EOP_0 = \theta_0$. Then draw P_0D normal to DE and construct the circle with diameter ED. Let the perpendicular PF from P to ED cut this circle at Q. Then the angle $EDQ = \phi$. For

$$\overline{EF} = l(1 - \cos\theta) = 2l\sin^2\left(\frac{\theta}{2}\right),$$

and assuming that $\angle EDQ$ really is ϕ, we have

$$\frac{\overline{EQ}}{\overline{ED}} = \sin\phi = \frac{\overline{EF}}{\overline{EQ}},$$

so that

$$\overline{EF} = \overline{ED}\sin^2\phi,$$

which from Fig. 9·1 becomes

$$\overline{EF} = 2l\sin^2\left(\frac{\theta_0}{2}\right)\cdot\sin^2\phi.$$

Hence $\sin\left(\dfrac{\theta}{2}\right) = \sin\left(\dfrac{\theta_0}{2}\right)\cdot\sin\phi$, as above. Substitution into (9·1–10)

now yields

$$\frac{d\phi}{\sqrt{1 - k^2 \sin^2 \phi}} = \sqrt{\frac{g}{l}}\, dt, \tag{9·1–11}$$

and on integration we have

$$t = \sqrt{\frac{l}{g}} \int_0^\phi \frac{d\phi}{\sqrt{1 - k^2 \sin^2 \phi}}, \tag{9·1–12}$$

where t is the time taken by the particle in moving between the positions $\theta = \theta$ and $\theta = 0$. The integral appearing here is the well known elliptic integral $F(k, \phi)$ connected with the elliptic functions.[1] Its values are tabulated in Peirce's *Table of Integrals*. Let us note a few special cases. For example, take $\theta_0 = 10°$ and calculate the quarter period, i.e., let $\phi = \pi/2$. Then $k = .0872$ and we have, denoting the period by P,

$$P = 6.2952 \sqrt{\frac{l}{g}}.$$

To the same number of places, $2\pi = 6.2832$. This indicates that the simple formula (9·1–8) is accurate for amplitude angles less than $10°$ with an error of less than .2%. For $\theta_0 = 20°$ we have $k = .1736$ and $P = 6.3312\sqrt{l/g}$. The error for a single period is still less than 1%. For many practical purposes the integrand in (9·1–12) may be expanded in a series and the integration carried out term by term. Thus expanding $(1 - k^2 \sin^2 \phi)^{-\frac{1}{2}}$,

$$t = \sqrt{\frac{l}{g}} \int_0^\phi (1 + \tfrac{1}{2}k^2 \sin^2 \phi + \cdots)\, d\phi$$

$$= \sqrt{\frac{l}{g}}\left\{ \phi + \frac{k^2}{4}(\phi - \tfrac{1}{2}\sin 2\phi) + \cdots \right\}. \tag{9·1–13}$$

Hence for the period P we have

$$P = 2\pi\sqrt{\frac{l}{g}}\left[1 + \frac{k^2}{4} + \cdots \right] = 2\pi\sqrt{\frac{l}{g}}\left(1 + \frac{\theta_0^2}{16} + \cdots \right), \tag{9·1–14}$$

if we recall that $k = \sin\theta_0/2 = \theta_0/2$, if θ_0 is small. The formula (9·1–14) is frequently very useful for small initial amplitudes.[2]

---

[1] See E. B. Wilson, *Advanced Calculus*, Dover Publications, New York, 1958, p. 503.
[2] For further discussion of the pendulum, reference may be made to P. G. Tait and W. J. Steele, *Dynamics of a Particle*, 7th ed., Macmillan, London, 1900, Chap. VI.

9·2. Motion of a Particle on a Smooth Surface of Arbitrary Form.   Let us suppose that the equation of the surface on which a particle is constrained to move is given by

$$\phi(x, y, z) = 0. \tag{9·2-1}$$

The particle (of mass m) is acted on by the external force $\mathbf{F}$ with components F_x, F_y, F_z, while the surface exerts on it a reaction force $\mathbf{R}$, with components R_x, R_y, R_z.   Now if the surface is smooth the force $\mathbf{R}$ acts along the *normal* and hence

$$R_x = \lambda R, \quad R_y = \mu R, \quad R_z = \nu R, \tag{9·2-2}$$

where λ, μ, ν are the direction cosines of the normal drawn in the direction of $\mathbf{R}$, and will be functions of x, y, and z in general, being constant only for the case of a plane.   The component equations of motion of the particle are then

$$\left.\begin{aligned} m\ddot{x} &= F_x + \lambda R, \\ m\ddot{y} &= F_y + \mu R, \\ m\ddot{z} &= F_z + \nu R. \end{aligned}\right\} \tag{9·2-3}$$

Let us multiply these equations through by $\dot{x}$, $\dot{y}$, $\dot{z}$ respectively and add.   We then get

$$\frac{m}{2}\frac{d(\dot{x}^2)}{dt} + \frac{m}{2}\frac{d(\dot{y}^2)}{dt} + \frac{m}{2}\frac{d(\dot{z}^2)}{dt} = \frac{1}{2}m\frac{d(v^2)}{dt}$$

$$= \dot{x}F_x + \dot{y}F_y + \dot{z}F_z$$

$$+ R(\dot{x}\lambda + \dot{y}\mu + \dot{z}\nu). \tag{9·2-4}$$

Now $\dot{x}$, $\dot{y}$, $\dot{z}$ are proportional at any point to the direction cosines of the tangent to the surface at that point since the particle is constrained to remain on the surface.   Hence $\dot{x}\lambda + \dot{y}\mu + \dot{z}\nu$ is proportional to the cosine of the angle between the tangent and the normal to the surface and is thus zero.   Eq. (9·2-4) may then be written

$$\tfrac{1}{2}md(v^2) = F_x\,dx + F_y\,dy + F_z\,dz. \tag{9·2-5}$$

Integration yields

$$\tfrac{1}{2}mv^2 = \int (F_x\,dx + F_y\,dy + F_z\,dz) + C. \tag{9·2-6}$$

If the external forces involved are *conservative* (Sec. 4·1), we may write the integral as $-V(x, y, z)$ and have

$$\tfrac{1}{2}mv^2 + V(x, y, z) = C, \tag{9·2-7}$$

where C is a constant.   This is the energy equation and we note the interesting fact that as might have been anticipated the constraints do not enter it.   The actual path followed by the particle can obviously not be determined by the second integration of (9·2–7) alone for this furnishes but one of the necessary equations.   As long as the time is involved the number of the latter is three (i.e., we must express x, y, z in terms of t).   We get the remaining two by eliminating R among the eqs. (9·2–3).   These yield

$$\frac{m\ddot{x} - F_x}{\lambda} = \frac{m\ddot{y} - F_y}{\mu} = \frac{m\ddot{z} - F_z}{\nu}. \qquad (9\cdot2\text{–}8)$$

On integrating these two equations we get two relations involving x, y, z, and t.   Elimination of the time yields a relation among x, y, and z, which represents a second surface.   The intersection of this with the surface $\phi(x, y, z) = 0$ is the path of the particle, while the equation (9·2–7) can then be used to give the " time equation," that is, the equation which expresses the rate at which the motion takes place along the path.   This is, in formal outline, the general method for solving a problem in constrained motion on a smooth surface.

As an illustration of the preceding general method let us consider some aspects of the motion of a material particle under the influence of gravity, but constrained to move in a smooth hemispherical bowl. For the sake of simplicity we shall choose the z axis vertical and directed downward, and take the origin at the center of the sphere.   At the point $P(x, y, z)$ the direction cosines of the *inward* drawn normal (**R** is directed in) are (Fig. 9·2)

$$\lambda = -\frac{x}{a}, \quad \mu = -\frac{y}{a}, \quad \nu = -\frac{z}{a}, \qquad (9\cdot2\text{–}9)$$

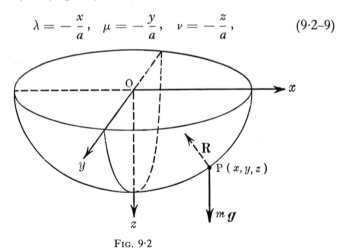

Fig. 9·2

if a is the radius of the bowl.   Moreover

$$F_x = 0, \quad F_y = 0, \quad F_z = mg. \qquad (9\cdot2\text{–}10)$$

Therefore the equations of motion (9·2–3) become

$$m\ddot{x} = -\frac{Rx}{a}, \quad m\ddot{y} = -\frac{Ry}{a}, \quad m\ddot{z} = mg - \frac{Rz}{a}. \quad (9\cdot2\text{–}11)$$

The " power " equation [i.e. (9·2–4) — that which gives the time rate of change of energy] then becomes

$$\frac{1}{2} m \frac{d}{dt} (\dot{x}^2 + \dot{y}^2 + \dot{z}^2) = mg\dot{z}. \quad (9\cdot2\text{–}12)$$

Incidentally we can readily verify that

$$\dot{x}\lambda + \dot{y}\mu + \dot{z}\nu = 0,$$

a relation which we have just shown must hold from general considerations. In the present case it becomes

$$\dot{x}x + \dot{y}y + \dot{z}z = 0. \quad (9\cdot2\text{–}13)$$

But since the equation of the surface is

$$x^2 + y^2 + z^2 = a^2, \quad (9\cdot2\text{–}14)$$

eq. (9·2–13) follows at once by differentiation with respect to the time. Integration of eq. (9·2–12) gives

$$\tfrac{1}{2}v^2 = gz + c, \quad (9\cdot2\text{–}15)$$

where c is a constant of integration. If the initial value of z is z_0 and the initial velocity v_0, then $c = \tfrac{1}{2}v_0^2 - gz_0$. The case where $v_0 = 0$ for $z = z_0$ is a special one and will be treated later. Here we wish to discuss the general case. Now eliminating R among the equations (9·2–11) we have

$$\frac{\ddot{x}}{x} = \frac{\ddot{y}}{y} = \frac{(\ddot{z} - g)}{z}. \quad (9\cdot2\text{–}16)$$

The first equation can be integrated once. Thus

$$y\dot{x} - x\dot{y} = b, \quad (9\cdot2\text{–}17)$$

where b is an arbitrary constant. It is not easy to integrate the other equation, but we can obviate this difficulty by recalling from eq. (9·2–13) that

$$x\dot{x} + y\dot{y} = -z\dot{z}. \quad (9\cdot2\text{–}18)$$

Now if we square the eqs. (9·2–17) and (9·2–18) and add, the result is

$$(x^2 + y^2)(\dot{x}^2 + \dot{y}^2) = b^2 + z^2\dot{z}^2. \quad (9\cdot2\text{–}19)$$

This may be reduced very easily to the form

$$\dot{x}^2 + \dot{y}^2 + \dot{z}^2 = \frac{b^2 + a^2\dot{z}^2}{a^2 - z^2} . \qquad (9\text{·}2\text{–}19a)$$

Combining (9·2–19a) with (9·2–15), however, gives

$$\dot{z}^2 = \frac{2(gz + c)(a^2 - z^2) - b^2}{a^2} . \qquad (9\text{·}2\text{–}20)$$

On separating the variables

$$\frac{dz}{\sqrt{2(gz + c)(a^2 - z^2) - b^2}} = \frac{dt}{a} . \qquad (9\text{·}2\text{–}21)$$

The integral involved here is an elliptic integral.   Much may be learned about the resultant motion without actually evaluating it.   Thus we note first that the expression under the radical must be real.   Let us investigate its roots, noting that in our problem z is necessarily restricted to the region $0 \leq z \leq a$.   If we call the expression, $\Psi(z)$, the following relations are true

$$\Psi(a) = -b^2, \quad \Psi(-a) = -b^2. \qquad (9\text{·}2\text{–}22)$$

while

$$\Psi(z_0) > 0,$$

and hence z may not in general take on the value a.   Since $\Psi(z)$ is positive for $z = z_0$ and negative for $z = a$, it must have at least one root between z_0 and a.   Moreover since $\Psi(-a)$ is also negative, there is another root between $z = z_0$ and $z = -a$.   As a matter of fact, there is a third root between $z = -a$ and $z = -\infty$, since $\Psi(-\infty) = +\infty$.   Call the three roots $\alpha, \beta,$ and γ.   In the type of motion in which we are interested both α and β are positive and the result is that the motion of the particle takes place between the two horizontal circles corresponding to $z = \alpha$ and $z = \beta$.

Now let

$$\frac{\alpha + \beta}{2} = f, \quad \frac{\alpha - \beta}{2} = h, \qquad (9\text{·}2\text{–}23)$$

and introduce the angular variable ϕ, where

$$z = f + h \cos 2\phi. \qquad (9\text{·}2\text{–}24)$$

Then

$$z - \alpha = z - (f + h) = -2h \sin^2 \phi, \qquad (9\text{·}2\text{–}25)$$

while

$$z - \beta = z - (f - h) = 2h \cos^2 \phi. \qquad (9\text{·}2\text{–}26)$$

Since

$$\Psi'(z) = -2g(z - \alpha)(z - \beta)(z - \gamma),$$

it therefore follows that

$$\Psi'(z) = 8gh^2 \sin^2 \phi \cos^2 \phi \cdot (z - \gamma)$$
$$= 8gh^2 \sin^2 \phi \cos^2 \phi \cdot (f - \gamma + h \cos 2\phi). \qquad (9\cdot2\text{–}27)$$

We now recall from (9·2–20) that

$$\dot{z}^2 = \frac{\Psi'(z)}{a^2}. \qquad (9\cdot2\text{–}28)$$

But from (9·2–24)

$$\dot{z} = -2h\dot{\phi} \sin 2\phi. \qquad (9\cdot2\text{–}29)$$

The combination of (9·2–29), (9·2–28), and (9·2–27) yields finally

$$\dot{\phi}^2 = \frac{gh}{a^2 k^2} (1 - k^2 \sin^2 \phi), \qquad (9\cdot2\text{–}30)$$

where

$$k^2 = \frac{2h}{f + h - \gamma}. \qquad (9\cdot2\text{–}31)$$

Separating the variables in (9·2–30) gives

$$\frac{d\phi}{\sqrt{1 - k^2 \sin^2 \phi}} = \frac{\sqrt{gh}}{ak} dt, \qquad (9\cdot2\text{–}32)$$

so that the time corresponding to any value of ϕ is

$$t = \frac{ak}{\sqrt{gh}} \int_0^\phi \frac{d\phi}{\sqrt{1 - k^2 \sin^2 \phi}}. \qquad (9\cdot2\text{–}33)$$

This expression is in the same form as (9·1–12) encountered in the study of the simple pendulum. Hence as far as motion in the z direction is concerned the particle oscillates approximately as a simple pendulum. When $\phi = 0$, $z = f + h$, while for $\phi = \pi/2$, $z = f - h$. Since in our case both α and β are positive, if $\alpha > \beta$, f and h are both positive and the integration from $\phi = 0$ to $\phi = \pi/2$ corresponds to the motion from $z = \alpha$ to $z = \beta$, i.e., a half-period. We then have, if P represents the period of the motion in the z direction,

$$\frac{P}{2} = \frac{ak}{\sqrt{gh}} K, \qquad (9\cdot2\text{–}34)$$

where

$$K = \int_0^{\pi/2} \frac{d\phi}{\sqrt{1 - k^2 \sin^2 \phi}} = F\left(k, \frac{\pi}{2}\right).$$

Now the quarter period of a simple pendulum is given (see Sec. 9·1) by

$$\frac{P}{4} = \sqrt{\frac{l}{g}}\, K. \tag{9·2–35}$$

Hence the length of the simple pendulum which will have the same period as the motion in the z direction of the particle here considered will be given by

$$\frac{2ak}{\sqrt{gh}} = 4\sqrt{\frac{l}{g}}\,,$$

or

$$l = \frac{a^2 k^2}{4h}\,. \tag{9·2–36}$$

A more detailed discussion together with the treatment of the motion in x and y with diagrams of actual experiments will be found in Webster's *Dynamics* (pp. 48 ff.).

We ought, however, to note the special case where $v_0 = 0$ for $z = z_0$ [see eq. (9·2–15)]. This corresponds to the case where the particle is let go from *rest* at any point. What is the result? In this case we have

$$c = -gz_0. \tag{9·2–37}$$

But since $\dot{z}$ must also be zero initially (i.e., when $z = z_0$) it follows from eq. (9·2–20) that

$$b = 0. \tag{9·2–38}$$

If now we introduce spherical coördinates defined as in Fig. 9·3, with

$$x = a \sin \theta \cos \phi,$$
$$y = a \sin \theta \sin \phi,$$
$$z = a \cos \theta, \tag{9·2–39}$$

eq. (9·2–17) with $b = 0$ becomes

$$-a^2 \sin^2 \theta \cdot \dot{\phi} = 0. \tag{9·2–40}$$

Now let us look at eq. (9·2–15) which since

$$v^2 = a^2(\dot{\theta}^2 + \sin^2 \theta \cdot \dot{\phi}^2), \tag{9·2–41}$$

becomes [recalling (9·2–40)]

$$a^2 \dot{\theta}^2 = 2(gz + c)$$
$$= 2(ga \cos \theta + c). \tag{9·2–42}$$

If now we differentiate with respect to the time we have

$$2a^2\dot\theta\ddot\theta = -2ag\dot\theta \sin \theta,$$

or

$$\ddot\theta + \frac{g}{a} \sin \theta = 0. \qquad (9\cdot2\text{--}43)$$

But this is the equation of the simple pendulum swinging in a plane — the problem already discussed fully in Sec. 9·1. Hence when the particle is allowed to drop from rest from its initial position the motion is that of a simple pendulum. The more complicated motion previously discussed results when the initial motion implies an initial velocity different from zero and arbitrarily directed. It should be noted, of course, that even if the initial velocity is not zero, if it is directed in the great circle containing the lowest point of the bowl, the motion is that of a simple pendulum. For in this case the particle must remain in the initial diametral plane.

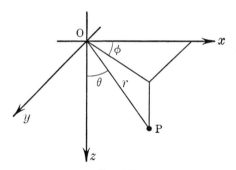

FIG. 9·3

9·3. Constraints and the Principles of Mechanics. D'Alembert's Principle — Dynamics Reduced to Statics.

Thus far our study of dynamics has been based on our interpretation of Newton's three laws of motion outlined in Chapter 1. It is important to realize, however, that there are other ways of stating the principles of mechanics. Two of these are closely connected with the motion of particles subject to constraints and hence we may well consider them at this place. The first is the celebrated principle of D'Alembert, enunciated in 1743, which provides a foundation for mechanics that effectively reduces dynamics to statics. We shall confine our attention to this principle in the present section and use Mach's method of presenting it.[1]

---

[1] Ernst Mach, *The Science of Mechanics*, English translation, Open Court Publishing Company, Chicago, 1902. This is an extremely valuable storehouse of information on the principles of mechanics. Every serious student of mechanics should read it.

Consider the system of n particles of masses $m_1, m_2, \ldots, m_n$, three of which are indicated in Fig. 9·4. Suppose that the forces $\mathbf{F}_1{}^i, \mathbf{F}_2{}^i, \ldots, \mathbf{F}_n{}^i$ act on them respectively. We shall call these the *impressed* forces. If the masses were subject to no constraints (i.e., if they were not connected in any way or forced to move along certain curves or surfaces) they would then move with accelerations given

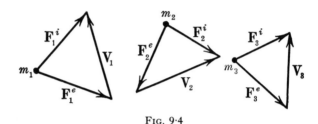

FIG. 9·4

by $\mathbf{a}_1 = \mathbf{F}_1{}^i/m_1$, etc. Let us suppose, however, that due to the constraints the actual motions are such as would be produced in free bodies by the action of the forces $\mathbf{F}_1{}^e, \mathbf{F}_2{}^e, \ldots, \mathbf{F}_n{}^e$. That is to say, $\mathbf{F}_n{}^e = m_n \mathbf{a}_n$, where $\mathbf{a}_n$ is the *actual* acceleration of the n-th particle. These may be termed the *effective* forces. Now let us form the vector differences

$$\left.\begin{aligned} \mathbf{F}_1{}^i - \mathbf{F}_1{}^e &= \mathbf{V}_1, \\ \mathbf{F}_2{}^i - \mathbf{F}_2{}^e &= \mathbf{V}_2, \\ & \quad \cdot \\ & \quad \cdot \\ & \quad \cdot \\ \mathbf{F}_n{}^i - \mathbf{F}_n{}^e &= \mathbf{V}_n. \end{aligned}\right\} \qquad (9\cdot3\text{--}1)$$

D'Alembert's principle then consists in the hypothesis that if the system of forces $\mathbf{V}_1, \mathbf{V}_2, \ldots, \mathbf{V}_n$ (sometimes referred to as " lost " forces) alone were to act the system would remain in equilibrium. This can be expressed analytically by the use of the principle of virtual work (Sec. 5·6) in the form

$$\sum_{j=1}^{n} \mathbf{V}_j \cdot \delta \mathbf{r}_j = 0. \qquad (9\cdot3\text{--}2)$$

It is important to emphasize that $(9\cdot3\text{--}2)$ does not by any means necessarily mean that $\sum \mathbf{V}_j = 0$. The dynamical problem is essentially reduced to one in static equilibrium. In the employment of D'Alembert's principle the essential problem is the correct choice of the impressed forces. The constraint forces do not enter, but one must be careful not to treat a genuine impressed force as a constraint force and leave it out.

A better understanding of the principle may be gained by a few simple examples.   First let us take the case of a single particle on a smooth inclined plane.   Consulting Fig. 9·5 we see that the impressed

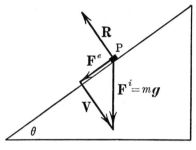

FIG. 9·5

force in this case is the weight, of magnitude mg, while the effective force is $\mathbf{F}^e$ acting along the plane.   In this case there is but one particle and a single $\mathbf{V} = \mathbf{F}^i - \mathbf{F}^e$.

Application of (9·3–2) leads at once to

$$(\mathbf{F}^i - \mathbf{F}^e) \cdot \delta\mathbf{r} = 0, \qquad (9·3\text{–}3)$$

where $\delta\mathbf{r}$ is taken down the plane.

Hence

$$\mathbf{F}^i \cdot \delta\mathbf{r} = mg \sin\theta\, \delta r,$$

while

$$\mathbf{F}^e \cdot \delta\mathbf{r} = F^e\, \delta r = ma\, \delta r.$$

We therefore have finally since δr is arbitrary,

$$F^e = ma = mg \sin\theta,$$

or

$$a = g \sin\theta, \qquad (9·3\text{–}4)$$

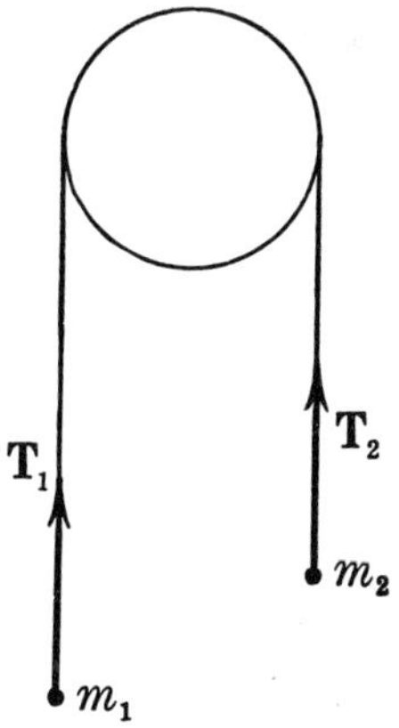

FIG. 9·6

the usual expression for the acceleration of the particle down the plane.   This is doubtless a rather long-winded way of getting at a simple result.   Nevertheless it is often desirable to emphasize the meaning of a general principle by the use of a very simple example. Let us try another illustration, this time one involving two particles. The simplest case of this kind is probably Atwood's machine, already worked out in Sec. 2·1 by means of Newton's laws.   Consulting Fig. 9·6 we see that the impressed forces are the weights $m_1\mathbf{g}$ and $m_2\mathbf{g}$ respectively. The tensions $\mathbf{T}_1$ and $\mathbf{T}_2$ are constraint forces and do not enter the expression of the principle.   The latter now takes the form

$$(m_1\mathbf{g} - m_1\mathbf{a}_1) \cdot \delta\mathbf{r}_1 + (m_2\mathbf{g} - m_2\mathbf{a}_2) \cdot \delta\mathbf{r}_2 = 0. \qquad (9·3\text{–}5)$$

If we follow the pattern of Sec. 5·6 we find it convenient to represent $\delta\mathbf{r}_1$ and $\delta\mathbf{r}_2$ as both directed vertically. The expansion of the dot product in (9·3–5) then yields

$$(m_1g - m_1a_1)\,\delta r_1 + (m_2g - m_2a_2)\,\delta r_2 = 0. \qquad (9\cdot3\text{–}6)$$

But from the geometry of the constraints we must have

$$\delta r_1 = -\delta r_2, \quad a_1 = -a_2. \qquad (9\cdot3\text{–}7)$$

Therefore the solution (with δr_1 arbitrary) follows in the usual form

$$a_1 = \frac{m_1 - m_2}{m_1 + m_2}g. \qquad (9\cdot3\text{–}8)$$

The reader should work out other and more complicated examples using the principle. (See, for instance, the problems at the end of the chapter.)

In advanced texts on mechanics D'Alembert's principle is often made the starting point for the development of the whole subject. This is true, for example, in the celebrated treatise *Méchanique analytique* of Lagrange (1811). This work should be of considerable historical interest to the student, for it marks the climax of the eighteenth century attempts to make mechanics a branch of mathematical analysis. In the preface the author proudly boasts: "There are no figures in this work." It constitutes a monument of analysis. We shall have occasion in Chapter 13 to refer to Lagrange's form of the equations of motion of a dynamical system.

9·4. Gauss's Principle of Least Constraint. Another very significant principle of mechanics closely connected with the idea of motion subject to constraint is due to Gauss. It was elaborated by him in 1829 in an attempt to reduce all mechanics to a single generalization.

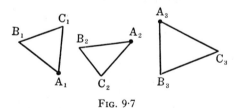

FIG. 9·7

Suppose that we have given a system of n particles of masses $m_1, m_2, m_3, \ldots, m_n$ occupying the positions $A_1, \ldots, A_n$. Three of them are indicated in the accompanying figure (Fig. 9·7). Let us now imagine that if the particles were perfectly free to move under the action of certain external forces, they would undergo during an infinitesimal time interval $d\tau$ the infinitesimal displacements $\overline{A_1B_1}$, $\overline{A_2B_2}, \ldots , \overline{A_nB_n}$. The system being subjected to certain constraints (i.e., the masses being perhaps connected to each other by rods or cords, or constrained to move along certain curves or surfaces), suppose that the *actual* displacements during the above time interval are $\overline{A_1C_1}$, $\overline{A_2C_2}, \ldots , \overline{A_nC_n}$. Gauss's principle now states that the *actual* displacement of the system under the constraints is such that the sum

$$m_1\overline{B_1C_1}^2 + \cdots + m_n\overline{B_nC_n}^2, \tag{9·4–1}$$

is a *minimum*, that is, less for the actual motion than for any other possible motion of the same system under the same constraints. This sum may be looked upon as the analytical expression for the total constraint, and hence the principle is known as that of *least constraint*. It is interesting to note that the static case is included in this principle, for if the total constraint for *every possible* motion is greater than it would be for *rest*, equilibrium will prevail, i.e., the system once at rest will remain at rest.

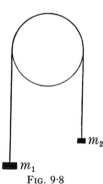

FIG. 9·8

Gauss intended this as a fundamental postulate by the assumption of which all the problems of mechanics can be solved. It is necessarily connected with the Newtonian laws of motion and D'Alembert's principle, and indeed we shall show that it may be deduced from the latter. Nevertheless for the moment let us assume it and work out a fairly simple problem in dynamics to understand its essential content.

We choose the Atwood machine again. Examining the situation once more as in Fig. 9·8 we note that if m_1 and m_2 were free of constraint, in the time $d\tau$ they would each fall vertically *from rest* the distance

$$s = \tfrac{1}{2}g(d\tau)^2. \tag{9·4–2}$$

Actually, however, m_1 falls with acceleration of magnitude a and hence in time $d\tau$ travels the distance

$$s' = \tfrac{1}{2}a(d\tau)^2. \tag{9·4–3}$$

The total constraint is thus

$$\frac{m_1}{4}(a - g)^2(d\tau)^4 + \frac{m_2}{4}(-a - g)^2(d\tau)^4. \tag{9·4–4}$$

This, according to the principle, is to be a minimum. Hence, differentiating with respect to a and setting the result equal to zero, we have

$$\frac{m_1}{2}(a - g)(d\tau)^4 + \frac{m_2}{2}(a + g)(d\tau)^4 = 0,$$

or

$$a(m_1 + m_2) = g(m_1 - m_2), \tag{9·4–5}$$

and therefore

$$a = \frac{m_1 - m_2}{m_1 + m_2}g, \tag{9·4–6}$$

as usual.

Let us now show that the principle of least constraint follows from that of D'Alembert.

Referring again to Fig. 9·7, we recall that $\overline{A_jB_j}$ is the displacement which the mass m_j would undergo under the application of the *impressed* force $F_j{}^i$ if it were free to do so. $\overline{A_jC_j}$ is the displacement it actually undergoes under the action of the *effective* force $F_j{}^e$, the deviation due to the constraints being $\overline{B_jC_j}$. Now imagine (see Fig. 9·9) that instead

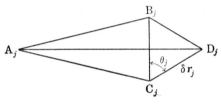

Fig. 9·9

of going to C_j the particle were to go to D_j with a corresponding deviation $\overline{B_jD_j}$. Let us denote $\overline{C_jD_j}$ by δr_j, and suppose it makes the angle θ_j with $\overline{C_jB_j}$. We then have

$$\overline{B_jD_j}{}^2 = \overline{C_jB_j}{}^2 + \delta r_j{}^2 - 2\,\delta r_j\overline{C_jB_j}\cos\theta_j, \tag{9·4–7}$$

whence multiplying by m_j and summing up over all the particles there results

$$\sum m_j\overline{B_jD_j}{}^2 - \sum m_j\overline{C_jB_j}{}^2 = \sum m_j\,\delta r_j{}^2$$
$$- 2\sum m_j\overline{C_jB_j}\,\delta r_j\cos\theta_j. \tag{9·4–8}$$

Now since all the above displacements are supposed to take place from rest in the same time $d\tau$, it follows that

$$\overline{A_jB_j} = ka_{ij}, \quad \overline{A_jC_j} = ka_{ej}, \quad \overline{C_jB_j} = ka_{cj}, \tag{9·4–9}$$

where k is a constant and a_{ij} and a_{ej} are the magnitudes of the accelerations produced by the impressed and effective forces respectively and a_{cj} is the magnitude of the acceleration that would correspond to the particular constraint which acts here (assuming it were able to produce an acceleration). Thus we may think of the actual (effective) acceleration as produced by subtracting an " equivalent " acceleration due to the constraint from the acceleration that would be produced in the particle if it were free to move. Then

$$m_j\overline{A_jB_j} = kF_j{}^i, \quad m_j\overline{A_jC_j} = kF_j{}^e, \quad m_j\overline{C_jB_j} = kV_j. \quad (9\cdot4\text{--}10)$$

Now according to D'Alembert's principle

$$\sum \mathbf{V}_j \cdot \delta \mathbf{r}_j = 0. \quad (9\cdot4\text{--}11)$$

Therefore from eq. $(9\cdot4\text{--}10)$

$$2\sum m_j \overline{C_jB_j}\, \delta r_j \cos \theta_j = 0, \quad (9\cdot4\text{--}12)$$

and finally from $(8\cdot4\text{--}8)$

$$\sum m_j \overline{B_jD_j}{}^2 - \sum m_j \overline{C_jB_j}{}^2 = \sum m_j\, \delta r_j{}^2. \quad (9\cdot4\text{--}13)$$

The right-hand side of this equation is always positive.

It follows then from $(9\cdot4\text{--}13)$ that the $\sum m_j\overline{C_jB_j}{}^2$ must be *less* for the *actual* motion than for any other alternative motion compatible with the constraints. This is the essential content of the principle of least constraint.

The student will do well to apply the principles of D'Alembert and least constraint to other simple examples. In a later portion of the book it will be shown how still more general mechanical principles may replace or supplement them. Their introduction in this place is for the purpose of emphasizing the important fact that there are several ways of expressing the laws of mechanics, depending on the point of view which is taken.

PROBLEMS

1. A particle is constrained to move under gravity in a vertical circle of radius R. If it starts from rest where the tangent to the circle is vertical, how long will it take it to reach the lowest point of the circle?

2. In Problem 1, find the expression for the reaction of the circle on the particle as a function of vertical distance above the lowest point.

3. A particle of mass m is fixed to one end of a string of length l and the other end is attached to a fixed point. The particle is then constrained to move in a horizontal circle with uniform angular velocity ω. Find the inclination of the string to the vertical and the relation between the tension in the string and the angular velocity. Compute the length of the equivalent simple pendulum. (This arrangement is known as a conical pendulum. Suggest a practical use of it.)

4. The cycloid is the locus of a fixed point on a circle which rolls along a fixed axis. Show that the parametric equations of an inverted cycloid with its lowest point at the origin (see figure) are $x = a\,(\theta + \sin\theta)$, $y = a\,(1 - \cos\theta)$. Find the time it takes for a particle to descend under gravity from rest from any point on an *inverted* cycloid to the lowest point. Show that this time is independent of the point from which the descent takes place. Comment on the significance of this result and its possible practical application.

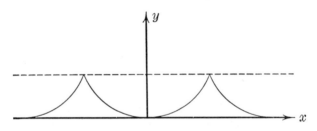

5. A particle moves under the influence of gravity on the convex side of a vertical circle with center at the ground. If it starts from rest at the top, where will it leave the circle?

6. A particle is constrained to move in a straight line under the influence of a force directed toward a fixed point at a perpendicular distance a from the line and varying inversely as the square of the distance from the point. Discuss the motion and in particular compute the approximate time required by the particle to travel from $x = h$ to $x = 0$, where $x = 0$ corresponds to the position of the fixed point, and $h \ll a$.

7. A smooth inclined plane of mass M and angle α is free to move on a perfectly smooth horizontal plane. A particle of mass m is free to move on the inclined plane. Discuss the motion of both particle and inclined plane.

8. Use the principle of D'Alembert to obtain the motion of the simple pendulum. Solve the same problem with the principle of least constraint.

9. Solve the problem of the simple lever by the principles of D'Alembert and least constraint.

10. A mass m_1 is attached to a string wrapped about a wheel of mass M and radius R, while a mass m_2 is attached to a string wrapped about the axle of mass m and radius r. Find the accelerations of m_1 and m_2 respectively by the principles of D'Alembert and least constraint (see figure at top of page 271).

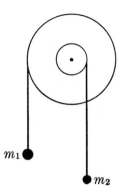

11. A man of mass m runs up a ramp in the form of a cycloid (Cf. Problem 4) with initial slope zero. If he runs at constant speed *along* the ramp, find the power exerted against gravity as a function of the instantaneous slope.

12. A particle of mass m_1 is constrained to move on a vertical straight line AB while attached to a string passing over a smooth peg P, with a particle of mass m_2 attached to the other end of the string. Use D'Alembert's principle to find the expressions for the instantaneous vertical accelerations of m_1 and m_2.

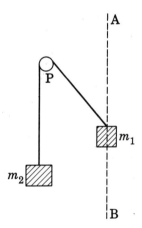

CHAPTER 10

OSCILLATIONS

10·1. A Simple Problem in Vibration. Some of the most important cases of constrained motion are those in which the particles are connected by rods and strings. Thus consider the following simple example later to be generalized. Imagine (Fig. 10·1) a particle of mass m attached at the point P to a horizontal, elastic string (whose mass is so small in comparison with m that it may be considered negligible) fastened at the two ends A and B and stretched with tension τ. The distances AP and PB are represented by l_1 and l_2 respectively. The particle is pulled aside

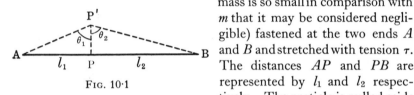

FIG. 10·1

a *short* distance PP' perpendicular to AB and let go. We are to find the resulting motion, assumed to be rectilinear. Call the displacement at any instant ξ and suppose it is very much less than $l(= l_1 + l_2)$. We shall make the simplifying assumption that the alteration in the tension with the stretching of the string is too slight to be taken into account. The total vertical component of force on the particle is then

$$-\tau(\cos \theta_1 + \cos \theta_2). \tag{10·1–1}$$

Now

$$
\left.
\begin{aligned}
\cos \theta_1 &= \frac{\xi}{\sqrt{\xi^2 + l_1{}^2}}, \\[2mm]
\cos \theta_2 &= \frac{\xi}{\sqrt{\xi^2 + l_2{}^2}}.
\end{aligned}
\right\} \tag{10·1–2}
$$

But if $\xi \ll l_1$ and $\xi \ll l_2$, as we have assumed, we can write to a sufficiently good approximation

$$\cos \theta_1 = \frac{\xi}{l_1}, \quad \cos \theta_2 = \frac{\xi}{l_2}, \tag{10·1–3}$$

so that the equation of motion of the particle becomes

$$m\ddot{\xi} = -\tau\xi \left(\frac{1}{l_1} + \frac{1}{l_2}\right). \tag{10·1–4}$$

This is the equation of *simple harmonic motion* (see Sec. 2·3) with frequency

$$\nu = \frac{1}{2\pi} \sqrt{\frac{\tau(l_1 + l_2)}{ml_1l_2}} = \frac{1}{2\pi} \sqrt{\frac{\tau l}{ml_1l_2}}, \qquad (10 \cdot 1 - 5)$$

where l is the total length of the string. If $l_1 = l_2 = l/2$, we get the simple case

$$\nu = \frac{1}{\pi} \sqrt{\frac{\tau}{ml}}. \qquad (10 \cdot 1 - 6)$$

This problem should be compared with the simple pendulum and the simple spring treated previously (Secs. 2·3 and 9·1). It affords a simple illustration of the small oscillations of a dynamical system about a position of equilibrium. We may use it indeed as an introduction to a more extended discussion of this important topic.

10·2. Oscillations of a Dynamical System with One Degree of Freedom — Dissipation. We have had occasion in several preceding sections so far to note the occurrence of simple harmonic oscillations of small amplitude. We need recall only the simple pendulum, the simple spring and the mass particle fixed on a horizontal string (Sec. 10·1). Such oscillations are so important throughout all physics that it will be desirable to discuss their general features with greater elaboration.

We shall at first restrict ourselves to the case of a system with a single degree of freedom. By this is meant a particle or collection of particles whose state of motion at any instant is completely determined by *one* variable, which may of course be quite general in nature, i.e., a linear displacement, angular displacement or some complicated combination of these. In our present discussion we shall be content to use a linear displacement as our variable, and shall denote it by the letter ξ. Associated with the system will be a certain *mass* designated by m and a certain *stiffness* denoted by f. The meaning of the latter is as follows. Suppose that a static force $\mathbf{F}_1$ is necessary to produce a static displacement of the system of magnitude ξ_1. Then

$$f = \frac{F_1}{\xi_1} \qquad (10 \cdot 2 - 1)$$

is defined as the *stiffness* coefficient or more simply the stiffness of the system.[1] If now the latter is displaced a slight amount from its

---

[1] It is here assumed that the stiffness remains constant, i.e., every time the static force is F_1 the corresponding displacement is ξ_1. This implies, as we shall see later in Chap. 11, that the system is elastic. But see the comments at the end of this section.

equilibrium position and then allowed to move freely the equation of motion is clearly

$$m\ddot{\xi} = -f\xi, \qquad (10\cdot2\text{--}2)$$

leading to simple harmonic motion with frequency $\nu = \dfrac{1}{2\pi}\sqrt{\dfrac{f}{m}}$ and period $P = 2\pi\sqrt{\dfrac{m}{f}}$. Thus in the case of the vibration problem treated in Sec. 10·1, the effective stiffness is represented by $f = \tau l/l_1 l_2$, while the mass is the mass of the particle. It may be pointed out that there are certain cases where the equivalent mass (i.e., that entering into the formula) is *not* the whole mass of the oscillating system. This is notably true in the case of a membrane or diaphragm.

However, at present we are more interested in another matter. We have already noted the fact that the eq. (10·2–2) can never adequately represent the true state of affairs for any oscillatory motion occurring in nature, since it implies that once the system is oscillating it continues so indefinitely; this is contrary to experience. We must recognize that there is always present a certain resistance to the motion leading to dissipation, so that ultimately unless some external influence intervenes, rest results. The question arises: how shall this resistance be introduced into the equation of motion? Obviously the resistance may be thought of as equivalent to a force, in nature somewhat like the force of friction in that it is always opposite in direction to the motion. It can hardly be supposed to be proportional to the displacement or any function thereof. On the other hand it does seem reasonable to assume that it is a function of the velocity. Let us therefore suppose that in addition to the *restoring* force of magnitude $-f\xi$ due to the stiffness there is present a resistance force of magnitude $-R\dot{\xi}$, where R will be termed the damping factor or coefficient. It must be emphasized that this is a pure hypothesis, since we have no *a priori* justification for the first power rather than the second or higher. And the essential confirmation of the correctness of this assumption will appear only after the equation of motion thus constructed has been integrated and the resulting motion compared with experience.

The equation of motion on this hypothesis now becomes

$$m\ddot{\xi} = -f\xi - R\dot{\xi},$$

or more simply

$$m\ddot{\xi} + R\dot{\xi} + f\xi = 0. \qquad (10\cdot2\text{--}3)$$

The solution of this equation is given in texts on differential equations, but we may proceed rather simply as follows. The form of the left-hand side indicates an exponential function of the time.   Hence we assume for our solution

$$\xi = Ae^{\lambda t}, \qquad (10\cdot2\text{–}4)$$

where A is an arbitrary constant and λ is to be determined.   We then have

$$\dot{\xi} = A\lambda e^{\lambda t}, \quad \ddot{\xi} = A\lambda^2 e^{\lambda t},$$

and therefore on substitution

$$m\lambda^2 + R\lambda + f = 0. \qquad (10\cdot2\text{–}5)$$

This is the condition which λ must satisfy in order that $(10\cdot2\text{–}4)$ may be a solution of the equation $(10\cdot2\text{–}3)$.   Solving we find

$$\lambda = -\frac{R}{2m} \pm \sqrt{\frac{R^2}{4m^2} - \frac{f}{m}}, \qquad (10\cdot2\text{–}6)$$

and consequently the solution becomes

$$\xi = e^{-R/2m\cdot t}\left(Ae^{\sqrt{R^2/4m^2 - f/m}\cdot t} + Be^{-\sqrt{R^2/4m^2 - f/m}\cdot t}\right), \qquad (10\cdot2\text{–}7)$$

where now the *two* arbitrary constants A and B must enter since we get a solution with the minus sign as well as with the plus sign.   There are three special cases to consider according as

$$\frac{R^2}{4m^2} \lesseqgtr \frac{f}{m}. \qquad (10\cdot2\text{–}8)$$

Let us take first the case where $R^2/4m^2 < f/m$, i.e., where the damping factor R is relatively small.   The radical is then imaginary and we may write

$$\xi = e^{-R/2m\cdot t}\left(Ae^{i\sqrt{f/m - R^2/4m^2}\cdot t} + Be^{-i\sqrt{f/m - R^2/4m^2}\cdot t}\right), \qquad (10\cdot2\text{–}9)$$

with $i = \sqrt{-1}$.   It will be necessary here to recall one or two facts about complex numbers.   Any such number may be represented by a point P in the xy plane with coördinates x and y.   The number itself is then written

$$z \equiv x + iy. \qquad (10\cdot2\text{–}10)$$

But there is another way of expressing this, namely in terms of polar coördinates, for $x = r\cos\theta$ and $y = r\sin\theta$ (Fig. 10·2), whence

$$z = r(\cos\theta + i\sin\theta). \qquad (10\cdot2\text{–}11)$$

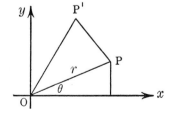

FIG. 10·2

The angle θ is called the *amplitude* or *argument* of the complex number while r is called its *modulus* or *absolute value*. Thus

$$r = \sqrt{x^2 + y^2}.$$

Now consider the complex number

$$w = \cos\theta + i\sin\theta. \tag{10·2–12}$$

This has the modulus unity and we may represent it by a point P in our diagram for which $r = 1$. If we displace P to P' on the unit circle, w changes to $w + dw$ and θ changes to $\theta + d\theta$. But we have from (10·2–12) at once

$$dw = (-\sin\theta + i\cos\theta)\, d\theta$$

$$= i(\cos\theta + i\sin\theta)\, d\theta, \tag{10·2–13}$$

whence

$$dw = iw\, d\theta. \tag{10·2–14}$$

Integrating,

$$\log w = i\theta + C,$$

or

$$w = C'e^{i\theta}, \tag{10·2–15}$$

and since $w = 1$ for $\theta = 0$, $C' = 1$ and hence

$$w = e^{i\theta}. \tag{10·2–16}$$

This extremely important connection between the imaginary exponential and the circular functions enables us to write at once in place of (10·2–9)

$$\xi = e^{-R/2m\cdot t}[(A + B)\cos\gamma t + (A - B)i\sin\gamma t], \tag{10·2–17}$$

where for simplicity we have set $\gamma = \sqrt{f/m - R^2/4m^2}$. In expressing the result in this form it is necessary to admit that A and B may be complex numbers. Write $A = a_1 + ia_2$ while $B = b_1 + ib_2$. Then if we separate ξ into real and imaginary parts we have

$$\xi = e^{-R/2m\cdot t}[(a_1 + b_1)\cos\gamma t - (a_2 - b_2)\sin\gamma t$$

$$+ i\{(a_2 + b_2)\cos\gamma t + (a_1 - b_1)\sin\gamma t\}]. \tag{10·2–18}$$

From the form of the solution it is seen that both the real and imaginary parts are equally solutions and moreover are essentially of the same form. We shall choose to use the real part (and indeed make this our general rule in problems of this kind), and writing $a_1 + b_1 = A'$ and $a_2 - b_2 = B'$, our result is

$$\xi = e^{-R/2m\cdot t}[A'\cos\gamma t - B'\sin\gamma t]. \tag{10·2–19}$$

This result can be put into even more compact form if we introduce the new variables C and ϵ where

$$A' = C \cos \epsilon \quad \text{and} \quad B' = C \sin \epsilon. \qquad (10\cdot2\text{--}20)$$

With these new constants we get for the displacement of the system

$$\xi = Ce^{-R/2m\cdot t} \cos (\gamma t + \epsilon). \qquad (10\cdot2\text{--}21)$$

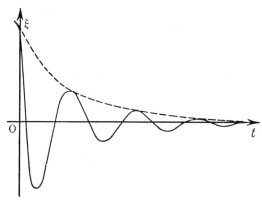

FIG. 10·3

We are now ready to interpret the final answer physically.   If we plot ξ as a function of t the result is indicated in Fig. 10·3 and represents an oscillation of frequency

$$\nu = \frac{\gamma}{2\pi}, \qquad (10\cdot2\text{--}22)$$

the amplitude of which decays steadily with the progress of time. It is often called a *damped* oscillation.   Two arbitrary constants are involved: C, the initial *amplitude*, and ϵ, the initial *phase*.   By definition the phase of the motion at any instant t is

$$\phi = \gamma t + \epsilon. \qquad (10\cdot2\text{--}23)$$

With regard to the frequency we note that if the damping is small, i.e., if $R^2/4m^2 \ll f/m$, the frequency does not differ noticeably from that of the corresponding undamped oscillator.   Thus slight damping has little effect on the *frequency* of a simple harmonic oscillator.   This is well borne out by experiments on pendulums, springs, tuning forks, etc., and serves as one check on the reasonableness of our equation of motion for the oscillator.

The magnitude of the damping effect is given by the term $R/2m$. The reciprocal of this quantity, viz., $2m/R$, is often called the " decay modulus ": it represents the time taken for the oscillation amplitude to decay to $1/e$-th of its original value. For small damping it is accordingly very large. Another commonly used measure of the damping is the so-called "logarithmic decrement." It is the logarithm to the base e of the ratio of two successive amplitudes. Thus if $P(= 1/\nu)$ is one period of the motion,

$$\log \frac{Ce^{-R2/m \cdot t_1}}{Ce^{-R/2m \cdot (t_1 + P)}} = \frac{R}{2m} P \qquad (10 \cdot 2 - 24)$$

is the logarithmic decrement.

It will be worth while to pause and consider a little the evaluation of the constants C and ϵ from the initial conditions. Suppose that when $t = 0$, $\xi = \xi_0$. We then have from (10·2–21)

$$\xi_0 = C \cos \epsilon. \qquad (10 \cdot 2 - 25)$$

This alone is not sufficient to determine both constants. We might of course note the displacement at some later time and so obtain another relation from which together with (10·2–25) C and ϵ may be calculated. Actually it is simpler to use the initial *velocity* for this purpose. Thus differentiating (10·2–21) with respect to the time yields

$$\dot{\xi} = C\left(-\frac{R}{2m}\right) e^{-R/2m \cdot t} \cos(\gamma t + \epsilon) - Ce^{-R/2m \cdot t} \gamma \sin(\gamma t + \epsilon). \qquad (10 \cdot 2 - 26)$$

Now when $t = 0$, if $\dot{\xi} = \dot{\xi}_0$ we have

$$\dot{\xi}_0 = -\frac{RC}{2m} \cos \epsilon - C\gamma \sin \epsilon, \qquad (10 \cdot 2 - 27)$$

whence we find using (10·2–25)

$$\tan \epsilon = -\frac{\dot{\xi}_0 + \dfrac{R}{2m} \xi_0}{\gamma \xi_0}, \qquad (10 \cdot 2 - 28)$$

while C is finally obtained as

$$C = \frac{\sqrt{\gamma^2 \xi_0^2 + \left(\dot{\xi}_0 + \dfrac{R}{2m} \xi_0\right)^2}}{\gamma}. \qquad (10 \cdot 2 - 29)$$

In case the damping is so slight as to be negligible, i.e., $R/2m \ll 1$, we have approximately

$$\tan \epsilon = -\frac{\dot{\xi}_0}{\xi_0 \sqrt{\dfrac{f}{m}}}, \qquad (10 \cdot 2 - 30)$$

and

$$C = \sqrt{\frac{\xi_0^2 \dfrac{f}{m} + \dot{\xi}_0^2}{\dfrac{f}{m}}}$$

$$= \sqrt{\xi_0^2 + \frac{m}{f} \dot{\xi}_0^2}. \tag{10·2-31}$$

Before entering upon further discussion of these damped oscillations and their interesting analogies throughout the realm of physics we must dispose of the other two cases indicated in (10·2–8). Take first the rather unusual case where

$$\frac{f}{m} = \frac{R^2}{4m^2}. \tag{10·2-32}$$

Here the roots of (10·2–5) are both equal to $-R/2m$ and our procedure must be somewhat modified. Instead of substituting $\xi = Ae^{\lambda t}$ as in (10·2–4) we let

$$\xi = e^{\lambda t}\chi(t), \tag{10·2-33}$$

where $\chi(t)$ is at first an undetermined function of t. Then

$$\dot{\xi} = \lambda e^{\lambda t}\chi + e^{\lambda t}\dot{\chi},$$

$$\ddot{\xi} = \lambda^2 e^{\lambda t}\chi + 2\lambda e^{\lambda t}\dot{\chi} + e^{\lambda t}\ddot{\chi},$$

and on substitution into the equation of motion

$$m(\lambda^2\chi + 2\lambda\dot{\chi} + \ddot{\chi}) + R(\lambda\chi + \dot{\chi}) + f\chi = 0, \tag{10·2-34}$$

or rearranging

$$\chi(m\lambda^2 + R\lambda + f) + \dot{\chi}(2m\lambda + R) + m\ddot{\chi} = 0. \tag{10·2-35}$$

Now since (10·1–5) is satisfied by $\lambda = -R/2m$, the above reduces to

$$\ddot{\chi} = 0. \tag{10·2-36}$$

Therefore

$$\chi = A + Bt, \tag{10·2-37}$$

where A and B are arbitrary constants, will satisfy the equation. The solution in this case then becomes

$$\xi = e^{-R/2m \cdot t}(A + Bt). \tag{10·2-38}$$

We note at once that (10·2–38) does not represent an oscillation. Depending on the initial conditions there are various possible types of curves. Taking the case where A and B are both positive, if $A < 2mB/R$, a curve of type I with a maximum displaced from $t = 0$ results, while if $A = 2mB/R$ the curve is of type II with maximum at the origin, and finally if $A > 2mB/R$, there is no maximum but ξ decreases steadily to zero as time progresses. All three represent what is called *critically* damped motion. Obviously if A and B are of different signs, ξ will become zero for finite t, and somewhat more complicated curves than those shown in Fig. 10·4 will result. The reader should investigate these for himself.

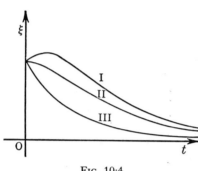

Fig. 10·4

We finally consider the case where $R^2/4m^2 > f/m$, i.e., γ imaginary. Here again, as inspection of eq. (10·2–7) shows, *no* oscillations are present. We can represent the result somewhat more simply if we introduce some simple initial conditions, say $\xi = \xi_0$ and $\dot{\xi} = 0$ for $t = 0$. Then with $\gamma' = i\gamma$ (where γ' is real) the solution (10·2–7) is

$$\xi = e^{-R/2m \cdot t}(Ae^{\gamma't} + Be^{-\gamma't}).$$

The initial condition gives

$$\xi_0 = A + B, \qquad\qquad (10\cdot2\text{–}39)$$

while since

$$\dot{\xi} = -\frac{R}{2m}e^{-R/2m \cdot t}(Ae^{\gamma't} + Be^{-\gamma't})$$

$$+ e^{-R/2m \cdot t}(A\gamma'e^{\gamma't} - B\gamma'e^{-\gamma't}),$$

for $t = 0$, we have

$$0 = -\frac{R}{2m}(A + B) + \gamma'(A - B)$$

$$= A\left[\gamma' - \frac{R}{2m}\right] - B\left[\gamma' + \frac{R}{2m}\right]. \qquad (10\cdot2\text{–}40)$$

Solving for A and B from (10·2–39) and (10·2–40), we have

$$A = \frac{\xi_0\left[\gamma' + \dfrac{R}{2m}\right]}{2\gamma'},$$

$$\left.\begin{array}{c}\\ \\ \\ \\ \end{array}\right\} \qquad (10\cdot2\text{–}41)$$

$$B = \frac{\xi_0\left[\gamma' - \dfrac{R}{2m}\right]}{2\gamma'}.$$

Then for the displacement there results

$$\xi = \frac{\xi_0 e^{-R/2m \cdot t}}{2\gamma'}\left[\gamma'(e^{\gamma't} + e^{-\gamma't}) + \frac{R}{2m}(e^{\gamma't} - e^{-\gamma't})\right]. \quad (10\cdot2\text{--}42)$$

Now using hyperbolic functions we may write

$$e^{\gamma't} + e^{-\gamma't} = 2\cosh\gamma't,$$

$$e^{\gamma't} - e^{-\gamma't} = 2\sinh\gamma't,$$

whence it follows that the displacement is

$$\xi = \frac{\xi_0 e^{-R/2m \cdot t}}{\gamma'}\left[\gamma'\cosh\gamma't + \frac{R}{2m}\sinh\gamma't\right]. \quad (10\cdot2\text{--}43)$$

The reader should plot this as an exercise.

Physically the last two cases, in which $R^2/4m^2 \geqq f/m$, correspond to rather considerable damping such as may be made manifest by the motion of a pendulum in a very viscous fluid like molasses or heavy tar. Strictly speaking they thus lie outside the realm of oscillations which are the theme of this chapter. Nevertheless there are some interesting analogies in other branches of physics.

A rather interesting case of damped motion occurs when the mass of the system is so small that the term $m\ddot{\xi}$ in (10·2–3) can be neglected. The equation of " motion " then becomes

$$R\dot{\xi} + f\xi = 0, \quad (10\cdot2\text{--}44)$$

with solution

$$\xi = \xi_0 e^{-ft/R}. \quad (10\cdot2\text{--}45)$$

This means physically that the system has been started off with initial displacement ξ_0 and initial velocity $-\xi_0 f/R$. Obviously the displacement goes asymptotically to zero as t increases and there is no oscillation. In time $\tau = R/f$, ξ becomes ξ_0/e and it is said that the system has relaxed to $1/e$-th of the initial displacement. The time R/f is then called the " relaxation time."

The notion of relaxation time is important in many physical phenomena. Thus when we try to stretch a wire by hanging a weight on it the increase in length given by Hooke's law does not immediately take place. The elementary physics relation

$$F = f\xi \quad (10\cdot2\text{--}46)$$

for the stretching force corresponding to stretch ξ assumes an equilibrium condition which does not prevail at the instant that the force is applied. Hence to study the problem of stretching a wire *dynamically* we must replace (10·2–46) by an equation which takes account of the velocity with which the stretching process proceeds. The simplest form of such an equation is

$$F = f\xi + R\dot{\xi},\qquad\qquad(10\cdot2\text{–}47)$$

which for *constant* applied force F has the solution

$$\xi = F/f\cdot(1 - e^{-ft/R}).\qquad\qquad(10\cdot2\text{–}48)$$

After time $\tau = R/f$, ξ reaches to within $1/e$ of F/f, which is the final stretch. Hence once more we term R/f the relaxation time of the process.

Every physical phenomenon in which there is a time lag in the attainment of the effect of a given cause will show a relaxation time. Hence the notion is of considerable importance in physics.

10·3. Energy of Damped Oscillations.   Time Averages.   Let us revert to the oscillations discussed in the previous section and consider them from the standpoint of the energy involved.   It will be recalled that eq. (10·2–2) refers to the motion of a *conservative* system (Sec. 4·1), for on multiplying through both sides by $\dot{\xi}dt$, we have

$$d(\tfrac{1}{2}m\dot{\xi}^2) + d(\tfrac{1}{2}f\xi^2) = 0,$$

or

$$\tfrac{1}{2}m\dot{\xi}^2 + \tfrac{1}{2}f\xi^2 = C.\qquad\qquad(10\cdot3\text{–}1)$$

The first term on the left is the kinetic energy K of the oscillator, while the second term is the potential energy V, for by definition it is the work done while the oscillator is displaced an amount ξ against the restoring force $-f\xi$.   The sum of the kinetic and potential energies is the *total* energy, which in this case is constant.

The situation is different, however, as soon as dissipation is taken into account.   Thus if we multiply eq. (10·2–3) by $\dot{\xi}$, we obtain

$$\dot{K} + \dot{V} = -R\dot{\xi}^2 = \dot{U},\qquad\qquad(10\cdot3\text{–}2)$$

where the total energy is represented by U.   In other words the energy of the system is decreasing with the time at the rate $R\dot{\xi}^2$.   This is then the rate of dissipation of energy and one-half of it has been called by Lord Rayleigh[1] the *dissipation function*.   The system under consideration is no longer a conservative but a *dissipative* system.

Let us digress for a moment to note that an important concept in connection with oscillating systems is that of *time average*.   Just as one forms the arithmetical mean or average of a number of similar quantities by adding them and dividing by the number, so one may

---

[1] *Theory of Sound*, Vol. I, §81.

form the *average* of the function of a variable over a given range or interval of values of the variable by *integrating* the function over this interval and dividing the result by the magnitude of the interval. Considering the matter geometrically, if $z = f(t)$ is the function and we plot it as in the attached illustrative figure (Fig. 10·5), the average of $f(t)$ over the interval from $t = t_0$ to $t = t_1$ is denoted by $\overset{t}{\overline{f(t)}}$ (the t above the bar may be left off if it is perfectly definite that the average is with respect to t), where

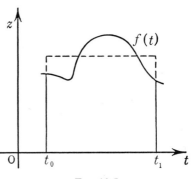

FIG. 10·5

$$\overset{t}{\overline{f(t)}} = \frac{1}{t_1 - t_0} \cdot \int_{t_0}^{t_1} f(t)\, dt. \qquad (10\cdot3\text{--}3)$$

It is thus evident that $\overset{t}{\overline{f(t)}}$ is the ordinate which when multiplied by the magnitude of the interval gives an area equal to the actual area between the curve and the t axis from t_0 to t_1.

We may now discuss $\bar{K}$ and $\bar{V}$ for the case of an oscillator. Taking first for simplicity the case of an *undamped* oscillator we have

$$\xi = A \cos (2\pi v t + \epsilon), \qquad (10\cdot3\text{--}4)$$

where v is the frequency, A the amplitude and ϵ the initial phase. Then

$$\dot{\xi} = -2\pi v A \sin (2\pi v t + \epsilon). \qquad (10\cdot3\text{--}5)$$

The kinetic and potential energies become respectively

$$K = 2\pi^2 v^2 A^2 m \sin^2 (2\pi v t + \epsilon), \qquad (10\cdot3\text{--}6)$$

$$V = \tfrac{1}{2} f A^2 \cos^2 (2\pi v t + \epsilon), \qquad (10\cdot3\text{--}7)$$

and we note that $K + V = $ constant, as must necessarily be the case. The averages over a single period $P = 1/v$ are then

$$\bar{K} = \frac{2\pi^2 v^2 m A^2}{P} \int_0^P \sin^2 (2\pi v t + \epsilon)\, dt, \qquad (10\cdot3\text{--}8)$$

$$\bar{V} = \frac{f A^2}{2P} \int_0^P \cos^2 (2\pi v t + \epsilon)\, dt. \qquad (10\cdot3\text{--}9)$$

Now

$$\frac{1}{P} \int_0^P \sin^2 (2\pi v t + \epsilon)\, dt = \frac{1}{4\pi v P} \left[(2\pi v t + \epsilon) - \tfrac{1}{2} \sin 2(2\pi v t + \epsilon) \right]_0^P .$$

Since $\sin 2(2\pi + \epsilon) = \sin 2\epsilon$, the above reduces to $\frac{1}{2}$, and hence

$$\bar{K} = \pi^2 \nu^2 m A^2. \tag{10·3–10}$$

Similarly

$$\frac{1}{P}\int_0^P \cos^2 (2\pi \nu t + \epsilon)\, dt = \frac{1}{4\pi \nu P}\left[(2\pi \nu t + \epsilon) + \frac{1}{2}\sin 2(2\pi \nu t + \epsilon)\right]_0^P$$

$$= \frac{1}{2},$$

and therefore

$$\bar{V} = \frac{fA^2}{4}. \tag{10·3–11}$$

But the frequency of the oscillation is

$$\nu = \frac{1}{2\pi}\sqrt{\frac{f}{m}},$$

so that $f = 4\pi^2\nu^2 m$. It thus develops that

$$\bar{K} = \bar{V} \tag{10·3–12}$$

over a single period. Obviously the same result will hold over any number of periods. In fact it may be noted that since

$$\frac{1}{\tau}\int_0^\tau \left.\begin{matrix} \sin^2 \\ \cos^2 \end{matrix}\right\} (2\pi \nu t + \epsilon)\, dt \doteqdot \frac{1}{2}, \tag{10·3–13}$$

as the time interval τ grows greater, even if it is not a multiple of one period, the average kinetic energy over *any* interval of time large compared with one period is equal to the average potential energy. In general in what follows, when we speak of a time average for an oscillating system we shall mean that taken over such an interval.

The reader may find it of interest to compare with the above the *space* averages of V and K, though the latter are not usually of such physical interest as the time average.

10·4. Forced Oscillations of a Dissipative System.

The oscillations discussed in the previous two sections are what may be called "free" or "natural" oscillations. Suppose now that a periodic force of frequency $\nu = \omega/2\pi$ and amplitude F_0 is applied to a dynamical system with *one* degree of freedom. The differential equation of the motion is then

$$m\ddot{\xi} + R\dot{\xi} + f\xi = F_0 \cos \omega t. \tag{10·4–1}$$

We shall find that there is considerable advantage in using complex quantities rather freely in this problem. Thus instead of using merely the *real* part of a complex force on the right side of (10·4–1), let us use $F_0e^{i\omega t}$, i.e., a complex force. The actual justification of this step may be made in the following manner. The oscillator equation may just as well be written

$$m\ddot{\xi}' + R\dot{\xi}' + f\xi' = F_0 \sin \omega t. \tag{10·4–2}$$

If now we multiply through (9·4–2) by i and add to (9·4–1) we obtain

$$m(\ddot{\xi} + i\ddot{\xi}') + R(\dot{\xi} + i\dot{\xi}') + f(\xi + i\xi') = F_0e^{i\omega t}. \tag{10·4–3}$$

This equation may be written

$$m\ddot{\xi} + R\dot{\xi} + f\xi = F_0e^{i\omega t}, \tag{10·4–4}$$

if we agree to let ξ now represent a *complex displacement* as in (10·4–3). On solving (10·4–4) we must ultimately take the real part of the resulting ξ (although, of course, the imaginary part would likewise describe equally well the behavior of the system under the influence of the force). The solution of (10·4–4) consists really of two parts, of which the first is that which has already been obtained in Sec. 10·2, while the second is that which on substitution will yield $F_0e^{i\omega t}$ on the right side instead of zero. The first is called the *transient*, for in any case it is more or less rapidly damped to zero. It is the second, or what may be called the *steady state*, solution in which we are interested here.

From the form of the right side, we are led at once to substitute

$$\xi = Ae^{i\omega t}, \tag{10·4–5}$$

whence

$$\dot{\xi} = i\omega Ae^{i\omega t}; \quad \ddot{\xi} = -\omega^2 Ae^{i\omega t}. \tag{10·4–6}$$

On substitution there follows for A

$$A = \frac{F_0}{i\omega R + f - m\omega^2}, \tag{10·4–7}$$

and the steady state solution is then

$$\xi = \frac{F_0e^{i\omega t}}{i\omega R + f - m\omega^2}. \tag{10·4–8}$$

The real part of this is now found at once by rationalizing the denominator. We multiply both numerator and denominator by $-i\omega R + f - m\omega^2$ and have

$$\xi = \frac{F_0[-i\omega R + f - m\omega^2]e^{i\omega t}}{(f - m\omega^2)^2 + \omega^2 R^2}. \tag{10·4–9}$$

Therefore

$$\xi_{\text{real}} = \frac{F_0\{(f - m\omega^2) \cos \omega t + \omega R \sin \omega t\}}{\omega^2 R^2 + (f - m\omega^2)^2}. \tag{10·4–10}$$

Let us introduce the angle α where

$$\cos \alpha = \frac{f - m\omega^2}{\sqrt{(f - m\omega^2)^2 + \omega^2 R^2}},$$

$$\sin \alpha = \frac{\omega R}{\sqrt{(f - m\omega^2)^2 + \omega^2 R^2}},$$

or

$$\tan \alpha = \frac{\omega R}{f - m\omega^2}. \tag{10·4–11}$$

Our expression for the displacement then becomes

$$\xi_{real} = \frac{F_0 \cos(\omega t - \alpha)}{\sqrt{\omega^2 R^2 + (f - m\omega^2)^2}}. \tag{10·4–12}$$

The angle α is the *phase difference* between the force and the displacement. Before we discuss the displacement further it will be worth while to obtain the expression for $\dot{\xi}$, the velocity, which is often more important in application than ξ itself. From (10·4–6) we have

$$\dot{\xi} = i\omega\xi. \tag{10·4–13}$$

Hence from (10·4–8) there follows

$$\dot{\xi} = \frac{F_0 e^{i\omega t}}{R + i\left(m\omega - \dfrac{f}{\omega}\right)}, \tag{10·4–14}$$

and if we evaluate the real part as above we get

$$\dot{\xi}_{real} = \frac{F_0 \cos(\omega t - \beta)}{\sqrt{R^2 + \left(m\omega - \dfrac{f}{\omega}\right)^2}}, \tag{10·4–15}$$

where

$$\tan \beta = \frac{m\omega - \dfrac{f}{\omega}}{R}, \tag{10·4–16}$$

and β is the phase difference between the force and the velocity. Comparing (10·4–16) with (10·4–11) we see that

$$\tan \alpha = -\frac{1}{\tan \beta}. \tag{10·4–17}$$

Hence

$$\alpha - \beta = \frac{2}{\pi}. \tag{10·4–18}$$

This means that ξ and $\dot{\xi}$ differ in phase by $\pi/2$.

Now if we examine the expressions for ξ_{real} and $\dot{\xi}_{real}$ we note that the system is always *forced* to *oscillate* under the action of the periodic force, but that the *amplitude* of the resulting oscillation depends on the magnitudes of $R, f, m,$ and ω, and of course may be very small indeed. On the other hand it may also be rather large. We note that if the characteristics of the system (R, f, m) are fixed, there is a value of the frequency of the applied force which makes $\sqrt{R^2 + (m\omega - f/\omega)^2}$ a *minimum* and hence the amplitude of $\dot{\xi}_{real}$ a *maximum*. This happens for

$$\omega = \omega_0 = \sqrt{\frac{f}{m}}.$$
(10·4–19)

When this occurs, the system is said to be in *resonance* with the force and the corresponding frequency

$$\nu_0 = \frac{\omega_0}{2\pi} = \frac{1}{2\pi}\sqrt{\frac{f}{m}}$$
(10·4–20)

is called the *resonance frequency*. For resonance then we have

$$\dot{\xi}_{res.} = \frac{F_0}{R} \cdot \cos \omega_0 t,$$
(10·4–21)

since the phase difference β_0 for resonance is equal to zero. On the other hand the resonance displacement is

$$\xi_{res.} = \frac{F_0}{\omega_0 R} \cdot \cos \left(\omega_0 t - \frac{\pi}{2}\right).$$
(10·4–22)

It is easily seen that the amplitude of the displacement is not quite a maximum for the resonance frequency. It reaches its maximum for that frequency for which $\sqrt{\omega^2 R^2 + (f - m\omega^2)^2}$ is a minimum. The usual test shows that this takes place for

$$\omega = \omega_1 = \sqrt{\frac{f}{m} - \frac{R^2}{2m^2}}.$$
(10·4–23)

As a matter of fact if the damping is small the term $R^2/2m^2$ is negligible compared with f/m and $\omega_0 \doteq \omega_1$ approximately. Moreover, if we recall (10·2–22) we remember that the so-called *natural* or *free* oscillation frequency is $1/2\pi \cdot \sqrt{f/m - R^2/4m^2}$ and this for small damping is approximately the same as the resonance frequency. We shall then attach most significance to the latter frequency.

Coming back to the phase we see that for resonance the force and the velocity of the system are exactly in phase, while the displacement and the force are out of phase by $\pi/2$. Any one who has pushed a swing will recall that the way to produce swings of large amplitude is to time the pushes so that they reach their maximum force when the displacement from equilibrium is *smallest*, *not* at the end of each swing.

The question of energy dissipation is an interesting one. As we have already shown in Sec. 10·3, the rate of dissipation is $R\dot{\xi}^2$. Hence the *average* rate (in *time* of course) is

$$\bar{D} = \frac{1}{\tau} \int_0^\tau R\dot{\xi}^2 \, dt$$

$$= \frac{F_0^2 R}{R^2 + \left(m\omega - \dfrac{f}{\omega}\right)^2} \cdot \frac{1}{\tau} \int_0^\tau \cos^2(\omega t - \beta) \, dt. \qquad (10\text{·}4\text{--}24)$$

Now we have already shown (Sec. 9·3) that

$$\frac{1}{\tau} \int_0^\tau \cos^2(\omega t - \beta) \, dt \doteq \tfrac{1}{2}, \qquad (10\text{·}4\text{--}25)$$

if τ is much greater than a single period $P = \dfrac{2\pi}{\omega}$. Incidentally the student should show that on the other hand the average of $\sin(\omega t - \beta)$ $\cos(\omega t - \beta)$ is zero. These results will be useful in the solution of special problems, and will be assumed from now on. We thus have

$$\bar{D} = \frac{F_0^2 R}{2\left[R^2 + \left(m\omega - \dfrac{f}{\omega}\right)^2\right]} \cdot \qquad (10\text{·}4\text{--}26)$$

This may be put into simpler form if we recall that

$$\cos \beta = \frac{R}{\sqrt{R^2 + \left(m\omega - \dfrac{f}{\omega}\right)^2}} \cdot \qquad (10\text{·}4\text{--}27)$$

Therefore

$$\bar{D} = \frac{F_0^2}{2R} \cos^2 \beta. \qquad (10\text{·}4\text{--}28)$$

This form is particularly interesting because it is clear from it that when $\beta = 0$, i.e., when resonance ensues, $\bar{D}$ is a maximum equal to

$$\bar{D}_{\text{res.}} = \frac{F_0^2}{2R} \cdot \qquad (10\text{·}4\text{--}29)$$

On the other hand when $\beta = \pi/2$, i.e., when force and velocity are out of phase (or force and displacement in phase or differing by π), $\bar{D} = 0$.

We have now to ask what connection $\bar{D}$ has with the rate of contribution of energy by the force to the system. The latter will clearly be

$$\dot{W} = \dot{\xi} F_0 \cos \omega t, \qquad (10\text{·}4\text{–}30)$$

that is, the product of the force by the velocity (which is the *power*). For the average we then have

$$\bar{W} = \frac{F_0{}^2}{\sqrt{R^2 + \left(m\omega - \dfrac{f}{\omega}\right)^2}} \overline{\cos \omega t \cdot \cos (\omega t - \beta)}$$

$$= \frac{1}{2} \frac{F_0{}^2 \cos \beta}{\sqrt{R^2 + \left(m\omega - \dfrac{f}{\omega}\right)^2}}, \qquad (10\text{·}4\text{–}31)$$

whence from (10·4–27)

$$\bar{W} = \frac{F_0{}^2}{2R} \cos^2 \beta = \bar{D}. \qquad (10\text{·}4\text{–}32)$$

In words, the rate at which the force contributes energy to the system is on the average just equal to the rate at which the system has its energy dissipated. This could indeed have been predicted from general considerations. The interesting thing is that when the system is in resonance with the force, the flow of energy *into* the system as well as the rate of dissipation *by* the system is a maximum.

The damping exercises a very important and characteristic effect on the resonance. Let us look into this. Writing (10·4–31) again we have

$$\bar{W} = \frac{1}{2} \frac{F_0{}^2 R}{R^2 + \left(m\omega - \dfrac{f}{\omega}\right)^2}$$

$$= \frac{1}{2} \frac{F_0{}^2 R}{R^2 + m^2 \omega_0{}^2 x^2}, \qquad (10\text{·}4\text{–}33)$$

where we have put for convenience

$$\frac{\omega}{\omega_0} - \frac{\omega_0}{\omega} = x. \qquad (10\text{·}4\text{–}34)$$

If now we plot $\bar{W}$ as a function of x we get curves of the type indicated in the following figure (Fig. 10·6). When $x = 0$, $\omega = \omega_0$, and hence the value of $\bar{W}$ at the origin represents the resonance or maximum value. As ω deviates from ω_0, $\bar{W}$ falls off to either side. The rapidity of the dropping off determines the sharpness or broadness of the resonance. The latter is fixed by the value of $d\overline{\overline{W}}/dx$. Thus

$$\frac{d\overline{\overline{W}}}{dx} = -\frac{F_0{}^2 R m^2 \omega_0{}^2 x}{(R^2 + m^2\omega_0{}^2 x^2)^2} . \qquad (10\cdot4\text{--}35)$$

For $x > 0$, i.e., $\omega > \omega_0$, $\dfrac{d\overline{\overline{W}}}{dx}$ is *negative* and varies with R in such a way that the *smaller* R is, the *greater* is the absolute value of $\dfrac{d\overline{\overline{W}}}{dx}$.

On the other hand at $\omega = \omega_0$ for *small* R, $\overline{\overline{W}}$ is *large*. We may summarize by saying that for *small* damping factor the resonance peak is *high* but *sharp*, whereas for *large* damping factor the peak is *low* and *blunt*, i.e., the resonance is broad. This may be seen even more simply

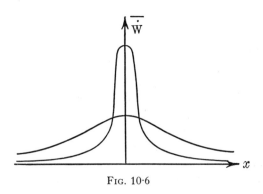

Fig. 10·6

by a direct inspection of (10·4–33). The relation of the height of the peak to R can be seen by substituting $x = 0$, and the relative sharpness of the peaks can be inferred from the fact that when R is large one has to choose a larger value of x to reduce the value of $\overline{\overline{W}}$ in the same proportion than when R is smaller.

Recent research in connection with mechanical oscillations has shown the value of introducing a notation borrowed from the theory of electrical oscillations. To go back to the expression for $\dot{\xi}$ [eq. (10·4–14)] the amplitude of the velocity is controlled by the expression in the denominator, viz.,

$$R + i\left(m\omega - \frac{f}{\omega}\right). \qquad (10\cdot4\text{--}36)$$

This quantity will be denoted by Z and will be termed the *mechanical impedance* of the oscillating system. It is a complex quantity. If we split it into real and imaginary parts

$$Z = Z_1 + iZ_2, \qquad (10\cdot4\text{--}37)$$

we have

$$Z_1 = R, \tag{10·4-38}$$

and

$$Z_2 = m\omega - \frac{f}{\omega}. \tag{10·4-39}$$

The real part is called the *mechanical resistance*, while the imaginary part is called the *mechanical reactance*. The absolute value of the impedance is

$$|Z| = \sqrt{R^2 + \left(m\omega - \frac{f}{\omega}\right)^2}, \tag{10·4-40}$$

so that we may write

$$\dot{\xi}_{real} = \frac{F_0}{|Z|} \cdot \cos(\omega t - \beta), \tag{10·4-41}$$

i.e., for a given force the velocity amplitude varies inversely as the absolute value of the impedance. For the resonance case the impedance becomes real and reduces to the resistance. The significance of these terms will become clearer when we have discussed the electrical circuit analogy (cf. Sec. 10·6). But this notation has proved of value even in connection with mechanical problems.[1]

10·5. The Acoustic Resonator as an Illustration of Oscillatory Motion.
In order to emphasize the importance of the mechanics of simple oscillating systems, we may well pause here to consider some applications to physical problems. These are very numerous. We shall choose only a few typical illustrations.

Consider first the action of an acoustic resonator. This instrument (indicated diagrammatically in Fig. 10·7) consists usually of a hollow metal sphere with a small opening which may or may not have the form of a tubular neck. When a number of vibrating tuning forks of various frequencies are brought near the opening successively, it may be found that for one particular fork the resonator appears to

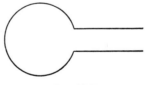

Fig. 10·7

amplify the sound many times, while for the others little effect of this nature is observed. This phenomenon reminds one at once of the resonance condition discussed in Sec. 10·4. Hence we try to treat the

---

[1] A very useful book on mechanical oscillations is that of J. P. Den Hartog, *Mechanical Vibrations*, 3rd ed., McGraw-Hill, New York, 1958. Also see P. M. Morse, *Vibration and Sound*, 2nd ed., McGraw-Hill, New York, 1948.

action as a *mechanical* problem. The student will find that this is a characteristic attitude taken by the physicist. Whenever an experimental phenomenon shows signs of similarity with some result of classical mechanics, the temptation is very strong to apply mechanical reasoning to the more exact description of the phenomenon. The justification of this process has come in the remarkable success which has so far attended it. It should be remarked, to be sure, that very recent physics has shown a tendency to get away from this program. However, we may well doubt that this tendency will ever be completely successful, so strong is the feeling of human minds for mechanical pictures. In any case we can hardly exaggerate in emphasizing the importance of mechanical methods in all the branches of physics.

Now if the acoustic resonator is a problem in mechanics we must decide what it is that *moves*. Here of course it is necessary to make an assumption, which however is not so very arbitrary. We postulate that the thing which moves is the *air* in the opening, and that there is a certain amount of it which moves *approximately* as a *whole*. If there is a neck (and this is the case we shall discuss here) we shall take as the *mass* of the moving air

$$m = \rho l S, \tag{10.5-1}$$

where ρ is the density of the air, l the length of the neck and S its area of cross-section. If we denote the displacement of the air by ξ, the kinetic reaction then is

$$\rho l S \ddot{\xi}. \tag{10.5-2}$$

We must next look for the *stiffness* of the system. It seems reasonable that this will be found in the air in the chamber of the resonator which is alternately compressed and expanded as the air in the neck moves *in* and *out*, and hence acts like an elastic cushion for the latter. In order now to find the stiffness coefficient we must avail ourselves of a little elementary knowledge of elasticity and fluids (cf. Chapters 11 and 12). If a fluid of volume V changes its volume by an amount dV under the influence of pressure p (force per unit area — see Sec. 12.1 on hydrostatics) the necessary pressure is related to dV in the following way

$$\frac{p}{-\dfrac{dV}{V}} = B, \tag{10.5-3}$$

where B is the so-called *volume elasticity* or *bulk modulus*. The relation (10.5-3) is indeed the form *Hooke's law* (see Sec. 11.1) takes for fluids. Now in the problem under discussion, V will represent the volume of the resonator chamber and dV will be the change brought about in V by the motion of the " plug " of air in the neck.   Hence we have

$$dV = -S\xi, \tag{10·5-4}$$

for the volume change accompanying the air displacement ξ.   The stiffness coefficient f has been defined previously to be the ratio of the force necessary to produce the displacement ξ to ξ itself.   We therefore have

$$f = \frac{Sp}{\xi},$$

and using eqs. (10·5–3) and (10·5–4) we get

$$f = \frac{S^2B}{V}. \tag{10·5-5}$$

We have finally to look for the damping factor.   This is much the most difficult task.   It might be thought that we shall find dissipation in the viscous resistance of the air itself and also in the friction at and absorption by the walls of the neck.   These factors certainly enter but a more elaborate calculation than is appropriate for this book indicates that they alone are incompetent to account for the observed dissipation.   Rather it develops that we must consider the *radiation* of sound energy from the opening of the resonator.   From elementary physical principles it is clear that this radiation must exist, otherwise the amplification of the resonator at resonance could not be at all so evident.   Its analytical calculation, however, is a rather difficult matter, since it is dependent on concepts connected with wave motion which we shall not discuss until Chapter 11.   However, it will do no harm to state here the result: the radiation produces a damping force of the following magnitude

$$R\dot{\xi} = \frac{\rho\omega^2S^2}{2\pi c}\dot{\xi}, \tag{10·5-6}$$

where c is the velocity of sound and $\omega = 2\pi\nu$, ν being the frequency of the radiated sound.   The interesting point to note is that the damping force proves to be proportional to $\dot{\xi}$ as we assumed in the general mechanical case (Sec. 10·2).   This furnishes a useful confirmation of our previous assumption.   We may now write the equation of motion for the resonator as follows

$$\rho lS\ddot{\xi} + \frac{\rho\omega^2S^2}{2\pi c}\dot{\xi} + \frac{S^2B}{V}\xi = F_0e^{i\omega t}, \tag{10·5-7}$$

where $F_0e^{i\omega t}$ is the external force acting on the resonator due to the tuning fork, microphone or whatever other source of sound is used.

We note at once the mathematical similarity between this equation and (10·4–4). It is not necessary to carry through the solution. As an exercise the reader may show, for example, that the resonance frequency of the resonator is given *approximately* by

$$\frac{c}{2\pi}\sqrt{\frac{S}{lV}}. \tag{10·5–8}$$

Here $c = \sqrt{B/\rho}$, the usual expression for the velocity of sound in a fluid (see Sec. 12·6). The form (10·5–8) would be strictly exact were it not for the damping which introduces a small correction term similar to that noted in the mechanical problem, eq. (10·2–22). Further details about the resonator, including for example the case of a resonator with *no* neck, and the general expression for the amplification are to be found in textbooks on acoustics.[1] Our purpose here has been to emphasize the mechanical analogy, and it should be stressed that every theoretical development for the mechanical system in Sec. 10·4 has its counterpart in the acoustical system constituted by the resonator.

10·6. Electrical Oscillations. The concepts developed in Sec. 10·4 are of great value in electricity also, as we shall now proceed to illustrate with the simplest possible example. In developing it we shall assume merely the most elementary facts about electric currents such as the student should know from his first course in physics.

Let us suppose that we join a coil of heavy wire having inductance L but negligible resistance in series with a coil of wire of resistance R (wound back on itself to render its inductance negligible), and also insert in the circuit a condenser of capacity C. A source of alternating electromotive force $E = E_0 e^{i\omega t}$ is now placed across all three (see the diagrammatic sketch in Fig. 10·8). As in the case of the mechanical system we may consider this circuit a system having a certain " mass " (inertia), stiffness coefficient and damping factor. The quantity which here corresponds to the

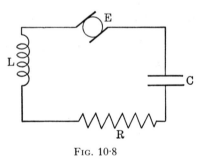

FIG. 10·8

mechanical displacement is the charge q. The kinetic reaction of the system is $L\ddot{q} = L\dot{I}$, where $\dot{q} = I$, the current flowing in the circuit; for $L\dot{I}$ is the back electromotive force due to the change of current (and hence of flux) through the inductance. We therefore look upon L as

---

[1] See, for example, Stewart and Lindsay, *Acoustics*, Van Nostrand, Princeton, N.J., 1930, p. 47 ff. Also see Lindsay, *Mechanical Radiation*, McGraw-Hill, New York, 1960.

the effective *mass* of the circuit.   An electromotive force E_c placed across the condenser of capacity C produces a charge $Q = E_c C$, and hence the stiffness coefficient, which is the ratio of force to corresponding displacement in the pure mechanical case, and which therefore would naturally be the ratio of electromotive force to electric displacement (or charge), in the present case is $1/C$.   Finally the damping force is $RI = R\dot{q}$, for this is of course the meaning of electrical resistance. The complete equation of motion for the forced oscillations of such a system is then

$$L\ddot{q} + R\dot{q} + \frac{q}{C} = E_0 e^{i\omega t}. \tag{10·6–1}$$

Once again the form is mathematically equivalent to eq. (10·4–4). The solution leads to the resonance frequency

$$\omega_0 = \sqrt{\frac{1}{LC}}, \tag{10·6–2}$$

which is the frequency for which the current is a maximum.   The frequency for which q is a maximum is, corresponding to (10·4–23),

$$\omega_1 = \sqrt{\frac{1}{LC} - \frac{R^2}{2L^2}}, \tag{10·6–3}$$

which again does not usually differ very much from ω_0, unless the resistance is very large.   The absolute value of the *impedance* of the electrical circuit is

$$Z = \sqrt{R^2 + \left(L\omega - \frac{1}{\omega C}\right)^2}, \tag{10·6–4}$$

and we note its analogy with the mechanical impedance (9·4–39). The reader is advised to find the electrical analogy for every important fact concerning the mechanical system, and refer for the physical significance to some text on electrical oscillations.[1]

10·7. The Oscillator in Atomic Theory.   Other important applications of harmonic oscillations are encountered in atomic theory. It will be recalled that in the atomic theory of the constitution of matter all bodies are assumed to be composed of small particles called *molecules* whose constituents in turn are *atoms* consisting of electrically charged particles called *electrons* and *nuclei*.   We have already had

---

[1] See, for example, A. O. Williams, Jr., *Electronics*, Van Nostrand, 1953, Chap. 8. See also L. Page and N. I. Adams, *Principles of Electricity*, 3rd ed., Van Nostrand, Princeton, N.J., 1958.

occasion in Sec. 3·11 to note the Bohr theory of the structure of hydrogen, the simplest of the atoms. Here the nucleus is a simple positively charged particle with most of the mass of the atom, and moving about it is a single electron negatively charged to the same magnitude as the positive charge of the nucleus, namely 4.8×10^{-10} electrostatic units. The nucleus of the hydrogen atom is called the *proton*. This is one of the constituents of the nuclei of other and more massive atoms. Besides protons, nuclei also contain *neutrons*, which are elementary particles possessing no electrical charge but having mass approximately equal to that of the proton. The positive charge of the nucleus is due to the protons alone, whereas the mass of the nucleus comes from the protons and neutrons together.

The atoms in a molecule are held together by mutual forces among their constituent particles. To assess these completely is indeed a complicated problem. However, to a first approximation much may be accomplished by lumping all the attractive forces between two atoms of a molecule into a single term varying with some appropriate power of the distance of separation, and doing likewise with the repulsive forces. This formulation seems reasonable from an examination of the individual electrostatic forces of attraction and repulsion between the individual particles of positive and negative sign. In general then we may write for the magnitude of the force between two atoms

$$F = a/r^p - b/r^q, \tag{10·7-1}$$

where p and q are usually two different integers, and a and b are constants. Here r is the separation of the two atoms. Now from the discussion in Chapter 6 (Sec. 6·1) it follows that we can reduce the motion of the two atoms subject only to their mutual force interaction to the motion of a single particle with the reduced mass and with displacement coördinate equal to r. Since the molecule must have some stability, it follows that for a certain value of r, say r_0, $F = 0$. However in the neighborhood of this equilibrium position, certain motions are possible. Thus let $r = r_0 + x$, where x is very small compared with r_0. Then

$$F = \frac{a}{(r_0 + x)^p} - \frac{b}{(r_0 + x)^q}$$

$$= \frac{a}{r_0^p} - \frac{b}{r_0^q} - \left(\frac{pa}{r_0^{p+1}} - \frac{qb}{r_0^{q+1}} \right) x + \cdots. \tag{10·7-2}$$

Now if x is small enough the expansion may be cut off at the second term. Moreover from the equilibrium condition just mentioned

$$a/r_0^p - b/r_0^q = 0. \tag{10·7-3}$$

Hence the net force corresponding to displacement x from equilibrium is

$$F = -\left(\frac{pa}{r_0^{p+1}} - \frac{qb}{r_0^{q+1}}\right) x. \qquad (10\cdot7\text{--}4)$$

If the term in the parentheses is positive, it is clear that the motion of the two atoms will be simple harmonic along the line joining them and indeed with frequency

$$\nu = \frac{1}{2\pi} \sqrt{\frac{(pa/r_0^{p+1} - qb/r_0^{q+1})}{m}}, \qquad (10\cdot7\text{--}5)$$

where m is the reduced mass. If the term in the parentheses were to be negative, we should not get harmonic motion, but in this case it is clear that the equilibrium at $r = r_0$ could not be stable.

The whole analysis of this chapter may be applied to the oscillations of charged particles like those mentioned in the preceding paragraph. Many actual cases have been studied ideally by supposing that the electrons attached to atoms vibrate as linear oscillators. In particular they may be considered to be subjected to damping forces which must be compensated for by external periodic forces to keep the vibrations going. The latter will in this case clearly be electric fields which, for example, may be due to radiation falling on the substance which is composed of the charged particles. If the frequency of an imposed field is equal to the natural frequency of the oscillator we shall expect all the phenomena of *resonance*, with resulting absorption of the incident radiation. This is properly the subject of investigation by the electromagnetic theory of optics, which is too imposing a region for us to enter here. The student, however, will find there ample illustration of the properties of oscillations discussed from the mechanical point of view in this chapter.

The following interesting question may be raised: since the Bohr theory is based on the idea that not *all* the possible mechanical motions of the electrons in an atom are allowed but only certain ones, specifically picked out by a process of *quantization* (Sec. 3·11), should not the same treatment be applied to the harmonic oscillator? The answer to this question is in the affirmative.

The total energy of such an oscillator assumed for simplicity to be *undamped* [Sec. 10·3, eqs. (10·3–6) and (10·3–7)] is given by

$$U = T + V = 2m\pi^2\nu^2 A^2, \qquad (10\cdot7\text{--}6)$$

where m is the mass, ν the frequency and A the amplitude of the oscillator. As far as classical mechanics is concerned, for a given oscillator this may have *any* value whatever, depending on the choice of amplitude. Of course in most mechanical problems the amplitude must not be too great if the oscillation is to be simple harmonic at all — but within this range *all* values are mechanically possible. However, the quantum theory prescribes that the oscillator may exist only in those states of motion for which the space integral of the momentum over a *complete* cycle is equal to an *integral* multiple of the fundamental constant of action, viz., h, the so-called *Planck's constant*. We may write the quantum condition [cf. (3·11–1)] in the case of linear oscillatory motion thus:

$$2 \int_{A}^{+A} m\dot{x}\, dx = nh, \tag{10·7–7}$$

when n is an integer. The factor 2 enters since the integration must be extended from $x = +A$ to $x = -A$ and *back* to $x = +A$. Since

$$x = A \sin(2\pi vt + \epsilon)$$

we have

$$\dot{x} = 2\pi vA \cos(2\pi vt + \epsilon)$$

$$= 2\pi vA \sqrt{1 - \frac{x^2}{A^2}}, \tag{10·7–8}$$

and therefore on substituting into the integral the result is

$$4\pi vm \int_{-A}^{+A} \sqrt{A^2 - x^2}\, dx = 2\pi^2 vmA^2 = nh. \tag{10·7–9}$$

This at once yields for the allowed energy values

$$U_n = 2\pi^2 mv^2 A^2 = nhv. \tag{10·7–10}$$

It then develops that the permitted energy values for the simple harmonic oscillator are integral multiples of the quantity hv, which thus appears as a fundamental unit of energy in atomic theory. It is called the *energy quantum* and plays a role of overwhelming importance in the modern theory of atomic structure.[1] What we wish to emphasize at this place, however, is the fact that the imposition of the quantum condition leads to the introduction of a certain *discreteness* into the problem of oscillator motion, a discreteness which contrasts markedly with the essential *continuity* of the possible states of motion in classical mechanics. The necessity for this discreteness arises from the fact that any theory of atomic structure must account for the essentially

---

[1] The student may here refer again to the books on atomic physics mentioned in Sec. 3·11.

discontinuous nature of atomic phenomena. It is pertinent to remark further that the method of quantization used in the Bohr theory has been replaced recently by a new one, namely that of the so-called *wave mechanics*. A brief survey of this is presented in Chapter 14, and the problem of the oscillator is there worked out on the basis of the new view.

10·8. Oscillations of a System with Several Degrees of Freedom.

So far in our study of oscillations we have restricted ourselves to systems with one degree of freedom. There are, however, many interesting features associated with systems of two or more degrees of freedom. The following is a simple example. Consider the case of a horizontal string AB (Fig. 10·9) of negligible mass loaded with two mass particles at P_1 and P_2. We let $\overline{AP_1} = \overline{P_2B} = \overline{P_1P_2} = a$, for simplicity. The

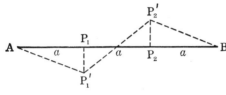

Fig. 10·9

mass of the particle at P_1 is m_1 while that at P_2 is m_2. The ends A and B are fastened, the string being stretched with tension τ.[1] The particles are displaced slightly from their equilibrium position and then let go; we have to determine their subsequent motion, assumed to lie in the vertical plane through the string. Let the displacements at any instant be ξ_1 and ξ_2 respectively. We have then to write down the equations of motion. Consulting the figure, we see that the restoring force on the first particle, assuming the tension is unaltered by the displacement, is

$$\tau\left[\frac{\xi_1}{a} - \frac{\xi_2 - \xi_1}{a}\right] = \frac{\tau}{a}[2\xi_1 - \xi_2], \qquad (10\cdot8\text{–}1)$$

while that on the second is

$$\tau\left[\frac{\xi_2}{a} + \frac{\xi_2 - \xi_1}{a}\right] = \frac{\tau}{a}[2\xi_2 - \xi_1]. \qquad (10\cdot8\text{–}2)$$

[1] Actually, of course, the weight of the particles will keep the string from maintaining an exact horizontal line in the equilibrium position. Nevertheless if the tension is sufficiently great the deviation is for our purposes negligible.

The equations of motion when the system is free are therefore[1]

$$m_1\ddot{\xi}_1 + \frac{\tau}{a}(2\xi_1 - \xi_2) = 0, \Bigg\}$$
$$m_2\ddot{\xi}_2 + \frac{\tau}{a}(2\xi_2 - \xi_1) = 0. \Bigg\} \qquad (10\cdot8-3)$$

To solve these equations, let us introduce the " operators "

and

$$D_1 \cdot = \left(m_1\frac{d^2}{dt^2} + \frac{2\tau}{a}\right)\cdot, \Bigg\}$$
$$D_2 \cdot = \left(m_2\frac{d^2}{dt^2} + \frac{2\tau}{a}\right)\cdot, \Bigg\} \qquad (10\cdot8-4)$$

the meaning of these being that when D_1 operates on ξ_1 we get

and similarly

$$D_1\xi_1 = m_1\ddot{\xi}_1 + \frac{2\tau}{a}\xi_1, \Bigg\}$$
$$D_2\xi_2 = m_2\ddot{\xi}_2 + \frac{2\tau}{a}\xi_2. \Bigg\} \qquad (10\cdot8-5)$$

If now we write the equations in this form they become

$$D_1\xi_1 - \frac{\tau}{a}\xi_2 = 0, \Bigg\}$$
$$D_2\xi_2 - \frac{\tau}{a}\xi_1 = 0. \Bigg\} \qquad (10\cdot8-6)$$

Let us multiply through the first equation by τ/a and operate on the second by D_1. We then have

$$\frac{\tau}{a}D_1\xi_1 - \frac{\tau^2}{a^2}\xi_2 = 0,$$

$$D_1D_2\xi_2 - \frac{\tau}{a}D_1\xi_1 = 0.$$

Adding these two equations yields

$$D_1D_2\xi_2 - \frac{\tau^2}{a^2}\xi_2 = 0, \qquad . \qquad (10\cdot8-7)$$

[1] It is to be noted that we are here neglecting dissipation. This is solely for the sake of making the analysis simple. For more details consult Rayleigh, *Theory of Sound*, Dover Publications, New York, 1945, para. 120 ff.

so that ξ_1 has been eliminated. The resulting equation for ξ_2 is then

$$m_1 m_2 \ddddot{\xi}_2 + \frac{2\tau}{a}(m_1 + m_2)\ddot{\xi}_2 + \frac{3\tau^2}{a^2}\xi_2 = 0. \tag{10·8–8}$$

There is a precisely similar equation for ξ_1, viz.,

$$m_1 m_2 \ddddot{\xi}_1 + \frac{2\tau}{a}(m_1 + m_2)\ddot{\xi}_1 + \frac{3\tau^2}{a^2}\xi_1 = 0. \tag{10·8–9}$$

Let us try the solution

$$\xi_1 = Ae^{\theta t}. \tag{10·8–10}$$

Substitution into eq. (10·8–9) yields

$$m_1 m_2 \theta^4 + \frac{2\tau}{a}(m_1 + m_2)\theta^2 + \frac{3\tau^2}{a^2} = 0. \tag{10·8–11}$$

Solution for θ^2 gives

$$\theta^2 = \frac{-\dfrac{2\tau}{a}(m_1 + m_2) \pm \sqrt{\dfrac{4\tau^2}{a^2}(m_1 + m_2)^2 - \dfrac{12\tau^2}{a^2}m_1 m_2}}{2m_1 m_2}. \tag{10·8–12}$$

There are thus *four* values of θ, as there should be since the equation (10·8–9) is of the fourth order. They are rather hard to handle in the general case where $m_1 \neq m_2$. To simplify the subsequent solution, let us at this point assume $m_1 = m_2 = m$. We then have from (10·8–12)

$$\theta^2 = \frac{-\dfrac{4\tau m}{a} \pm \dfrac{2\tau m}{a}}{2m^2} = \frac{-3\tau}{ma} \text{ or } \frac{-\tau}{ma}. \tag{10·8–13}$$

Hence

$$\theta = \pm i\sqrt{\frac{3\tau}{ma}} \text{ or } \pm i\sqrt{\frac{\tau}{ma}}, \tag{10·8–14}$$

and the solutions for both ξ_1 and ξ_2 take the form

$$\xi_1 = A_1 e^{i\sqrt{3\tau/ma}\cdot t} + A_1' e^{-i\sqrt{3\tau/ma}\cdot t}$$
$$+ B_1 e^{i\sqrt{\tau/ma}\cdot t} + B_1' e^{-i\sqrt{\tau/ma}\cdot t}, \tag{10·8–15}$$

$$\xi_2 = A_2 e^{i\sqrt{3\tau/ma}\cdot t} + A_2' e^{-i\sqrt{3\tau/ma}\cdot t}$$
$$+ B_2 e^{i\sqrt{\tau/ma}\cdot t} + B_2' e^{-i\sqrt{\tau/ma}\cdot t}. \tag{10·8–16}$$

If we reduce to *real* form (as in Sec. 9·1) we have finally

$$
\left.
\begin{aligned}
\xi_1 &= a_1 \cos\left(\sqrt{\frac{3\tau}{ma}}\,t + \epsilon_1\right) + b_1 \cos\left(\sqrt{\frac{\tau}{ma}}\,t + \epsilon_1'\right), \\
\xi_2 &= a_2 \cos\left(\sqrt{\frac{3\tau}{ma}}\,t + \epsilon_2\right) + b_2 \cos\left(\sqrt{\frac{\tau}{ma}}\,t + \epsilon_2'\right),
\end{aligned}
\right\}
\tag{10·8–17}
$$

where the amplitudes a_1, b_1, a_2, b_2, and the phases ϵ_1, ϵ_2, ϵ_1', ϵ_2' are not all independent. In fact, since we started originally with two second order equations, we must have only *four* independent arbitrary constants. If we substitute (10·8–17) back into (10·8–3) with $m_1 = m_2 = m$, we obtain after some algebraic manipulation the following simple results:

$$
a_2 = a_1, \quad b_2 = -b_1, \quad \epsilon_2 = \epsilon_1, \quad \epsilon_2' = \epsilon_1'. \tag{10·8–18}
$$

Physically we may interpret (10·8–17) as follows. Both particles have a motion which is the result of compounding two simple harmonic oscillations with frequencies

$$
\nu_1 = \frac{1}{2\pi}\sqrt{\frac{\tau}{ma}}, \quad \nu_2 = \frac{1}{2\pi}\sqrt{\frac{3\tau}{ma}}. \tag{10·8–19}
$$

These two frequencies may be called the *characteristic* frequencies of the system, and the latter may be said to have two distinct *modes* of oscillation. It may be remarked that since the two frequencies ν_1 and ν_2 are incommensurable the resulting motion will not in general be *periodic*, i.e., unless one of the two amplitudes happens to be zero. The four phase constants and amplitudes must be determined by the initial conditions of the motion. We have already said enough about these conditions in our discussion of the case of one degree of freedom to render it unnecessary to enter on details here. We should, however, stress the fact that the final solution for both particles is obtained by *adding* or *superposing* separate terms which are themselves solutions. The reason for the possibility of this is to be found in the *linearity* of the original equations of motion (10·8–8, 9), i.e., in the fact that they contain no second or higher powers of the ξ's or any of their derivatives. It is the special characteristic of a linear equation that the sum of two or more solutions is a solution (see Sec. 11·5, where this is demonstrated). The differential equations of oscillatory motion for small disturbances from equilibrium are always linear equations, as may well be suspected from the simple illustration treated here. Hence the solution in each case will consist of a *superposition* of special modes of oscillation. This is known as the *superposition* principle. We shall have other illustrations of it later.

As might be supposed the only modification made in this result by the introduction of damping factors will be to make the amplitude of each mode contain a term of the form $e^{-\lambda t}$ (λ being real) which damps out the resulting oscillations as time progresses.

The general problem (of which ours is a special case) of the motion of n equal mass particles attached at equal intervals along a finite string stretched with tension τ is of great historical interest for it was first solved by Lagrange in his famous treatise " Méchanique analytique," using the powerful general methods introduced by him into mechanics. We merely note that as one might expect from our special case the motion of each particle is the superposition of n simple harmonic motions each with a characteristic frequency.   There are then n distinct *modes* of oscillation.

As other interesting physical illustrations of the oscillations of a system of two or more degrees of freedom, we may note: (1) the vibrations of coupled resonators, i.e., two resonators joined in series; (2) coupled electrical circuits with resistance, inductance and capacity (here the damping can rarely be neglected), such as are encountered in every radio set; and (3) coupled oscillations of charged electric particles, such as the ions in a crystal.   In each case the method of attack outlined above may be employed and the results interpreted analogously to the mechanical case.

In the case of electrical oscillations an *operational* method of attack originated by Oliver Heaviside has been of great utility and can of course be applied to oscillating systems in general.[1]

PROBLEMS

1. Compare the *space* average of the kinetic energy of a simple harmonic oscillator over the space interval from $x = 0$ (the equilibrium position) to $x = A$, where A is the amplitude, with the corresponding average of the potential energy and comment on the result.

2. In the case of a simple harmonic oscillator derive an expression for the fractional part of a whole period which it spends in a small interval Δx at distance x from its equilibrium position.   Construct curves plotting the fractional time as a function of x for several different amplitudes and comment on their physical significance.

3. The schematic diagram shows a mass m able to move vertically under the action of two massless springs with stiffness coefficients f_1 and f_2 respectively.

[1] For details see, for example: R. V. Churchill, *Modern Operational Mathematics in Engineering*, McGraw-Hill, New York, 1944; H. S. Carslaw and J. C. Jaeger, *Operational Methods in Applied Mathematics*, Oxford Univ. Press, New York, 1941; N. W. McLachlan, *Modern Operational Calculus*, Macmillan, London, 1948.

Find the resonance frequency of the system if it performs simple harmonic oscillations. Find the percentage change in the resonance frequency if f_1 and f_2 change by Δf_1 and Δf_2 respectively (where $|\Delta f_1| \ll f_1$ and $|\Delta f_2| \ll f_2$).

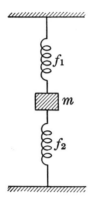

4. A mass of 50 grams is attached to the center of a horizontal string 20 cm long stretched with a tension equivalent to 2000 gram wt. Assuming that the mass of the string is negligible, find the resonance frequency of the system as a simple harmonic oscillator. Calculate the equivalent stiffness of the system. If it is observed that the amplitude of vibration is reduced in the ratio 1 to e (Naperian base) in 5 seconds, find the damping coefficient and the logarithmic decrement.

5. Referring to Problem 4, use the damping coefficient to calculate the natural frequency of oscillation and the frequency for maximum amplitude. Calculate the mechanical impedance of the system at (a) the resonance frequency and (b) a forced frequency of 50 cycles/sec.

6. A certain tuning fork of frequency 256 cycles has its amplitude diminished in the ratio $1/e$ in about 5900 cycles. Calculate the decay modulus and the logarithmic decrement. Find the value of the interval ω/ω_0 [see eq. (10·4–33)] in which the intensity of resonance (i.e., $\bar{W}$) falls to one-half its maximum value. If the tuning fork is placed before the opening of an air resonator of equal natural frequency, the number of cycles to bring about the amplitude reduction specified is 3300. Discuss the physical reason for this and calculate ω/ω_0 for this case also. Plot representative curves for $\bar{W}$ in the two cases.

7. A Helmholtz resonator of natural frequency 256 cycles/sec is in the form of a sphere with volume 1053 cm³. If the diameter of the opening is 3.02 cm, calculate the effective length of the neck on the opening. (The use of the word " effective " implies that there may actually be no neck present, yet there is a plug of air vibrating in the opening and the length in question may be considered to give the dimension of this plug. See Stewart and Lindsay, " Acoustics," p. 47.)

8. If the resonator in Problem 7 is excited by a tuning fork of frequency 256 which exerts a maximum force of 25 dynes at the opening, compute the maximum displacement velocity of the air in the opening. Do the same for the case of a fork of frequency 512 exerting the same force.

9. A mechanical vibrating system has a mass of 100 grams and a stiffness factor of 1.6×10^7 dynes/cm and a damping coefficient of 200 dynes sec/cm. Calculate the resonance and natural frequencies and find the percentage difference.

10. Find the decay modulus and logarithmic decrement for the system specified in Problem 9. If the system is excited by a force of frequency 100 cycles/sec with a maximum of 10 grams wt, calculate the average rate of dissipation of energy by the system.

11. Find the expression for the natural frequency of the oscillations of an electric circuit made up of resistance R, inductance L, and capacitance C in series.

12. The cosine of the phase angle between impressed electromotive force and current in an electric circuit containing resistance, inductance, and capacitance in series is called the *power factor*. Suggest a reason for this name and calculate the power factor in a case where the resistance is 1 ohm, the inductance is 4 millihenrys (a henry is the inductance of a circuit in which an impressed e.m.f. of one volt causes the current to grow at the rate of one ampere per sec) and the capacitance is 3 microfarads (a *farad* is the capacitance of a condenser for which a charge of one coulomb corresponds to a difference of potential of one volt). If a periodic e.m.f. of 100 volts with frequency 60 cycles/sec is impressed on this circuit, calculate the average rate of dissipation of energy by the circuit.

13. The figure shows two electric circuits coupled together. Find the characteristic resonance frequencies of the system.

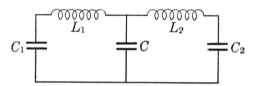

14. Consider two masses m_1 and m_2 joined together by a light rod whose longitudinal elasticity is so very large compared with its mass that the latter may be neglected. If the masses are displaced in the direction of the rod, set up and solve the equations of motion of the system. Show that the frequency of the motion is

$$\nu = \frac{1}{2\pi} \sqrt{\frac{f(m_1 + m_2)}{m_1 m_2}},$$

where f is the stiffness coefficient of the rod (i.e., $f = YS/l$ where Y is Young's modulus, $S =$ cross-sectional area of the rod, and l is its length). What will be the effect on the frequency if the mass of the rod (say m_r) is not neglected? Why in this problem is there but *one* natural frequency instead of *two*?

15. In the schematic diagram m_1 and m_2 are masses suspended by springs with stiffness f_1 and f_2 respectively. Assume that a harmonic force of frequency $\omega/2\pi$ acts on m_1. Find the steady-state displacement of each mass. What

happens when the resonance frequency of m_2 by itself is equal to $\omega/2\pi$? (This is the principle of the Frahm vibration absorber.)

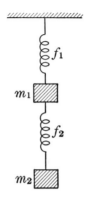

16. According to classical electrodynamics an accelerated electron radiates energy at the rate $\frac{2}{3}e^2f^2/c^3$ where e is the charge on the electron, c the velocity of light, and f is the acceleration. Assuming an electron in simple harmonic motion with frequency ν calculate the amount of energy radiated during a single period. Find the number of periods it would take to reduce the energy of the motion to one-half its original value.

17. The string of a simple pendulum is gradually shortened at a rate very slow compared with the period of the pendulum. Calculate the *average* work that is done in the shortening over a single period. Derive the expressions for the kinetic and potential energies of the pendulum and show that during the shortening process the value of E/ν remains unaltered, E being the total energy. Prove that $E/\nu = \oint p \; dx$, where p is the momentum of the pendulum bob. (E/ν is called an *adiabatic invariant*, and its invariance in such a process as indicated is of great importance in atomic theory. N.B. $\oint p \; dx$ is the integral taken over one complete cycle of the motion.)

18. In the diatomic molecule of hydrogen chloride the masses of the hydrogen and chlorine atoms are respectively:

$$m_H = 1.66 \times 10^{-24} \text{ gram} \quad \text{and} \quad m_{Cl} = 5.9 \times 10^{-23} \text{ gram.}$$

The vibration frequency has been found to be 8.721×10^{13} cycles/sec. What is the effective stiffness of the system? If the force curve is fitted with a function like that shown in (10·7–1) with $p = 2$ and $q = 3$, and it is known that $r_0 = 1.28 \times 10^8$ cm, find the constants a and b. Find the force associated with a displacement 10^{-9} cm from equilibrium.

19. Use D'Alembert's principle to write the equations of motion of the system consisting of three equally spaced particles of masses m_1, m_2, and m_3 respectively, attached to a stretched horizontal string of length l. Find the frequencies of the system.

20. An oscillator in which the restoring force is not simply proportional to the displacement but is asymmetrical with respect to the displacement is called

an anharmonic oscillator. Its equation of motion can be written in the form

$$m\ddot{\xi} + f_1\xi \times f_2\xi^2 = 0,$$

where $f_2\xi^2$ is the anharmonic term. Show that this represents the asymmetry just mentioned.

Solve the equation approximately by a series expansion involving successive approximations. Thus write

$$\xi = \epsilon\xi_1(t) + \epsilon^2\xi_2(t) + \epsilon^3\xi_3(t) + \ldots,$$

where ϵ is an arbitrary parameter. Show that ξ_1, ξ_2, ξ_3 satisfy the following differential equations

$$m\ddot{\xi}_1 = -f_1\xi_1$$
$$m\ddot{\xi}_2 = -f_1\xi_2 - f_2\xi_1^2$$
$$m\ddot{\xi}_3 = -f_1\xi_3 - 2f_2\xi_1\xi_2.$$

Solve the first equation for ξ_1 in the usual fashion and substitute the solution into the second equation. Solve the second equation for ξ_2, etc. Find the resultant solution out to terms in ϵ^3 and show that it involves harmonics of the natural frequency of the equivalent harmonic oscillator. Discuss a case in which it might be possible to detect these.

Chapter 11

DEFORMABLE BODIES AND WAVE MOTION

11·1. Strain and Stress. Hooke's Law. In our work so far we have studied the motion of particles, both singly and in groups. But our only treatment of the behavior of large scale solids such as are actually met in physical experiments has been the discussion of the motion of rigid bodies, the constitution of which has been supposed to be such that the distance between any two points of the body remains forever unaltered no matter what forces act on it. This means that such a body can never be deformed. It was pointed out in that connection that the rigid body is a highly idealized concept, even though valuable for the description of many phenomena. However, there are enough illustrations of the deformation of bodies, changes in size and shape, to make it necessary to deal with these problems at some length and by methods differing in some important respects from those already used in treating particle motion. For we shall now effectively consider a large scale body as a *continuous medium*, rather than as made up of discrete particles, and the continuity thus assumed will play an important role in our theoretical considerations. We shall have occasion to note the great theoretical importance of the distinction between particle and medium motion.

For the moment, however, let us confine our attention to the possible changes in size and shape which a finite portion of a continuous material medium can undergo. Such alterations are called *strains*, and we may classify them under a relatively few simple types.

Perhaps the simplest is change in volume without change of shape. Suppose we have a body of volume V and by the application of appropriate forces the volume is changed by an amount ΔV. This may be either positive or negative, corresponding to an expansive or compressive strain. It is advisable to fix upon a definite measure of volume strain, and for convenience we shall agree to call

$$\delta_V = \frac{\Delta V}{V} \qquad (11\cdot1\text{--}1)$$

the measure of the *volume strain*. It is the change in volume per unit volume, and implies the possibility of a change in the average density, ρ, of the body.   It need not be the same for all parts of the body; if we divide the body into volume elements the δ_V for each element will not necessarily be the same.   In this case the strain is said to be *non-uniform*. For the present we shall concern ourselves primarily with uniform strains.   Since the mass m of the body is not changed, and since

$$m = \rho V, \qquad (11\cdot1\text{--}2)$$

we can also write for the volume strain

$$\delta_V = \frac{\Delta V}{V} = -\frac{\Delta \rho}{\rho}, \qquad (11\cdot1\text{--}3)$$

a relation which will later be useful.   There is a special case of volume strain which we ought to notice, viz., a *linear strain*.   Suppose the distance between any two points in the unstrained body is l.   Under strain the distance becomes $l + \Delta l$.   The linear strain is then defined by

$$\delta_l = \frac{\Delta l}{l}. \qquad (11\cdot1\text{--}4)$$

It is seen at once that there is a relation between linear and volume strains.   For consider a cube of side l.   The volume is $V = l^3$.   If the alterations are small enough so that they may be treated approximately as differentials we have

$$\Delta V = 3l^2 \, \Delta l, \qquad (11\cdot1\text{--}5)$$

so that on dividing through by V there results

$$\delta_V = 3\delta_l. \qquad (11\cdot1\text{--}6)$$

Hence a small uniform volume strain δ_V may be considered as replaced by three equal linear strains in three mutually perpendicular directions of magnitude $\delta_V/3$.   It must be emphasized again that this implies strains small enough so that δ_V^2 and δ_V^3 etc., may be neglected compared with δ_V.   It is with strains of this order of magnitude that we shall deal exclusively in this chapter.   Liquids and gases can undergo volume strain as well as solids.   On the other hand linear strain is confined to solids.

A particularly interesting case of linear strain is that of a long cylindrical wire.   If the wire is stretched in the direction of its length a positive linear strain ensues.   There is a concomitant lateral strain, i.e., the diameter of the wire is decreased.   If we denote the lateral strain by $\delta_D = \Delta D/D$, where D is the diameter of the wire, then

$$\sigma = \frac{\delta_D}{\delta_l} \qquad (11\cdot1\text{--}7)$$

is known as Poisson's ratio.   Its significance will be discussed in the next section.

Volume and linear strains are often grouped together under the caption, *dilatational* strains.

The last type of strain to be discussed is the so-called *shear*. Consider the cross section of a cube, $ABCD$ (Fig. 11·1). Holding fixed the plane of which $\overline{AB}$ is the trace, allow all the other parallel planes in the cube to be shifted toward the right parallel to themselves, each one an amount proportional to its distance from AB, so that the square cross section $ABCD$ becomes the rhombus $ABFE$. In this case the cube is said to have been *sheared* and the strain is known as a *shearing strain*. More particularly it is a *uniform* shearing strain. Now what shall be chosen as the measure of the strain? It is customary to take for this the value of the angle θ, which for small shears will be approximately equal to $\overline{DE}/\overline{AD}$, i.e., tan θ. An important thing about a shear is that no volume change is involved, it being wholly a change in shape, as far as the body as a whole is concerned. Of course *length* alterations are involved, and it is clear from an inspection of Fig. 11·1 that all lengths originally parallel to the diagonal $\overline{AC}$ are *increased* while all those originally parallel to the diagonal $\overline{BD}$ are *decreased* by the shear. As simple experience amply indicates it is not possible to subject most liquids and gases to shearing strain. Nevertheless the shear does have meaning for very viscous liquids as well as for solids (cf. Sec. 12·1).

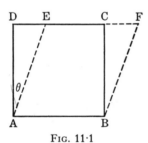

FIG. 11·1

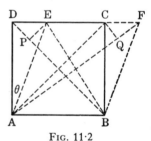

FIG. 11·2

We shall now prove a significant theorem about shearing strains. For this purpose consult Fig. 11·2, which is like Fig. 11·1, except that the diagonals $\overline{AC}$ and $\overline{BD}$ have been drawn, as well as the new diagonals $\overline{AF}$ and $\overline{BE}$. Let us draw $\overline{EP}$ perpendicular to $\overline{BD}$, and $\overline{CQ}$ perpendicular to $\overline{AF}$. Now since the shear is small the angle CFQ is still approximately 45°, and hence, approximately,

$$\overline{QF} = \frac{\overline{CF}}{\sqrt{2}}, \qquad (11\cdot1\text{–}8)$$

while to the same approximation

$$\overline{AC} = \overline{AQ}.$$

Hence the positive linear strain along the one diagonal is

$$\frac{\overline{QF}}{\overline{AC}} = \frac{\dfrac{\overline{CF}}{\sqrt{2}}}{\sqrt{2}\,\overline{AD}} = \frac{1}{2}\frac{\overline{DE}}{\overline{AD}} = \frac{\theta}{2}, \qquad (11\cdot1\text{–}9)$$

since θ is so small that, as we have said before, $\theta \doteqdot \tan\theta$. We can show similarly that the negative linear strain along the other diagonal has the same magnitude, viz., approximately,

$$\frac{\overline{DP}}{\overline{BD}} = \frac{\theta}{2}. \qquad (11\cdot1\text{–}10)$$

We have thus shown that a shear strain θ may be considered as equivalent to a positive linear strain $\theta/2$ at right angles to a negative linear strain $\theta/2$, both being at 45° to the sheared planes.

We have been considering so far only the *geometry* of deformation. The strains just defined are always associated with *forces* which are applied to the body in question, and the equal and opposite reaction forces with which the body acts on the external influence. These forces may always be considered as distributed over some area or areas of the body, and the force per unit area is denominated the *stress*. Corresponding then to different types of *strain*, we have different types of *stress*. For example, with volume strain will be associated what may be called *compressive stress* (or sometimes *hydrostatic stress* or *pressure*. See Sec. 12·1). Suppose we consider once more a cube of side l. If on every unit of area of every face of the cube the same force acts normal to the surface, it is said to be under the action of a compressive or expansive stress, depending on the direction of the force with respect to the outward drawn normal. As we shall have occasion to note in Sec. 12·1, the former is true when a body is submerged in a fluid — in so far as the action of the fluid on the body is concerned.

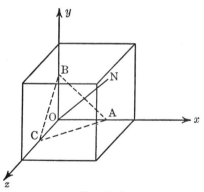

Fig. 11·3

The idea of compressive stress gains increased significance from the fact that if we draw any plane whatever through the cube just considered, the normal stress on this plane will be the same as that on the faces of the cube. To show this consider (Fig. 11·3) a cube placed with one vertex at O, the origin of a system of rectangular coördinates.   Let the plane be the one which has intercepts $\overline{OA}$, $\overline{OB}$, $\overline{OC}$ on the x, y, z axes respectively.   We shall represent its equation by

$$ax + by + cz = d, \qquad (11\cdot1\text{--}11)$$

where

$$\overline{OA} = \frac{d}{a}, \quad \overline{OB} = \frac{d}{b}, \quad \overline{OC} = \frac{d}{c}. \qquad (11\cdot1\text{--}12)$$

$\overline{ON}$ represents the normal to the plane through the origin.   We know from analytic geometry that the direction cosines of the normal are

$$\frac{a}{\sqrt{a^2 + b^2 + c^2}}, \quad \frac{b}{\sqrt{a^2 + b^2 + c^2}}, \quad \frac{c}{\sqrt{a^2 + b^2 + c^2}}. \qquad (11\cdot1\text{--}13)$$

We wish to calculate the stress on the plane ABC.   Let the stress on each face of the cube be denoted by p.   Then the force on the area OBC in the yz plane is in magnitude pS_{OBC} (where S_{OBC} stands for the magnitude of this area), and its direction is along the positive x axis. This force also acts on the area ABC.   Its component normal to the plane will then be (recalling the significance of the direction cosine)

$$pS_{OBC} \frac{a}{\sqrt{a^2 + b^2 + c^2}}. \qquad (11\cdot1\text{--}14)$$

If now we proceed with the other faces similarly we find for the total normal *force* on the plane ABC due to the compressive stress on all the faces of the cube,

$$\frac{p}{\sqrt{a^2 + b^2 + c^2}} [aS_{OBC} + bS_{OAC} + cS_{OAB}]. \qquad (11\cdot1\text{--}15)$$

But to find the normal *stress* we must divide the *force* by the area. Hence the stress is

$$\frac{p}{\sqrt{a^2 + b^2 + c^2}} \left[\frac{aS_{OBC} + bS_{OAC} + cS_{OAB}}{S_{ABC}} \right]. \qquad (11\cdot1\text{--}16)$$

Now, however, since S_{OBC} is the projection of S_{ABC} on the yz plane

$$\frac{S_{OBC}}{S_{ABC}} = \frac{a}{\sqrt{a^2 + b^2 + c^2}}, \qquad (11\cdot1\text{--}17)$$

and similarly for the others.   Hence the normal stress reduces to

$$\frac{p}{\sqrt{a^2 + b^2 + c^2}} \left[\frac{a^2 + b^2 + c^2}{\sqrt{a^2 + b^2 + c^2}} \right] = p, \qquad (11\cdot1\text{--}18)$$

as was to be proved.

Corresponding to *linear strain* we may set *tensile stress*, which is the force per unit area acting on every cross section perpendicular to the direction of the strain. Finally corresponding to shearing strain we have shearing stress, which is the tangential force per unit area parallel to the shearing planes.

The next and very important question is: What is the relation between each strain and the corresponding stress? The answer to this is found in the celebrated *law of Hooke*. For a great many bodies actually observed in nature the ratio of the stress to the strain is approximately a constant for a certain range of variation of the stress. Such bodies are termed *elastic* bodies and the study of their behavior is often called *elasticity*, for when the external stress is removed these bodies resume more or less approximately their original size and shape in distinction to *plastic* bodies, which to a large extent retain their deformation. It must be emphasized that there is no hard and fast line between elasticity and plasticity, for a body may be elastic with respect to a certain type of stress and plastic with respect to another. For example, a viscous fluid is plastic with respect to shearing stresses but approximately elastic with respect to compressive stresses. We shall have occasion in Sec. 11·3 to discuss this aspect of the nature of deformable bodies in a little more detail. (Recall also the discussion of relaxation phenomena in Sec. 10·2.)

We now wish to introduce the expressions for Hooke's law for the different types of stress-strain combinations. First consider volume strains. Denoting as before the compressive stress by p, with δ_V as the corresponding volume strain, it is found that the ratio p/δ_V has a value which for many bodies over a wide range of values of p is constant. Thus we set

$$\frac{p}{\delta_V} = -B. \qquad (11\cdot1\text{–}19)$$

The positive constant B is called the *bulk modulus*, or *modulus of volume elasticity*. We may perhaps regard it as the most significant of the moduli of elasticity since it applies to fluids as well as to solids. Its reciprocal is called the *compressibility* of the substance. Some characteristic values will be found in the following table of elastic moduli. It is important to note that since δ_V is nondimensional, B has the dimensions of p.

Considering next linear strains, if we have a substance in the form of a wire or rod and the longitudinal or tensile stress applied is f_t, with corresponding linear strain δ_l, the ratio

$$\frac{f_t}{\delta_l} = Y \qquad (11\cdot1\text{–}20)$$

is constant for many solids over a considerable range of values of f_t, and the constant Y so defined is called *Young's modulus*. Like B it has the dimensions of force per unit area.

TABLE OF VALUES OF ELASTIC MODULI[1]

Substance	Y Young's Modulus (dynes/cm^2)	μ Shear Modulus (dynes/cm^2)	B Bulk Modulus (dynes/cm^2)	σ Poisson's Ratio
Aluminum	7×10^{11}	2.5×10^{11}	12×10^{11}	0.40
Brass (cold rolled)	9	3.5	7	0.29
Copper	12	4.3	20	0.40
Glass (window)	7	2.7	5.8	0.30
Glycerine	—	—	0.50	—
Gold	8	3.0	8.3	0.34
Granite	5	1.8	5	0.34
Lucite	5.6	2.15	4.9	0.31
Mercury	—	—	0.27	—
Nickel	20	7.1	37	0.41
Polystyrene	3.9	1.5	3.6	0.32
Silver	7.5	2.7	11.5	0.39
Steel	18	7	25	0.38
Water	—	—	0.21	—
Wood (mean)	0.5	—	—	—

Finally if the shearing stress be denoted by f_s and the corresponding shearing strain is θ, we have

$$\frac{f_s}{\theta} = \mu, \qquad (11\cdot1\text{--}21)$$

where μ is constant over a wide range and is known as the *shear modulus* or *rigidity* of the substance. It has the same units as B and Y. These are the three principal moduli of elasticity for homogeneous, isotropic media. We have now to inquire concerning the possible relations among them.

11·2. Relations Among the Elastic Moduli. Consider a rectangular parallelepiped[2] (Fig. 11·4) of sides a, b, c, in the directions

[1] These values are averages only.   The accurate determination of elastic constants is a very difficult problem and much depends on the purity and heat treatment of the material.   The values for Aluminum, Copper, Steel, Glass, Lucite, Polystyrene are taken from W. C. Schneider and C. J. Burton, *J. App. Phys.* **20**, 48, 1949.   Most of the other values are from *Handbook of Chemistry and Physics* (Chemical Rubber Publishing Co., Cleveland, 30th ed., 1948).   All values are given for room temperature and in the case of the liquids for approximately atmospheric pressure.

[2] It should be emphasized that we are here confining our attention to homogeneous, isotropic media whose properties are the same in every part and in every direction. This rules out consideration of crystalline media whose elastic properties are in general very complicated.

of the x, y, z axes respectively, where $a < b < c$. Suppose that the tensile stress f_t acts along the z axis on the surface $FDEB$. Then there will be a stress f_t acting along the negative z axis also on the surface $CGAO$, since the body as a whole is assumed to be in equilibrium. Associated with f_t there will be the linear strain in the z direction f_t/Y and the concomitant lateral strain $\sigma f_t/Y$ perpendicular to the z axis, where σ is Poisson's ratio. Now suppose on the other hand that f_t acts along the x axis. We then have a linear strain f_t/Y along the x axis and a concomitant lateral strain $\sigma f_t/Y$ perpendicular to the x axis. Finally suppose that f_t acts along the y axis; there is then a linear strain f_t/Y along this axis and the concomitant lateral strain $\sigma f_t/Y$ perpendicular to the y axis. If now all these stresses act simultaneously we have total linear strains in the x, y, z directions respectively as follows:

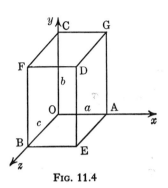

FIG. 11.4

$$\delta_x = \delta_y = \delta_z = \frac{f_t}{Y}(1 - 2\sigma). \qquad (11\cdot2\text{--}1)$$

But in this case the resulting deformation is essentially that due to a uniform stress $f_t = p$ on each face of the rod. This is equivalent to a compressive stress and the corresponding volume strain is

$$\delta_V = \frac{f_t}{B}. \qquad (11\cdot2\text{--}2)$$

Now we have shown (Sec. 11·1) that a volume strain δ_V is equivalent to three mutually perpendicular linear strains each equal in magnitude to $\delta_V/3$. Hence we must have from (11·2–1)

$$\frac{f_t}{3B} = \frac{f_t}{Y}(1 - 2\sigma), \qquad (11\cdot2\text{--}3)$$

whence there follows the important relation

$$Y = 3B(1 - 2\sigma), \qquad (11\cdot2\text{--}4)$$

connecting Y, B, and σ.

The shear modulus μ may now be introduced. We have already shown that a shearing strain θ may be replaced by two linear strains $\theta/2$ in magnitude at right angles to each other and of opposite sign. Hence in the present case if the positive linear stress f_t acts along the

y axis and the negative stress $-f_t$ acts along the x axis the result will be a shearing strain at an angle of 45° to both linear strains and of magnitude

$$\theta = \frac{2}{Y} f_t (1 + \sigma).$$ (11·2–5)

Now it can be shown, however, that a tensile stress f_t in the y direction and a lateral negative stress $-f_t$ in the x direction are equivalent to a shearing stress of magnitude f_t acting at an angle of 45° to the other stresses.   For suppose we consider the cross section of the parallelepiped in the xy plane with the stresses f_t as indicated (Fig. 11·5). Cut the parallelepiped with a plane parallel to the z axis and with trace LC in the xy plane making angle 45° with AG.   Now the resultant of the force Sf_t acting on the area S parallel to the z axis (the trace of which on the xy plane is GL) and Sf_t acting on the equal area (the trace of which is CG) will be in magnitude $\sqrt{2}Sf_t$ and its direction will be *parallel* to the 45° plane just introduced.   Hence the stress on this latter plane will be $\sqrt{2}Sf_t/\sqrt{2}S = f_t$, if we recall that the area of the 45° plane is $\sqrt{2}$ times the areas it cuts off on the faces of the parallelepiped.   Hence the statement made above is justified.   But if the shearing stress $f_s = f_t$ acts, the resulting shearing strain is

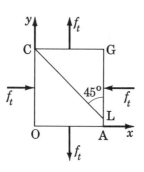

FIG. 11·5

$$\theta = \frac{f_t}{\mu},$$ (11·2–6)

where μ is the shear modulus.   This must be the same shearing strain at that given in (11·2–5), for its direction is the same and it corresponds so precisely the same set of external stresses acting on the body.   Hence we may equate and get

$$Y = 2\mu(1 + \sigma),$$ (11·2–7)

an important relation connecting Y, μ and σ.   By means of (11·2–4) and (11·2–7), the bulk and shear moduli B and μ respectively may be expressed in terms of Young's modulus and Poisson's ratio.   By the elimination of the latter between the two equations we may also obtain the relation connecting Y, B, and μ

$$Y = \frac{9B\mu}{\mu + 3B},$$ (11·2–8)

showing that the three moduli are not independent; from a knowledge of any two, the third may be derived. If now we eliminate Y between the eqs. (11·2–4) and (11·2–7), we obtain some information about σ. Thus

$$3B(1 - 2\sigma) = 2\mu(1 + \sigma). \qquad (11\text{·}2\text{–}9)$$

It is to be noted that B and μ are essentially *positive* quantities. Hence in order that both sides of (11·2–9) may have the same sign, σ must not be *greater* than $\frac{1}{2}$. On the other hand it must not be *less* than -1, since otherwise the term $1 + \sigma$ would be negative while $1 - 2\sigma$ would be positive. Hence we may state the important inequality relation for σ

$$-1 < \sigma < \tfrac{1}{2}. \qquad (11\text{·}2\text{–}10)$$

It is interesting to notice in the table at the end of the preceding section that σ for many substances has values ranging around $\frac{1}{4}$ or $\frac{1}{3}$. Poisson devised a theory of elasticity according to which σ for all elastic solids should be exactly $\frac{1}{4}$. The theory is however not particularly well substantiated except as far as order of magnitude is concerned.

It may be well to mention here briefly some of the experimental methods for determining the elastic moduli. The evaluation of Young's modulus is doubtless familiar to the student as it forms a part of almost every elementary laboratory routine. The length of a long vertical wire of the substance to be examined is measured when stretched by a weight. A known weight is then added and the elongation very carefully measured with a micrometer microscope. This enables the linear strain δ_l to be calculated, and the stress having been computed from the extra weight and the area of cross section of the wire, Y follows from the formula defining it.

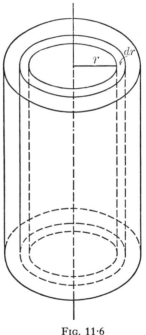

Fig. 11·6

The determination of μ or B is a more difficult matter. Usually μ is the quantity investigated, whence B may be calculated by means of eq. (11·2–8). We shall discuss only one method of getting the shear modulus, the theory of which is interesting on its own account. This is the torsion of a right circular cylinder. Consider (Fig. 11·6) such a solid in the form of a wire of radius a and height h fastened vertically at the upper end.   Suppose now that a torque in the form of a couple is applied to the lower end of the wire twisting the wire at this end through an angle θ about its axis. Any cylindrical element or sheet of the wire of radius r and thickness dr will suffer a shear.   The magnitude of the shearing strain will be understood from the following figure (Fig. 11·7) where an enlarged version of a portion of the cylindrical sheet (of unit height, let us say) is presented.   Consider a part of this ring enclosed between two diametral planes.   This is marked in dotted lines in the figure (A–$BCDE$) and is approximately a parallelepiped.   Now when the wire is twisted and the ring sheared, the part just considered assumes the shape shown by the full lines (A–$FGH\mathcal{J}$).   The shearing strain is then approximately $\overline{BF}$ since $\overline{AB}$ has been chosen of unit length.   But $\overline{BF} = r\phi$, where ϕ is the angle of twist per unit height of the element.   It follows that since the twist is θ for the cylinder of height h, the shearing strain for the ring element of radius r but height h will be

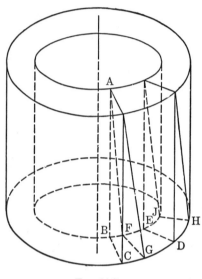

Fig. 11·7

$$\frac{r\theta}{h} .$$

$$(11 \cdot 2 – 11)$$

Then the shearing stress f_s will necessarily be given as

$$f_s = \frac{\mu r \theta}{h} ,$$

$$(11 \cdot 2 – 12)$$

where μ is the shear modulus of the material composing the wire. The shearing stress is the force per unit area on the base of the cylindrical element, and hence the *torque* or force moment per *unit* area about the axis of the cylinder due to the shearing stress is

$$r f_s = \frac{\mu r^2 \theta}{h} ,$$

$$(11 \cdot 2 – 13)$$

while the torque for the whole base area of the *element* is

$$2\pi r \, dr \cdot r f_s = \frac{2\pi \mu r^3 \theta \, dr}{h} .$$

$$(11 \cdot 2 – 14)$$

The total torque on the base area of the *complete* cylinder is obtained by integrating the preceding expression from 0 to a.   Finally for the shearing torque we have

$$M = \frac{\pi \mu a^4}{2h} \theta. \qquad (11 \cdot 2\text{--}15)$$

Suppose now that a heavy disc or rod is rigidly attached to the free end of the wire, and that its moment of inertia about the axis of the wire is I. If the disc is turned through an angle θ from its equilibrium position there will be exerted on it a restoring torque of magnitude M given by eq. (11·2–15).   Hence the equation for the rotational motion of the disc after its release will be (see Sec. 8·5)

$$I\ddot{\theta} = -\frac{\pi \mu a^4}{2h} \theta. \qquad (11 \cdot 2\text{--}16)$$

But from our previous study we observe that this is the equation of angular simple harmonic motion, with frequency

$$\nu = \frac{1}{2\pi} \sqrt{\frac{\pi \mu a^4}{2hI}}. \qquad (11 \cdot 2\text{--}17)$$

The experimental measurement of ν, h, a, and I suffices to determine μ, the rigidity, from the above expression.

11·3. Elastic Limit.   Fatigue and Heredity.   Our treatment of the first two sections has implied the validity of Hooke's law.   For the most interesting applications of the study of deformable bodies this law will generally be assumed, together with the existence of the elastic moduli and their relations. However, it is well to recognize that this law is valid only within limits.   Suppose we take a piece of wire and strain it, plotting the tensile stress against the linear strain.   The result in general will be somewhat as shown in Fig. 11·8. From O to A the stress is very closely a linear function of the

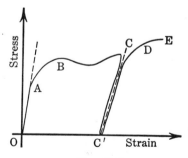

FIG. 11·8

strain, i.e., Hooke's law holds.   As long as we remain within this region of stress and strain the wire behaves as an elastic medium, i.e., resumes its original length on the removal of the stress.   However, after the strain indicated by A has been reached, further stress does not lead to a corresponding strain in accordance with the relation

$$\frac{\text{stress}}{\text{strain}} = K, \tag{11·3–1}$$

where K is a constant.   Rather the stress-strain curve becomes bent as in the region from A to B: a small increase in stress leads to a much larger increase in strain than the above relation (11·3–1) would indicate. On release from stress in this state the wire does *not* recover its original length at once and sometimes not even after a very long time.   The point A may be said to mark the *elastic limit* of the original specimen while the point B represents what may be called the *yield point*, because beyond it the elongation increases very rapidly and the wire becomes plastic in that the strain depends on the time a given stress acts: if the stress is maintained the wire may and in many cases does break.   However, in some cases the specimen appears to regain its elasticity after the point B has been reached and for such the curve begins to mount again. Suppose in this process, say at point C, the load is removed.   It is then found that the original stress-strain curve is not followed at all, but that the change follows a curve like CC', more or less straight, so that the complete removal of stress now leaves a permanent strain, of magnitude OC'.   This is known as a *permanent set*.   The further application of stress leads to a new stress-strain curve following $C'C$ and also more or less straight, i.e., effectively the elastic limit has been raised by the stretching and is now beyond the yield point of the unstretched specimen. It should be noted that the interval between the elastic limit and the breaking point varies greatly from substance to substance, being greater for ductile substances as one might expect.

The stress-strain curve in Fig. 11·8 is a static curve, i.e., the values of the strain there shown are the equilibrium values attained after the stress has been applied.   We have already commented in Sec. 10·2 on the fact that the strain never builds up to its full value *immediately* on application of stress, but that time is taken for this process.   This served as an illustration of the concept of *relaxation* time.   The temporal change of strain in a solid subjected to stress has been called " creep " by metallurgists and is obviously of considerable practical importance in materials which have wide commercial use.   Much attention to this phenomenon has recently been paid by physicists.[1]

Within the elastic limit a wire will return to its original length on release from stress but this process also shows a relaxation effect.

[1] Cf. for example, F. Seitz, *The Physics of Metals*, McGraw-Hill, New York, 1943. This book discusses in considerable detail both the elastic and plastic properties of solids, particularly metals, both polycrystalline and the single crystal state.

Substances differ greatly in the rate at which the original length is regained and with some a considerable time is required. For example while quartz shows almost no delay, that for a glass fiber may amount to several hours, as may readily be shown by a simple experiment (more easily perhaps for torsion than for extension). This is known as the *elastic after-effect* or *lag*. Its magnitude appears to depend on the amount of non-homogeneity in the structure of the substance. This is probably why it is so small in quartz, for example, since quartz is very homogeneous. This is true of crystals in general. Glass on the other hand is a composite mixture of fairly large aggregates and hence less homogeneous. It is possible to give a rather good purely mechanical

analogy of the *after-effect* phenomenon by means of the model indicated in Fig. 11·9. A weight B is attached to the horizontal support A by means of the spring S_1 and by means of the spring S_2 to the weight C which is immersed in a very viscous liquid (molasses, for example). Now suppose that B is moved down a little. If it is held for such a short time that C in the meantime has not had a chance to move perceptibly, when B is released it will spring back to its original position (oscillating slightly about it). But if B is kept in the displaced position long enough, C will move down slowly, and when B is released it will not oscillate about its original position at once, since

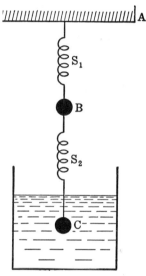

Fig. 11·9

this would correspond to a stretching of the spring S_2. After a time C regains its original equilibrium position whereupon B does the same. Another thing we should notice is that the oscillations of B die away the more rapidly the greater the viscosity of the liquid in which C is immersed, i.e., the greater the elastic after-effect. We should therefore expect that when wires which show a large after-effect are set vibrating either longitudinally or torsionally the vibrations will become rapidly damped out. This is a very striking effect and may be thought of as due to a kind of internal *viscosity* of the metal very similar to viscosity in fluids. There is an interesting property of this viscosity of metals which was discovered by Lord Kelvin. Suppose a wire is forced to vibrate for a considerable length of time; it is then found that the rate of damping for free oscillations is much greater than for the same wire before it was vibrated.   The wire acts as if it were tired.   On being allowed to rest, recovery ensues and the rate of damping decreases again.   This effect is known as elastic *fatigue*.   Another illustration of the same effect is found in the fact that repeated application of a stress may so weaken a metal that it breaks at less than the normal breaking point.

In the phenomena of elasticity we find an interesting illustration of a new physical concept.   It has been seen that the ordinary stress-strain relation holds only over a limited range and even here the phenomena of relaxation, elastic after-effect, and fatigue present themselves. It is just as if the elastic state of a wire at a given instant does not depend on the strain at that instant but on the whole previous strain history of the wire.   The question then appears to be one of *heredity*: the inheritance of the previous states is a controlling factor in any present state. The problem is particularly interesting because it introduces a new type of mathematical method into physics.   We shall illustrate this briefly.   Strictly speaking, even within the elastic limit, we ought to write Hooke's law in the form

$$\delta = Kf + \phi, \tag{11.3-2}$$

where f is the stress, δ the strain, K a constant, and ϕ is a quantity which depends on all the values which f has taken on from the time when the first stress was applied to the specimen up to the time t being considered.   A quantity of this sort which depends on a *whole range* of values of another quantity is known as a *functional*.   The simplest illustration is provided by the area under a curve between two ordinates.   Thus consider the curve $y = f(x)$ (Fig. 11·10).   The area included between the curve, the x axis and the two ordinates at $x = a$ and $x = b$ is a functional of $f(x)$, for it clearly depends on the whole set of values of $y = f(x)$ between a and b.   We may write

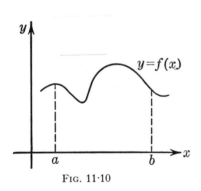

Fig. 11·10

$$A = \int_a^b f(x)\,dx \equiv F|[f_a{}^b(x)]|, \tag{11.3-3}$$

to indicate this type of quantity.

Let us illustrate briefly by a definite problem, the torsion of a wire. Letting θ be the angle of torsion and M the magnitude of the applied torque, we can rewrite eq. (11·3–2) as follows,

$$\theta = KM + \phi, \tag{11·3–4}$$

where M is a function of time, viz., $M(t)$. We shall now assume that *unit* torque applied to the wire during a time interval of $d\tau$ from τ to $\tau + d\tau$ not only produces a certain torsion in the wire at this moment but also contributes a torsion at the future time t of amount $\phi(t, \tau)\, d\tau$. Hence the resultant torsion angle θ at the time t will be given by $KM(t)$ plus the sum of all the residual terms $\phi(t, \tau)M(\tau)\, d\tau$. This sum of course must be an integral over all the time elapsing from the initial treatment at time t_0 to t. So we now write for the angle the " generalized " Hooke's law

$$\theta(t) = KM(t) + \int_{t_0}^{t} \phi(t, \tau)M(\tau)\, d\tau. \tag{11·3–5}$$

If we knew the previous torque at every instant and also knew the function $\phi(t, \tau)$ we might compute the resultant torsion. The function $\phi(t, \tau)$ is known as the *coefficient of heredity*, and the eq. (11·3–5) is known as an *integral equation* because in general knowing $\theta(t)$ and $\phi(t, \tau)$ we are interested in finding $M(t)$, which occurs under the integral sign. The solution of this problem is too difficult for presentation here. We merely wish to emphasize the fact of its existence in an endeavor to describe analytically the phenomena of elastic after-effect and fatigue, with which it might be supposed to be rather hopeless to deal in any symbolic way. The student interested in hereditary elasticity and in heredity problems in physics in general will find some interesting material in Volterra, *Theory of Functionals*, London, 1930.[1] Integral equations are becoming constantly more important in the solution of physical problems.

11·4. Rheology. In the preceding section we have seen that the perfectly elastic solid which when deformed follows Hooke's law for the relation between stress and strain is an ideal case. All materials, when stressed, take time for the strain to build up to the Hooke's law value corresponding to the stress; in other words, they show relaxation effects. This means that even for a constant stress the strain must vary from the instant of the imposition of the stress. A possible equation for this behavior would be, for tensile stress f and linear strain δ,

$$f = Y\delta + R\dot{\delta} \tag{11·4–1}$$

[1] Or see Vito Volterra, *Theory of Functionals and of Integral and Integro–differential Equations*, Dover Publications, New York, 1959, pp. 188 ff.

where Y is Young's modulus and R is a constant measuring the stress per unit rate of change of strain. If f is constant the solution of (11·4–1) is

$$\delta = \frac{f}{Y}(1 - e^{-Yt/R}).\qquad(11\cdot4\text{–}2)$$

When $t = 0$, $\delta = 0$, which is consistent with the fact that at the instant the stress is applied the strain starts from zero. For $t = \infty$, $\delta = f/Y$, or the Hooke's law value of the strain. Actually δ approximates this value in a much shorter time if R is a sufficiently small quantity. Thus, for time

$$\tau = R/Y \qquad(11\cdot4\text{–}3)$$

δ attains to within $1/e$ of the value f/Y. It is customary to call τ the relaxation time of the deformation process (see Sec. 10·2, particularly eq. 10·2–45).

The important point is that eq. (11·4–1) implies that the solid material effectively " flows " as a result of the imposition of the stress, though the flow is not that of the solid as a whole.

The study of the flow of materials in this sense is now termed *rheology* (from the Greek root *rheo-* meaning " flow "). It deals with all deformations of materials under stress. Strictly speaking it excludes from its consideration gases and ideal fluids, but viscous liquids which will be discussed in Chapter 12 come in its province. Liquids which display shear elasticity as well as viscosity (viscoelastic materials), such as high polymers, are rheological substances. The practical importance of rheology is shown by the properties of gels, which are colloidal disperse systems like gelatin, collagen, agar, and certain rubbers. Certain gels are thixotropic, i.e., can pass from the solid state to the liquid through mechanical agitation without temperature change and then revert to the solid form after the agitation ceases. Examples are provided by paints and printing inks.

The rheological behavior of a body is determined by its rheological equation of state, i.e., the equation connecting stress and deformation and their time rates of change. Hooke's law is the simplest rheological equation of state, while that given in (11·4–1) is higher in complexity and closer to the real behavior of many substances.

For a so-called Newtonian viscous fluid the rheological state equation has the form

$$f = \eta\dot{\delta},\qquad(11\cdot4\text{–}4)$$

where f is the tangential or shear stress in the direction of deformation and δ is now the shear strain. The quantity η is the coefficient of viscosity. We have already introduced this for gases in Chapter 7.

A modification of eqs. (11·4–1) and (11·4–4) takes into account the fact already mentioned in Sec. 11·3 that below the yield stress f_y the material is elastic, while for stresses above this value the material is plastic, i.e., flows under constant stress. Thus for such a situation we can write

$$f = f_y + \eta_{pl}\,\dot{\delta}, \tag{11·4–5}$$

where η_{pl} is called the plastic viscosity.

The reader might wonder whether meaning could be attached to a rheological equation of the form

$$\dot{\delta} = \frac{f}{\eta} + \frac{\dot{f}}{Y}. \tag{11·4–6}$$

This would appear to represent the behavior of a substance which has both elasticity (represented by the Y term) and viscosity (represented by the η term). Indeed if the coefficient of viscosity is infinite the above equation reduces effectively to Hooke's law. It becomes the equation for a viscous fluid if Young's modulus becomes infinitely great.

It must be emphasized that the state equations mentioned in this brief survey are of phenomenological character, that is, they do not pretend to account for the occurrence of the rheological constants η, Y, R, etc., nor for the existence of the equations themselves. For this it is necessary to examine the structure of the material in greater detail. There has been much recent interest in this subject, particularly with respect to the rheological behavior of crystals which are the most homogeneous of solids. It has been shown that the plastic deformation of crystals can be accounted for by the assumption in them of certain defects called dislocations which can move with a certain amount of freedom when stress is applied.[1]

11·5. Wave Motion. The detailed treatment of the motion of an elastic solid is in general a difficult subject. However, there is a particular type of such motion which is of such importance throughout physics that we must give it considerable attention. This is known as *wave motion*. Suppose that a strain is produced at some point in an elastic medium. What happens throughout the rest of the medium? For the sake of simplicity (though with no loss in generality as far as the fundamental ideas are concerned), in answering this question we

[1] For more details on rheology see *Rheology—Theory and Applications*, edited by F. R. Eirich, Vol. 1, Academic Press, New York, 1956. This volume also treats of dislocation theory in crystals. For a simplified account of the latter, see the popular book *Atomic Structure and the Strength of Metals* by N. F. Mott, Pergamon Press, New York, 1956.

shall confine ourselves here to the special case of an infinitely long wire or rod placed along the x axis and subjected to a tensile stress which we shall denote by X. This is a force per unit area acting solely along the x axis. Consulting Fig. 11·11, where a portion of the rod is indicated and represented by a rectangular parallelepiped, we consider the motion of a thin section of the rod of length dx. The area of cross-section being S, the stress force on the element by the portion of the rod to the left is

$$SX,$$

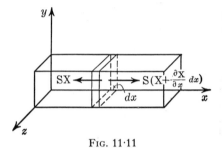

Fig. 11·11

while that due to the portion of the rod to the right is

$$S\left(X + \frac{\partial X}{\partial x}\,dx\right).$$

Hence the net force in the positive x direction is $S\dfrac{\partial X}{\partial x}\,dx$. The equation of motion results from equating this to the kinetic reaction $\rho S\ddot{\xi}\,dx$ where ρ is the mean density of the rod material and ξ is the displacement of the section considered to move as a whole. We therefore have

$$\rho\ddot{\xi} = \frac{\partial X}{\partial x}. \qquad (11\text{·}5\text{--}1)$$

Now from Hooke's law there at once results

$$X \div \frac{\partial \xi}{\partial x} = Y, \qquad (11\text{·}5\text{--}2)$$

where Y is Young's modulus [Sec. 11·1, eq. (11·1–20)], and $\dfrac{\partial \xi}{\partial x}$ is the linear strain. On substitution from (11·5–2) into (11·5–1) we get the equation

$$\rho\ddot{\xi} = Y \frac{\partial^2 \xi}{\partial x^2}. \qquad (11\text{·}5\text{--}3)$$

The analysis leading to (11·5–3) is faulty in that it neglects the fact that the *size* of the element $S\,dx$ changes as it moves. However, this turns out to be a very small change if ξ is small and hence the equation is correct for *small* displacements.[1]

In order to understand how the various parts of the rod move we must solve to find ξ as a function of x and t. Eq. (11·5–3) is a partial

[1] See R. B. Lindsay, *Concepts and Methods of Theoretical Physics*, Van Nostrand, Princeton, N.J., 1951, p. 320.

differential equation of the second order and a detailed discussion of its solution would require a good deal of mathematics. We shall however proceed as simply as possible. Since the equation says that the second time derivative of ξ is a constant times the second space derivative, it is natural to inquire whether or not a solution in the general form

$$\xi = f(x + ct) \tag{11·5-4}$$

is possible, where f is an *arbitrary differentiable function* and c is a constant, whose value is to be determined in such a way as to fit the solution. On this assumption then

$$\dot{\xi} = cf', \quad \ddot{\xi} = c^2 f'', \tag{11·5-5}$$

where we have set

$$f' = \frac{df(x + ct)}{d(x + ct)},$$

and correspondingly for f''. Moreover, similarly

$$\frac{\partial^2 \xi}{\partial x^2} = f''. \tag{11·5-6}$$

If now we resubstitute into the differential equation (11·5-3) we get

$$\rho c^2 f'' = Yf'', \tag{11·5-7}$$

which shows that our choice of a solution works provided we have

$$c = \pm \sqrt{\frac{Y}{\rho}}. \tag{11·5-8}$$

In other words c may be either positive or negative but must have the magnitude $\sqrt{Y/\rho}$. Since both $+\sqrt{Y/\rho}$ and $-\sqrt{Y/\rho}$ yield solutions, we may have either

$$\xi = f_1(x - ct), \tag{11·5-9}$$

or

$$\xi = f_2(x + ct). \tag{11·5-10}$$

Since moreover

$$\frac{\partial^2(f_1 + f_2)}{\partial t^2} = \ddot{f_1} + \ddot{f_2},$$

and

$$\frac{\partial^2(f_1 + f_2)}{\partial x^2} = \frac{\partial^2 f_1}{\partial x^2} + \frac{\partial^2 f_2}{\partial x^2},$$

it follows that

$$\xi = A_1 f_1(x - ct) + A_2 f_2(x + ct) \tag{11·5-11}$$

is also a solution where A_1 and A_2 are arbitrary constants. In other words the *sum* of two solutions of the differential equation (11·5–3) each multiplied by an arbitrary constant is also a solution. The same is true of *any* linear combination of solutions. This is an important property of *linear* differential equations, i.e., those in which no squares or higher powers of the dependent variable or any of its derivatives enter.

Let us now inquire into the physical significance of the solution (11·5–11). We first consider f_1 alone. The value of the function f_1 at the point $x = x_0$ and the time $t = t_0$ is

$$\xi_{00} = f_1(x_0 - ct_0). \qquad (11\cdot5\text{–}12)$$

Its value at x_0 at the later time t_1 is

$$\xi_{01} = f_1(x_0 - ct_1), \qquad (11\cdot5\text{–}13)$$

where ξ_{01} is in general different from ξ_{00}. But if we take its value at t_1 at the point x_1, where

$$x_1 - x_0 = c(t_1 - t_0), \qquad (11\cdot5\text{–}14)$$

we clearly have

$$\begin{aligned}\xi_{11} &= f_1[x_0 + c(t_1 - t_0) - ct_1] \\ &= f_1(x_0 - ct_0) \\ &= \xi_{00}. \qquad (11\cdot5\text{–}15)\end{aligned}$$

In other words the value of ξ for x_0, t_0 is the *same* as its value for x_1, t_1, provided the distance from x_0 to x_1 is equal to the time elapsing between t_0 and t_1 multiplied by c. It is just as if the value of ξ had been *propagated* from x_0 to x_1 in the time interval $t_1 - t_0$ with the velocity c. Hence $f_1(x - ct)$ may be taken to represent a disturbance (denoted by ξ) which is propagated in the positive x direction with velocity equal to c. We call this propagated disturbance a *wave* and the type of motion described is *wave motion*. Since ξ is a function of t and x only, the wave here defined is known as a *plane wave*, corresponding to propagation in one direction only. The

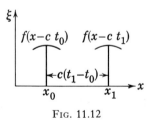

FIG. 11.12

matter is rendered more evident from an examination of the figure (Fig. 11·12) where we have plotted two functions of x, namely $f(x - ct_0)$ and $f(x - ct_1)$, which are the values of ξ for the time instants t_0 and t_1 respectively. It is as if we had taken snapshot pictures of the way ξ

varies with x at the two instants t_0 and t_1. The result is the same for both times except that the whole figure is shifted bodily so that each point of the first picture is displaced through the distance $c(t_1 - t_0)$ to make the second picture. The reader is urged to investigate all this very carefully for himself in order to form a clear notion of what a wave really means. He should note carefully, for example, that while to be sure the motion of particles or parts of the medium is involved, the wave motion is *not their* motion, but rather the motion *through* the medium of the configuration which *they* produce. Thus in the physical problem under discussion what we have shown is that if the long wire is stretched at some place in the direction of its length, thus producing a disturbance of the parts of the wire in the vicinity of this point and then let go, the *disturbance* moves along the wire with velocity $c = \sqrt{Y/\rho}$, constituting what is called an *elastic wave*. Moreover the wave travels in both directions, for if $f_1(x - ct)$ corresponds to wave motion in the positive x direction, $f_2(x + ct)$ will correspond to similar motion with the same velocity in the negative x direction. It must be emphasized, moreover, that there is nothing essentially *periodic* about this motion, though, as we shall see, periodic or harmonic waves are undoubtedly the most important type. We ought also to note that in the case discussed the direction of propagation coincides with the direction of displacement: the wave is said to be *longitudinal* (see Sec. 11·6).

The numerical magnitude of the velocity of an elastic wave in a rod or wire is of some interest. If we consider steel, for example, with $\rho = 7.8$ grams/cm^3 and $Y = 2 \times 10^{12}$ dynes/cm^2 (varying of course with the special composition), we get $c = 5.06 \times 10^5$ cm/sec $= 5060$ meters/sec. This indeed is the velocity with which sound travels along a steel bar, since the sound is propagated by elastic disturbance.

It is now in order to discuss in a general way some of the properties of *simple harmonic* waves. For a wave of this kind progressing in the positive x direction the displacement may be written

$$\xi = A \cos k(x - ct), \quad (11\cdot5\text{--}16)$$

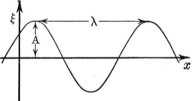

Fig. 11·13

where A is called the *amplitude* of the wave, c is the velocity and k is a constant which must have the dimensions of a reciprocal distance, since the argument of the cosine must be non-dimensional (i.e., a pure number). It is seen that (11·5–16) actually has the form of the function f_1 in (11·5–11). Now let us plot ξ as a function of x for a certain instant of time t. The result is given in Fig. 11·13. In wave nomenclature the places where ξ is a maximum are called *crests*; those corresponding to minima are called *troughs*. The distance between any two successive crests is called one *wave length* and designated by λ. Since the cosine function has a period of 2π, i.e.,

$$\cos z = \cos (2\pi + z),$$

it follows that for any instant t

$$k(x - ct) + 2\pi = k(x + \lambda - ct), \qquad (11\cdot5\text{--}17)$$

and therefore

$$k = \frac{2\pi}{\lambda}. \qquad (11\cdot5\text{--}18)$$

Moreover at any particular place there is simple harmonic motion [recall that $\cos (-kct) = \cos kct$] of frequency

$$\nu = \frac{kc}{2\pi} = \frac{\omega}{2\pi}, \qquad (11\cdot5\text{--}19)$$

so that

$$k = \frac{\omega}{c} = \frac{2\pi\nu}{c}. \qquad (11\cdot5\text{--}20)$$

We shall call ν the *frequency* of the *wave*, but shall often use $\omega = 2\pi\nu$ in its place for convenience and call it the *angular frequency*. Finally the *period* of the simple harmonic wave is

$$P = \frac{2\pi}{\omega} = \frac{1}{\nu}, \qquad (11\cdot5\text{--}21)$$

and we have the important relation for a simple harmonic wave

$$P = \frac{2\pi}{kc} = \frac{\lambda}{c}, \qquad (11\cdot5\text{--}22)$$

the period appearing as the ratio of wave length to velocity. It is clear that we may write the expression for ξ in the following equivalent forms

$$\xi = A \cos \frac{2\pi}{\lambda} (x - ct)$$

$$= A \cos (kx - \omega t)$$

$$= A \cos 2\pi \left(\frac{x}{\lambda} - \frac{t}{P} \right). \qquad (11\cdot5\text{--}23)$$

The choice is a matter of convenience. We shall perhaps use

$$\xi = A \cos (\omega t - kx), \qquad (11\cdot5\text{--}24)$$

most frequently, reversing the order of the time and space terms. This is, of course, purely arbitrary.

At this place it may be desirable to point out the value of the complex notation in expressing displacement in wave motion. Thus analogously to eq. (10·4–5) in Sec. 10·4 we set

$$\xi = Ae^{i(\omega t - kx)}, \qquad (11\cdot5\text{--}25)$$

where the amplitude A is now in general to be considered complex. In operating with wave displacements, particularly in differentiation and integration, this form of expression is very advantageous. Of course it should be emphasized that in general only the real or the imaginary parts separately have physical significance.

The wave dealt with in the last few paragraphs has been one traveling in the positive x direction. Naturally all that has been said will apply equally well to the wave in the negative x direction, where the displacement is denoted by

$$\xi = Be^{i(\omega t + kx)}. \qquad (11\cdot5\text{--}26)$$

In most cases where solid media are in question there will be waves traveling in both directions simultaneously and the resultant displacement will then be the sum of (11·5–25) and (11·5–26). We shall discuss special cases in Sec. 11·6.

The quantity $\omega t \pm kx$ is called the *phase* of the wave, provided the amplitude is real. If the latter is complex, we can always write it $A = A_0e^{i\varepsilon}$, where A_0 and ϵ are real quantities. The phase now takes the form $\omega t \pm kx + \epsilon$, and ϵ is called the initial phase at the origin.

When a medium is traversed by a wave, a certain amount of energy is associated with the motion in each unit volume. In the case of a harmonic wave the kinetic energy may be easily calculated. Suppose such a wave travels in the x direction along a rod of cross-sectional area S. Then the kinetic energy in a length Δx of the rod comprising a volume $S \Delta x$ is

$$\tfrac{1}{2}\rho S\dot{\xi}^2 \, \Delta x, \qquad (11\cdot5\text{--}27)$$

for $\rho S \, \Delta x$ is the mass involved, if ρ is the density of the rod. Hence the kinetic energy per unit volume at any place x at a given time instant t is $K = \tfrac{1}{2}\rho\dot{\xi}^2$. Now for $\dot{\xi}$ we have, consulting eq. (11·5–24) and supposing the initial phase zero,

$$\dot{\xi} = -A\omega \sin(\omega t - kx), \qquad (11\cdot5\text{--}28)$$

so that the kinetic energy per unit volume or kinetic energy density becomes

$$K = \tfrac{1}{2}\rho A^2\omega^2 \sin^2(\omega t - kx). \qquad (11\cdot5\text{--}29)$$

This is of course a function of x and t.   At any place it varies periodically with time and at any instant it varies periodically from point to point. Rather more important is the *average* kinetic energy density.   Thus for any value of x we have for the time average

$$\overset{t}{\bar{K}} = \tfrac{1}{2}\rho A^2 \omega^2 / \tau \cdot \int_0^\tau \sin^2 (\omega t - kx)\, dt, \qquad (11\cdot5\text{–}30)$$

where τ is much greater than one period of the wave.   Since x is considered constant, the evaluation of the integral gives the same result as $(10\cdot3\text{–}13)$.   Thus

$$\overset{t}{\bar{K}} = \tfrac{1}{4}\rho A^2 \omega^2. \qquad (11\cdot5\text{–}31)$$

Keeping the time constant, let us find the *space* average of the kinetic energy density over a distance long compared with the wave length, viz.,

$$\overset{x}{\bar{K}} = \tfrac{1}{2}\rho A^2 \omega^2 / x_0 \cdot \int_0^{x_0} \sin^2 (\omega t - kx)\, dx, \qquad (11\cdot5\text{–}32)$$

where $x_0 \gg \lambda$, the wave length.   The form of the integral is precisely the same in the two cases and hence

$$\overset{x}{\bar{K}} = \overset{t}{\bar{K}}. \qquad (11\cdot5\text{–}33)$$

Therefore we may speak merely of the *average* kinetic energy density as

$$\bar{K} = \tfrac{1}{4}\rho A^2 \omega^2. \qquad (11\cdot5\text{–}34)$$

Since the medium is strained by the passage of the wave there will also be *potential energy* associated with the wave.   This will, however, obviously depend on the character of the strain corresponding to the wave and hence must be specially investigated in each particular case. In this place as a simple illustration let us consider again the solid rod of density ρ and Young's modulus Y.   The potential energy associated with the element Δx of the rod is the work done by the variable force due to stress, viz., SX, in changing the length Δx from $(\Delta x)_1$ to $(\Delta x)_2$, i.e., by $\Delta(\Delta x)$.   Thus we have

$$V = S \int_{(\Delta x)_1}^{(\Delta x)_2} X d(\Delta x). \qquad (11\cdot5\text{–}35)$$

Now the change $d(\Delta x)$ is the differential of the linear strain times the original length.   Hence we may write

$$d(\Delta x) = d \left(\frac{\partial \xi}{\partial x} \right) \Delta x. \qquad (11\cdot5\text{–}36)$$

Consequently (11·5–35) becomes

$$V = S\Delta x \int_0^{\frac{\partial \xi}{\partial x}} X d\left(\frac{\partial \xi}{\partial x}\right)$$

$$= YS \Delta x \int_0^{\frac{\partial \xi}{\partial x}} \frac{\partial \xi}{\partial x} d\left(\frac{\partial \xi}{\partial x}\right), \tag{11·5–37}$$

using (11·5–2). We finally obtain

$$V = \frac{YS \Delta x}{2}\left(\frac{\partial \xi}{\partial x}\right)^2. \tag{11·5–38}$$

For the plane harmonic wave (11·5–24) we get for the potential energy density

$$V = \frac{YA^2k^2}{2}\sin^2(\omega t - kx). \tag{11·5–39}$$

It is of interest to observe from a comparison with (11·5–29) that for this type of wave motion

$$V = K, \tag{11·5–40}$$

identically. Hence the total energy density is

$$U = \rho\omega^2A^2 \sin^2(\omega t - kx). \tag{11·5–41}$$

The *average* total energy density is therefore

$$\bar{U} = \tfrac{1}{2}\rho\omega^2A^2. \tag{11·5–42}$$

We must be careful not to conclude that the relation (11·5–40) is true for all kinds of waves. Nevertheless the special case here discussed is rather important in practice.

Another important allied concept which deserves mention in this place is that of the *intensity* of a wave. This is defined as the *average rate of flow of energy per unit area perpendicular to the direction of propagation.* If we consider any cross-section of the rod, for example, as the wave passes this cross-section it may be thought of as carrying energy with it and the amount of energy carried per unit area per second is clearly (for a plane wave at least) the product of the energy density and the velocity of the wave. Hence we have the following expression for the intensity in the case of a plane harmonic wave traversing a rod [from eq. (11·5–42)]

$$I = \tfrac{1}{2}\rho c A^2 \omega^2. \tag{11·5–43}$$

It may perhaps be worth while to express this in terms of the maximum stress in the rod, X_{max}, associated with the wave.   Since

$$X = Y \frac{\partial \xi}{\partial x},$$

and

$$\frac{\partial \xi}{\partial x} = Ak \sin (\omega t - kx),$$

we have

$$X_{max} = AkY = A\omega \rho c. \tag{11·5–44}$$

Therefore

and

$$\left. \begin{aligned} A^2 \omega^2 &= \frac{X^2_{max}}{\rho^2 c^2}, \\ I &= \frac{1}{2} \frac{X^2_{max}}{\rho c}. \end{aligned} \right\} \tag{11·5–45}$$

The intensity is thus proportional to the square of the maximum tensile stress produced in the rod.   This is a very significant equation.

11·6. Transverse Waves in a String.   In our study of wave motion in a solid rod in the previous section we were concerned with waves in which the direction of propagation coincides with the material displacement.   Such waves are known as *longitudinal* waves and are of great importance, particularly in acoustics (Sec. 12·6).   However, there is another type of wave, of equal significance, in which the displacement is perpendicular to the direction of propagation.   Such waves are known as *transverse* waves.   As a matter of fact both types of waves are set up in every disturbance of an elastic solid, though in a fluid only the former can exist.   The mathematical discussion of transverse wave motion in a general elastic solid is rather involved and we shall not enter upon it here. However, we encounter a very interesting illustration of transverse waves in the problem of the vibrating string.   Imagine a perfectly flexible string (Fig. 11·14) stretched with tension τ.   Let the equilibrium position of the string

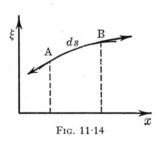

FIG. 11·14

be the x axis (we neglect its thickness, of course), and denote the *transverse* displacement of any point by ξ.   We suppose that all displacements take place in the same plane.   We shall also assume that the tension τ is constant and may be considered to a sufficient degree of approximation as unchanged when the string is deformed. This in turn implies that the displacement ξ is to be very small compared with the length of the string. We now discuss the motion of an element of the string from A to B of length ds, whose projection on the x axis is dx. Let us find the restoring force acting on the element AB in the direction of the displacement. The upward component of τ at A is

$$-\tau \frac{\partial \xi}{\partial s} = -\tau \left[\frac{\partial \xi}{\partial x} - \frac{1}{2} \left(\frac{\partial \xi}{\partial x} \right)^3 + \cdots \right], \qquad (11\cdot6\text{–}1)$$

which we get by expanding

$$\frac{\partial \xi}{\partial s} = \frac{\dfrac{\partial \xi}{\partial x}}{\sqrt{1 + \left(\dfrac{\partial \xi}{\partial x} \right)^2}}, \qquad (11\cdot6\text{–}2)$$

recalling that both $\partial \xi / \partial s$ and $\partial \xi / \partial x$ are small. As a matter of fact, it will be a sufficiently good approximation, if we write for the upward component at A

$$-\tau \frac{\partial \xi}{\partial x}. \qquad (11\cdot6\text{–}3)$$

What is now the upward component of the tension at B? It must be, to a first approximation,

$$\tau \left[\frac{\partial \xi}{\partial x} + \frac{\partial}{\partial x} \left(\frac{\partial \xi}{\partial x} \right) dx \right], \qquad (11\cdot6\text{–}4)$$

whence the total upward force on the element AB is the sum of $(11\cdot6\text{–}3)$ and $(11\cdot6\text{–}4)$ namely

$$\tau \frac{\partial}{\partial x} \left(\frac{\partial \xi}{\partial x} \right) dx. \qquad (11\cdot6\text{–}5)$$

Equating the kinetic reaction of the element to the force on it yields the equation of motion

$$\rho \ddot{\xi} \, dx = \tau \frac{\partial^2 \xi}{\partial x^2} \, dx,$$

or

$$\rho \ddot{\xi} = \tau \frac{\partial^2 \xi}{\partial x^2}, \qquad (11\cdot6\text{–}6)$$

where ρ is here the mass per unit length of the string and assumed to be a constant. We have here made the same sort of approximation as in deriving $(11\cdot5\text{–}3)$ by neglecting the stretching of the string element in its displacement.   Eq. (11·6–6) is the usual wave equation, and hence the displacement ξ is propagated along the string with velocity

$$c = \sqrt{\frac{\tau}{\rho}}. \tag{11·6–7}$$

If we recall the discussion in Sec. 11·5, we see that since in general there may be waves in both directions the most general expression for the displacement at distance x and at time t is

$$\xi = f_1(ct - x) + f_2(ct + x). \tag{11·6–8}$$

Let us, however, confine our attention to the motion of the string when the displacement at any point is simple harmonic, i.e., consider only harmonic waves.   From Sec. 11·5 we then write

$$\xi = Ae^{i(\omega t - kx)} + Be^{i(\omega t + kx)}, \tag{11·6–9}$$

where A and B are complex amplitudes, $\omega = 2\pi\nu$, ν being the frequency of the wave and $k = \omega/c$, where c is the velocity [eq.(11·6–7)].   There are now four arbitrary constants involved, since A and B, being complex, each involve two constants.   Moreover there is nothing to specify the frequency, which is therefore also arbitrary.

   We shall now suppose that the string is finite and of length l, and is moreover fastened at the ends so that no motion takes place there. We then have the boundary conditions that for all t

$$\xi = 0 \quad \text{for} \quad x = 0, l. \tag{11·6–10}$$

Substitution into (11·6–9) then yields

$$\left. \begin{array}{l} (A + B)e^{i\omega t} = 0, \\ e^{i\omega t}(Ae^{-ikl} + Be^{ikl}) = 0. \end{array} \right\} \tag{11·6–11}$$

From the first of these two equations we get

$$A = -B, \tag{11·6–12}$$

and hence from the second

$$e^{-ikl} - e^{ikl} = 0. \tag{11·6–13}$$

Expressing eq. (11·6–13) in terms of trigonometric functions gives

$$\sin kl = 0, \tag{11·6–14}$$

which leads to

$$kl = n\pi, \tag{11·6–15}$$

where n is any integer.   This immediately limits the possible frequencies of the harmonic waves in the string to the set given by

$$\nu_n = \frac{nc}{2l} = \frac{n}{2l}\sqrt{\frac{\tau}{\rho}}. \tag{11·6–16}$$

The lowest frequency of the set, viz., $\nu_1 = c/2l$, is called the *fundamental*. The higher frequencies $\nu_2, \ldots, \nu_n, \ldots$ are called the *harmonics*. It is interesting to see that the imposition of the boundary conditions (11·6–10) in addition to removing some of the arbitrary constants from the solution has also introduced a certain *discreteness* into the problem. This is a significant result, for it is the first element of discreteness we have encountered in the motion of a *continuous* medium. Corresponding to each frequency ν_n there is a definite mode of oscillation, viz.,

$$\xi_n = A_n[e^{i(2\pi\nu_n t - k_n x)} - e^{i(2\pi\nu_n t + k_n x)}]. \qquad (11\cdot6\text{–}17)$$

For practical purposes we shall put this into its *real* form. Letting $2A_n = a_n + ib_n$,

$$\xi_{n,\text{ real}} = \frac{a_n}{2}\left[\cos\left(2\pi\nu_n t - k_n x\right) - \cos\left(2\pi\nu_n t + k_n x\right)\right]$$

$$-\frac{b_n}{2}\left[\sin\left(2\pi\nu_n t - k_n x\right) - \sin\left(2\pi\nu_n t + k_n x\right)\right]. \quad (11\cdot6\text{–}18)$$

If we expand the trigonometric expressions and simplify, there finally results

$$\xi_{n,\text{ real}} = \sin k_n x[a_n \sin 2\pi\nu_n t + b_n \cos 2\pi\nu_n t], \qquad (11\cdot6\text{–}19)$$

with $k_n = 2\pi\nu_n/c$. For any integral value of n, eq. (11·6–19) represents a solution of the wave equation (11·6–6) and a possible displacement propagation for the string. Now the wave equation (11·6–6) is a *linear* partial differential equation, and we have already seen (Sec. 11·5) that the individual solutions of such an equation are additive, giving new solutions. It would therefore follow that the most general expression for the displacement when harmonic waves of all frequencies ν_n travel along the string, is given by

$$\xi_{\text{real}} = \sum_{n=0}^{\infty} \sin k_n x[a_n \sin 2\pi\nu_n t + b_n \cos 2\pi\nu_n t]. \quad (11\cdot6\text{–}20)$$

What does this solution mean physically? It means that if we bring about an initial transverse displacement of any point on the string the resulting displacement in time of all other points is given by the infinite series (11·6–20).

It must be emphasized that (11·6–20) no longer represents a single progressive wave. Rather as the superposition of progressive harmonic waves in opposite directions along the finite string it represents what is called a standing or stationary wave. Thus each point of the string is executing harmonic motion of frequency given by the bracketed terms of (11·6–20) and with amplitudes proportional to $\sin k_n x$ (not a function of time). This introduces a feature not present in the usual progressive wave. For we see that for any particular mode of oscillation characterized by the integer n there exist $n - 1$ equally spaced points of the string (exclusive of the end points) at which the displacement is always zero. These are given by the condition

$$\sin k_n x = 0,$$

and measured from one end of the string the corresponding values of x are

$$x = l/n, \quad 2l/n, \cdots (n - 1)l/n.$$

The points in question are called *nodes* or nodal points. The reader should show that the distance between successive nodes is one half the wave length of the corresponding standing wave. A knowledge of this and the frequency of excitation suffices (from 11·5–22) to permit the evaluation of the velocity of the wave. The midpoints between successive nodes are referred to as loops since there the displacement reaches its maximum during each period of the motion.

Our next task is to discuss the evaluation of the constants a_n and b_n. Let us denote the initial displacement of any point on the string by ξ_0. This is a function of x, of course. We therefore have from (11·6–20), (dropping the subscript " real," since this is now understood)

$$\xi_0 = \sum_{n=0}^{\infty} b_n \sin k_n x. \tag{11·6–21}$$

Moreover, let us denote the initial *velocity* of any point on the string by $\dot{\xi}_0$, also a function of x. Since

$$\dot{\xi} = \sum_{n=0}^{\infty} \sin k_n x \cdot 2\pi \nu_n [a_n \cos 2\pi \nu_n t - b_n \sin 2\pi \nu_n t], \tag{11·6–22}$$

we have

$$\dot{\xi}_0 = \sum_{n=0}^{\infty} 2\pi \nu_n a_n \sin k_n x. \tag{11·6–23}$$

We now have to evaluate a_n and b_n from the eqs. (11·6–21) and (11·6–23). This might appear to be rather difficult. Let us, however, multiply both sides of eq. (11·6–21) by $\sin k_s x$, where s is a *particular* integer, and integrate the result as x goes from 0 to l. This gives

$$\int_0^l \xi_0 \sin k_s x \, dx = \sum_{n=0}^{\infty} \int_0^l b_n \sin k_n x \cdot \sin k_s x \, dx. \tag{11·6–24}$$

From (11·6–16)

$$k_s = \frac{2\pi\nu_s}{c} = \frac{s\pi}{l},$$ (11·6–25)

and

$$\int_0^l \sin\frac{s\pi x}{l}\cdot\sin\frac{n\pi x}{l}\,dx$$

$$= \left(\frac{\sin(s-n)\pi x/l}{2(s-n)\pi/l} - \frac{\sin(s+n)\pi x/l}{2(s+n)\pi/l}\right)\Bigg]_0^l,$$ (11·6–26)

so that if $n \neq s$, the integral *vanishes*. On the other hand if $n = s$, we have

$$\int_0^l \sin^2 s\pi\frac{x}{l}\cdot dx = \frac{l}{2s\pi}\left(\frac{s\pi}{l}x - \sin\frac{s\pi x}{l}\cos\frac{s\pi x}{l}\right)\Bigg]_0^l = \frac{l}{2}.$$

Hence of all the integrals in the sum on the right-hand side of (11·6–24) only one is different from zero, namely that for which $n = s$. Its value is $l/2$. We therefore have

$$b_s = \frac{2}{l}\int_0^l \xi_0 \sin k_s x\,dx,$$ (11·6–27)

which enables us to calculate b_s if we know ξ_0. A precisely similar procedure with eq. (11·6–23) leads to

$$a_s = \frac{2}{s\pi c}\int_0^l \dot{\xi}_0 \sin k_s x\,dx.$$ (11·6–28)

What the two eqs. (11·6–27, 28) really mean is this: if we know the actual *displacement* and *velocity* of *every* point on the string at a single definite instant we can compute the configuration of the string, i.e., the position and velocity of every point, for every future instant, tracing out its whole subsequent history. There is an interesting bit of mathematics connected with this result. The initial position of the string can be anything compatible with the conditions imposed, i.e., it can be mathematically speaking any continuous function of x. What we have then shown is that any such function of x can be expanded in a certain bounded interval into an infinite series of circular functions of x, viz., (11·6–21), and we have shown how to calculate the coefficients. Such a series is called a *Fourier series*, and is of very great importance in many physical problems such as are encountered for example in the theory of the conduction of heat, oscillations of media, orbits in celestial mechanics and atomic structure theory. The student at this point should obtain a reasonable degree of familiarity with this type of series. We have not discussed it here with any rigor, since we have not taken up, for example, the conditions for its convergence.[1]   But we have at any rate pointed out some of its physical significance.

Further discussion of the motion of a stretched string lies really in the province of acoustics.[2]

One important additional point about harmonic waves deserves mention here. The form of the solution (11·6–19) for a stationary wave in a string suggests that we may seek a solution of the wave equation (11·6–6) for harmonic waves by writing

$$\xi = f(x)e^{i\omega t}, \qquad (11\cdot6\text{–}29)$$

where ω is again the angular frequency and $f(x)$ is a function of x alone. Then

$$\ddot{\xi} = -\omega^2 f(x)e^{i\omega t},$$

and

$$\frac{\partial^2 \xi}{\partial x^2} = \frac{d^2 f}{dx^2} e^{i\omega t}.$$

Hence (11·6–6) (with the use of (11·6–7)) takes the form

$$\frac{d^2 f}{dx^2} + k^2 f = 0, \qquad (11\cdot6\text{–}30)$$

with $k = \omega/c = 2\pi/\lambda$, as usual. This is the differential equation of what may be called the space part of a harmonic plane wave in the x direction.   Its solution is of course

$$f = Ae^{ikx} + Be^{-ikx}, \qquad (11\cdot6\text{–}31)$$

indicating at once that a stationary wave is a possible solution of the wave equation.   The method of solution implied in the choice (11·6–29), in which ξ appears as a product of a function of x alone by a function of t alone is called separation of *variables*.[3]

11·7. Dispersion of Waves in a Solid Rod.   The discussion in Sec. 11·5 of longitudinal wave propagation in a solid rod was adequate for the case of a long, slender rod and for harmonic waves of relatively low frequency.   However it neglected a factor of considerable theoretical importance in the theory of wave propagation.   We recall from Sec. 11·2 that whenever a solid is subjected to a tensile strain in a given direction, there is always a lateral strain at right angles to this direction associated

---

[1] See E. B. Wilson, *Advanced Calculus*, Dover Publications, New York, 1958, pp. 458 ff.

[2] See H. Lamb, *Dynamical Theory of Sound*, 2nd ed., Dover Publications, New York, 1960, Chap. II.   Also R. B. Lindsay, *Mechanical Radiation*, McGraw-Hill, New York, 1960, Chap. 4.

[3] For more details consult R. B. Lindsay, *Mechanical Radiation*, pp. 24 ff.

with it.   In fact the latter strain is equal to the former multiplied by Poisson's ratio σ.   Hence when a longitudinal disturbance is propagated along a solid rod, there is bound to be a corresponding lateral disturbance. How can we take account of it?   The detailed analysis in terms of the elastic behavior of the solid is rather complicated, but fortunately a simple consideration, due to Lord Rayleigh,[1] enables us to see rather quickly the effect of taking the lateral motion into account.

If we denote the density of the solid by ρ and the area of cross-section of the rod by S, the kinetic energy associated with the longitudinal wave disturbance in the element dx is

$$dK = \tfrac{1}{2}\rho S \dot{\xi}^2 \, dx \qquad (11\cdot7\text{–}1)$$

if we denote the displacement from equilibrium in the x direction by ξ. If the length of the rod is l, the total kinetic energy due to longitudinal motion is

$$K = \tfrac{1}{2}\rho S \int_0^l \dot{\xi}^2 \, dx. \qquad (11\cdot7\text{–}2)$$

But if the rod at the same time undergoes lateral displacement, there must be some kinetic energy associated with this motion also.   If we denote the lateral displacement in the rod at distance r from the central axis by η, the kinetic energy of lateral displacement for the element dx is then

$$dK' = \tfrac{1}{2}\rho \int_0^a 2\pi r \, dr \, \dot{\eta}^2 \, dx, \qquad (11\cdot7\text{–}3)$$

if the radius of the rod is a.   Now from the definition of Poisson's ratio we have

$$\frac{\eta}{r} = \sigma \frac{\partial \xi}{\partial x}. \qquad (11\cdot7\text{–}4)$$

Substitution into (11·7–3) yields for the total kinetic energy due to lateral motion

$$K' = \rho \int_0^l \int_0^a \pi r^3 \sigma^2 \, dr \left(\frac{\partial \dot{\xi}}{\partial x}\right)^2 dx,$$

$$= \frac{\rho S a^2 \sigma^2}{4} \int_0^l \left(\frac{\partial \dot{\xi}}{\partial x}\right)^2 dx. \qquad (11\cdot7\text{–}5)$$

Now in Sec. 11·5 we did not discuss the case of a finite rod of length l. However in Sec. 11·6 we did take up the analogous case of the vibrating string, for which the analysis is similar.   The general solution for harmonic waves is

$$\xi = A e^{i(\omega t - kx)} + B e^{i(\omega t + kx)}. \qquad (11\cdot7\text{–}6)$$

[1] *Theory of Sound*, Dover Publications, New York, 1945, Vol. 1, p. 252.

Let us confine our attention first to the case of a rod free at both ends. Clearly the boundary condition is no longer $\xi = 0$ at $x = 0, l$. Rather we have to assume that at a free end, the longitudinal strain vanishes, i.e., $\partial\xi/\partial x = 0$. Since

$$\frac{\partial\xi}{\partial x} = -ikAe^{i(\omega t - kx)} + ikBe^{i(\omega t + kx)}, \qquad (11\cdot7\text{--}7)$$

the imposition of the conditions yields

$$\sin kl = 0,$$

or

$$kl = n\pi. \qquad (11\cdot7\text{--}8)$$

The solution (11·7–6) becomes

$$\xi = A' \cos \frac{n\pi x}{l} e^{i\omega t}. \qquad (11\cdot7\text{--}9)$$

Hence

$$\frac{\partial\dot{\xi}}{\partial x} = -i\omega A' \frac{n\pi}{l} \sin \frac{n\pi x}{l} e^{i\omega t},$$

$$\dot{\xi} = i\omega A' \cos \frac{n\pi x}{l} e^{i\omega t}. \qquad (11\cdot7\text{--}10)$$

In evaluating the kinetic energies K and K' we can neglect the time factors. Then so far as space dependence is concerned

$$K = \tfrac{1}{2}\rho S \int_0^l \omega^2 A'^2 \cos^2 \frac{n\pi x}{l} dx$$

$$= \tfrac{1}{4}\rho S\omega^2 A'^2 l. \qquad (11\cdot7\text{--}11)$$

Similarly

$$K' = \frac{\rho Sa^2\sigma^2}{4} \int_0^l \omega^2 A'^2 \frac{n^2\pi^2}{l^2} \sin^2 \frac{n\pi x}{l} dx$$

$$= \frac{\rho Sa^2\sigma^2\omega^2 A'^2\pi^2 n^2}{8l}. \qquad (11\cdot7\text{--}12)$$

Now each kinetic energy expression may be thought of as one half the product of an effective mass and the square of the maximum velocity $\omega A'$. The effect of taking into account the lateral motion is therefore essentially to attribute greater effective mass to the vibrating rod. In fact we have (denoting the effective mass by M)

$$\frac{M + \Delta M}{M} = \frac{K + K'}{K} = 1 + \frac{n^2\pi^2 a^2\sigma^2}{2l^2}. \qquad (11\cdot7\text{--}13)$$

But since the natural frequency of the rod as a vibrator is inversely proportional to the square root of the mass, the actual frequency ν', taking into account the lateral motion, will bear to the frequency ν associated with the simple longitudinal motion the relation

$$\nu'/\nu = \sqrt{\frac{1}{1 + n^2\pi^2 a^2 \sigma^2/2l^2}}$$

$$\doteq 1 - n^2\pi^2 a^2 \sigma^2/4l^2. \tag{11·7–14}$$

Since the frequency is directly proportional to the wave velocity with the reciprocal of the wave length as the factor, we can write (11·7–14) in the form

$$c'/c = 1 - \pi^2\sigma^2(a/\lambda)^2, \tag{11·7–15}$$

reflecting that $\lambda = 2l/n$. Here c is the effective velocity of longitudinal waves in the rod, disregarding the lateral motion, where (11·5–8)

$$c = \sqrt{Y/\rho}. \tag{11·7–16}$$

Hence (11·7–15) says that the velocity is changed by the lateral motion to c' and indeed in such a way that it depends on the wave length. When wave velocity depends on wave length or frequency we say that there is velocity dispersion. Eq. (11·7–15) is a dispersion relation. In particular if we plot c'/c as a function of λ, we see that for $\lambda \gg a$ the ratio approaches unity, whereas when λ decreases c'/c becomes steadily smaller. Clearly we cannot apply the formula for arbitrarily small λ, since ultimately c'/c will become negative. The formula must be considered only an approximation in which λ must not be allowed to get smaller than a. In any case we note that when λ approaches a in magnitude the lateral motion makes itself most noticeable in its effect on the phase velocity. This is physically reasonable. We now wish to explore an interesting physical consequence of (11·7–15).

11·8. Group Velocity. In order to explore the possible significance of the dispersion relation (11·7–15), let us consider two plane harmonic waves of the same amplitude A moving in the positive x direction. We shall suppose that the first has the frequency ν_1 and moves with velocity c_1 and the second has the frequency ν_2 and moves with the velocity c_2, which is different from c_1. The resultant wave is the superposition of the two and may be written in the form

$$\xi = A \cos\left(\omega_1 t - \frac{\omega_1}{c_1}x\right) + A \cos\left(\omega_2 t - \frac{\omega_2}{c_2}x\right). \tag{11·8–1}$$

By a simple trigonometric identity this may be rewritten as

$$\xi = 2A \cos \left[\left(\frac{\omega_1 + \omega_2}{2} \right) t - \left(\frac{\omega_1/c_1 + \omega_2/c_2}{2} \right) x \right]$$

$$\cdot \cos \left[\left(\frac{\omega_1 - \omega_2}{2} \right) t - \frac{(\omega_1/c_1 - \omega_2/c_2)}{2} x \right]. \quad (11 \cdot 8\text{--}2)$$

Let us suppose that ω_1 and ω_2 differ only by a quantity $\Delta\omega$ which is small compared with either. We therefore write

$$\omega_2 = \omega_1 + \Delta\omega.$$

Similarly

$$\omega_2/c_2 = \omega_1/c_1 + \Delta(\omega/c).$$

With these substitutions we have

$$\xi = 2A \cos \left[\left(\omega_1 + \frac{\Delta\omega}{2} \right) t - \left(\frac{\omega_1}{c_1} + \frac{\Delta(\omega/c)}{2} \right) x \right]$$

$$\cdot \cos \left[\frac{\Delta\omega}{2} \cdot t - \frac{\Delta(\omega/c)}{2} x \right]. \quad (11 \cdot 8\text{--}3)$$

Now the first cosine wave in (11·8–3) is one whose frequency and velocity (strictly frequency over velocity) differ only slightly from these quantities for the first wave in (11·8–1). On the other hand the second cosine wave has a much smaller frequency or longer period. We may therefore think of the term

$$2A \cos \left[\frac{\Delta\omega}{2} t - \frac{\Delta(\omega/c)}{2} x \right] \quad (11 \cdot 8\text{--}4)$$

as constituting a *varying* amplitude of the first cosine wave in (11·8–3). If indeed we were to plot ξ in (11·8–3) we should find something like the sketch in Fig. 11·15 in which the heavy profile (both dotted and full)

FIG. 11·15

corresponds to (11·8–4), while the other cosine curve with smaller period represents the first cosine wave in (11·8–3) with its amplitude *modulated* by (11·8–4). The two superposed waves may be said to constitute a *group* and the heavy profile in Fig. 11·15 represents the progression of the group. It travels with a different velocity from the individual waves. From a knowledge of wave propagation earlier in this chapter and in particular the relations developed in Sec. 11·5, we see indeed that the velocity represented by the heavy profile is

$$c_g = \frac{\Delta\omega}{\Delta(\omega/c)}.$$ (11·8–5)

This is called the *group velocity*. It is strictly the velocity with which the modulated amplitude of the superposed waves travels in the x direction. We have evaluated its expression for the simple case of a group made up of only two waves. Closer inspection shows that the formula (11·8–5) holds, no matter how many component waves there are in the group.

We must now examine (11·8–5) more closely. Note that the changes denoted by $\Delta\omega$ and $\Delta(\omega/c)$ must take place in the vicinity of the mean frequency and phase velocity of the waves in the group, which we may denote as ω_0 and c_0 respectively. We may then interpret the ratio on the right-hand side as a genuine derivative taken at the mean values and write for the group velocity

$$c_g = \left[\frac{d\omega}{d(\omega/c)} \right]_0$$

$$= \left[\frac{d\omega}{\dfrac{d\omega}{c} - \dfrac{1}{c^2}\dfrac{dc}{d\omega}d\omega} \right]_0$$

$$= \frac{c_0}{1 - \dfrac{\omega_0}{c_0}\left(\dfrac{dc}{d\omega}\right)_0}$$ (11·8–6)

where $(dc/d\omega)_0$ means the rate of change of velocity with frequency taken at the mean frequency. We see that if $(dc/d\omega)_0 = 0$, i.e., if there is no dispersion, then $c_g = c_0$ and the group velocity is the same as the phase velocity of all waves in the group. On the other hand, if $(dc/d\omega)_0 > 0$, then $c_g > c_0$; whereas if $(dc/d\omega)_0 < 0$, then $c_g < c_0$. In order to examine the situation prevailing in the solid rod discussed in Sec. 11·7, we must express (11·8–6) in terms of wave length. Utilizing the fundamental relation (11·5–22), we can show that (11·8–6) becomes

$$c_g = c_0 - \lambda_0 \left(\frac{dc}{d\lambda}\right)_0.$$ (11·8–7)

Now we may rewrite (11·7–15) in the form

$$\underline{c}' = \sqrt{Y/\rho}(1 - \pi^2\sigma^2 a^2/\lambda^2)$$ (11·8–8)

for the dependence of the now variable phase velocity c' on the wave length λ. Hence, leaving off the prime on c for simplicity,

$$\left(\frac{dc}{d\lambda}\right)_0 = 2\sqrt{Y/\rho}\ \pi^2\sigma^2a^2/\lambda_0^3. \tag{11·8–9}$$

Therefore the group velocity becomes

$$c_g = c_0 - 2\sqrt{Y/\rho}\cdot\pi^2\sigma^2a^2/\lambda_0^2. \tag{11·8–10}$$

This shows that the group velocity is always smaller than the mean phase velocity c_0 in the group. As was pointed out in Sec. 11·7, the formula must not be expected to hold for too small values of λ_0.

11·9. Wave Pulses. The discussion of wave motion in the preceding section was confined to general wave functions of the form $f(x \pm ct)$, which are infinitely extended in space and time. Even the harmonic waves like (11·5–24), to which we have restricted most of our attention, have the same ideal character. This did not hinder us from combining such waves to find the resultant disturbance in a finite medium like a stretched string, nor from examining standing waves and characteristic frequencies or harmonics. But the question arises: how can one handle the case of an actually occurring progressive wave which is certainly not infinite in extent? All practical progressive wave trains are finite in both space and time. An illustration is presented in Fig. 11·16, which shows a snapshot picture of a finite harmonic wave

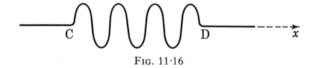

Fig. 11·16

train at $t = 0$. From $x = -\infty$ to C there is no disturbance. From C to D there is a harmonic disturbance of the form $A\cos(\omega_0 t - k_0 x)$, and from C to $x = +\infty$ there is again zero disturbance. As t increases the whole pattern moves off to the right with a certain speed. Such a situation is described as a harmonic *wave pulse*.

It may be very desirable to try to represent such a wave pulse as a superposition of an infinite number of component harmonic waves of various frequencies. Obviously the conditions on these components must be rather stringent, since everywhere to the left of C and to the right of D they must add up precisely to zero, whereas between C and D, the addition must yield precisely the sine wave. It is not perhaps surprising that one cannot meet these conditions with components of discrete frequencies. The only way to do it is to let the frequencies of the components vary *continuously* over a wide range (effectively infinite) and hence represent the pulse not by a sum over harmonic components as in the case of stationary waves in a string (Sec. 11·6) but by an integral taken over the continuously varying frequency. Thus if the pulse is given by the function $f(x, t)$ as a function of time and distance along the x axis, we might try the expression

$$f(x, t) = \int_{-\infty}^{+\infty} A(k) \cos(\omega t - kx)\, dk \qquad (11\cdot9\text{--}1)$$

where indeed we use the wave parameter k (which is equal to $2\pi/\lambda$ or ω/c) in place of the angular frequency ω as the running variable to represent the various components. In (11·9–1) $A(k)\, dk$ becomes, so to speak, the amplitude of the harmonic components with wave parameters extending over the interval from k to $k + dk$. By a mathematical analysis which we shall not go through here[1] it can be shown that under certain conditions (11·9–1) will hold and

$$A(k) = \frac{1}{2\pi} \int_{-L/2}^{L/2} \cos k_0 w \cos kw \, dw \qquad (11\cdot9\text{--}2)$$

where w is a new variable defined as

$$w = u - c\tau \qquad (11\cdot9\text{--}3)$$

and u is a variable having the dimensions of length and τ a variable having the dimensions of time. The quantity L is the length of the pulse. Thus, to refer again to Fig. 11·16,

$$f(x, t) = \cos k_0(x - Vt) \quad \text{for} \quad |x - ct| < L/2$$

$$f(x, t) = 0 \quad \text{for} \quad |x - ct| > L/2. \qquad (11\cdot9\text{--}4)$$

Integration now yields

$$A(k) = \frac{1}{\pi} \left[\frac{\sin(k_0 - k)L/2}{(k_0 - k)} + \frac{\sin(k_0 + k)L/2}{(k_0 + k)} \right]. \qquad (11\cdot9\text{--}5)$$

It is clear that the first term in the bracket in (11·9–5) will predominate over the second unless k is very much larger than k_0, and in such a case both terms become very small. Hence for practical purposes only the first term need be retained and we write

$$A(k) = \frac{\sin(k_0 - k)L/2}{\pi(k_0 - k)}. \qquad (11\cdot9\text{--}6)$$

[1] R. B. Lindsay, *Concepts and Methods of Theoretical Physics*, Van Nostrand, Princeton, N. J., 1951, p. 342.

If we plot this as a function of $k_0 - k$, the result resembles Fig. 11·17. It is seen that the maximum amplitude $A(k)$ results when $k = k_0$ and the amplitude falls off in an oscillating fashion as k becomes smaller or greater than k_0.   For

$$(k_0 - k)L = \pm 2n\pi \qquad (11\cdot9\text{--}7)$$

where n is integral, $A(k) = 0$.   This enables us to set up an interesting reciprocal relation between the length L of the pulse and the effective spread of k values in the wave components which have to be superposed in order to make up the pulse.   If we denote the length of the pulse by Δx and let $k_0 - k$ be Δk, we can express the content of (11·9–7) in the form of the inequality

$$\Delta k \cdot \Delta x \geqslant 2\pi. \qquad (11\cdot9\text{--}8)$$

This means that the longer the wave pulse (Δx), the shorter is the range of wave parameters (Δk) necessary for the resolution of the pulse into

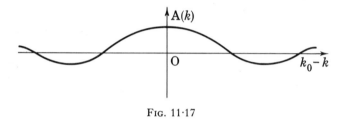

Fig. 11·17

harmonic waves extending throughout all space and over all time.   On the other hand, the shorter the pulse the longer is the range Δk.   An important practical application of this result occurs in the construction of an amplifier to amplify a pulse electrically.   Depending on the narrowness of the pulse, the amplifier must have a frequency response sufficiently wide to allow for the whole frequency band into which the pulse is resolved.   Distortion will otherwise result.

An interesting theoretical significance of the inequality (11·9–8) will emerge in connection with the discussion of the so-called indeterminacy principle of quantum mechanics in Chapter 14.

11·10. Types of Elastic Waves in Solids.   We have discussed in Sections 11·5 and 11·6 the special cases of longitudinal waves in a solid rod and transverse waves in a string.   As has already been indicated, the problem of the general motion of an elastic solid disturbed from equilibrium demands rather more extensive analysis than we wish to embark on here.   This is particularly true of solids like crystals which have different properties in different directions.   However, we ought to note the principal results for the case of an isotropic solid, viz., one whose properties are independent of direction.   Such a solid possesses, as we have seen, both shear and volume elasticity.   The former involves distortion of the medium and hence implies the existence of transverse waves, while the latter provides for the existence of longitudinal waves. Thus in the general motion of an elastic solid we shall expect to find both types of waves present.   The mathematical analysis substantiates this expectation and shows that the longitudinal wave in an extended solid medium travels with a velocity

$$c_L = \sqrt{\frac{B + \frac{4}{3}\mu}{\rho}} \tag{11·10--1}$$

while the transverse wave has a velocity

$$c_T = \sqrt{\frac{\mu}{\rho}}, \tag{11·10--2}$$

where B and μ have their usual significance as elastic moduli (Sec. 11·1). We therefore have $c_L > c_T$ for all solids.   It will be recalled that for a long narrow rod the velocity of the longitudinal wave reduces to

$$c = \sqrt{\frac{Y}{\rho}}, \tag{11·10--3}$$

where Y is Young's modulus.   Comparison shows that for a large number of solids c_L is greater than c by about 10%.

The foregoing formulas suggest that the elastic constants of solids may be determined by the measurement of the velocities of the corresponding types of waves.   This has indeed been carried out with success by employing standing waves in solid rods similar to those already discussed for the finite string in Sec. 11·6.   In recent years it has been possible to drive such rods at very high frequencies (e.g., 100 megacycles or higher).   This is particularly true of piezo-electric crystals which alternately contract and expand when placed across an alternating high voltage.   The fact that the modes are very sharply defined by the dimensions of the specimen (cf. the length l in Sec. 11·6) makes it possible to maintain oscillations of very specific frequency and indeed to stabilize the frequency of high frequency electric (radio) circuits in which the vibrating crystals are placed.

11·11. The Elastic Medium Theory of Light.   The student will recall from his study of elementary physics that there have been two principal theories for the propagation of light.   The first, championed by Newton, is the so-called *corpuscular* theory according to which light travels as very small particles moving in straight lines through space in all directions from a given source. The second is the *wave* theory suggested by Huyghens, which considers the transmission of light as a wave propagation in a medium. Of the two theories the latter has been the more successful if we leave out of consideration the phenomena connected with the emission and absorption of light, which seem to demand a particle description based on the ideas of the quantum theory.

Now in our discussion of wave motion we have seen that in every case it is a disturbance in a *medium* which is propagated as a wave. Hence if the transmission of light is a wave propagation, what is the medium which is disturbed? This is a problem to which physicists gave considerable attention during the nineteenth century, beginning with Fresnel, who was the first to put the wave theory on its feet mathematically speaking, and continuing with the work of Green, Neumann, MacCullagh, Lord Kelvin and Lord Rayleigh, all men of outstanding eminence. Let us consider briefly the nature of the problem as an illustration of the mechanical theory developed in this chapter. It was only natural to assume that the light-bearing medium is analogous to an elastic medium of some kind. Now we have noted that in an elastic solid any disturbance is in general propagated by both *transverse* and *longitudinal* waves. The only elastic medium through which waves of but one type are propagated is a fluid, as we shall see in the next chapter (for a fluid has volume elasticity only and is unable to support shearing stress). In this case longitudinal waves only are transmitted. The fact that a light wave can be polarized shows definitely that it must be a transverse wave. Hence the light-bearing medium cannot be a fluid, but must be an elastic solid. Here, however, the problem at once arises: how shall one get rid of the longitudinal wave that accompanies the transverse wave? We have seen that the longitudinal wave travels with velocity $c_L = \sqrt{\dfrac{B + 4\mu/3}{\rho}}$, while the transverse wave has the velocity $c_T = \sqrt{\mu/\rho}$. Therefore it is impossible to get rid of the former type of wave merely by imagining the medium to possess no volume elasticity, viz., $B = 0$. To overcome this difficulty Green made the assumption that $B \doteq \infty$, so that c_L is infinite. Effectively then the longitudinal wave is not propagated at all, and this would seem to be satisfactory enough. Unfortunately difficulties arise when the theory is applied to the specific problem of the reflection and refraction of light and extended to the case of anisotropic media like crystals. Hence it would seem that Green's theory must be abandoned. Lord Kelvin proposed a theory in which $B = -4\mu/3$ so that $c_L = 0$. Such a medium has negative volume elasticity and hence will be *unstable*, i.e., a positive stress will lead to expansion instead of contraction. Of course, one might imagine such a medium as filling the whole universe or as being rigidly attached to a fixed containing vessel acting as its boundary. It is hardly necessary to say that the mathematical development of any one of these theories is extremely complicated. Nevertheless Lord Kelvin worked all his life in the endeavor to construct such a mechanical theory of light. It must be confessed that the result has not been particularly successful. We are now inclined to believe that the electromagnetic theory of Maxwell is more satisfactory. Incidentally, however, it should be pointed out that Maxwell originally based his theory on mechanical grounds, so that we are still justified in considering the generally accepted theory of light propagation as one which in the last analysis can be visualized in a dynamical framework.

PROBLEMS

1. The shear modulus of a certain substance is equal to 1.24×10^{11} dynes/cm², and Young's modulus for the same substance is 3.2×10^{11} dynes/cm². Calculate the value of the bulk modulus for this substance. Also compute Poisson's ratio. Do the same for a quartz fiber for which $Y = 5.179 \times 10^{11}$ dynes/cm² and $\mu = 2.88 \times 10^{11}$ dynes/cm². Comment on any interesting feature of the result.

2. The value of Young's modulus for steel is 2×10^{12} dynes/cm², and the coefficient of linear (thermal) expansion for the same substance is 1.2×10^{-5} per degree centigrade. What compressive force must be applied to the ends of a steel cylinder 2 cm in diameter to prevent it from expanding longitudinally when the temperature is raised by 40°C?

3. A body suffers tensile strains δ_x, δ_y, δ_z, along the x, y, and z directions respectively. Show that the resultant strain is equivalent to a uniform volume dilatation equal in magnitude to $(\delta_x + \delta_y + \delta_z)$ plus two shears, one in the xy plane of magnitude $\frac{2}{3}(\delta_x + \delta_y + \delta_z) - 2\delta_y$ and the other in the xz plane of magnitude $\frac{2}{3}(\delta_x + \delta_y + \delta_z) - 2\delta_z$.

4. A steel wire 100 cm long and 0.1 cm in radius is suspended from a rigid ceiling. A homogeneous horizontal disc of mass 1000 grams and radius 10 cm is attached at its center to the free end. How much twisting force must be applied at the periphery of the disc to turn the latter through an angle of 10°? If the disc is released and allowed to move freely, what will be the period of its motion?

5. A circular cylindrical wire spring is said to be flat if, when the spring is stretched, each turn of wire is approximately parallel to a plane perpendicular to the axis of the cylinder. One end of such a spring of radius a is attached to a rigid ceiling while the other is stretched by the imposition of a vertical force F. Show that the equivalent stiffness of the spring is given by the expression (when $r \ll a$)

$$f = \frac{\mu \pi r^4}{2a^2 l},$$

where μ = shear modulus of the wire, r = radius of the wire, and l = total length of the wire in the spring. Discuss the significance of the condition $r \ll a$.

6. Calculate the potential energy per unit volume in a solid rod subjected to a longitudinal stress of magnitude X.

7. A homogeneous solid beam of square cross-section with side a is bent into the arc of a circle of radius R. If x denotes distance measured normally to the central axis of the beam and L is the magnitude of the bending torque at any point about an axis normal to the plane of bending and passing through the central axis, show that the rate of change of L with x is given by

$$\frac{dL}{dx} = \frac{2 Y a x^2}{R},$$

where Y is Young's modulus for the material of the beam. Hence find that the total bending torque necessary is

$$L = Y a^4 / 12 R.$$

8. A possible dynamical variant of Hooke's law to take account of the " relaxation " effect (see 10·2) may be written in the form

$$X = A\delta + B\dot{\delta},$$

where X is the stress and δ the corresponding strain, while A and B are elastic constants. Suppose $X = 0$ for $0 < t < t_0$, $X = X_0 =$ constant for $t_0 < t < t_1$ and $X = 0$ for $t > t_1$. Find the way in which δ varies with the time (choosing arbitrary but reasonable values for A and B). Discuss elastic after-effect on this basis.

9. Show that $\xi = f(x + ct)$ represents a wave in the negative x direction with velocity c. Investigate by graphical methods or otherwise the physical character of the wave $f(x - ct) - f(x + ct)$. Do the same for the expression $f(x - ct) + f(x + ct)$.

10. A wave $\xi = f(x - ct)$ progresses in the positive x direction with velocity c. At the point $x = x_0$ a rigid barrier is interposed. Describe the character of the motion of the medium to the left of the barrier.

11. Use the relations among μ, B and Y to compare c_L, c_T, and $c = \sqrt{Y/\rho}$ (Sec. 11·10). Discuss the physical significance of the difference between c_L and c.

12. A plane sinusoidal acoustic wave in air of frequency 512 cycles/sec has a displacement amplitude 10^{-6} cm. If it progresses along the x axis with the velocity of sound at 20°C, and the origin is taken at the point where the displacement ξ is zero at $t = 0$, plot to scale the wave form at $t = 1$ sec for a distance of a wave length or so. Also plot the variation of ξ at $x = 5$ cm as a function of t for two or three periods.

13. In the preceding problem, find the displacement velocity, i.e., $d\xi/dt$ at $x = 5$ cm and $t = 1$ sec. Find the acceleration, i.e., $d^2\xi/dt^2$ under the same conditions. Plot both quantities in the same way in which you plotted ξ in Problem 12.

14. Show that the intensity of a compressional wave in a rod may be represented by $\overline{X_x\dot{\xi}}$, where the bar indicates the time average. Compare this expression with (11·5–45).

15. A flexible string 80 cm long with a mass of 4 grams is stretched with a tension of 84×10^6 dynes. Find the fundamental and first two harmonics of the string. The string is pulled aside at its midpoint a distance 0.5 cm and let go. Find the amplitudes of the fundamental and first two harmonics in the resulting standing wave pattern. Prove that all harmonics of even order are absent from the motion of the string.

16. The string in Problem 15 is struck at its midpoint (while in its equilibrium position) with such force as to give it an initial velocity there of 10 cm/sec. Find the amplitudes of the fundamental and first two harmonics in the resulting standing wave pattern.

17. Calculate the average kinetic and potential energies for the first two harmonics in the motions of the string discussed in Problems 15 and 16.

18. Show that the differential equation for wave motion through a dissipative medium may to a first approximation be written in the form

$$\ddot{\xi} + R\dot{\xi} = c^2 \frac{\partial^2 \xi}{\partial x^2}.$$

Obtain a particular solution of this equation in the form of a damped harmonic wave. Obtain the expression for the distance which a disturbance will travel before its amplitude is diminished in the ratio $1/e$. Suggest possible physical characteristics which make a medium dissipative.

19. A narrow solid rod of length l and line density ρ is clamped rigidly at its two ends. What are the natural frequencies for *longitudinal* vibration of the rod? Obtain also the expression for the natural frequencies for the case of a rod clamped at one end and free at the other. Work the same problem for a rod free at both ends but clamped at the center.

20. The phase velocity of a harmonic flexural wave in a solid rod is

$$c = \frac{c_l}{\sqrt{1 + \lambda^2/4\pi^2 K^2}}$$

where c_l is the longitudinal wave velocity in the rod ($c_l = \sqrt{Y/\rho}$, where Y is Young's modulus and ρ is the density), λ is the wave length, and K is the radius of gyration of the rod about an axis through the center normal to the length.

Find the group velocity for flexural waves and express it in terms of the phase velocity. Specialize to the case of a rod of circular cross section and radius a. Work out a numerical case. What happens at very long wave length, i.e., $\lambda \gg 2\pi K$?

21. Find the amplitude of the Fourier component with wave number k in the representation of the square wave pulse:

$$f(x - ct) = C = \text{non-vanishing constant for } |x - ct| < L/2$$
$$f(x - ct) = 0 \text{ for } |x - ct| > L/2.$$

Chapter 12

MECHANICS OF FLUIDS

12·1. Fluids at Rest.   Fundamental Principles of Hydrostatics. In Chapter 11 we introduced the idea of a deformable body and discussed its behavior. We saw there that the most general kind of deformation may be considered to be a combination of a *dilatation* (change of volume) with a *shear* (change of shape.) In the case of physical solids the application of stress yields in general both kinds of strains, but there is a class of substances of such a nature that the application of stress gives rise to dilatation *only* and never to shears. Such substances are called *fluids* or better *perfect fluids*, for they represent limiting ideal cases of the actual fluids encountered in nature. The line between actual solids and actual fluids is sometimes hard to draw. Under very great stresses most solids at ordinary room temperature begin to act like fluids, and a solid like pitch, for example, flows at room temperature under the stress produced by its own weight, though for impulsive stresses (i.e., those of short duration) it may behave like other solids in manifesting both shears and dilatations. Naturally all substances become fluids at sufficiently high temperatures and appropriate pressures.

From what we have just said it should be possible to deduce the principles governing the behavior of fluids from the fundamental relations for deformable bodies in general. The rigorous derivation demands the use of more general stress-strain analysis than we have given in the previous chapter. Fortunately we are able to visualize the deduction in a rather simple way. Let us imagine a volume element of fluid as given in the figure (Fig. 12·1), and consider further any plane surface element in this box. Suppose that the fluid is at rest, i.e., in equilibrium under the action of external forces. There will still be a stress on the surface element; and this stress will be a compressive stress, i.e., one tending to produce dilatation only, since by definition a perfect fluid can not be sheared. Now if the compressive stress on the area (to which we shall hereafter refer as the *pressure*) were to be inclined to the area at any other angle than 90°, it would have a nonvanishing component *along* the surface. But this would lead to shearing and, since a perfect fluid can not support a shear, motion would have to ensue parallel to the surface. This contradicts the initial assumption of equilibrium. Hence we reach the important conclusion, amply verified by simple experiments, that in a perfect fluid at rest the stress or pressure on any surface element whatever is normal to the surface. To state the same result in slightly different form, at any point in a perfect fluid the pressure is normal to any surface element passing through this point and independent of the direction of this element. This statement includes the famous principle of Pascal.

Let us now examine the condition that a fluid may be in equilibrium under the action of an external force **F** acting on *unit* mass. Let F_x, F_y, F_z denote the x, y, z components of **F** respectively. Consider an element of fluid contained in the parallelepiped with sides dx, dy, and dz (Fig. 12·2). Let the pressure at the midpoint P of the volume

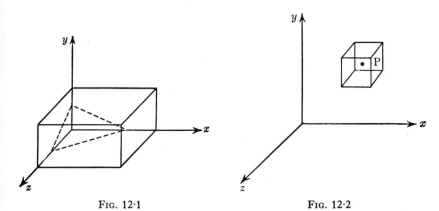

FIG. 12·1   FIG. 12·2

be p. Then the normal force on the face parallel to and nearer the yz plane is $\left(p - \dfrac{\partial p}{\partial x}\dfrac{dx}{2}\right) dy\,dz$, while that on the farther parallel face is $\left(p + \dfrac{\partial p}{\partial x}\dfrac{dx}{2}\right) dy\,dz$. Hence the fluid in the element is acted on by a force due to pressure whose component in the x direction is

$$-\frac{\partial p}{\partial x}\,dx\,dy\,dz. \qquad (12·1\text{–}1)$$

The analogous components in the y and z directions are $-\dfrac{\partial p}{\partial y}\,dx\,dy\,dz$ and $-\dfrac{\partial p}{\partial z}\,dx\,dy\,dz$. Now if the element is to be in equilibrium under the influence of the external force, the total force components on the element in the x, y, and z directions must vanish. That is, we must have (recalling that $\mathbf{F}$ represents the force per unit mass)

$$\left.\begin{array}{l} \rho F_x \, dx \, dy \, dz - \dfrac{\partial p}{\partial x} \, dx \, dy \, dz = 0, \\[2ex] \rho F_y \, dx \, dy \, dz - \dfrac{\partial p}{\partial y} \, dx \, dy \, dz = 0, \\[2ex] \rho F_z \, dx \, dy \, dz - \dfrac{\partial p}{\partial z} \, dx \, dy \, dz = 0, \end{array}\right\} \qquad (12\cdot1\text{--}2)$$

or more compactly,

$$F_x = \frac{1}{\rho}\frac{\partial p}{\partial x}, \quad F_y = \frac{1}{\rho}\frac{\partial p}{\partial y}, \quad F_z = \frac{1}{\rho}\frac{\partial p}{\partial z}, \qquad (12\cdot1\text{--}3)$$

where ρ is the density. These are the fundamental equations of *hydrostatics*. If we employ the vector operator ∇ introduced in Sec. 4·5 we can express the physical content of these three equations by the single equation

$$\mathbf{F} = \frac{1}{\rho}\nabla p. \qquad (12\cdot1\text{--}4)$$

We see that if we write the change in pressure between two closely neighboring points in the fluid at rest as dp, we have the total differential

$$dp = \rho F_x \, dx + \rho F_y \, dy + \rho F_z \, dz = \rho \mathbf{F}\cdot d\mathbf{r} \qquad (12\cdot1\text{--}5)$$

if we use the more economical vector notation. Here $d\mathbf{r}$ is the vector separation between the two neighboring points (see Sec. 4·1). The problem of ascertaining the distribution of pressure in the fluid is the problem of solving the total differential equation (12·1–5).

We may express the general solution in the form

$$p = \Phi(x, y, z) + C, \qquad (12\cdot1\text{--}6)$$

where C is a constant of integration whose value depends on the pressure at some specified point in the fluid. If in some way the pressure were to be increased at this point, eq. (12·1–6) states that the pressure is increased by the *same amount* at every other point in the fluid. This is sometimes referred to as the law of the *transmissibility of pressure*. It is usually considered a part of Pascal's principle for fluids at rest.

We shall consider one special case, namely that in which the external force is *gravity*. Suppose that it acts downward along the z axis, i.e.,

$$F_x = F_y = 0, \quad F_z = -g. \qquad (12\cdot1\text{--}7)$$

Then p varies with z alone and we have

$$\frac{dp}{dz} = -\rho g. \qquad (12{\cdot}1{-}8)$$

The integration can be carried out only if we know the way in which ρ depends on z. If the fluid is incompressible (i.e., an ideal *liquid*) ρ is constant, and we have

$$p = -\rho g z + C, \qquad (12{\cdot}1{-}9)$$

C being an arbitrary constant which may be put equal to zero if the origin is taken at a point where the pressure is zero, viz., at the surface of the liquid (assuming that there is a vacuum above the surface). It is to be noted that the negative sign enters (12·1–9) because the positive direction of z is *upward* and p *decreases* as one goes up. In practical applications it is usually more convenient to measure z downward and use the positive sign. (See, for example, Sec. 12·2.) In words, (12·1–9) states that in an incompressible fluid at rest under the action of gravity alone the pressure varies directly as the depth. This is well substantiated by experimental investigation of liquids in which the variation of ρ with depth is negligible for moderate depths.

12·2. Principle of Archimedes — Stability of Floating Bodies.

We can apply the results of the preceding section very appropriately to the problem of the calculation of the resultant force exerted by a liquid on an object immersed in it. Let us first take a special case for the sake of simplicity. Imagine a rectangular parallelepiped with dimensions a, b, c immersed so that one pair of faces is parallel to the surface of the liquid. In Fig. 12·3 the cross-section is shown, where $\overline{AB} = a$, and $\overline{BC} = c$. Suppose that $\overline{AB}$ is at a distance z_0 below the surface. To calculate the total force exerted by the liquid on the parallelepiped we must find the x, y, and z components. The x component of the force, for example, will be found by multiplying the

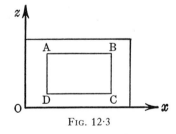

FIG. 12·3

element of area at every point by the x component of the pressure at that point and then summing up over the whole surface of the body. The procedure for the other components is analogous. Now from the way we have chosen our special case it is clear that the x and y components will be zero since the forces on opposite faces cancel out in pairs. The z component, however, is not zero. Let us suppose that the pressure at the surface of the liquid is p_0.   At the top of the body $(\overline{AB})$ it is then by eq. (12·1–9)

$$p_1 = p_0 + \rho g z_0,$$

while at the bottom $(\overline{DC})$ it is

$$p_2 = p_0 + \rho g(z_0 + c).$$

The areas of the top and bottom are the same, viz., $S = ab$, so that there is a *downward* force on the top face of magnitude

$$S(p_0 + \rho g z_0),$$

and an *upward* force on the bottom face of magnitude

$$S(p_0 + \rho g(z_0 + c)).$$

Hence the total force in the z direction is an *upward* force of magnitude

$$F_z = \rho g c S. \tag{12·2–1}$$

Now since cS is the volume of the body and $\rho g c S$ accordingly the weight of the liquid displaced by the body, it follows that *the liquid exerts on the immersed body a buoyant force equal to the weight of the displaced liquid.* This is the principle of Archimedes.   We have derived it here for a very special case.   In the general case of a body of any shape we should have for the component of force in the z direction (gravity alone being assumed to act)

$$F_z = \iint p \cos \gamma \, dS, \tag{12·2–2}$$

where p is the pressure acting on the area element dS and γ is the angle between the normal to dS and the z axis.   The integration is to be carried out over the *whole* surface of the body.   Since gravity acts vertically along the z axis we see that even in the general case the x and y components are zero, i.e.,

$$F_x = F_y = 0. \tag{12·2–3}$$

In order to calculate F_z it is convenient to transform the surface integral into a volume integral.   Suppose we consider again an elementary parallelepiped dx, dy, dz cut out of the body as shown in Fig. 12·2. We have already seen in the preceding section that the net force on this element in the z direction is

$$-\frac{\partial p}{\partial z} dx \, dy \, dz. \tag{12·2–4}$$

Consequently we can get the resultant force on the whole body by evaluating the integral

$$-\iiint \frac{\partial p}{\partial z}\,dx\,dy\,dz, \tag{12·2–5}$$

the integration being extended over the whole volume of the body; this must also give us F_z. In other words the volume integral (12·2–5) is equivalent to the surface integral (12·2–2). We have here a special simplified case of the so-called *divergence theorem* or, more generally, *Green's theorem*, which the student will encounter in all advanced work in physics, and of which we shall give a more extensive account in the next section. Now we know from eq. (12·1–8) that in the present case $\frac{\partial p}{\partial z} = -\rho g$, where ρ is the density of the liquid. Hence for the resultant force we get

$$F_z = \rho g \iiint dx\,dy\,dz$$

$$= \rho g V, \tag{12·2–6}$$

where V is the volume of the body. The result is then the same as for the special case. It should be noted that although in our discussion we have used the word " liquid," everything we have said is true of *fluids* in general.

We have thus seen that a liquid exerts a buoyant force on an object immersed in it. This force is directed vertically upward and is in magnitude equal to the weight of the displaced liquid. We can also see that it must pass through the center of gravity of the body; for if we imagine the body to be removed, the force which the rest of the liquid exerts on the portion of liquid taking the place of the body must remain the same. But if this force did not pass through the center of gravity this particular portion of the fluid would not be in equilibrium with regard to rotation, and hence the hydrostatic conditions of the problem would be violated.

Let us next give our attention to the special case of a body floating on the surface of a liquid. In this case the buoyant force must clearly be numerically the same as the weight of the body. Hence by the principle of Archimedes a floating body displaces its own weight of liquid. We have just seen that the buoyant force acts upward through the center of gravity of the displaced liquid. This is called the *center of buoyancy* of the body. The weight of course acts through the center of gravity of the body itself. Hence a floating body is acted on by a *couple*, whose moment vanishes only when the center of gravity and the center of buoyancy lie in the same vertical line.

If a floating body is slightly displaced from its position of equilibrium while the center of gravity G of the body (I and II, Fig. 12·4) remains fixed in the body, the center of buoyancy C will necessarily move with respect to it, since the shape of the immersed portion has now altered. Suppose that it moves from C to C' (II, Fig. 12·4), tracing out the curve CC' in the body. The center of curvature of this curve, M, is called the *metacenter* and its height above the center of gravity is called the *metacentric height*. We shall denote it by h. For not too great angles of roll, M may be considered as the point of intersection of the vertical through C' and the line $\overline{CG}$ extended. The metacentric height is the important criterion for the stability of a floating object, e.g., a ship. If this height is positive, i.e., if M lies *above* G, the rolling produces a couple which tends to right the ship; while, if it is negative (M *below* G) the resulting couple tends to produce further rolling. The equilibrium is therefore *stable* in the former case and *unstable* in the latter. If M coincides with G, the equilibrium will be neutral, which is just as bad as instability as far as a ship is concerned. It is clear that the higher the metacentric height the greater the stability. However, it can be shown[1] that the period of the roll varies as the inverse square root of the metacentric height. Hence a ship with a large h, generally known as a " stiff " ship, will roll more rapidly and hence not be so comfortable as a slowly rolling ship for which h is smaller. The latter is known as a " crank " ship. The tendency in ocean ships is to build them with as small a metacentric height as is consistent with safety.

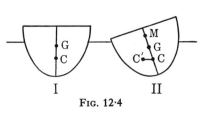

FIG. 12·4

12·3. The Equation of Continuity in Fluid Motion. As in the discussion of the motion of the vibrating string (Sec. 11·6), we shall carry through our analysis of fluid motion by concentrating attention on a small element of volume and observing its behavior over a short interval of time. We shall find that there are *two* fundamental ideas involved. The first is the expression of the fact that the body in question acts like a *continuous medium* and not merely as a discrete aggregate of particles.[2] We must consider once more the elementary parallelepiped $dx\ dy\ dz$ (Fig. 12·2) with the point P as its midpoint. Assume that this element is stationary and that the perfect fluid whose motion is being investigated flows through it. We shall suppose that

[1] See A. G. Webster, *Dynamics*, p. 474.

[2] The second, the idea involved in the equations of motion, will be treated in the next section.

the flow of the fluid is such that at time t, the components of the velocity of flow at $P(x, y, z)$ are u, v, w in the three coördinate directions respectively.   The x component of the velocity of flow at the face parallel to the yz plane and nearer to it will then be $u - \dfrac{\partial u}{\partial x} \dfrac{dx}{2}$ while that on the farther parallel face will be $u + \dfrac{\partial u}{\partial x} \dfrac{dx}{2}$.   Hence the rate of flow of fluid, i.e., the *mass* per second *into* the one face and *out* of the other will be

$$\left(\rho u - \frac{\partial(\rho u)}{\partial x} \frac{dx}{2}\right) dy\, dz, \qquad (12\cdot3\text{–}1)$$

and

$$\left(\rho u + \frac{\partial(\rho u)}{\partial x} \frac{dx}{2}\right) dy\, dz, \qquad (12\cdot3\text{–}2)$$

respectively,[1] if the density of the fluid at P at time t is ρ.   Therefore the excess of *outflow* over *inflow* will be given by the difference of $(12\cdot3\text{–}2)$ and $(12\cdot3\text{–}1)$ or

$$\text{Excess flow in } x \text{ direction} = \frac{\partial(\rho u)}{\partial x}\, dx\, dy\, dz. \qquad (12\cdot3\text{–}3)$$

Similarly we find for the excess flow in the y and z directions, $\dfrac{\partial(\rho v)}{\partial y}\, dx\, dy\, dz$ and $\dfrac{\partial(\rho w)}{\partial z}\, dx\, dy\, dz$ respectively.   Hence the total excess outflow is

$$\left(\frac{\partial(\rho u)}{\partial x} + \frac{\partial(\rho v)}{\partial y} + \frac{\partial(\rho w)}{\partial z}\right) dx\, dy\, dz, \qquad (12\cdot3\text{–}4)$$

which may be written more compactly in terms of the vector operator ∇ (see Sec. 4·5).

$$[\nabla \cdot (\rho \mathbf{q})]\, dx\, dy\, dz \qquad (12\cdot3\text{–}5)$$

where $\mathbf{q}$ is the resultant fluid flow velocity, i.e. the vector whose rectangular components are u, v, w respectively.   As indicated in Sec. 4·5 $\nabla \cdot$ is pronounced " del dot." $\nabla \cdot (\rho \mathbf{q})$ is also referred to as div$(\rho \mathbf{q})$ and called the divergence of the vector $\rho \mathbf{q}$.   The physical significance of this terminology should be clear from the discussion leading to eq. $(12\cdot3\text{–}4)$.

---

[1] Note that, strictly speaking, the velocity is not $u - \dfrac{\partial u}{\partial x}\dfrac{dx}{2}$ or $u + \dfrac{\partial u}{\partial x}\dfrac{dx}{2}$ over the *whole* face in each case, as it may vary with y and z.   However, our assumption is equivalent to neglecting differentials of order higher than the first.   Or, if the student wishes, he may equally well consider the velocities in question as *averages* over the faces concerned.

Since the fluid is a continuous medium and can neither be created nor destroyed the excess outflow must be compensated by a decrease in the mass of the fluid contained within the element. If the density at time t is ρ, the rate of change is $\partial\rho/\partial t$, and hence the rate of decrease of mass in the element is

$$-\frac{\partial\rho}{\partial t}\,dx\,dy\,dz. \qquad (12{\cdot}3\text{--}6)$$

Equating (12·3–4) and (12·3–6) we have the equation

$$\dot{\rho} + \frac{\partial(\rho u)}{\partial x} + \frac{\partial(\rho v)}{\partial y} + \frac{\partial(\rho w)}{\partial z} = 0. \qquad (12{\cdot}3\text{--}7)$$

In vector operator notation this takes the form

$$\dot{\rho} + \nabla\cdot(\rho\mathbf{q}) = 0. \qquad (12{\cdot}3\text{--}8)$$

This is known as the *equation of continuity*, one of the most important equations in the physics of continuous media. It may be worth while to point out that this equation holds for *any* deformable continuous indestructible medium, though it plays perhaps its most significant role in connection with fluids. If the fluid is *incompressible* and *homogeneous*, the equation of continuity reduces to the simpler form

$$\nabla\cdot\mathbf{q} = 0. \qquad (12{\cdot}3\text{--}9)$$

We can understand the physical significance of this equation more clearly if we consider the flow of fluid through any closed surface of arbitrary form. It is clear that if we divide the surface into a large number of area elements dS, we can get the total rate of flow (in mass per second) *out* of the surface by multiplying the density by the component of the velocity normal to each area element and further by dS (in each case the *outward* normal is to be considered positive), and then integrating over the whole surface. Denoting the magnitude of the normal velocity (a function of x, y, z, t) by q_N, we have for the total outflow

$$\iint \rho q_N\,dS. \qquad (12{\cdot}3\text{--}10)$$

But we have already seen that we can represent the total outflow through an elementary parallelepiped by (12·3–4), and hence the flow through the whole portion of the fluid contained inside the surface considered is given by the volume integral

$$\iiint \left[\frac{\partial(\rho u)}{\partial x} + \frac{\partial(\rho v)}{\partial y} + \frac{\partial(\rho w)}{\partial z}\right] dx\,dy\,dz. \qquad (12{\cdot}3\text{--}11)$$

Now (12·3–10) and (12·3–11) represent the same thing and therefore may be equated. If the normal to the area element dS has the direction cosines $\cos \alpha$, $\cos \beta$, $\cos \gamma$ we can at once write

$$q_N = u \cos \alpha + v \cos \beta + w \cos \gamma, \qquad (12\cdot3\text{–}12)$$

and on the equating of (12·3–10) and (12·3–11) we finally have

$$\iint \rho(u \cos \alpha + v \cos \beta + w \cos \gamma) \, dS$$

$$= \iiint \left[\frac{\partial(\rho u)}{\partial x} + \frac{\partial(\rho v)}{\partial y} + \frac{\partial(\rho w)}{\partial z} \right] dx \, dy \, dz. \qquad (12\cdot3\text{–}13)$$

This again may be more compactly expressed in terms of vector notation as

$$\int \rho \mathbf{q} \cdot \mathbf{n} \, dS = \int \nabla \cdot (\rho \mathbf{q}) \, d\tau \qquad (12\cdot3\text{–}14)$$

where $d\tau$ is the element of volume, i.e.,

$$d\tau = dx \, dy \, dz$$

and

$$\mathbf{n} = \mathbf{i} \cos \alpha + \mathbf{j} \cos \beta + \mathbf{k} \cos \gamma$$

is the *unit* vector (i.e., magnitude equal to 1) normal to the area element dS.

Eq. (12·3–14) is a form of the divergence theorem or Green's theorem already mentioned in Sec. 12·2.

There is an interesting consequence of the vanishing of the divergence of **q**, which as we have just seen [eq. (12·3–9)] is the case for a homogeneous incompressible fluid. At every point in space the velocity **q** has a definite magnitude and direction. We can then construct curves whose *tangents* at every point are in the direction of **q** at that point. These curves are called *lines of flow*. Let us suppose that **q** does not change with the time so that the lines maintain a definite permanent shape. They are then called *stream lines*. It is clear that a group of them may be considered

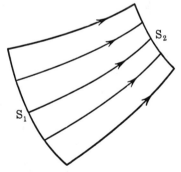

FIG. 12·5

as generating a surface; this is called a *tube of flow* (see Fig. 12·5). Now suppose we have such a tube of flow and terminate it by the surfaces

S_1 and S_2 respectively. Assume that the fluid is incompressible so that the divergence is zero. The total mass of fluid flowing per second out of the element of volume formed by the bounded tube is therefore likewise zero. But since there can be no flow either out or in through the sides of the tube (which are parallel to the lines of flow), it must

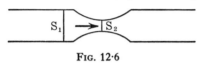

FIG. 12·6

follow that the total normal flow *in* through S_1 equals the total normal flow *out* through S_2. This may be applied at once to the flow of a liquid through a tube or pipe with a constriction (Fig. 12·6). Suppose the axis of the tube lies along the x axis. Letting the cross-sectional area at the unconstricted part be S_1 and that of the constriction be S_2, if we consider the flow through a portion of the tube with boundaries S_1 and S_2, we immediately have from the above that

$$S_1 u_1 = S_2 u_2, \qquad (12\cdot3\text{--}15)$$

where u_1 and u_2 are the velocities at S_1 and S_2 respectively. For the flow through a constricted pipe the velocity at any point varies inversely as the area of cross-section. We shall have occasion to note a practical application of this in Sec. 12·5.

12·4. The Equations of Motion of a Perfect Fluid. In order to discuss further the motion of a perfect fluid we must consider its *acceleration*. Suppose at the point $P(x, y, z)$ the velocity components are u, v, w at the time t, while at the nearby point $Q(x + dx, y + dy, z + dz)$ the corresponding quantities at the time $t + dt$ are $u + du$, $v + dv$, $w + dw$. Since du, dv, dw depend on x, y, z, and t, we have

$$\left. \begin{aligned} du &= \frac{\partial u}{\partial t} dt + \frac{\partial u}{\partial x} dx + \frac{\partial u}{\partial y} dy + \frac{\partial u}{\partial z} dz, \\[1em] dv &= \frac{\partial v}{\partial t} dt + \frac{\partial v}{\partial x} dx + \frac{\partial v}{\partial y} dy + \frac{\partial v}{\partial z} dz, \\[1em] dw &= \frac{\partial w}{\partial t} dt + \frac{\partial w}{\partial x} dx + \frac{\partial w}{\partial y} dy + \frac{\partial w}{\partial z} dz. \end{aligned} \right\} \qquad (12\cdot4\text{--}1)$$

Now if the particle of fluid which was at P at time t is at Q at time $t + dt$, it follows that

$$dx = u \, dt, \quad dy = v \, dt, \quad dz = w \, dt,$$

and du, dv, dw will be the increments in the velocity components of this particle in the time dt.   Hence

$$
\left.
\begin{aligned}
\frac{du}{dt} &= \frac{\partial u}{\partial t} + u\frac{\partial u}{\partial x} + v\frac{\partial u}{\partial y} + w\frac{\partial u}{\partial z}, \\[6pt]
\frac{dv}{dt} &= \frac{\partial v}{\partial t} + u\frac{\partial v}{\partial x} + v\frac{\partial v}{\partial y} + w\frac{\partial v}{\partial z}, \\[6pt]
\frac{dw}{dt} &= \frac{\partial w}{\partial t} + u\frac{\partial w}{\partial x} + v\frac{\partial w}{\partial y} + w\frac{\partial w}{\partial z},
\end{aligned}
\right\}
\tag{12·4-2}
$$

will be the components of the *acceleration* of the particle which was at P at time t and is at Q at time $t + dt$.   The reader must distinguish carefully between $\dfrac{du}{dt}$ and $\dfrac{\partial u}{\partial t}$.   The latter refers merely to the rate of change of u with time at a *particular* place.   The former gives the genuine rate of change of u for a particle moving from place to place.

We have already had occasion in this chapter to note how much more economically certain equations may be written if vector notation is employed.   Eq. (12·4–2) provides another excellent example.   If we multiply these equations by the unit vectors $\mathbf{i}, \mathbf{j}, \mathbf{k}$ respectively and add, the left-hand side becomes the resultant vector acceleration $\mathbf{a}$ of the fluid flow.   Thus

$$
\mathbf{a} = \mathbf{i}\frac{du}{dt} + \mathbf{j}\frac{dv}{dt} + \mathbf{k}\frac{dw}{dt}. \tag{12·4-3}
$$

On the right-hand side, it is clear we may write (since $\mathbf{q} = \mathbf{i}u + \mathbf{j}v + \mathbf{k}w$)

$$
\dot{\mathbf{q}} = \mathbf{i}\frac{\partial u}{\partial t} + \mathbf{j}\frac{\partial v}{\partial t} + \mathbf{k}\frac{\partial w}{\partial t} \tag{12·4-4}
$$

for the rate of change of fluid flow velocity at a *particular* place.   The rest of the right-hand side might seem to present some difficulties, but if we use the vector operator ∇ in standard fashion it is not hard to show that

$$
\begin{aligned}
\mathbf{i}\left(u\frac{\partial u}{\partial x} + v\frac{\partial u}{\partial y} + w\frac{\partial u}{\partial z}\right) &+ \mathbf{j}\left(u\frac{\partial v}{\partial x} + v\frac{\partial v}{\partial y} + w\frac{\partial v}{\partial z}\right) \\[4pt]
&+ \mathbf{k}\left(u\frac{\partial w}{\partial x} + v\frac{\partial w}{\partial y} + w\frac{\partial w}{\partial z}\right) = (\mathbf{q}\cdot\nabla)\mathbf{q}.
\end{aligned}
\tag{12·4-5}
$$

The right side of this identity is to be interpreted as follows. From the operator ∇ we construct a new operator $\mathbf{q} \cdot \nabla$ by dot-multiplying ∇ with $\mathbf{q}$. Thus

$$(\mathbf{q} \cdot \nabla) = (\mathbf{i}u + \mathbf{j}v + \mathbf{k}w) \cdot \left(\mathbf{i}\frac{\partial}{\partial x} + \mathbf{j}\frac{\partial}{\partial y} + \mathbf{k}\frac{\partial}{\partial z} \right) = u\frac{\partial}{\partial x} + v\frac{\partial}{\partial y} + w\frac{\partial}{\partial z} \cdot$$

(12·4–6)

This operator when allowed to operate on $\mathbf{q}$ produces (12·4–5).

Let us concentrate our attention once more on the volume element $d\tau$ shown in Fig. 12·2 and suppose that at a given instant the pressure at P, the center of the element, is p. We have already seen in Sec. 12·1 that the components of the force on the fluid in the element due to variation in pressure from place to place are $-\dfrac{\partial p}{\partial x}\, d\tau,\ -\dfrac{\partial p}{\partial y}\, d\tau,\ -\dfrac{\partial p}{\partial z}\, d\tau$ in the x, y, z directions respectively. As was pointed out previously this means that the total force on the element due to pressure can be written in vector notation as $-\nabla p\, d\tau$. If in addition an external force $\mathbf{F}$ is assumed to act on unit mass of the fluid, the resultant force on the element $d\tau$ is

$$\mathbf{F}\rho\, d\tau - \nabla p\, d\tau. \tag{12·4–7}$$

Equating this to the mass times the resultant acceleration of the element and canceling out the volume $d\tau$ on both sides of the equation leads to the vector equation of motion of the fluid in the form

$$\frac{d\mathbf{q}}{dt} = \dot{\mathbf{q}} + (\mathbf{q} \cdot \nabla)\mathbf{q} = \mathbf{F} - \frac{\nabla p}{\rho} \cdot \tag{12·4–8}$$

The reader should for his own satisfaction write the three corresponding component equations, though we need not set them down here.[1]

A first integration of the equation of motion for the case of an incompressible homogeneous fluid yields information about the energy of the fluid. We shall assume that the external force is associated with a potential Ω (see Sec. 4·5) so that

$$\mathbf{F} = -\nabla\Omega. \tag{12·4–9}$$

Then dot multiply through eq. (12·4–8) by $\mathbf{q}$ and obtain

$$\mathbf{q} \cdot \frac{d\mathbf{q}}{dt} = -\mathbf{q} \cdot \nabla\Omega - \mathbf{q} \cdot \frac{\nabla p}{\rho} \cdot \tag{12·4–10}$$

[1] This is the hydrodynamic equation of motion in the form due to Euler. It may be noted that if, instead of concentrating attention on a *given element of space* and discussing the flow through this element as time passes, we study the whole history of *every particle* of fluid as it moves through space, we obtain the equation of motion in the form due to Lagrange. For most purposes that of Euler is more valuable. For that of Lagrange see Horace Lamb, *Hydrodynamics*, 6th ed., Dover Publications, New York, 1945, pp. 12 ff.

As we have already seen in Sec. 1·11, we can write

$$\mathbf{q} \cdot \frac{d\mathbf{q}}{dt} = \frac{1}{2} \frac{d}{dt} (\mathbf{q} \cdot \mathbf{q}). \qquad (12 \cdot 4\text{--}11)$$

Moreover by expanding and recalling that $u = \dfrac{dx}{dt}$, etc., it develops that

$$\mathbf{q} \cdot \nabla \Omega = \frac{d\Omega}{dt}. \qquad (12 \cdot 4\text{--}12)$$

We may therefore rewrite (12·4–11) as

$$\tfrac{1}{2}\rho \frac{d}{dt} q^2 + \rho \frac{d\Omega}{dt} = -\mathbf{q} \cdot \nabla p, \qquad (12 \cdot 4\text{--}13)$$

where $\mathbf{q} \cdot \mathbf{q} = q^2$, the square of the fluid flow speed.   Our next step is to multiply (12·4–13) by the volume element $d\tau$ and integrate over the whole space occupied by the fluid.   The result is

$$\frac{d}{dt} \left\{ \int \tfrac{1}{2}\rho q^2 \, d\tau + \int \rho \Omega \, d\tau \right\} = -\int \mathbf{q} \cdot \nabla p \, d\tau. \qquad (12 \cdot 4\text{--}14)$$

By applying the rule of differentiation of a product we can readily show . that

$$\nabla \cdot (p\mathbf{q}) = p \nabla \cdot \mathbf{q} + \mathbf{q} \cdot \nabla p, \qquad (12 \cdot 4\text{--}15)$$

which is indeed a well-known vector operation identity.   Since we agreed to limit our discussion to a homogeneous incompressible fluid, we have $\nabla \cdot \mathbf{q} = 0$ (eq. 12·3–9) and hence the right hand side of (12·4–14) becomes $-\displaystyle\int \nabla \cdot (p\mathbf{q}) \, d\tau$.   We can then at once apply the divergence theorem (12·3–14) to express the volume integral in terms of an integral over the surface enclosing the volume.   Thus

$$\int \nabla \cdot (p\mathbf{q}) \, d\tau = \int p\mathbf{q} \cdot \mathbf{n} \, dS. \qquad (12 \cdot 4\text{--}16)$$

Note that the presence of ρq in (12·3–14) does not prevent us from applying the theorem to $p\mathbf{q}$ in the form (12·4–16).   We may then rewrite (12·4–14) in the form

$$\frac{d}{dt} \left\{ \int \tfrac{1}{2}\rho q^2 \, d\tau + \int \rho \Omega \, d\tau \right\} = -\int p\mathbf{q} \cdot \mathbf{n} \, dS. \qquad (12 \cdot 4\text{--}17)$$

Now $\int \frac{1}{2}\rho q^2 \, d\tau$ is the total kinetic energy of the flowing fluid, whereas $\int \rho\Omega \, d\tau$ is the total potential energy of the fluid due to the external force $\mathbf{F}$. Calling these K and V_Ω respectively we have

$$\frac{d}{dt}(K + V_\Omega) = -\int p\mathbf{q} \cdot \mathbf{n} \, dS. \qquad (12\cdot4\text{--}18)$$

Examination of the right-hand side reveals that $p\,dS$ is the force in the area dS due to the fluid pressure p, while $\mathbf{q} \cdot \mathbf{n}$ is the component of fluid velocity normal to the surface dS. But the product of force and the velocity component in the direction of the force is the power or rate at which the force does work (eq. $1\cdot11$--20). If we look upon $K + V_\Omega$ as the total energy of the fluid, eq. ($12\cdot4$--18) says that the time rate of change of the total energy in a given volume is equal to the negative of the rate at which the pressure of the fluid does work on the fluid outside this volume or alternatively to the rate at which energy flows across the surface enclosing the volume. This is a kind of work-energy theorem for a homogeneous incompressible fluid. It says that the only way for the total energy of the fluid inside the given volume to change is through the flow of energy across the surface surrounding the volume. This result bears a close analogy with Poynting's theorem in electromagnetism.[1]

12·5. Steady Flow of a Fluid. Bernoulli's Theorem and Applications. One of the simplest cases of fluid motion is that in which the velocity at any place does not change with the time even though it may change from place to place. This means that in the equation of motion ($12\cdot4$--8) $\dot{\mathbf{q}}$ vanishes. Such motion is known as steady flow and the lines of flow are stream lines, as has already been mentioned in Sec. $12\cdot3$. The fundamental equation of fluid motion now becomes

$$(\mathbf{q} \cdot \nabla)\mathbf{q} = \mathbf{F} - \frac{\nabla p}{\rho}. \qquad (12\cdot5\text{--}1)$$

Let us denote the vector element of distance along a stream line as $d\mathbf{s}$. Then

$$d\mathbf{s} = \mathbf{q} \, dt = (\mathbf{i}u + \mathbf{j}v + \mathbf{k}w) \, dt. \qquad (12\cdot5\text{--}2)$$

We now dot-multiply ($12\cdot5$--1) with $d\mathbf{s}$ (and in the process assume again that $\mathbf{F} = -\nabla\Omega$). We get

$$[(\mathbf{q} \cdot \nabla)\mathbf{q}] \cdot d\mathbf{s} = -\nabla\Omega \cdot d\mathbf{s} - \frac{\nabla p \cdot d\mathbf{s}}{\rho}. \qquad (12\cdot5\text{--}3)$$

---

[1] Cf. R. B. Lindsay, *Concepts and Methods of Theoretical Physics*, Van Nostrand, Princeton, N.J., 1951, pp. 403 ff.

The left-hand side is a trifle complicated, but if we go back to (12·4–2), which lists the components of $(\mathbf{q}\cdot\nabla)\cdot\mathbf{q}$, and utilize (12·5–2) we can ultimately show that

$$[(\mathbf{q}\cdot\nabla)\mathbf{q}]\cdot d\mathbf{s} = q\left[u\frac{du}{ds} + v\frac{dv}{ds} + w\frac{dw}{ds}\right]dt. \qquad (12\cdot5\text{–}4)$$

Similarly

$$\nabla\Omega\cdot d\mathbf{s} = q\frac{d\Omega}{ds}dt \qquad (12\cdot5\text{–}5)$$

and

$$\frac{\nabla p\cdot d\mathbf{s}}{\rho} = \frac{q}{\rho}\frac{dp}{ds}dt. \qquad (12\cdot5\text{–}6)$$

Consequently (12·5–3) becomes, if we multiply through by ds,

$$u\,du + v\,dv + w\,dw = -d\Omega - \frac{dp}{\rho}. \qquad (12\cdot5\text{–}7)$$

If we integrate this along a stream line the result is

$$\int_s (u\,du + v\,dv + w\,dw) = -\int_s d\Omega - \int_s \frac{dp}{\rho},$$

or

$$\tfrac{1}{2}q^2 = -\Omega - \int\frac{dp}{\rho} + C, \qquad (12\cdot5\text{–}8)$$

where C is a constant of integration. The $\int\frac{dp}{\rho}$ cannot be evaluated until we know the relation between p and ρ. But if we are dealing with a liquid (an incompressible fluid, effectively), ρ is constant and the equation becomes

$$\tfrac{1}{2}\rho q^2 + \rho\Omega + p = C' \qquad (12\cdot5\text{–}9)$$

where C' is again a constant of integration. This equation is an expression for the famous theorem of Bernoulli. In the equation, $\tfrac{1}{2}\rho q^2$ is the kinetic energy per unit volume along the stream line, while $\rho\Omega$ is the potential energy per unit volume due to the external force. It is tempting therefore to treat the pressure p as an additional potential energy per unit volume, a kind of pressure-potential energy. On this assumption Bernoulli's theorem as derived here states in words that the total energy per unit volume *along any stream line* in steady flow is constant, though of course the value of the constant will in general change from one stream line to another. The theorem may then be looked upon as the expression for the conservation of energy in steady fluid flow along a stream line. It turns out to be possible to establish a similar conservation theorem in which the energy per unit volume is constant over the *whole* fluid. This demands, however, that the fluid shall have no rotational motion.[1]

Bernoulli's theorem is of considerable importance in practical hydraulics and we shall discuss a few applications here. Suppose in the first place we consider the steady flow through a *horizontal* tube with a constriction (Fig. 12·6). If we follow a single stream line from the place where the cross-sectional area is S_1 to the place where it is S_2, the velocity will change from q_1 to q_2 and the pressure from p_1 to p_2 while the potential energy due to the external force, which in this case is gravity, will change very little since there is little or no change in level involved. From the theorem we have accordingly

$$\tfrac{1}{2}\rho q_1{}^2 + p_1 = \tfrac{1}{2}\rho q_2{}^2 + p_2. \qquad (12\cdot5{-}10)$$

It therefore follows that at the place in the tube where the velocity is greatest the pressure is least and vice versa. We have already seen (Sec. 12·3) that in the steady flow through a tube the velocity varies inversely as the cross-section. Hence where the cross-section is smallest the pressure is least. An interesting practical application of this is the *Venturi water meter.* Substituting $q_2 = \dfrac{S_1}{S_2} q_1$ into $(12\cdot5{-}10)$ and solving for q_1 gives

FIG. 12·7

$$q_1 = S_2 \sqrt{\frac{2(p_2 - p_1)}{\rho(S_2{}^2 - S_1{}^2)}}, \qquad (12\cdot5{-}11)$$

whence a knowledge of the two areas of cross-section and of the difference in pressure at the two places, such as might be obtained by a suitably connected manometer, will give the velocity and also the discharge rate (volume flow per second) of the liquid in the tube.

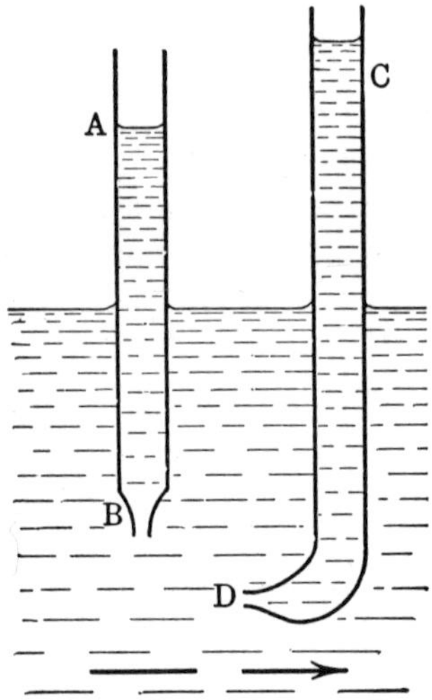

A rather simple device for measuring fluid velocity is the *Pitot* tube, illustrated schematically in Fig. 12·7. Two tubes AB and CD are placed with narrowed ends B and D in the pipe through which the fluid is flowing. The tube AB is strictly normal to the flow while CD is bent so that the orifice D faces

---

[1] R. B. Lindsay, *Concepts and Methods of Theoretical Physics,* Van Nostrand, Princeton, N.J., 1951, p. 351.

the flow. We should then expect approximately, at any rate, that the pressure of the liquid inside AB will be p, the same as that in the flowing liquid at this place. On the other hand, when the steady state is attained the pressure inside the tube CD will be p', where

$$p' = p + \tfrac{1}{2}\rho q^2, \qquad (12\text{·}5\text{–}12)$$

from Bernoulli's theorem, noting that the velocity in CD is zero. We then have simply

$$q = \sqrt{\frac{2}{\rho}(p' - p)}, \qquad (12\text{·}5\text{–}13)$$

the velocity being given at once in terms of the difference in pressure in the two tubes as measured by the difference in height of the liquid in the tubes. If this difference is h we have (Sec. 12·1)

$$p' - p = \rho g h, \qquad (12\text{·}5\text{–}14)$$

and the velocity becomes

$$q = \sqrt{2gh}. \qquad (12\text{·}5\text{–}15)$$

It must be emphasized that the application of the theorem of Bernoulli to this case is a rather bold approximation since the condition of the liquid in the neighborhood of the two openings is hardly compatible with the existence of steady flow. However, eqs. (12·5–13) and (12·5–15) are empirically justified to a fair degree of approximation.

Another application of the Bernoulli theorem is provided in the flow of a liquid out of an orifice in the bottom of a tank. Consider the tank in Fig. 12·8 with

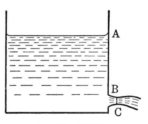

FIG. 12·8

the orifice B and suppose that the liquid in the tank is maintained at the level A by a steady fresh supply. If we follow a given stream line from A to B, we have for the energy per unit volume in the stream line at A,

$$\tfrac{1}{2}\rho q_A{}^2 + \rho g h_A + p_A, \qquad (12\text{·}5\text{–}16)$$

while that at B is

$$\tfrac{1}{2}\rho q_B{}^2 + \rho g h_B + p_B. \qquad (12\text{·}5\text{–}17)$$

Since the liquid is open to the air at both A and B, we have approximately $p_A = p_B$. Moreover, approximately, $q_A = 0$. Hence equating the energy at A to that at B, we have finally

$$q_B = \sqrt{2g(h_A - h_B)}. \qquad (12\text{·}5\text{–}18)$$

The result embodied in eq. (12·5–18) is known as *Torricelli's theorem*. It is, however, only roughly approximate, for this reason: observation indicates that the shape of the stream flowing out of the hole is not a circular cylinder; rather it narrows down after leaving the orifice and becomes narrowest at C, a point called the " vena contracta." Between the opening and C the stream lines converge and it is only at C that they become approximately parallel and the pressure approximately equal to that of the atmosphere. The more accurate equation to replace (12·5–18) is then

$$q_C = \sqrt{2g(h_A - h_C)}. \tag{12·5–19}$$

The size of the " vena contracta " depends on the type of opening. If the latter is merely a hole in a thin wall, the ratio of the area of the " vena contracta " to the area of the orifice is found by experiment to be approximately 0.62.

The discussion of the applications of Bernoulli's theorem has been so far for the case of an incompressible fluid. Application to a compressible fluid like a gas can, however, be handled if we revert to eq. (12·5–8) and evaluate the integral $\int \frac{dp}{\rho}$ by the substitution of the appropriate relation between p and ρ. If Boyle's law is satisfied we have

$$p = C\rho, \tag{12·5–20}$$

where C is a constant at any given constant temperature and therefore

$$\int \frac{dp}{\rho} = C \int \frac{d\rho}{\rho} = C \log \rho + C'$$

$$= C (\log p - \log C) + C', \tag{12·5–21}$$

and eq. (12·5–8) then becomes

$$\tfrac{1}{2}\rho q^2 + \rho \Omega + \rho C \log p = C'', \tag{12·5–22}$$

where C' and C'' are further constants. On the other hand if the gas law is the *adiabatic* one, which seems much more reasonable for gases moving with considerable velocities, we have, as the reader will recall from elementary physics,

$$p = K\rho^\gamma, \tag{12·5–23}$$

where K is another constant and γ is the ratio of the specific heat of the gas at constant pressure to that at constant volume. Then

$$\int \frac{dp}{\rho} = K\gamma \int \rho^{\gamma-2} \, d\rho = \frac{K\gamma\rho^{\gamma-1}}{\gamma - 1} + K'. \tag{12·5–24}$$

The eq. (12·5–8) now becomes

$$\tfrac{1}{2}\rho q^2 + \rho\Omega + \frac{\gamma}{\gamma-1}\,p = C''', \qquad (12\cdot5\text{–}25)$$

where C''' is a constant.   It is seen that the same qualitative statement of Bernoulli's theorem holds for gases as for liquids.   Hence the Pitot tube method may also be used to measure the velocity of a gas stream. Naturally the assumption of steady flow must still be made in spite of the fact that the presence of tubes, etc., introduces alterations in the flow.   Hence the resulting equations become quasi-empirical and adjustment of constants necessary in the calibration of the appropriate apparatus.

The student should investigate for himself such qualitative illustrations of Bernoulli's principle as the jet pump or aspirator and ship suction (the tendency of ships moving side by side to be drawn together), the Flettner rotor ship, the behavior of a ball in a jet, etc.

12·6. Waves in Fluids.   In Chapter 11 we discussed wave propagation through a deformable medium and the general properties of wave motion.   There are many important cases of waves in fluids, of which we shall consider only two, namely: (1) waves on the *surface* of a liquid, and (2) compressional waves through a liquid or gas.   Indeed we shall still further specialize the first type as follows.   Surface waves in a liquid are due to two causes, viz., the *surface tension* (see Sec. 12·8), and *gravity*.   The former are of relatively short wave length, while the latter are very long.   In our present treatment we shall confine our attention to the latter and particularize by considering the propagation of a gravity wave in a long straight canal.

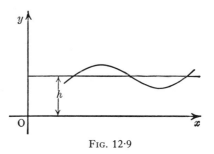

Fig. 12·9

Let the depth of the canal be h and suppose that it is small compared with the wave length.   The displacement of the surface is assumed to take place in the xy plane and to be so small that, as in the case of the transversely vibrating string (Sec. 11·6), we may neglect the squares and higher powers of it and its derivatives.   The x axis is taken as the horizontal bottom of the canal (see Fig. 12·9) so that the ordinate of the displaced surface is $h + \eta$, where η is the displacement in the y direction from the equilibrium position.   We shall assume that the pressure at any point (x, y) below the surface is the ordinary statical pressure.   This means that we are supposing that the vertical accelerations of the particles of fluid are so small that they may be neglected. Hence for the pressure in question we have

$$p = \rho g(h + \eta - y), \tag{12·6–1}$$

so that

$$\frac{\partial p}{\partial x} = \rho g \frac{\partial \eta}{\partial x}. \tag{12·6–2}$$

The equation of motion for the x direction (the external force being zero) is

$$\frac{\partial u}{\partial t} + u \frac{\partial u}{\partial x} = -\frac{1}{\rho} \frac{\partial p}{\partial x}. \tag{12·6–3}$$

Here we use the x component of eq. (12·4–8) and note (eq. 12·4–2) that u is independent of y and z. It is a function of x and t only. But since u is small, $u \frac{\partial u}{\partial x}$ is negligible compared with $\frac{\partial u}{\partial t}$, and (12·6–3) reduces to [using (12·6–2)],

$$\frac{\partial u}{\partial t} = -\frac{1}{\rho} \frac{\partial p}{\partial x} = -g \frac{\partial \eta}{\partial x}. \tag{12·6–4}$$

Now in this case $u = \frac{\partial \xi}{\partial t}$, where ξ is the *horizontal* displacement of the particles which were under equilibrium conditions in the plane at x. Hence we can write (12·6–4) in the form

$$\frac{\partial^2 \xi}{\partial t^2} = -g \frac{\partial \eta}{\partial x}. \tag{12·6–5}$$

We must now apply the equation of continuity [eq. (12·3–8)], which in the present problem reduces to the two dimensional form

$$\frac{\partial u}{\partial x} + \frac{\partial v}{\partial y} = 0, \tag{12·6–6}$$

so that

$$v = -\int_0^y \frac{\partial u}{\partial x} dy = -y \frac{\partial u}{\partial x}, \tag{12·6–7}$$

since $\frac{\partial u}{\partial x}$ is independent of y. Hence putting $v = \frac{\partial \eta}{\partial t}$ (*at the surface*) and $u = \frac{\partial \xi}{\partial t}$, this becomes (if we recall that $y = h$ at the surface)

$$\frac{\partial \eta}{\partial t} = -h \frac{\partial}{\partial t}\left(\frac{\partial \xi}{\partial x}\right). \tag{12·6–8}$$

Integrating with respect to the time yields

$$\eta = -h \frac{\partial \xi}{\partial x}, \qquad (12 \cdot 6\text{--}9)$$

leaving off the constant of integration which is independent of t. If we utilize (12·6–9) in (12·6–5) we have finally the equation

$$\frac{\partial^2 \xi}{\partial t^2} = gh \frac{\partial^2 \xi}{\partial x^2}, \qquad (12 \cdot 6\text{--}10)$$

for the behavior of ξ. If we had eliminated ξ instead of η we should have found

$$\frac{\partial^2 \eta}{\partial t^2} = gh \frac{\partial^2 \eta}{\partial x^2}. \qquad (12 \cdot 6\text{--}11)$$

We recognize at once that (12·6–10, 11) are examples of the one dimensional wave equation. Hence the disturbance on the surface is propagated with velocity

$$c = \sqrt{gh}. \qquad (12 \cdot 6\text{--}12)$$

Suppose, for example, that the wave is of the simple harmonic variety. Then (Sec. 11·5)

$$\xi = \xi_0 \cos (\omega t - kx), \qquad (12 \cdot 6\text{--}13)$$

where $\omega = 2\pi\nu$, ν being the frequency of the wave and $k = \omega/c$. The vertical displacement at the surface is then from (12·6–9)

$$\eta = -h\xi_0 k \sin (\omega t - kx). \qquad (12 \cdot 6\text{--}14)$$

The elimination of the time between (12·6–13) and (12·6–14) gives the path of the liquid particle at the surface, viz.,

$$\frac{\xi^2}{\xi_0^2} + \frac{\eta^2}{h^2 \xi_0^2 k^2} = 1. \qquad (12 \cdot 6\text{--}15)$$

This is the equation of an ellipse with semi-major and semi-minor axes ξ_0 and $\xi_0 hk$ respectively. Recalling that $k = 2\pi/\lambda$, where λ is the wave length, and that $h \ll \lambda$, we see that the vertical axis is much shorter than the horizontal.

It is interesting to note that for $h = 10$ feet, the velocity of these surface waves is approximately 18 ft/sec.

The above analysis forms the basis for the investigation of the *dynamical* theory of the tides, which attributes the latter to wave motion in the water on the earth due to the attraction of the moon and sun. The details would carry us too far afield here.

We shall now turn to *compressional* waves in a fluid. These are of particular interest since all sounds are transmitted by waves of this type (both in fluids and solids, as we have had occasion to notice).

In this case the equation of motion becomes rather simple. Thus suppose within a fluid at rest a disturbance is created at some point. This disturbance will involve displacements of small elements of the fluid from their equilibrium positions. We shall assume that these displacements and the corresponding velocities are small enough so that their powers higher than the first and their products may be neglected.

Hence the equation of motion of the fluid may be written, for *no* external forces (eq. 12·4–8):

$$\dot{\mathbf{q}} = -\frac{\nabla p}{\rho}. \qquad (12\cdot6\text{–}16)$$

It will now be assumed that there exists a function $\phi(x, y, z)$ such that

$$\mathbf{q} = -\nabla\phi. \qquad (12\cdot6\text{–}17)$$

We may call ϕ the velocity potential, since it is related to the flow velocity $\mathbf{q}$ in the same way as the potential V is related to the force $\mathbf{F}$ in eq. (4·5–17) (see also Sec. 4·1). It is shown in more advanced books[1] that the existence of the velocity potential implies that the fluid has no angular velocity about any axis, i.e., its motion is *irrotational*. If we substitute from (12·6–17) into (12·6–16) the result is

$$\nabla\dot{\phi} = \frac{\nabla p}{\rho}. \qquad (12\cdot6\text{–}18)$$

It will be convenient to write

$$p_e = p - p_0 \qquad (12\cdot6\text{–}19)$$

where p_0 is the mean equilibrium pressure of the fluid and p is its instantaneous variable value. The quantity p_e is termed the excess pressure. We shall similarly introduce the excess density ρ_e where

$$\rho_e = \rho - \rho_0 \qquad (12\cdot6\text{–}20)$$

where ρ_0 is the mean equilibrium density and ρ the instantaneous variable value. Further let

$$s = \rho_e/\rho_0 \qquad (12\cdot6\text{–}21)$$

where s is the fractional change in density and is known as the condensation.

We are going to assume that the fluid displacement and velocity changes are so small that $p_e \ll p_0$ and $\rho_e \ll \rho_0$ or $|s| \ll 1$. This permits us to replace ρ in (12·6–18) by ρ_0 and to write this equation as

$$\nabla\dot{\phi} = \nabla(p_e/\rho_0). \qquad (12\cdot6\text{–}22)$$

[1] R. B. Lindsay, *Concepts and Methods of Theoretical Physics*, Van Nostrand, Princeton, N.J., 1951, p. 353.

Since the gradients (see Sec. 4·5) of ϕ and p_e/ρ_0 are the same, it follows that ϕ and p_e/ρ_0 can differ only by a quantity constant in space (since the operator ∇ involves differentiation with respect to space alone). If we are interested only in those quantities which vary both in space and time, we can therefore write

$$\phi = p_e/\rho_0. \qquad (12\text{·}6\text{--}23)$$

This is consequently the form which the equation of motion of a fluid takes for very small irrotational disturbances from equilibrium.

But the equation of continuity must also be considered. Again utilizing the fact that ρ changes only a little from the equilibrium value ρ_0 we can write (12·3–8) in the form

$$\rho_0 \nabla \cdot \mathbf{q} = -\dot{\rho}_e. \qquad (12\text{·}6\text{--}24)$$

From (12·6–17) and (12·6–21) this becomes (see Sec. 4·5)

$$\nabla^2 \phi = \dot{s}. \qquad (12\text{·}6\text{--}25)$$

There will always be a relation between the excess pressure and excess density of the fluid. In fact this comes from the equation of state of the fluid (see Sec. 7·1). We shall write the relation here simply as

$$p_e/\rho_e = c^2, \qquad (12\text{·}6\text{--}26)$$

where c^2 is at present merely a parameter which will in general depend on the temperature of the fluid and may indeed depend on its pressure and density. We can write the relation (12·6–26) in the form

$$p_e = \rho_0 c^2 s \qquad (12\text{·}6\text{--}27)$$

and immediately substitute into (12·6–23), which becomes

$$\dot{\phi} = c^2 s. \qquad (12\text{·}6\text{--}28)$$

The condensation s may be eliminated between (12·6–25) and (12·6–28), yielding the second-order partial differential equation

$$c^2 \nabla^2 \phi = \ddot{\phi}. \qquad (12\text{·}6\text{--}29)$$

This reminds us of eq. (11·5–3) and indeed would reduce precisely to the form of this equation if ϕ were assumed to depend on x alone so that $\partial^2 \phi/\partial y^2 = \partial^2 \phi/\partial z^2 = 0$. For then eq. (12·6–29) would become

$$\ddot{\phi} = c^2 \frac{\partial^2 \phi}{\partial x^2} \qquad (12\text{·}6\text{--}30)$$

the solution to which, according to the discussion in Sec. 11·5, corresponds to the wave propagation of ϕ with velocity c.

It is shown in more advanced treatises[1] that eq. (12·6–29) is the differential equation for wave motion in three dimensions.

It is interesting to note that the wave equation (12·6–29) here results from the combination of the equation of *continuity* and the equation of *motion* for small displacements from equilibrium, the first of which expresses the fact that a continuous, indestructible medium is involved and the second gives the slight motion from equilibrium of a small part of that medium conceived to move as a whole, viz., as a *particle*. There are other illustrations of this duality which emphasize its fundamental significance in wave motion.[2]

The waves of acoustics are all included in the above analysis. The two types of such waves which are most important in practice are respectively *plane* and *spherical* waves. In the former ϕ is a function of t and one space variable, say x, only, and eq. (12·6–29) reduces to the form (12·6–30) as we have just seen. If we confine our attention here to plane harmonic waves as the most significant, we may write

$$\phi = A \cos(\omega t - kx), \tag{12·6–31}$$

where ω and k have the usual meaning and A is the velocity potential amplitude. The corresponding expressions for the particle velocity u, the particle displacement ξ, the excess pressure and the condensation may at once be obtained. Thus

$$\dot{\xi} = u = -\frac{\partial \phi}{\partial x} = -kA \sin(\omega t - kx), \tag{12·6–32}$$

$$s = \frac{1}{c^2} \frac{\partial \phi}{\partial t} = -\frac{Ak}{c} \sin(\omega t - kx), \tag{12·6–33}$$

$$\xi = \frac{A}{c} \cos(\omega t - kx), \tag{12·6–34}$$

$$p_e = \rho_0 c^2 s = -A\rho_0 ck \sin(\omega t - kx). \tag{12·6–35}$$

If we differentiate ξ with respect to x we obtain the important relation for acoustic wave transmission

$$s = -\frac{\partial \xi}{\partial x}. \tag{12·6–36}$$

Its physical meaning is as follows. If ξ increases in the positive x direction, s is negative corresponding to what may be called a *rarefaction*; similarly, decreasing ξ in the positive x direction corresponds to positive

---

[1] See, for example, R. B. Lindsay, *Mechanical Radiation*, McGraw-Hill, New York, 1960, pp. 24, 379.

[2] See, for example, R. B. Lindsay, *Proc. Nat. Acad. Sci.*, **17**, 420, 1931.

s and hence to a *condensation*. We ought to note that if ξ is always measured in the positive x direction then for a wave in the negative x direction, eq. (12·6–36) will become $s = +\dfrac{\partial \xi}{\partial x}$.

From eqs. (12·6–32, 33, 34, 35) we see at once that it is not only ϕ which satisfies the wave equation, but that u, s, and ξ are also solutions. Thus we have, for example

$$c^2 \frac{\partial^2 \xi}{\partial x^2} = \frac{\partial^2 \xi}{\partial t^2}, \quad \text{and} \quad c^2 \frac{\partial^2 s}{\partial x^2} = \frac{\partial^2 s}{\partial t^2}. \tag{12·6–37}$$

From the definition of phase (Sec. 11·5) we note that u, s, and p_e are in the same phase, that is, when p_e has a positive maximum, the same is true of u and s. However, while ξ and ϕ are in phase with each other, they are both out of phase with u, s, and p_e.

Examining now the expression (12·6–26) we see that the general formula for the velocity of an acoustic wave in a fluid is

$$c = \sqrt{\frac{p_e}{\rho_e}}. \tag{12·6–38}$$

The exact form of this will depend, of course, on the relation between p and ρ. If Boyle's law holds we have

$$c = \sqrt{\frac{p}{\rho}}. \tag{12·6–39}$$

This formula (derived originally by Newton) does not, however, agree with the experimentally observed result, giving values which are too low. It seems more reasonable to assume that the relationship between p and ρ is *adiabatic* (as suggested by Laplace), viz., such that [eq. (12·5–23)]

$$\frac{p_e}{\rho_e} = \frac{\gamma p}{\rho}.$$

We then have

$$c = \sqrt{\frac{\gamma p}{\rho}}, \tag{12·6–40}$$

which agrees very well with the experimental values.[1]

All the general discussion of wave motion in Sec. 11·6 finds application in acoustic waves. But we may perhaps here refer the

---

[1] The student should check this by the substitution of numerical values. He may also show that in the case of a liquid the expression for the velocity is $c = \sqrt{B/\rho}$, where B is the bulk modulus.

reader to some standard texts on acoustics[1] where, for illustration, the interesting features of spherical waves in fluids are also discussed in detail.

12·7. Viscous Fluids. Our treatment of fluid motion has so far been confined to perfect fluids in which shearing strains never occur. It is hardly necessary to re-emphasize the *ideal* nature of the perfect fluid, and the fact that all fluids found in nature depart from this to a greater or lesser degree by displaying *viscosity*. Indeed in our short discussion of the kinetic theory of matter (Sec. 7·1) we noted that if a fluid is assumed to be composed of molecules in rapid motion there must be a tangential drag exerted on any layer of moving molecules by the contiguous layers. We there defined the coefficient of viscosity η as the tangential force per unit velocity gradient, and proceeded to find out a few interesting things about it in the case of a gas. For many problems of fluid flow like those treated in the previous sections the effect of viscosity is so slight that it may safely be neglected. However, there are some problems in which it is of considerable importance and we ought to mention one or two of these.

First let us observe that there is a connection between viscosity and the steady flow of a fluid. It will be recalled that in flow of this kind there exist *stream lines* which maintain their position as long as the flow lasts. Now in the flow of actual fluids it is found that while it is possible to have steady flow of a liquid through a tube for reasonably small velocities, in general as the velocity of flow increases there is a breakup of the stream lines and the motion may be said to become *turbulent*. There appears to exist for each fluid a certain *critical velocity* below which steady motion is possible but above which turbulence ensues. This may be readily shown, for example, by allowing a small amount of coloring matter to be transported in a flowing liquid. For small flow velocities it will be observed to follow a regular stream line, while eventually a velocity is attained for which the stream line is broken up and the coloring matter distributed generally throughout the tube. Now experiment indicates that for a viscous fluid this critical velocity is directly proportional to the coefficient of viscosity and inversely proportional to the density. This is a somewhat remarkable result, for it indicates that steady motion is possible for fluids of small viscosity only at very low flow velocities unless the density is also very small, while steady flow is possible over a considerable range of velocities for a very viscous fluid. We have an illustration of this in the steady flow of lava from a volcano.

[1] For example, P. M. Morse, *Vibration and Sound*, McGraw-Hill, New York, 2nd ed., 1948; also R. B. Lindsay, *Mechanical Radiation*, McGraw-Hill, New York, 1960.

The result mentioned at the end of the preceding paragraph is closely connected with the existence of a certain constant in the form of a dimensionless number called the Reynolds number after Osborne Reynolds, the British engineer who made numerous contributions to fluid mechanics. We present here a simplified, phenomenological approach to the evaluation of this number. In any real fluid it seems reasonable to suppose (at any rate Reynolds assumed it) that the inertia force on the fluid at any point must be proportional to the viscous force at the same point for all similar geometrical configurations, i.e., configurations which may differ in size but must be of the same shape. Now the inertia force per unit volume according to eq. (12·4–8) has the dimensions of $\rho q^2/l$ where ρ is the density of the fluid, q the magnitude of fluid velocity and l is some characteristic length involved in the geometrical configuration, e.g., the diameter of a pipe through which the flow takes place or the length of an object opposing fluid flow, etc. Similarly the viscous force per unit volume from (7·3–1) has the dimensions $\eta q/l^2$, where η is the coefficient of viscosity. Hence the assumption just made yields

$$\frac{\rho q^2}{l} \bigg/ \frac{\eta q}{l^2} = \rho q l/\eta = \mathscr{R}, \qquad (12\text{·}7\text{–}1)$$

where $\mathscr{R}$ is the Reynolds number, a dimensionless quantity. It is a constant for all geometrically similar configurations. Thus if in one state of flow of the fluid, the relevant quantities are ρ_1, q_1, l_1 and η_1 respectively, and for a geometrically similar configuration the corresponding quantities are ρ_2, q_2, l_2 and η_2 respectively, we shall have

$$\rho_1 q_1 l_1/\eta_1 = \rho_2 q_2 l_2/\eta_2. \qquad (12\text{·}7\text{–}2)$$

The Reynolds number may be simplified by introducing the kinematic viscosity ν which is defined as η/ρ. Then

$$\mathscr{R} = q l/\nu. \qquad (12\text{·}7\text{–}3)$$

The value of the number lies in the fact that knowing it enables us to predict the flow in one configuration from a knowledge of the flow in a geometrically similar configuration. We see that a high Reynolds number means that the inertia forces predominate over the viscous forces per unit volume, whereas a low Reynolds number means that the viscous forces predominate.

In the steady flow of water through a tube 1 mm in diameter at a velocity of 1 cm/sec, since the viscosity of water at room temperature is 10^{-3} poises, the Reynolds number comes out to be 10. (Note that the choice of l in Reynolds number is bound to be somewhat arbitrary.) On the other hand turbulence in channels and tubes occurs for Reynolds numbers of the order of 5000 to 10,000.

One might suppose that for very large Reynolds numbers, in which the viscous effects appear to be negligible compared with inertia effects, the fluid would move as an ideal fluid.   However, this neglects the behavior close to boundary surfaces to which the fluid adheres to a certain extent. It is only far from such surfaces that a so-called " frictionless " fluid (or a fluid with very small viscosity) moves ideally.   At the wall or boundary a so-called " boundary layer " is formed within which the fluid velocity varies from that in the free fluid to zero at the solid surface. In the boundary layer the frictional forces and inertia forces become of the same order of magnitude.   This provides a means for estimating the thickness of the boundary layer.   Thus suppose a fluid flows over a flat plate of length l in the direction of the flow.   If the thickness of the boundary layer is δ, the viscous force per unit volume there is of the order $\eta q/\delta^2$, while the inertia force per unit volume is still $\rho q^2/l$, where q is the flow velocity at the edge of the layer away from the plate surface. If we equate these quantities we get

$$\delta = \sqrt{\eta l/\rho q}. \qquad (12\text{-}7\text{-}4)$$

In the flow of water over a plate 1 meter long with $q = 10$ cm/sec, $\delta \doteq 1/10$ cm.

Much of the study of the flow of fluids past solids as in aerodynamics, for example, is involved with the boundary layer concept.[1]

Let us now discuss the steady flow of a viscous Newtonian fluid (cf. Sec. 11·4) through a circular tube.   We shall assume that the radius of the tube is R and that its axis lies along the x axis.   We also suppose that the fluid is flowing with velocity u in the positive x direction. Consider a coaxial cylindrical shell whose inner surface has the radius r while the outer surface has the radius $r + dr$.   Due to the viscosity there will be a *tangential* stress *per unit area* of the inner surface of magnitude

$$X_r = \eta \frac{du}{dr}, \qquad (12\text{-}7\text{-}5)$$

where η is the coefficient of viscosity and $\dfrac{du}{dr}$ is the velocity gradient normal to the axis of the tube.   This follows at once from the definition of η.   Then the tangential force on the whole inner surface for a length l of tube is

$$2\pi r l \eta \frac{du}{dr}. \qquad (12\text{-}7\text{-}6)$$

---

[1] See L. Prandtl, *Essentials of Fluid Dynamics*, Blackie and Son, Ltd., London, 1952, pp. 103 ff.; also R. W. Pohl, *Physical Principles of Mechanics and Acoustics*, Blackie and Son, Ltd., London, 1932, pp. 215 ff.

The corresponding tangential force on the outer surface of the shell will then be

$$2\pi r l \eta \frac{du}{dr} + \frac{d}{dr}\left(2\pi r l \eta \frac{du}{dr}\right) dr. \tag{12·7–7}$$

There will thus be a *net* tangential force on the shell in the positive x direction of

$$\frac{d}{dr}\left(2\pi r l \eta \frac{du}{dr}\right) dr.$$

The flow is supposed to be steady. Hence the above force must be equilibrated by a force due to the difference in pressure $p_l - p_0$ at the two ends of the tube. The force due to the latter will be $(p_l - p_0)2\pi r\, dr$; equating the two equal forces gives the differential equation

$$\frac{d}{dr}\left(2\pi r l \eta \frac{du}{dr}\right) = (p_l - p_0)2\pi r. \tag{12·7–8}$$

A first integration yields

$$2\pi r l \eta \frac{du}{dr} = (p_l - p_0)\pi r^2 + C_1, \tag{12·7–9}$$

while the second gives

$$u = \frac{(p_l - p_0)r^2}{4\eta l} + \frac{C_1 \log r}{2\pi \eta l} + C_2. \tag{12·7–10}$$

We must now suppose that at the boundary of the tube the viscosity causes the fluid to be at rest. Hence $u = 0$ for $r = R$. Moreover, the value of u for $r = 0$, i.e., along the axis, must be finite. Hence the coefficient of $\log r$ must vanish. This means $C_1 = 0$. From the previous condition we get

$$C_2 = -\frac{(p_l - p_0)R^2}{4\eta l},$$

and we finally have for the velocity u at any distance r from the axis

$$u = \frac{(p_l - p_0)(r^2 - R^2)}{4\eta l}. \tag{12·7–11}$$

We may at once calculate the rate of volume flow per second passing any cross-section of the tube by integrating $2\pi r u\, dr$ from $r = 0$ to $r = R$. We get

$$\int_0^R 2\pi r u\, dr = \frac{\pi R^4}{8\eta} \cdot \frac{(p_0 - p_l)}{l}. \tag{12·7–12}$$

This is known as *Poiseuille's* formula. In words it states that the volume rate of steady flow of a viscous fluid through a cylindrical tube varies directly as the fourth power of the radius and directly as the pressure gradient, while inversely as the coefficient of viscosity. For very small tubes the velocity may thus become very small. Poiseuille verified the formula by experiments on the flow through capillary tubes. Incidentally the formula may be used to determine the coefficient of viscosity.

As might be expected, the passage of an acoustic wave through a viscous fluid is accompanied by an attenuation of the intensity of the wave. This is particularly marked in the case where the transmission takes place through a very narrow tube.[1]

Some of the most important problems in applied physics are connected with the resistance experienced by a solid object in moving through a viscous fluid. We shall mention but one illustration. By means of analysis beyond the scope of this book Stokes showed that the resisting force on a sphere of radius a moving through a medium of viscosity η with constant velocity v is given by

$$F = 6\pi\eta av, \qquad (12\cdot7\text{--}13)$$

which the reader may be willing to accept as physically plausible, at any rate. This formula is fundamental for the work of Millikan on the measurement of the charge on the electron by the behavior in electrostatic fields of very small electrically charged drops of oil. Thus consider an oil drop of radius a (actually in the neighborhood of 10^{-4} cm) and of density ρ_0 falling under the action of gravity in a fluid of density ρ at rest. There are then three forces acting on the drop, viz., *gravity*, of magnitude

$$\tfrac{4}{3}\pi a^3 \rho_0 g;$$

the *buoyancy*, of magnitude (by Archimedes' principle)

$$\tfrac{4}{3}\pi a^3 \rho g;$$

and the *resistance* of the fluid given by the law of Stokes above. In the steady state when the velocity is constant, the balance of forces requires that

$$\tfrac{4}{3}\pi a^3(\rho_0 - \rho)g = 6\pi\eta av, \qquad (12\cdot7\text{--}14)$$

so that the velocity of fall is therefore

$$v = \tfrac{2}{9}a^2 \frac{(\rho_0 - \rho)}{\eta} g. \qquad (12\cdot7\text{--}15)$$

[1] See, for example, Stewart and Lindsay, *Acoustics*, pp. 67 ff.

It must be emphasized that this formula holds only for values of the Reynolds number $\mathscr{R}$ much smaller than unity; i.e., viscous forces must predominate.

In the experiment to determine the charge on the electron, a charge is given to the drop by illuminating the region in which it moves with X-rays or ultraviolet light. Suppose that this charge is e, the smallest possible charge, i.e., that of the electron. An electric field is then applied to the space where the drop is moving and in the vertical direction. If the intensity of the field is E, i.e., E dynes per unit charge, the total force on the charged drop due to the field is eE and if E is adjusted until the drop comes to rest we must have for equilibrium

$$eE = \tfrac{4}{3}\pi a^3(\rho_0 - \rho)g. \qquad (12\cdot7\text{--}16)$$

If we could measure all quantities here we could then solve for e. However, a is very difficult if not impossible to measure accurately. Fortunately we can solve for it from eq. (12·7–15) and then substitute into eq. (12·7–16), finally obtaining

$$e = \frac{18\pi}{\sqrt{2E}} \frac{(v\eta)^{3/2}}{\sqrt{g(\rho_0 - \rho)}} . \qquad (12\cdot7\text{--}17)$$

As a matter of fact the values of e obtained by this formula, though of value as first approximations, are found to depend on the pressure of the air and hence cannot be exact. The drops are so small that the molecular constitution of the air must be taken into consideration. That is, Stokes's law, which is based on the assumption that the fluid in question is perfectly continuous, must be modified. We shall not enter into further discussion here.[1]

12·8. Surface Phenomena. Capillarity. It would hardly be appropriate to leave the subject of fluids without some elementary reference to the phenomena associated with liquid-gas and liquid-solid interfaces. These phenomena are of great importance in applied physics and physical chemistry.

It is a common observation that the surface of a liquid exposed to the atmosphere appears to act like a more or less tight skin or membrane covering the body of the liquid. This property is manifested in a variety of ways. It is very evident, for example, in the apparent violation of the laws of hydrostatics shown in the floating of a needle or particles of sand on the surface of water. It is also displayed in the characteristic form of liquid drops, all tending toward the spherical shape, the sphere

---

[1] See R. A. Millikan, *Electrons (+ and —), Protons, Photons, Neutrons, Mesotrons, and Cosmic Rays*, Chicago, rev. ed., 1947, pp. 90 ff.

having the smallest surface enclosing a given volume. It is as if the surface tries to contract as much as possible. The student will recall other illustrations of the same nature from elementary physics.

Another common observation is the rise of certain liquids in tubes of small bore, called *capillary* (i.e., hairlike) tubes. Indeed it is this name which has become associated with the whole subject under discussion.

In beginning our survey of these phenomena we shall assume that if a straight line is drawn in the surface of a liquid the portion of the surface on one side of the line exerts on that on the other side a force which is directly proportional to the length of the line. The coefficient of proportionality or force per unit length is called the *surface tension*, which we shall denote by the symbol T_s. It is dependent on the nature of the liquid and the substance above its surface, and also on the state of the surface and the temperature, decreasing with increase of the latter. It is, however, independent of the size of the surface, differing therein from the superficial tension in an elastic sheet or membrane. For the latter, being due to the action of external forces, increases with the further stretching of the surface.

Perhaps the clearest way to visualize the meaning of surface tension is to consider a simple experiment which, if done carefully enough, is competent to give an approximate value of T_s for the case of several liquids. A piece of perfectly clean thin metal wire (e.g., platinum) is bent into the form of a rectangular framework (Fig. 12·10) and suspended in the liquid from one arm of a balance. As the metal frame is pulled out of the liquid with a two faced film attached to the sides of the frame it is necessary to balance the tendency of this film to contract by placing weights in the balance pan. When equilibrium is attained it will be found that the counterpoising weight is independent of the magnitude of the surface film formed. The value of the surface tension may then be computed from the simple equation

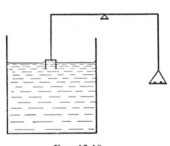

FIG. 12·10

$$2lT_s = mg, \qquad (12\cdot8-1)$$

where mg is the counterpoising weight and l is the horizontal length of the film. The factor 2 enters from the fact that the film has *two* surfaces. Of course it must be noted that the extension of film surface possible without breaking varies a good deal with the liquid used, and the values obtained in this way vary greatly with the cleanness of the surface. The slightest contamination, as for example with oil from hair or fingers, suffices to reduce the value of T_s materially.

An understanding of the nature of surface tension may be gained if we examine the phenomenon in terms of the molecular theory which considers the liquid to be composed of a large number of molecules (much like those of a gas — Sec. 7·1) moving about with considerable velocity, but also exerting on each other attractive forces which are rather small when the molecules are at ordinary distances, but which become extremely large when the molecules are very close to each other. Certain evidence makes it probable that this sphere of molecular action, as it is called, is usually of the order of 10^{-7} cm, hence about ten times the order of magnitude of molecular dimensions. In the interior of a liquid a given molecule will be surrounded by other molecules on all sides and hence be under the influence of a force which is approximately the same in every direction. This, however, is not the case with a molecule in the surface of the liquid, for the attraction of the gas molecules above the surface will be far outweighed by the attraction of the molecules of the liquid. Hence there will act on such a molecule a resultant downward force, and it is this force which we may look upon as producing the effect of a tight skin on the surface. That this is indeed only an approximate picture of the phenomenon will be recognized from the observed fact that on the molecular theory it is necessary to assume that conditions on the surface of a liquid in contact with a gas containing vapor of the liquid are by no means static, since rapidly moving molecules of the liquid are continually escaping into the region above the liquid, and concomitantly vapor molecules are flying back into the liquid. The reader will recall that when the average number traveling in each direction per unit of time is the same the vapor above the liquid is said to be *saturated*. If the number escaping is greater than the number regained there is a net *evaporation* of the liquid into vapor form, while if the tendency of the process is in the other direction we speak of the *condensation* of the vapor. By reason of this state of affairs it is perhaps better to consider the surface phenomena from the standpoint of *energy*. The kinetic energy of a molecule moving entirely in the interior of the liquid is affected only by collisions with its neighbors, but when such a molecule approaches the surface it must lose kinetic energy because of the effective force tending to pull it back. It will then gain potential energy, so that the molecules in the surface will have on the average greater potential energy than those in the interior. Now we have already had occasion to notice that the most stable equilibrium of an aggregate of particles corresponds to the least potential energy compatible with the constraints, etc., (Sec. 5·6). Hence the surface will so behave as to keep the total potential energy as small as possible. This may be brought about, however, by keeping the area of the surface as small as possible. Hence the tendency which gives the effect of a tight membrane over the surface. This moreover accounts for the previously mentioned tendency for drops to assume the spherical form. The foregoing molecular discussion also accounts qualitatively for the observed fact that the surface tension decreases with increase of the temperature.

The considerations above may also be applied in an interesting manner to the stretching of the surface of a liquid. This involves the transfer of molecules from the interior to the surface with consequent increase in potential energy and decrease in the kinetic energy. But, as we have seen, the *temperature* depends on the average value of the latter. Hence if the temperature is not to fall, heat must be absorbed by the surface during the stretching. This is in addition to the mechanical work done against the surface tension during the process of expansion. The mechanical equivalent of the heat absorbed plus the mechanical work done per *unit* increase in area will be called the total *surface energy* of the liquid. The reader will find no difficulty in showing that the mechanical work per unit increase in area is numerically equal to the *surface tension*. At any temperature (at which the liquid exists as such) the surface energy is always numerically greater than the surface tension.

When a solid object is brought into contact with a liquid so as to be partially immersed, it is observed that one of two things will happen: either the liquid will appear to run a certain distance up the side of the object as in *A* (Fig. 12·11) or will appear to be depressed somewhat in the vicinity of the object as in *B*. In the first case the liquid is said to

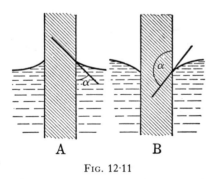

wet the object, while in the second case it does not wet the object. To put the matter somewhat crudely we may say that there is an attraction between the liquid molecules and those of the object, which in the immediate neighborhood of the object (in case the latter is wet) outbalances the mutual attraction of the liquid molecules. This, for example, is true when the liquid is pure water and the solid is glass.

A   B

Fig. 12·11

On the other hand, in mercury which does not " wet " glass, the mutual action of the liquid molecules is greater than the attraction of the mercury-glass molecules and hence the mercury surface is depressed in the neighborhood of a glass plate. The angle between the surface of the

liquid and the surface of the solid is known as the angle of contact —
represented by α in Fig. 12·11. It varies with the cleanness of the
surfaces, but experiment indicates that it is fairly definite for a given
pair of clean surfaces. For example in the case of mercury in contact
with glass it is about 140°, while for water in contact with glass it is
practically zero.

These considerations are very approximate, and we must emphasize
that capillary phenomena have been the subject of much theorizing
extending from the time of Laplace and (later) Gauss down to the
present period. The subject is still incomplete owing to our ignorance
of the precise nature of the cohesive forces between molecules both of
the same and different kinds.

Nevertheless we can derive a few more elementary results. Consider
first the rise of a liquid in a capillary tube as indicated in Fig. 12·12.
Let the radius of the tube be a and suppose it is placed in a liquid of
density ρ which wets it. Let the angle of contact be α (an acute angle)
and assume that the surface tension
of the liquid in contact with air is
T_s. Where the liquid is in contact
with the tube there will then be a
force whose vertical component
acts upward and has the magnitude

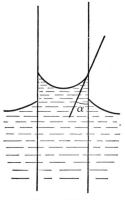

$$2\pi a T_s \cos \alpha.$$

The liquid will therefore rise in
the tube until this force is balanced
by the weight of the column of
liquid above the surface of the
liquid into which the tube has been
placed. Since the upper surface
of the liquid in the tube is not

Fig. 12·12

level, the height of the column is not a definite quantity, but we can
nevertheless take for it the average height (i.e., that which it would
have if it were level) and call this h. The weight of the column then
becomes

$$\rho g h \pi a^2,$$

and hence equating this to the former quantity, we get

$$2\pi a T_s \cos \alpha = \rho g h \pi a^2, \tag{12·8–2}$$

or

$$h = \frac{2T_s \cos \alpha}{\rho g a}, \tag{12·8–3}$$

for the height, which thus proves to be inversely proportional to the radius of the tube. If cos α is negative there is no capillary rise, but a *depression* instead. This occurs in the case of mercury in glass, where $\alpha = 140°$, as has already been mentioned. The law given by eq. (12·8–3) is known as *Jurin's law*. It can be used to determine T_s by an alternative method to that described in the first part of the section. The reader may show that the same law applies to the capillary rise between two vertical plates placed in a liquid which wets them, provided that a now refers to half the distance between the plates.

The form of the liquid surface at rest under gravity in the neighborhood of a solid object can under certain conditions be determined very readily by an elementary method due to Maxwell. This is the case, for example, when the object is a vertical flat plate of great breadth.

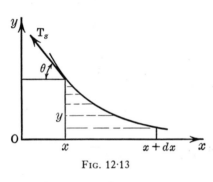

We assume that the object is wet by the liquid. Let us take a section of the surface (considered as a cylinder) in the xy plane (Fig. 12·13). It is understood that for $y = 0$ the surface is plane and the section parallel to the x axis. Consider the infinitesimal slice of unit thickness whose projection on the xy plane is the area between the ordinates corresponding to x and $x + dx$. Since this portion is in

Fig. 12·13

equilibrium the total force on it in the x direction, say, must vanish. First let us consider the force due to the surface tension. At the left the horizontal component is (since T_s is the force per *unit length*)

$$-T_s \cos \theta = - \frac{T_s}{\sqrt{1 + \left(\frac{dy}{dx}\right)^2}}, \qquad (12·8–4)$$

where dy/dx is the slope of the curve at the point in question. At the right, on the other hand, the horizontal component is

$$T_s \left[\cos \theta + \frac{d \cos \theta}{dx} dx\right]. \qquad (12·8–5)$$

The net horizontal component is the sum of (12·8–4), and (12·8–5) or

$$T_s \frac{d \cos \theta}{dx} dx,$$

which from (12·8–4) is equal to

$$\frac{-T_s \dfrac{dy}{dx}\dfrac{d^2y}{dx^2}\,dx}{\left[1+\left(\dfrac{dy}{dx}\right)^2\right]^{3/2}}.\tag{12·8–6}$$

This force must be balanced by the hydrostatic forces against the two vertical ends of the element. If we assume for simplicity that there is a vacuum above the surface, then the pressure at any point in the portion of the liquid which we are considering will be zero or negative. Thus for any value of y, it will be

$$-\rho g y.$$

Hence the total thrust on unit breadth of the end of the element at x is

$$-\rho g \int_0^y y\,dy = -\frac{\rho g}{2}y^2.\tag{12·8–7}$$

At $x + dx$, the corresponding thrust in the *opposite* direction is

$$-\frac{\rho g}{2}\left(y+\frac{dy}{dx}dx\right)^2 = -\frac{\rho g}{2}\left(y^2+2y\frac{dy}{dx}dx\right),\tag{12·8–8}$$

if we neglect differentials of order higher than the first. Hence the net thrust due to hydrostatic pressure is

$$-\rho g y \frac{dy}{dx}dx.\tag{12·8–9}$$

Since the surface tension force and the hydrostatic thrust balance, we must have

$$\frac{T_s\dfrac{d^2y}{dx^2}}{\left[1+\left(\dfrac{dy}{dx}\right)^2\right]^{3/2}}=\rho g y.\tag{12·8–10}$$

From analytic geometry we recall that

$$\frac{\dfrac{d^2y}{dx^2}}{\left[1+\left(\dfrac{dy}{dx}\right)^2\right]^{3/2}}=\frac{1}{R},$$

where R is the radius of curvature of the surface at the point in question. Hence eq. (12·8–10) becomes

$$\rho g y = \frac{T_s}{R}.\tag{12·8–11}$$

Strictly speaking there should be a constant of integration added to $\rho g y$ to give the value of T_s/R for $y = 0$. But since we have assumed that the surface becomes a plane when $y = 0$ (i.e., at considerable distance from the immersed plate), we have $R \doteq \infty$ for $y = 0$, and hence the constant will vanish. Therefore (12·8–11) is correct *in this case* as it stands. It describes the form of the surface in terms of the radius of curvature. It is, however, possible to put it into more usable form if we multiply through (12·8–10) by $\dfrac{dy}{dx}\, dx$ obtaining

$$\rho g y \, dy = -T_s d \left[\frac{1}{\sqrt{1 + \left(\dfrac{dy}{dx}\right)^2}} \right], \qquad (12\cdot8\text{–}12)$$

as may be verified immediately. Integration then yields

$$\tfrac{1}{2}\rho g y^2 = -\frac{T_s}{\sqrt{1 + \left(\dfrac{dy}{dx}\right)^2}} + C. \qquad (12\cdot8\text{–}13)$$

Now $dy/dx = \tan \phi$, where ϕ is the slope of the curve (i.e., the supplement of θ), and hence we may write the above [recall eq. (12·8–4)]

$$\tfrac{1}{2}\rho g y^2 = T_s \cos \phi + C. \qquad (12\cdot8\text{–}14)$$

Now when $y = 0$, $\phi = \pi$ and hence $C = T_s$, so that

$$\tfrac{1}{2}\rho g y^2 = T_s(1 + \cos \phi), \qquad (12\cdot8\text{–}15)$$

or if we prefer to use θ,

$$\tfrac{1}{2}\rho g y^2 = T_s(1 - \cos \theta), \qquad (12\cdot8\text{–}16)$$

which is a somewhat more convenient form than (12·8–11). The complete equation in cartesian notation is rather complicated and will not be given here. We may note, however, that the same curve is encountered in the stretching of a uniform spring.[1] It may also be pointed out that the form of the surface is the same as that of the top of a liquid drop resting on a flat horizontal plate which it does not wet. It should be emphasized that the general problem of finding the capillary surface can not be handled by elementary methods and is extremely difficult.

The weight of the liquid raised by the capillary action is naturally equal to the volume above the plane level multiplied by ρg. Another expression for the same thing is, however, to be found by evaluating

[1] Thomson and Tait, *Treatise on Natural Philosophy*, Oxford University Press, 1867, Vol. 1, p. 455.

the total *vertical* component of the forces acting on the element considered in our previous discussion.   This is

$$T_s \frac{d \sin \theta}{dx} \, dx = T_s \cos \theta \cdot d\theta. \qquad (12\text{·}8\text{–}17)$$

Hence the total weight is simply

$$T_s \int_0^\theta \cos \theta \, d\theta = T_s \sin \theta. \qquad (12\text{·}8\text{–}18)$$

When two parallel vertical flat plates are placed in a liquid the
capillary rise or depression produces a force tending to cause the plates
to attract or repel each other.   We
can evaluate the magnitude of this
force in any case by the simple
analysis just given.   Thus consider
the case shown in Fig. 12·14 where
the plates are separated by a distance
l and the angles of contact are
respectively α_1 and α_2.   On the left
the liquid is drawn up to a height
h_1 above the low level outside the
plates and at the right to the
height h_2.   Considering first the
left plate, we see that there is a

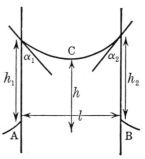

FIG. 12·14

force per unit breadth of plate acting at A tending to pull it towards the
right of magnitude

$$T_s \sin \alpha_1 + \tfrac{1}{2}\rho g h_1{}^2,$$

as is clear from the immediately preceding analysis.   On the other
hand acting at C there is a force T_s acting to pull it towards the left.
The net force toward the right is therefore

$$T_s(\sin \alpha_1 - 1) + \tfrac{1}{2}\rho g h_1{}^2. \qquad (12\text{·}8\text{–}19)$$

Now to go back to eq. (12·8–14), it develops that since $y = h$ (see
Fig. 12·14) for $\phi = \pi$, we have $C = T_s + \tfrac{1}{2}\rho g h^2$ and hence

$$\tfrac{1}{2}\rho g h_1{}^2 = \tfrac{1}{2}\rho g h^2 + T_s(1 + \cos \phi_1)$$
$$= \tfrac{1}{2}\rho g h^2 + T_s(1 - \sin \alpha_1). \qquad (12\text{·}8\text{–}20)$$

Hence the net force toward the right on the left plate becomes at
once

$$\tfrac{1}{2}\rho g h^2, \qquad (12\text{·}8\text{–}21)$$

and a precisely similar expression results for the net force on the right-
hand plate toward the left.   Here h is the height of the bottom of the
meniscus above the level of the liquid outside the two plates.   In the

case where the plates are both of the same material and close together $\alpha_1 = \alpha_2 = \alpha$, and we can apply eq. (12·8–3) for the capillary tube. Then the force pulling the plates together is approximately

$$\tfrac{1}{2}\rho g \cdot \frac{4T_s{}^2 \cos^2 \alpha}{\rho^2 g^2 a^2} = \frac{2T_s{}^2 \cos^2 \alpha}{\rho g a^2}, \qquad (12\cdot 8\text{--}22)$$

where here a is *half* the distance between the plates. The force of attraction between two nearby plates immersed in a liquid which wets both of them is therefore inversely proportional to the square of the distance between them. This is to be sure an approximate result. It will not apply, for example, when one of the plates is wet and the other not; in the latter case a *repulsion* rather than an attraction is observed to take place.[1]

From our study of the capillary rise it is clear that the pressure at a point immediately underneath the curved capillary surface in a tube is less or greater than the pressure in the gas above the surface according as the liquid rises or is depressed in the tube (Fig. 12·15, A, B). The

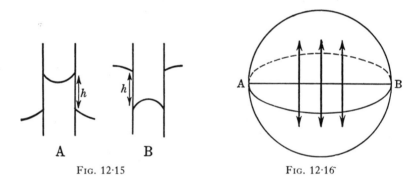

FIG. 12·15   FIG. 12·16

amount of pressure difference is given at once by $\rho g h$, where h is the rise or depression respectively. Hence employing the expression for h given in eq. (12·8–3) we have for the pressure difference

$$\Delta p = \frac{2T_s \cos \alpha}{a}, \qquad (12\cdot 8\text{--}23)$$

i.e., inversely proportional to the radius of the tube. This result suggests at once a more general one. Consider a sphere of liquid of radius R (Fig. 12·16). Draw any diametral plane AB. This will cut the spherical surface in a great circle of radius R, and about the periphery of this circle there will be a tension of T_s dynes per cm or a total force of

[1] The calculation in the latter case can be shown to follow from the usual analysis. See Prob. 21 at the end of the chapter.

$2\pi RT_s$ dynes tending to pull the two hemispheres (formed by the diametral plane) together. This must be balanced by an *excess* pressure (*over* the atmospheric) inside the sphere, which will exert a force on the diametral plane of magnitude $\Delta p \cdot \pi R^2$. Equating the two balanced forces we have

$$\Delta p = \frac{2T_s}{R} .$$ (12·8–24)

If instead of a sphere of liquid we have a hollow spherical film, such as a soap bubble, a similar result follows, except that since there are *two* surfaces to the film we now have

$$\Delta p = \frac{4T_s}{R}$$ (12·8–25)

for the excess pressure inside the bubble. Of course, in this case the student will need to prove that the pressure, which acts everywhere *normally* to the inner surface of the film produces an effective force $\Delta p \cdot \pi R^2$ across any diametral section (see Prob. 20 at the end of the chapter).

More elaborate analysis than we shall attempt here indicates that the pressure at any given point just inside a liquid surface due to the surface tension (i.e., the excess or defect over the pressure outside) is given by the formula

$$\Delta p = T_s \left(\frac{1}{R_1} + \frac{1}{R_2} \right),$$ (12·8–26)

where R_1 and R_2 are the so-called *principal radii of curvature* of the surface at the point considered. It is at once evident that for the special case of the sphere where $R_1 = R_2 = R$, the radius of the sphere, for all points, eq. (12·8–26) reduces to the previously derived simple form (12·8–24).

The accurate determination of the surface tension for different liquids under different physical conditions is a very important matter for modern physical chemistry.[1] We shall stop to notice but one of the many interesting modern problems connected with surface effects. Study of the behavior of solutions of chemical salts has shown that in most of these there is a difference between the *concentration* (i.e., the mass of dissolved salt per unit volume of the solvent) in the surface layer and in the interior portion of the solution. This phenomenon is known as *adsorption*, and we may speak of *positive* adsorption if the

[1] See, for example, Willows and Hatschek, *Surface Tension and Surface Energy*, 2nd ed., Philadelphia, 1919. The following books should also be consulted for studies on surface phenomena: N. K. Adam, *The Physics and Chemistry of Surfaces*, 3rd ed., Oxford University Press, 1941 ; E. K. Rideal, *Introduction to Surface Chemistry*, 2nd ed., Cambridge University Press, 1930; R. S. Burdon, *Surface Tension and the Spreading of Liquids*, 2nd ed., Cambridge University Press, 1949.

concentration is greater in the surface than in the bulk, or *negative* adsorption if the reverse is true. Now it is also found that, as might be expected, a dissolved substance alters the surface tension of the solvent. Thus for example it is observed that in the case of NaCl the solution of each gram-equivalent mass of salt in water *increases* the surface tension by 1.53 dynes/cm. On the other hand some substances lower the surface tension on solution. There is a close connection between the effect of concentration on the surface tension and the adsorption. Thus if u denotes the excess of dissolved substance (or solute) in the surface in grams/cm² over the bulk concentration, called C, the following formula first derived by Willard Gibbs,

$$u = - \frac{C}{RT} \cdot \frac{dT_s}{dC} \qquad (12\text{·}8\text{–}27)$$

holds, where T is the absolute temperature and R is the gas constant appropriate to the solution. Since many chemical reactions are found to take place most readily at the surfaces of substances it is clear that adsorption plays an extremely important rôle in chemistry.

For further information on modern aspects of surface tension phenomena, reference may be made to the comprehensive treatment of Freundlich in the text mentioned in the footnote. An interesting experimental study of the properties of soap films may be found in *Soap Films*, by A. S. C. Lawrence (G. Bell and Sons, London, 1929).

PROBLEMS

1. A vessel in the form of a rectangular parallelepiped of dimensions a, b, and c is filled with water to a height h. Calculate the total thrust due to the water on the bottom and each side of the vessel. Find the center of pressure on each side, i.e., the point where the resultant thrust on the side acts. Hint: If the x axis is taken as the line of intersection of the surface with one side and the y axis is the line perpendicular to this (i.e., parallel to the depth), show first that the coördinates of the center of pressure will be given by

$$x_c = \frac{\iint xp\ dx\ dy}{\iint p\ dx\ dy},$$

and

$$y_c = \frac{\iint yp\ dx\ dy}{\iint p\ dx\ dy},$$

where $p = f(x, y)$ as indicated in the text. The integration is to be carried out over the whole area in contact with the liquid.

2. Calculate the total thrust on an equilateral triangle of side a immersed vertically in a liquid of density ρ with the base parallel to the surface of the liquid and at distance h from the surface. Also compute the position of the center of pressure.

3. A hollow sphere of radius R is completely filled with water. What is the resultant vertical thrust on the inside surface? Compare the vertical thrusts on the upper and lower halves of the surface.

4. A cylindrical vessel of length l and radius a with plane ends is filled with water and rests with its axis horizontal. Compare the vertical thrusts on the upper and lower halves of the curved surface. Also calculate the total thrust on each end and determine the position of the center of pressure at each end.

5. A sphere floats with $\frac{1}{3}$ of its surface above water. Find its mean density.

6. A cylindrical can 30 cm long and 10 cm in diameter and weighing 100 grams cannot float stably in water in an upright position. Find the amount of mercury (density 13.6 grams/cm³) which must be placed in the can in order that it may just be able to float upright stably. How far will the can sink in the water?

7. Assuming Boyle's law, derive the law of variation of atmospheric pressure with height above the earth's surface.

8. Assuming the adiabatic law, derive the law of variation of atmospheric pressure with height above the earth's surface.

9. If the density in a certain liquid at rest varies linearly with the depth, find the expression for the pressure as a function of depth.

10. Find the total force that the air exerts on the walls, ceiling, and floor of a room 10 meters by 8 meters by 3 meters.

11. Prove that if an incompressible homogeneous fluid moves so that its velocity components satisfy the relations $u = kx/r$, $v = ky/r$ and $w = kz/r$, where $r = \sqrt{x^2 + y^2 + z^2}$ and k is a constant with the dimensions of velocity, the equation of continuity is satisfied. Interpret this type of motion physically.

12. Derive Bernoulli's theorem (eq. 12·5–9) by assuming that the total energy per unit volume along any stream line is constant (i.e., conservation of energy applied to fluid motion). Hint: Recall that the potential energy of a fluid per unit volume due to pressure is equal to the pressure (Sec. 12·4).

13. Water flows out of an orifice at the bottom of a vertical tank (see Fig. 12·8). If the area of cross section of the orifice is S_B and that of the tank is S_A, use Bernoulli's theorem and the equation of continuity to calculate the theoretical rate of flow out of the orifice and the rate of descent of the free surface in the tank. (Introduce numerical values to get order of magnitude.)

14. Use the result of the preceding problem to obtain the height of the free surface in the tank above the orifice at any time t after the flow has begun and draw a graphical sketch of the dependence of descent on the time.

15. How many gallons of water flow in 24 hours through a pipe 4 in. in diameter if at a constriction of 1.5 in. in diameter a mercury pressure gauge shows a difference in height of 1.8 in. from another in the unconstricted portion of the pipe?

16. Show how the Pitot tube may be used to measure the velocity of a rapid blast of air in a tube (such as might be produced by a blower). (Eq. 12·5–25.)

17. Deduce the dependence of the velocity of sound in a gas on the temperature and pressure.

18. By setting up the boundary conditions (continuity of pressure and continuity of volume displacement) at the interface between two fluid media, compute the relations between incident and reflected amplitudes and incident and transmitted amplitudes of an acoustic wave incident normally on the interface. (Take harmonic waves.) Discuss *phase* relations.

19. Defining the intensity of an acoustic wave as in Sec. 11·5, show that the intensity of a plane acoustic wave in a fluid may be written in the form

$$I = \frac{1}{2} \frac{p^2{}_{max}}{\rho_0 c},$$

where p_{max} is the maximum excess pressure in the fluid and ρ_0 and c have their usual significance. Comment on the connection with eq. 11·5–45.

20. Prove that the excess pressure inside a soap bubble produces an effective force across any diametral plane equal to the pressure times the area of a great circle of the sphere. (Sec. 12·8, eq. 12·8–24, etc.)

21. Two plane plates are introduced close together into a liquid, which wets the one but not the other. Show that the two plates will repel each other and calculate the magnitude of the repulsion, following the analysis of Sec. 12·8.

22. Prove that Jurin's law (12·8–3) applies equally well to the capillary rise between two parallel plates placed in a liquid which wets them.

23. Prove that when n equal small spheres of water coalesce so as to form a single drop the surface energy is diminished in the ratio $n^{-1/3}$.

24. What form does the one-dimensional equation of motion of a perfect fluid confined by rigid walls, viz.,

$$\frac{\partial u}{\partial t} + u \frac{\partial u}{\partial x} = -\frac{1}{\rho} \frac{\partial p}{\partial x},$$

take if the fluid is incompressible? If the pressure gradient is due entirely to gravity, find the acceleration of the fluid at any point and compare with Torricelli's theorem.

25. The wave length of a long gravity wave on water of depth 20 feet is 100 feet. If the wave amplitude parallel to the water surface is 2 feet, find the maximum value of the total particle displacement. Do the same for the total particle velocity and compare with the wave velocity.

26. A plane harmonic acoustic wave in the x direction has the particle displacement in the form $\xi = A \cos(\omega t - kx)$, where $k = \omega/c = 2\pi\nu/c$ and ν is the frequency. Find the expressions for the velocity potential ϕ, the condensation and excess pressure.

27. In Problem 26, if $\nu = 512$ cycles/sec and the wave is in air at 20° C, find A if the excess pressure amplitude is 10^{-1} dynes/cm². Also find the condensation amplitude.

28. Prove that the potential energy density in an acoustic wave in a fluid is $\frac{1}{2} \rho_0 c^2 s^2$. Show that for a plane wave the average potential energy density equals the average kinetic energy density. Show that the intensity of a plane wave is given by the product of the average energy density and the wave velocity.

29. In Problem 18 of Chapter 11 the damping coefficient R in the wave equation for acoustical waves in a fluid becomes $4\omega^2\eta/3\rho_0$, if the damping is due to viscosity (coefficient of viscosity $= \eta$ and the other symbols have their usual meaning). How far will a 100-cycle wave travel in air before its amplitude is decreased in the ratio $1/e$? Work the same problem for water. Take $\eta_{air} = 1.8 \times 10^{-4}$ dyne sec/cm² and $\eta_{water} = 1.14 \times 10^{-2}$ dyne sec/cm².

30. A vertical U-tube open at both ends is full of water to a length equal to l. If the height of the liquid on one side of the tube is changed momentarily and then left free to find its own level, show that the liquid surfaces oscillate in simple harmonic motion and find the expression for the period of the motion.

31. Prove that when a liquid surface is stretched, the mechanical work done per unit increase in area is numerically equal to the surface tension.

32. Show that the wave equation for plane elastic waves in the x direction in a linear compressible fluid medium can be obtained by a combination of
   (1) the equation of motion:
$$\rho_0 \ddot{\xi} = -\frac{\partial p_e}{\partial x},$$

   (2) the equation of continuity
$$\rho_0 \frac{\partial \xi}{\partial x} = -\rho_e,$$

   (3) the equation of state
$$p_e = c^2 \rho_e,$$

where ξ is the fluid displacement in the x direction, ρ_0 is the mean equilibrium density, ρ_e is the excess density $(\rho - \rho_0)$, p_e is the excess pressure $(p - p_0)$, and c^2 is at first a constant of proportionality.

33. Show that the wave equation for a linear, compressible *dissipative* fluid medium can be obtained from the three equations in the preceding problem if eq. (3) is modified to read

(3')
$$p_e = c^2 \rho_e + R\dot{\rho}_e.$$

Note from Sec. 11·4 that this is a relaxation equation. Show that the wave equation now takes the form

$$\ddot{\xi} = c^2 \frac{\partial^2 \xi}{\partial x^2} + R \frac{\partial^2 \dot{\xi}}{\partial x^2}.$$

Find a harmonic wave solution of this in the form

$$\xi = \xi_0 e^{-\alpha x} e^{i(\omega t - kx)}$$

and determine α in terms of the constant R. From the discussion in Sec. 11·4 give a possible physical interpretation of the constant R and the mechanism involved in eq. (3').

34. In Problem 33 show that the velocity of the wave depends on the frequency and find the dispersion relation.

35. Derive the expression for the group velocity from the dispersion relation obtained in Problem 34.

36. Find the velocity of sound in argon at 20° C and in oxygen at 200° C. Find the rate of change of velocity of sound with temperature for argon at 20° C and 200° C respectively.

Chapter 13

ADVANCED MECHANICS

13·1. Hamilton's Principle. In the previous chapters of this book we have based the various applications of mechanics for the most part on the principles set forth in Chapter 1, namely, the Newtonian " laws " of motion. We did indeed emphasize in Chapter 9 that there exist alternative ways of expressing the fundamental principles and we gave as examples D'Alembert's principle and the Gaussian principle of least constraint. It is important to realize that certain problems may be handled in a more direct and efficient fashion by some one principle than by others. The progress of mechanics has been marked by a continual search for new points of view. We wish in this chapter to discuss one which stresses primarily the use of the energy concept in the solution of mechanical problems. This is the celebrated *principle of Hamilton*. It will serve very usefully as an introduction to what is usually referred to as advanced mechanics and about which the reader of this book may well expect to learn a little since it is basic for theoretical physics in general. We shall state the principle as a postulate and then endeavor to illustrate its application.

Let us consider a dynamical system which may be composed of many particles and hence may require a large number of coördinates to specify its *state*, i.e., the position of every particle at every instant. The total number of coördinates needed for this specification is called the *number of degrees of freedom* of the system. Now associated with the system there will be a certain kinetic energy K and, if it is a conservative system, a potential energy V. The former will be a function of the *velocities* of the particles, the latter a function of their *positional* coördinates. Let us form the function

$$L = K - V. \tag{13·1-1}$$

Hamilton's principle now states that the motion of the system of particles between any two instants t_0 and t_1 takes place in such a way that the integral

$$\int_{t_0}^{t_1} L \, dt \tag{13·1-2}$$

has a value which is either *less* than its value for any other possible motion of the system in the interval from t_0 to t_1 or *greater* than its value for any other such possible motion. That is, the integral is either a maximum or a minimum or, as we may better say, has a *stationary* value with respect to other possible motions. We may perhaps render the matter somewhat clearer by using a pictorial representation. In Fig. 13·1 let us represent the state of the system at the instant t_0 by A

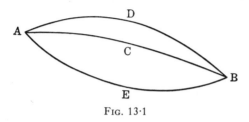

FIG. 13·1

and that at time t_1 by B. Let the path actually followed by the system be *ACB*, while *ADB* and *AEB* represent two " varied " paths — possible paths for the system and performed in the same time. Now it must be remarked that our representation is very general. In certain simple cases of the plane motion of a single particle *ACB*, *ADB*, and *AEB* may represent possible geometrical orbits from *point A* to *point B* in the plane with the understanding that to be comparable they must of course all be traversed in the *same* time, viz., in the interval $t_1 - t_0$, and must correspond to the same initial and final states respectively. On the other hand, the representation can be purely schematic, i.e., A may merely *represent* for convenience the state of a system of several particles, etc. But in any case the meaning of the principle is that the time integral $\int_{t_0}^{t_1} L\, dt$ along the actual path traversed, *ACB*, is either *greater* than that along *any other* paths such as *ADB* and *ACB* or it is *less* than that along any such paths. It is often convenient to state it as a *minimum* principle, i.e., that $\int_{t_0}^{t_1} L\, dt$ is a *minimum* along the actual dynamical path. While in most problems encountered in practice this is correct, it is not so in general. All we have a right to say is that it has a stationary value. The quantity L is termed the *Lagrangian* function or *kinetic potential*.

It must again be emphasized that we are here stating Hamilton's principle as a *postulate*, an assumption from which all special motions of bodies may be derived. As a first illustration of this view let us apply the principle to a simple problem. We shall take a single particle whose position is fixed by a single coördinate, for example, the distance along a straight line from some chosen origin. We are thus indeed restricting our attention to *linear* motion and hence our illustration is a very special one. The kinetic energy of the particle is then

$$K = \tfrac{1}{2}m\dot{x}^2, \tag{13·1–3}$$

if the particle is conceived to move along the x axis. Let us investigate the type of motion corresponding to a potential energy of the form

$$V = \tfrac{1}{2}kx^2, \tag{13·1–4}$$

where k is a constant. The principle of Hamilton now demands that the integral

$$\int_{t_0}^{t_1} (\tfrac{1}{2}m\dot{x}^2 - \tfrac{1}{2}kx^2)\, dt, \tag{13·1–5}$$

shall have a *stationary* value for the actual motion. This means that if we *vary* the true path *slightly* the corresponding variation of the integral will be *zero*. Of course, since in this case the geometrical shape of the path may not alter, a variation in the path signifies only an altered dependence of x on t, i.e., an altered mode of pursuing the linear path. The reader will remember that in the neighborhood of the maximum or minimum of a function of one independent variable t, the change in the function corresponding to a change dt in the variable is zero as far as first order quantities are concerned. If we denote the slight variation of the integral by

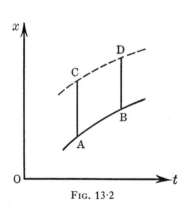

FIG. 13·2

$$\delta \int_{t_0}^{t_1} (\tfrac{1}{2}m\dot{x}^2 - \tfrac{1}{2}kx^2)\, dt,$$ we have therefore the condition

$$\delta \int_{t_0}^{t_1} (\tfrac{1}{2}m\dot{x}^2 - \tfrac{1}{2}kx^2)\, dt = 0. \tag{13·1–6}$$

Now the variation of the integral will clearly be the limit of the sum of the variations in the integrand over all the infinitesimal time intervals between t_0 and t_1. Hence we have

$$\int_{t_0}^{t_1} \delta(\tfrac{1}{2}m\dot{x}^2 - \tfrac{1}{2}kx^2)\, dt = 0. \tag{13·1–7}$$

We are thus faced with the task of reducing $\delta(\dot{x}^2)$ and $\delta(x^2)$ to some common basis. One would naturally try to do this by expressing both in terms of δx. Let us consider the curves in Fig. 13·2. *AB* represents an element of the course of x as a function of t. CD is a portion of the *varied* curve.   At A, the variation in x is δx.   It is seen that this is for a definite value of t.   At B, the value of x is

$$x + \dot{x}\, dt,$$

and hence we may represent BD as either

$$\delta(x + \dot{x}\, dt), \tag{13·1–8}$$

or

$$\delta x + \frac{d}{dt}(\delta x)\, dt. \tag{13·1–9}$$

Consequently (13·1–8) and (13·1–9) are equal and hence

$$\delta(\dot{x}\, dt) = \delta(dx) = \frac{d}{dt}(\delta x)\, dt = d(\delta x). \tag{13·1–10}$$

Therefore the operations of δ and d are interchangeable.   We can now write

$$\delta(x^2) = 2x\, \delta x, \tag{13·1–11}$$

and

$$\delta(\dot{x}^2) = 2\dot{x}\, \delta\dot{x} = 2\dot{x}\, \frac{d}{dt}(\delta x). \tag{13·1–12}$$

Eq. (13·1–7) then becomes

$$\int_{t_0}^{t_1} (m\dot{x}\, \delta\dot{x} - kx\, \delta x)\, dt = 0,$$

or using eq. (13·1–12),

$$\int_{t_0}^{t_1} \left[m\dot{x}\, \frac{d}{dt}(\delta x) - kx\, \delta x \right] dt = 0. \tag{13·1–13}$$

Let us now evaluate the integral

$$\int_{t_0}^{t_1} m\dot{x}\, \frac{d}{dt}(\delta x)\, dt$$

by integration by parts.   Letting $u = m\dot{x}$ and $dv = d/dt\, (\delta x)\, dt$, we have $du = m\ddot{x}\, dt$ and $v = \delta x$, so that

$$\int_{t_0}^{t_1} m\dot{x}\, \frac{d}{dt}(\delta x)\, dt = m\dot{x}\, \delta x \Big]_{t_0}^{t_1} - \int_{t_0}^{t_1} m\ddot{x}\, \delta x\, dt.$$

But the two paths must have the same end points, hence $\delta x = 0$ for $t = t_0$ and $t = t_1$.   Therefore eq. (13·1–13) becomes

$$\int_{t_0}^{t_1} (m\ddot{x} + kx)\, \delta x\, dt = 0. \tag{13·1–14}$$

It must be emphasized that this result holds for *all* δx, i.e., δx is perfectly arbitrary except that it be small and equal to zero for $t = t_0$ and t_1. Hence the only way for the integral to be zero for all δx is for us to have

$$m\ddot{x} + kx = 0. \qquad (13 \cdot 1\text{–}15)$$

This then appears as the differential equation of the motion, and we see at once (Sec. $2 \cdot 3$) that the latter is simple harmonic with frequency

$$\nu = \frac{1}{2\pi} \sqrt{\frac{k}{m}}. \qquad (13 \cdot 1\text{–}16)$$

Hence from the assumption of Hamilton's principle together with the knowledge of the potential energy function we have been able to derive the equation of motion independently of any other dynamical assumption except that the kinetic energy shall be of the form $\frac{1}{2}m\dot{x}^2$. In other words we have made no essential use of the Newtonian laws of motion. Hamilton's principle thus appears as an independent basis for the development of mechanics. A special case indeed is no proof of this statement. We have merely tried to suggest its validity without proving it. Nevertheless the general proof has been carried out and may be found in more advanced treatises.[1] The power of the principle is more manifest in the treatment of the motion of systems with more than one degree of freedom. We shall discuss this with some detail in the next section.

13·2. Generalized Coördinates and Lagrange's Equations.

As an illustration of a more general application of Hamilton's principle, let us consider a mechanical system composed of a number of particles. If these particles are totally unconnected the total number of degrees of freedom or number of coördinates needed to specify the system will be three times the number of the particles. However if the particles are connected or otherwise constrained to move in certain ways (see Chapter 9), the number of degrees of freedom will be reduced. Suppose the system in question has n. Now it should be clear that the choice of these n coördinates is possible in a very great variety of ways. They may of course be rectangular coördinates or certain combinations of these, or they may contain angles as well as lengths. In order to make our application most general we shall not specify the exact nature of the coördinates, but merely write them $q_1, q_2, \ldots, q_n$. All our description of the behavior of the system will then be in terms of the q's. In the last analysis, of course, the latter must be translated into some

---

[1] Cf. Lindsay and Margenau, *Foundations of Physics*, Dover Publications, New York, 1955, p. 131 for a deduction of Hamilton's principle from D'Alembert's principle.

definite known set, which appear particularly appropriate for the description on the ground of simplicity. The coördinates $q_1, \ldots, q_n$ have been termed *generalized coördinates*. To express the kinetic energy in terms of them we note that

$$K = \sum \tfrac{1}{2} m_i (\dot{x}_i{}^2 + \dot{y}_i{}^2 + \dot{z}_i{}^2), \tag{13·2–1}$$

the summation being extended over *all* the particles. Let us suppose that the equations defining the generalized coördinates are expressed in the form

$$x_i = x_i(q_1, \ldots, q_n), \, y_i = y_i(q_1, \ldots, q_n),$$
$$z_i = z_i(q_1, \ldots, q_n), \tag{13·2–2}$$

for any particular i. We therefore have

$$\dot{x}_i = \frac{\partial x_i}{\partial q_1} \dot{q}_1 + \cdots + \frac{\partial x_i}{\partial q_n} \dot{q}_n = \sum_{j=1}^{n} \frac{\partial x_i}{\partial q_j} \dot{q}_j, \tag{13·2–3}$$

with similar expressions for $\dot{y}_i$ and $\dot{z}_i$. Substituting now into the expression for K, we get finally

$$K = \sum_{kj} a_{kj} \dot{q}_k \dot{q}_j, \tag{13·2–4}$$

where the summation is extended over *both* k and j running from 1 to n, and the a_{kj} are (in general) functions of the $q_1, \ldots, q_n$. The kinetic energy thus appears as a *homogeneous quadratic* function of the time derivatives of the generalized coördinates, or as we may call them the generalized velocities.

Now how does it stand with the potential energy? For a conservative system V is a function of the position coördinates of the particles. Hence it will be a function of the $q_1, \ldots, q_n$. Let us next apply the principle of Hamilton to such a system of n degrees of freedom. We express the stationary character of the time integral of the Lagrangian function for the actual motion as follows:

$$\delta \int_{t_0}^{t_1} (T - V) \, dt = \int_{t_0}^{t_1} \sum_i \left[\frac{\partial L}{\partial q_i} \delta q_i + \frac{\partial L}{\partial \dot{q}_i} \delta \dot{q}_i \right] dt = 0, \tag{13·2–5}$$

employing (13·1–1). Now since $\delta \dot{q}_i = \dfrac{d}{dt}(\delta q_i)$ from Sec. 13·1, we may integrate by parts

$$\int_{t_0}^{t_1} \sum_i \frac{\partial L}{\partial \dot{q}_i} \delta \dot{q}_i \, dt,$$

precisely as in the special problem in Sec. 13·1. The result is

$$\int_{t_0}^{t_1} \sum \frac{\partial L}{\partial \dot{q}_i} \delta \dot{q}_i \, dt = \left[\sum \frac{\partial L}{\partial \dot{q}_i} \delta q_i \right]_{t_0}^{t_1} - \int_{t_0}^{t_1} \sum \frac{d}{dt} \left\{ \frac{\partial L}{\partial \dot{q}_i} \right\} \delta q_i \, dt$$

$$= - \int_{t_0}^{t_1} \sum \frac{d}{dt} \left\{ \frac{\partial L}{\partial \dot{q}_i} \right\} \delta q_i \, dt, \qquad (13 \cdot 2\text{--}6)$$

since the part integrated out vanishes at the two limits because $\delta q_i = 0$ at both limits. This merely means that all the paths of the system have the same termini. Hence the statement of the principle becomes

$$\int_{t_0}^{t_1} \sum \left\{ \left[\frac{\partial L}{\partial q_i} - \frac{d}{dt} \left(\frac{\partial L}{\partial \dot{q}_i} \right) \right] \delta q_i \right\} dt = 0. \qquad (13 \cdot 2\text{--}7)$$

Now the n variations δq_i are arbitrary (the q's are independent) and hence in order that the integral may vanish each separate bracket in the sum must vanish. This however gives us a set of n equations, viz.,

$$\frac{d}{dt} \left(\frac{\partial L}{\partial \dot{q}_i} \right) - \frac{\partial L}{\partial q_i} = 0, \qquad (13 \cdot 2\text{--}8)$$

as i runs from $1 \ldots n$. These are the celebrated *equations of Lagrange*. We see that they are differential equations of the second order and that their number is precisely equal to the number of degrees of freedom of the system. These equations form a very general description of the motion of the system, and their solution leads to the expression of each q_i as a function of the time. There will of course be $2n$ arbitrary constants of integration involved; their evaluation depends on the boundary conditions of the system.

Let us note incidentally that for the case of a system of one degree of freedom where $q_i (= q)$ becomes simply the geometrical displacement and $\dot{q}$ is the velocity, with $K = \frac{1}{2} m \dot{q}^2$, the single Lagrangian equation becomes the usual equation of motion, viz.,

$$\frac{d}{dt} (m \dot{q}) + \frac{\partial V}{\partial q} = 0,$$

or

$$m \ddot{q} = - \frac{\partial V}{\partial q}, \qquad (13 \cdot 2\text{--}9)$$

where $- \dfrac{\partial V}{\partial q}$ appears as the force acting on the system.

Examination discloses that the Lagrangian equations $(13 \cdot 2\text{--}8)$ can be written in a form reminiscent of Newton's second law, provided that we *define*

$$p_i = \frac{\partial L}{\partial \dot{q}_i} \qquad (13 \cdot 2\text{--}10)$$

as the *generalized momentum* associated with the coördinate q_i, and further call

$$\frac{\partial L}{\partial q_i}$$

the generalized force associated with coördinate q_i. Then eq. (13·2–8) says that the time rate of change of generalized momentum is equal to the generalized force, which reminds us of eq. (1·7–5). The reader might then be inclined to wonder wherein the advantage of Lagrange's equations consists. This comes principally from the fact that the Lagrangian equations being expressed in generalized form are immune to change in form when coördinates are transformed from one system to another: once we have expressed L in *any* system of coördinates, use of (13·2–8) *automatically* produces the correct equations of motion for those coördinates. It is apparent that this is not true of the simple Newtonian equation that mass times acceleration equals force. From an esthetic point of view the Lagrangian equations may be considered to have the additional merit of employing energy as the fundamental concept in their makeup; they make no mention of force.

13·3. Application of Lagrange's Equations.   We shall continue our discussion of Lagrange's equations with the solution of certain problems employing them.   As the first illustration let us consider the motion of a single mass particle in a central field of force.   We have, of course, treated this problem in the usual mechanical way in Sec. 3·6.   Our purpose here is to show how the general equations for such motion in *spherical coördinates* can be written with great ease by the Lagrangian method.   There is often a gain in utility through this procedure.   It will be recalled that the spherical coördinates r, θ, ϕ are defined through the accom-

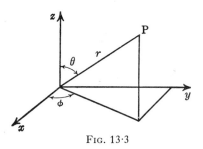

Fig. 13·3

panying figure (Fig. 13·3), the point P being on a sphere of radius r, and its longitude (with respect to Ox) and colatitude being, respectively, ϕ and θ. It is seen that the spherical coördinates are related to rectangulars by the relations

$$\left. \begin{aligned} x &= r \sin\theta \cos\phi, \\ y &= r \sin\theta \sin\phi, \\ z &= r \cos\theta. \end{aligned} \right\} \qquad (13\cdot3\text{–}1)$$

The kinetic energy of a particle is then

$$K = \tfrac{1}{2}m(\dot{x}^2 + \dot{y}^2 + \dot{z}^2)$$
$$= \frac{m}{2}(\dot{r}^2 + r^2\dot{\theta}^2 + r^2\sin^2\theta \cdot \dot{\phi}^2), \qquad (13\cdot3\text{--}2)$$

and, if the field is central (Sec. 3·6), the potential energy V is a function of r only, so that the Lagrangian function becomes

$$L = \frac{m}{2}(\dot{r}^2 + r^2\dot{\theta}^2 + r^2\sin^2\theta \cdot \dot{\phi}^2) - V(r). \qquad (13\cdot3\text{--}3)$$

the system being one with three degrees of freedom with $q_1 = r$, $q_2 = \theta$, and $q_3 = \phi$. The Lagrangian equations (13·2–8) are then

$$\frac{d}{dt}(m\dot{r}) + \frac{dV(r)}{dr} - mr(\dot{\theta}^2 + \sin^2\theta \cdot \dot{\phi}^2) = 0,$$

$$\frac{d}{dt}(mr^2\dot{\theta}) - mr^2\sin\theta\cos\theta \cdot \dot{\phi}^2 = 0, \qquad (13\cdot3\text{--}4)$$

$$\frac{d}{dt}(mr^2\sin^2\theta \cdot \dot{\phi}) = 0.$$

From these equations the whole theory of central motion can be followed out. It will be observed that the longitude ϕ does not appear explicitly in any of the equations (13·3–4). This means that the generalized momentum component associated with ϕ is constant. Or we can say that $\dot{\phi}$ is determined from the third equation in terms of r and θ, viz.,

$$\dot{\phi} = \frac{C}{mr^2\sin^2\theta}, \qquad (13\cdot3\text{--}5)$$

where C is a constant. This may be substituted into the first two equations yielding

$$\frac{d}{dt}(m\dot{r}) + \frac{dV}{dr} - mr\left(\dot{\theta}^2 + \frac{C^2}{m^2r^4\sin^2\theta}\right) = 0,$$

$$\frac{d}{dt}(mr^2\dot{\theta}) - \frac{C^2\cos\theta}{mr^2\sin^3\theta} = 0. \qquad (13\cdot3\text{--}6)$$

It is thus seen that the problem is effectively reduced to one with two degrees of freedom. We have already noted in Sec. 3·6 that central field motion takes place in a plane. It being most simple to take this plane as the plane $\phi = 0$ (i.e., the xz plane), we have $\dot{\phi} = 0$ (i.e., $C = 0$, above) and consequently may write

$$\left.\begin{aligned}\frac{d}{dt}(m\dot{r}) + \frac{dV}{dr} - mr\dot{\theta}^2 &= 0,\\[2mm] \frac{d}{dt}(mr^2\dot{\theta}) &= 0.\end{aligned}\right\}\qquad(13\text{·}3\text{--}7)$$

The law of areas, viz.,

$$mr^2\dot{\theta} = \text{const.,}\qquad(13\text{·}3\text{--}8)$$

follows at once from the second equation, and if we substitute this into the first we obtain ultimately, on substitution of $r = 1/u$, the eq. (3·6–15) which we used in our previous discussion of central field motion.

A somewhat more elaborate illustration of the use of Lagrange's equations is provided by the following problem. Two small metal spheres A and B of equal mass m are suspended from two points A' and B' at a distance a apart on the same horizontal line by insulating threads of equal length l (Fig. 13·4). They are then charged with equal charges $+e$. If A is pulled aside a *short* distance q_1 and B a *short* distance q_2 (both small compared with a) in the *plane* formed by the equilibrium positions of both threads, we are to determine the resulting motion in this plane. This is a system with two degrees of freedom. For the kinetic energy we have

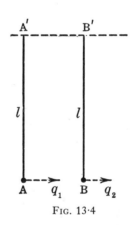

Fig. 13·4

$$K = \tfrac{1}{2}m(\dot{q}_1^2 + \dot{q}_2^2).\qquad(13\text{·}3\text{--}9)$$

The potential energy will be made up of two parts, viz., the gravitational and the electrostatic. The former is simply the sum of that for each sphere considered as the bob of a simple pendulum. Hence (Secs. 4·1 and 9·1)

$$V_g = \frac{1}{2}\frac{mg}{l}(q_1^2 + q_2^2).\qquad(13\text{·}3\text{--}10)$$

The student will recall that from Coulomb's law the electrostatic force of repulsion between the two point charges when separated by distance a is e^2/a^2. The potential energy for this force when the charged balls are displaced will then be

$$V_e = \frac{e^2}{a + q_2 - q_1}. \tag{13·3–11}$$

Hence for the Lagrangian function we have

$$L = \frac{1}{2} m(\dot{q_1}^2 + \dot{q_2}^2) - \frac{e^2}{a + q_2 - q_1} - \frac{1}{2} \frac{mg}{l} (q_1^2 + q_2^2), \tag{13·3–12}$$

to the approximation which considers the displacements as *small*.

We are now ready to write the Lagrangian equations for the motion. Thus

$$\frac{d}{dt} (m\dot{q_1}) + \frac{mg}{l} q_1 + \frac{e^2}{(a + q_2 - q_1)^2} = 0, \tag{13·3–13}$$

$$\frac{d}{dt} (m\dot{q_2}) + \frac{mg}{l} q_2 - \frac{e^2}{(a + q_2 - q_1)^2} = 0. \tag{13·3–14}$$

To solve, let us add the two equations. There results

$$\frac{d^2}{dt^2} (q_1 + q_2) = -\frac{g}{l} (q_1 + q_2). \tag{13·3–15}$$

On the other hand if we subtract the two equations we get ultimately

$$\frac{d^2}{dt^2} (q_2 - q_1) + \frac{g}{l} (q_2 - q_1) - \frac{2e^2}{m(a + q_2 - q_1)^2} = 0. \tag{13·3–16}$$

Since both q_1 and q_2 are supposed small compared with a, we may expand the last term on the left in (13·3–16) writing

$$\frac{d^2}{dt^2} (q_2 - q_1) + (q_2 - q_1) \left(\frac{g}{l} + \frac{4e^2}{ma^3} \right) - \frac{2e^2}{ma^2} = 0. \tag{13·3–17}$$

The solution of (13·3–15) is clearly

$$q_1 + q_2 = A_1 \cos (2\pi \nu_1 t + B_1), \tag{13·3–18}$$

where

$$\nu_1 = \frac{1}{2\pi} \sqrt{\frac{g}{l}}. \tag{13·3–19}$$

The solution of (13·3–17) is

$$q_2 - q_1 - \frac{2e^2}{ma^2 \left(\frac{g}{l} + \frac{4e^2}{ma^3} \right)} = A_2 \cos (2\pi \nu_2 t + B_2), \tag{13·3–20}$$

where

$$v_2 = \frac{1}{2\pi}\sqrt{\frac{g}{l} + \frac{4e^2}{ma^3}}.$$ (13·3–21)

We finally have for the two displacements

$$q_1 = \frac{-e^2}{ma^2\left(\frac{g}{l} + \frac{4e^2}{ma^3}\right)} + \frac{A_1}{2}\cos(2\pi v_1 t + B_1)$$

$$-\frac{A_2}{2}\cos(2\pi v_2 t + B_2), \quad (13·3–22)$$

$$q_2 = \frac{e^2}{ma^2\left(\frac{g}{l} + \frac{4e^2}{ma^3}\right)} + \frac{A_1}{2}\cos(2\pi v_1 t + B_1)$$

$$+\frac{A_2}{2}\cos(2\pi v_2 t + B_2). \quad (13·3–23)$$

It may be noted that by shifting the origin for each ball the distance

$$\frac{e^2}{ma^2\left(\frac{g}{l} + \frac{4e^2}{ma^3}\right)},$$ (13·3–24)

the constant term may be made to disappear.   In this case the motion of each ball appears as the composition of two simple harmonic motions with amplitudes and phases (A_1, A_2, B_1, B_2) which depend on the boundary conditions.

As a final illustration of the use of Lagrange's equations consider the situation depicted in Fig. 13·5.

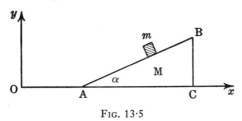

Fig. 13·5

Here a wedge with projection ABC on the xy plane and with mass M is able to slide freely on the horizontal plane.   The perfectly smooth slant surface AB of the wedge makes the angle α with the horizontal. On this surface a particle of mass m is free to move in the xy plane. The problem is to determine the motion of m as well as the wedge.

Referring to fixed axes as in the figure, we have for the kinetic and potential energies of the total system, respectively,

$$K = \tfrac{1}{2}M\dot{x}^2 + \tfrac{1}{2}m(\dot{x} + \dot{y}/\tan \alpha)^2 + \tfrac{1}{2}m\dot{y}^2, \qquad (13\cdot3\text{–}25)$$

$$V = mgy. \qquad (13\cdot3\text{–}26)$$

Here x is the distance OA, while y is the height of m above the x axis. The problem is one in two degrees of freedom. Note that we might equally well have chosen the x coördinate of m along with y as the second coördinate, i.e., $x + y/\tan \alpha$. The Lagrangian method dose not care what coördinates are used, provided that the number is correct for the nature of the system being studied, and provided that the Lagrangian function is correctly expressed in terms of the coördinates chosen. With the present choice we then have

$$L = \tfrac{1}{2}M\dot{x}^2 + \tfrac{1}{2}m\dot{y}^2 + \tfrac{1}{2}m(\dot{x} + \dot{y}/\tan \alpha)^2 - mgy. \qquad (13\cdot3\text{–}27)$$

The Lagrangian equations become at once

$$M\ddot{x} + m\ddot{x} + m\ddot{y}/\tan \alpha = 0,$$
$$m\ddot{y} + m\ddot{x}/\tan \alpha + m\ddot{y}/\tan^2 \alpha + mg = 0. \qquad (13\cdot3\text{–}28)$$

The solution of these equations for x and y is left as an exercise. Note the interesting limiting case of $m/M \to 0$.

13·4. Hamilton's Canonical Equations. The great merit of the equations of Lagrange discussed in the previous sections lies in their invariance in form with respect to changes in coördinates. This is the significance of the generalized coördinates $q_1 \ldots q_n$. The equations, however, are still second-order differential equations in the q's and the $\dot{q}$'s, and the question arises whether it would be possible to reduce them to first-order equations. From a mathematical point of view this should not be difficult provided we are willing to double their number. When we do this in the appropriate fashion we secure a set of $2n$ equations known as Hamilton's canonical equations.

We have already introduced the generalized conjugate momentum $p_j = \partial L/\partial \dot{q}_j$ in eq. (13·2–10). With the use of this the Lagrangian equations (13·2–8) do indeed become of the first order. Unfortunately they contain the $\dot{q}$'s as well as the q's and p's. We should like a set of equations involving only the q's and the p's. The procedure is the rather formal one of considering the new quantity H defined arbitrarily as

$$H = \sum_{j=1}^{n} p_j \dot{q}_j - L(q, \dot{q}). \qquad (13\cdot4\text{–}1)$$

This would indeed appear to be a function of p's, q's, and $\dot{q}$'s. If however we form its total differential we see that from the definition of p_j it really is a function of the p's and q's alone. Thus

$$dH = \sum_{j=1}^{n} p_j \, d\dot{q}_j + \sum_{j=1}^{n} \dot{q}_j \, dp_j - \sum_{j=1}^{n} \frac{\partial L}{\partial \dot{q}_j} \, d\dot{q}_j - \sum_{j=1}^{n} \frac{\partial L}{\partial q_j} \, dq_j. \quad (13 \cdot 4\text{--}2)$$

Because of the definition of p_j it follows that the first sum is canceled out by the third sum, so that the change in H depends solely on the changes in the p's and q's. Moreover

$$\frac{\partial H}{\partial p_j} = \dot{q}_j, \quad (13 \cdot 4\text{--}3)$$

$$\frac{\partial H}{\partial q_j} = \frac{\partial L}{\partial q_i} = -\dot{p}_j, \quad (13 \cdot 4\text{--}4)$$

where the last step in (13·4–4) comes from the use of Lagrange's equations. Eqs. (13·4–3) and (13·4–4) form a set of $2n$ first-order equations in the p's and q's. These are the canonical equations of Hamilton, sometimes known simply as Hamilton's equations for a system of particles with n degrees of freedom.

To understand these equations we first need to establish the physical meaning of the function H. Let us suppose the system is conservative so that the potential energy V is a function of the q's only. Then p_j becomes

$$p_j = \frac{\partial K}{\partial \dot{q}_j}, \quad (13 \cdot 4\text{--}5)$$

and H in (13·4–1) can be written

$$H = \sum_{j=1}^{n} \frac{\partial K}{\partial \dot{q}_j} \dot{q}_j - L(q, \dot{q}). \quad (13 \cdot 4\text{--}6)$$

From Euler's theorem on homogeneous functions[1] and the fact that K is a homogeneous quadratic function of the $\dot{q}$'s, we can write

$$\sum_{j=1}^{n} \frac{\partial K}{\partial \dot{q}_j} \dot{q}_j = 2K \quad (13 \cdot 4\text{--}7)$$

and hence

$$H = K + V. \quad (13 \cdot 4\text{--}8)$$

This means that H is equal to the total energy of the system. It is indeed the expression for the energy in terms of the q's and p's instead of the q's and $\dot{q}$'s. It is called the Hamiltonian function for short.

---

[1] See R. S. Burington and C. C. Torrance, *Higher Mathematics*, McGraw-Hill, New York, 1939, p. 113.

The significance of the Hamiltonian is clearer if we consider one or two examples. For a free particle, for which the constant potential energy may most conveniently be set equal to zero, we have $p = m\dot{q}$ and hence

$$H = p^2/2m. \tag{13·4-9}$$

The two canonical equations are

$$\dot{p} = -\frac{\partial H}{\partial q} = 0, \tag{13·4-10}$$

$$\dot{q} = \frac{\partial H}{\partial p} = p/m. \tag{13·4-11}$$

The second equation is merely the definition of the momentum in terms of the time derivative of the generalized coördinate q. The first equation says that the time rate of change of the conjugate momentum p is zero, so that p remains constant. This is really nothing but Newton's second law for this special case.

Take as another example the simple harmonic oscillator. Here the Hamiltonian becomes

$$H = p^2/2m + kq^2/2, \tag{13·4-12}$$

where k is the stiffness constant of the oscillator. The canonical equations are

$$\dot{p} = -\frac{\partial H}{\partial q} = -kq \tag{13·4-13}$$

$$\dot{q} = \frac{\partial H}{\partial p} = p/m. \tag{13·4-14}$$

Once again the first equation is Newton's second law, while the second is the identity corresponding to the meaning of p in terms of $\dot{q}$.

The value of the Hamiltonian equations is not indeed apparent from the above introduction. Nevertheless they serve as a useful jumping off place for the so-called transformation theory of mechanics.[1] They are also of great importance in the development of statistical mechanics. The generalization of the statistical notions set forth in Chapter 7 involves the introduction of the idea of *phase space*, where by the phase of a dynamical system we mean the total number of independent p's and q's necessary to describe it. The phase space for a given system is a rectangular coördinate space of $2n$ dimensions in which the position of each point is fixed by the $2n$ coördinates $q_1 \ldots q_n, p_1 \ldots p_n$. Physically each point thus represents not merely the location of the system in physical space (the q's) but also what the system is doing in the way

---

[1] See R. B. Lindsay, *Concepts and Methods of Theoretical Physics*, p. 158.

of motion (the p's). As the system moves through physical space, the corresponding phase point moves in phase space, and the resulting curve in phase space provides the whole history of the motion in physical space.

A simple example will make this point clear. Let us revert to the simple harmonic oscillator, which is a system of one degree of freedom. Hence the appropriate phase space has two dimensions corresponding to the single coördinate q and the single conjugate momentum p. It is therefore a plane, every point of which represents a possible phase of a system of one degree of freedom. But if the oscillator has a fixed energy E, not all p and q values are possible for it, as eq. (13·4–12) emphasizes. In fact the possible phase values are those which lie on the ellipse given by (13·4–12) with H put equal to E. (Fig. 13·6).

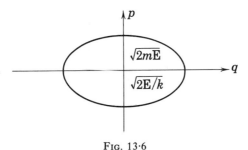

FIG. 13·6

The semimajor axis of the ellipse is $\sqrt{2E/k}$ and the semiminor axis $\sqrt{2mE}$. The ellipse tells in phase space the whole story of the to and fro motion of the oscillator in physical space. Every phase value which the oscillator can assume in its actual motion is represented by some point on the ellipse and by points on the ellipse only.

It is important to note that no phase curve for a conservative system can ever cross itself. The reader should be able to supply the reason himself.

PROBLEMS

1. Use Hamilton's principle to determine the path of a particle which moves freely in three-dimensional space, i.e., under the action of no forces.

2. Use Hamilton's principle to derive the equation of motion of a particle moving in a straight line with potential energy $= K/x$, where x is the distance of the particle from some arbitrarily chosen origin.

3. Using Euler's theorem for homogeneous functions, show that for a dynamical system with n degrees of freedom (Cf. eq. 13·2–4)

$$\sum_{i=1}^{n} \dot{q}_i \, \frac{\partial K}{\partial \dot{q}_i} = 2K.$$

4. Consider a conservative system. Define

$$p_i = \frac{\partial K}{\partial \dot{q}_i}$$

as the generalized momentum associated with q_i. Taking the q_i's in turn as the rectangular and spherical coördinates of a single particle, evaluate the corresponding p_i in each case and comment on its physical significance.

5. A particle of mass m moves along the x axis in simple harmonic motion. Calculate the time integral of the Lagrangian function over the actual dynamical path $x = A \sin \omega t$ from $t = 0$ to $t = T/4$, where $T = 2\pi/\omega$. Consider a varied path $x = A \sin \omega t + \lambda \sin 4\pi t/T$, which has the same end points as the dynamical path at $t = 0$ and $t = T/4$, if λ is a constant parameter. Find the time integral of the Lagrangian function over the varied path from $t = 0$ to $t = T/4$ and compare with the previous result. Connect this with the fundamental physical significance of Hamilton's principle.

6. Use Lagrange's equations to determine the motion of the masses in the frictionless pulley set-up shown in the accompanying figure. The movable pulley P_2 has mass $2m$.

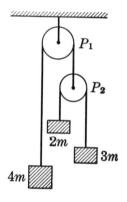

7. Referring to Fig.13·5, let the surface AB be completely rough and replace the particle m by a circular cylinder of mass m which can roll without slipping down the plane. Determine the motion of wedge and cylinder by the use of Lagrange's equations.

8. According to Fermat's principle, the ray of light from any point A to any other point B in space can be determined by the assumption that the time of travel from A to B is a minimum. Show that this leads to the experimentally observed laws of reflection and refraction of light at a plane surface. Show that Hamilton's principle applied to a light particle or photon of energy $h\nu$ is equivalent to Fermat's principle.

9. Write the Hamiltonian function for a particle in a uniform field of force and deduce the Hamiltonian equations. What is the curve in phase space for the motion of such a particle with constant energy E?

Consider the phase area in the pq plane lying between the two phase curves for energies E_1 and E_2 respectively. Further consider the portion of this phase region lying between the parallels to the q axis defined by the momentum values p_1 and p_2 respectively.   Show that at the end of time t_1 the phase points in this subregion will move to another subregion in the phase space which is equal in area to the first.   This is a case of Liouville's theorem, of importance in statistical mechanics.

10. A particle of mass m moving in an inverse-square central field of force is also acted on by a uniform field of intensity F along the z axis.   The potential energy thus has the form

$$V = -\frac{C}{r} + Fmz.$$

Express the Hamiltonian function in terms of parabolic coördinates ξ, η, ϕ, i.e., transform according to the following equations

$$x = \xi\eta \cos \phi$$
$$y = \xi\eta \sin \phi$$
$$z = (\eta^2 - \xi^2)/2.$$

Write the Hamiltonian equations of motion.

Chapter 14

RELATIVISTIC MECHANICS

14·1. The Theory of Relativity. In Sec. 1·12 we commented on the fact that the fundamental equations of motion of a particle in classical Newtonian mechanics remain invariant in form under a transformation of coördinates of the form

$$x' = x - vt,$$
$$y' = y, \qquad\qquad (14\text{·}1\text{-}1)$$
$$z' = z,$$

in which x, y, z are the rectangular coördinates of a mass particle in one inertial system, t is the time, and v is the *uniform* velocity of the reference system in which the coördinates of the same particle are x', y', z' with respect to the first system. We expressed this result by saying that the laws of mechanics have the same form in all inertial systems and hence it is impossible by mechanical means to detect the motion of an inertial system. This is the content of what has been called the Newtonian theory of relativity.

It might be thought that this simple point of view is completely adequate to handle all problems in mechanics. To be sure it contains a certain challenge: is there not some physical means besides a mechanical one through which one might detect the motion of an inertial system? Might one not hope to do this, for example, by using light signals? If light is a wave motion in a medium (Sec. 11·11) it is natural to suppose that its measured velocity will depend on the velocity of the light source through the medium; this is certainly the case for sound, whose effective velocity relative to the earth can be greater in moving air (i.e., a wind) than in still air. Since we know that the earth is moving relatively to the sun and other planets, we might expect to detect this motion, if it is genuine and not just an apparent result due to the motion of the sun and other bodies, by measuring the velocity of light in the direction of the motion and at right angles thereto. The results should be different by a very small amount (the velocity of light is of course enormously greater than any other terrestrial velocity) but still measurable. Many experiments were concocted in the late nineteenth and early twentieth centuries to try to detect this difference, among them the famous Michelson-Morley-Miller experiment.[1] The result of all these experiments was so nearly completely negative as to lead scientists like Poincaré and Einstein to put forth a new principle about motion, namely, that there is no means whatever by which the uniform motion of an inertial system can be detected. This is usually called the Einstein principle of relativity. It is obviously more general than the Newtonian principle. It means that the laws of nature for all phenomena must remain invariant in form in all inertial systems.

The question arises: does this more general relativity principle have any effect on the equations of mechanics? If it does not there would be no particular excuse for discussing it in a book on mechanics, though it would obviously be important in a treatise on light or electromagnetic theory. Actually it turns out to have some very important mechanical consequences for particles moving with velocities large enough to be appreciable fractions of the velocity of light. This we now wish to look into.

14·2.   The Transformation Equations of Relativity. Are eqs. (14·1–1) the equations which satisfy the Einstein principle of relativity as set forth in the previous section? It turns out that they are not. In particular, if we were to use them to go from one inertial system to another, we would find that the equations of electromagnetic theory, namely the so-called Maxwell electromagnetic field equations[2] do *not* retain their form invariant. This would mean that it should be possible to establish a difference between inertial systems by means of electromagnetic phenomena, in contradiction to the well-known experimental findings. Hence eqs. (14·1–1) cannot be the strictly correct transformation equations from one inertial system to another. Of course we know they work as such in mechanics for velocities ordinarily encountered in mechanical experiments. However this would not by any means guarantee that they would work for particles at very high velocities, and in fact the implication is plain that this is where they break down. How are we to find the proper equations to replace them?

Einstein[3] found them by assuming a very general principle of relativity, stating in effect that all physical laws have the same form in all inertial frames of reference and further utilizing the special case of light in postulating that the velocity of light in free space is the same in all inertial systems. For if it were not, one could use this fact to detect the motion of such a system in violation of the relativity principle.

---

[1] See R. B. Lindsay, *General Physics*, Wiley, New York, 1940, p. 514.

[2] See R. B. Lindsay, *Concepts and Methods of Theoretical Physics*, Van Nostrand, Princeton, N.J., 1951, p. 396.

[3] *Annalen der Physik*, **17**, 891 (1905).

Let us imagine two inertial frames S and S', and for the sake of simplicity but with no essential loss in generality, assume them to move with respect to each other with constant velocity v along their common x axes. The origin of S is O and that of S' is O' (see Fig. 14·1). A given investigator or observer may use either reference frame to describe the experiments he performs. If he uses S he fixes the position of any point in space by the rectangular coördinates x, y, z with reference to S and the time t of an event at this point by means of a clock fixed at that point. On the other hand if he chooses to refer the same event to the S' frame, he uses the coördinates x', y', z' of the point in S' and the time t' for this event as measured on a clock fixed in S'. The problem is to find the relations between x, y, z, t on the one hand and x', y', z', t' on the other to satisfy the demands of the relativity postulate.

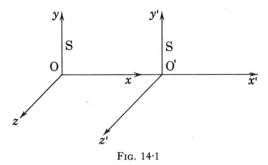

Fig. 14·1

But it is at once clear that we shall have to say something about t and t'. In the Newtonian version of relativity they were of course the same, and this seems a rather natural thing to assume until we reflect on how difficult it really is to give a categorical answer to the question: " What is the time on the star Sirius when it is 12 noon at a particular point on the earth's surface? " Poincaré, Lorentz, and Einstein found it advantageous not to assume that t and t' are the same, but to see how they must differ if the postulate of relativity is to hold. Einstein assumes that a clock is (ideally) located at every point in space, and that all these clocks are identical in structure and are observed to run the same way when examined at any one place. He has to make one further assumption, namely that the clocks must be synchronized. This is carried out by the following arbitrary though plausible process. Suppose we consider two points P_1 and P_2 each with its appropriate clock. Send a light signal from P_1 at time t_1 as indicated by P_1's clock. Suppose it reaches P_2 at time t_2 as shown on P_2's clock. By means of a mirror it is reflected back to P_1 and arrives there at time t_1' as shown on P_1's clock. The two clocks are said to be in synchronism if

$$t_2 = \tfrac{1}{2}(t_1 + t_1'). \qquad (14\cdot2\text{–}1)$$

This, in other words, is the time that P_2's clock must be adjusted to read in order for it to be synchronized with P_1's clock. It is further assumed that the relation between the two clocks is a reciprocal one, i.e., if P_2's clock is in synchronism with P_1's clock, then P_1's clock is in synchronism with P_2's clock.

We proceed to find the relations between x', y', z', t' and x, y, z, t, utilizing the situation depicted in Fig. 14·1. It is clear that two of the transformation equations are

$$y' = y,$$

$$z' = z.$$

Assume that the origins O and O' coincide when $t = t' = 0$. The clock attached to O is thus supposed to register zero when O coincides with O' and the clock attached to O' is supposed to register zero also at the moment of coincidence. We further suppose that all the clocks in the frame S are in synchronism with each other and likewise all the clocks in frame S' are in synchronism with each other.

The kinematic equation for the motion of O' as measured in the frame S is

$$x - vt = 0. \tag{14·2–2}$$

But measured in S', the motion of O' is given simply by

$$x' = 0. \tag{14·2–3}$$

These two equations must hold identically. Hence

$$x' = \gamma(x - vt), \tag{14·2–4}$$

where γ is a constant, at first arbitrary in nature. It should be emphasized that in writing (14·2–4) we are tacitly assuming that the transformation equations are to be linear in character. Obviously we could satisfy (14·2–2) and (14·2–3) identically by letting the square of x' be proportional to the cube of $x - vt$, etc. Our reason for taking the transformation equation as linear is simple: we wish to insure that to each event in the frame S there corresponds one and only one event in the frame S'.

If we now apply an argument similar to that above to the motion of O, we come out with the equation

$$x = \gamma'(x' + vt'). \tag{14·2–5}$$

Now the first postulate of relativity requires that

$$\gamma = \gamma', \tag{14·2–6}$$

since if this relation were not satisfied the law describing the relative motion of the two reference frames would have a different form depending on the frame in which it is expressed. If we eliminate x' between (14·2–4) and (14·2–5), we obtain

$$t' = t + (1 - \gamma^2)x/v\gamma. \tag{14·2-7}$$

We take the differentials of x' and t' in (14·2–4) and (14·2–7) respectively and obtain

$$dx' = \gamma(dx - v\,dt),$$

$$dt' = (1 - \gamma^2)/v\gamma \cdot dx + \gamma\,dt. \tag{14·2-8}$$

Division yields

$$\frac{dx'}{dt'} = \frac{\dfrac{dx}{dt} - v}{1 + \dfrac{dx}{dt} \cdot (1 - \gamma^2)/v\gamma^2}. \tag{14·2-9}$$

This expresses the instantaneous velocity of a particle dx'/dt' in the frame S' in terms of the instantaneous velocity dx/dt of the same particle in the frame S.

We now use the second postulate of Einstein, namely, that the velocity of light in free space is the same in all inertial systems, i.e., c. Hence if the particle is a photon, we have $dx'/dt' = dx/dt = c$ and (14·2–9) becomes

$$c = \frac{c - v}{1 + c(1 - \gamma^2)/v\gamma^2}, \tag{14·2-10}$$

which yields

$$\gamma = \frac{1}{\sqrt{1 - v^2/c^2}}. \tag{14·2-11}$$

The transformation equations we are seeking then become (from (14·2–4) and (14·2–7) respectively)

$$x' = \frac{x - vt}{\sqrt{1 - v^2/c^2}}, \quad y' = y, \quad z' = z,$$

$$t' = \frac{t - vx/c^2}{\sqrt{1 - v^2/c^2}}, \tag{14·2-12}$$

It is clear that for $v \ll c$, these reduce to the Newtonian form

$$x' = x - vt, \quad y' = y, \quad z' = z, \quad t' = t.$$

We anticipate then that any changes relativity will produce in the principles of mechanics will be of slight significance unless the velocity of the particle in question in the inertial system is comparable in magnitude with the velocity of light in free space.

We shall not develop here the usual kinematic consequences of these transformation equations, usually known as the Lorentz-Einstein transformation equations.[1]   We are more interested in the modifications they produce in the principles of mechanics.

14·3. The Relativistic Equation of Motion.   The problem we wish to solve is to find the form of the equation of motion for a particle that will remain invariant under the Lorentz-Einstein transformation discussed in the preceding section.   We shall find it convenient to write this in the form

$$\mathbf{F} = \frac{d}{dt}(m\mathbf{v}) \qquad (14\text{·}3\text{–}1)$$

as in Sec. 1·7, where $m\mathbf{v}$ is the instantaneous momentum of the particle and $\mathbf{F}$ is the resultant force on it.   Let us now suppose that the particle we are talking about is fixed at the origin O' of the frame S' and hence is moving with velocity $\mathbf{v}$ with respect to the origin O of the frame S (in Fig. 14·1).   We want to write the equation of motion of the particle in S' and then transform it to S and compare with (14·3–1).   It would seem to have the form

$$\mathbf{F}' = \frac{d}{dt'}(m_0\mathbf{v}'), \qquad (14\text{·}3\text{–}2)$$

where we now use m_0 for the mass to denote that it is a special mass; since the particle rides along with S'.   Now we might suppose that $\mathbf{v}'$ would be the vector with components dx'/dt', dy'/dt', dz'/dt', etc. But since the particle is attached rigidly to S', it is clear that $dx' = dy' = dz' = 0$ and hence this cannot be the meaning of v'.   Rather we must suppose that

$$v_x' = \frac{dx}{dt'} = \frac{dx}{dt}\frac{dt}{dt'} = v_x\frac{dt}{dt'},$$

$$v_y' = \frac{dy}{dt'} = \frac{dy}{dt}\frac{dt}{dt'} = v_y\frac{dt}{dt'}, \qquad (14\text{·}3\text{–}3)$$

$$v_z' = \frac{dz}{dt'} = \frac{dz}{dt}\frac{dt}{dt'} = v_z\frac{dt}{dt'},$$

where v_x, v_y, v_z are the components of $\mathbf{v}$ in S.   Now we concentrate attention on the first equation in (14·3–3) only and find dt/dt' from eq. (14·2–8).   Since $dx' = 0$, $dx = vdt$ and we substitute this into the second equation in (14·2–8), obtaining

$$dt' = \sqrt{1 - v^2/c^2}\, dt. \qquad (14\text{·}3\text{–}4)$$

[1] See R. B. Lindsay, *Concepts and Methods of Theoretical Physics*, pp. 477 f.

Consequently we have

$$\mathbf{v'} = \frac{\mathbf{v}}{\sqrt{1 - v^2/c^2}} . \tag{14.3-5}$$

Hence eq. (14.3–2) becomes

$$\mathbf{F'} = \frac{d}{dt'} \left(\frac{m_0 \mathbf{v}}{\sqrt{1 - v^2/c^2}} \right) = \frac{d}{dt} \left(\frac{m_0 \mathbf{v}}{\sqrt{1 - v^2/c^2}} \right) \cdot \frac{1}{\sqrt{1 - v^2/c^2}} . \tag{14.3-6}$$

This may be rewritten in the form

$$\sqrt{1 - v^2/c^2}\, \mathbf{F'} = \frac{d}{dt} \left(\frac{m_0 \mathbf{v}}{\sqrt{1 - v^2/c^2}} \right) . \tag{14.3-7}$$

This can only be identical with (14.3–1) if

$$\mathbf{F} = \mathbf{F'}\sqrt{1 - v^2/c^2}, \tag{14.3-8}$$

$$m = \frac{m_0}{\sqrt{1 - v^2/c^2}} . \tag{14.3-9}$$

The result of greatest interest is the fact that if m_0 is a scalar constant associated with the particle in the frame of reference in which it is at rest (the so-called rest mass), the mass m which we must associate with the particle in the frame with respect to which it is moving with speed v is no longer an invariant but varies with the velocity through the term $1/\sqrt{1 - v^2/c^2}$, i.e., it increases with velocity and approaches ∞ as $v \to c$.

We see again that the change in mass with velocity demanded by relativity is negligible for most problems in ordinary classical mechanics, since v is normally so much smaller than c. However, in atomic mechanics, where particles like electrons and ions can be given velocities approaching c in value, the relativistic correction can be very considerable.

14.4. Energy in Relativistic Mechanics. The definition of energy in relativistic mechanics is approached by the same method as in classical mechanics. We recall that in Sec. 1.11 we formed the space integral of the resultant force and called this the change in the kinetic energy. Now we have

$$\int_{\mathbf{r}_0}^{\mathbf{r}_1} \mathbf{F} \cdot d\mathbf{r} = m_0 \int_{\mathbf{r}_0}^{\mathbf{r}_1} \frac{d}{dt} (\mathbf{v}/\sqrt{1 - v^2/c^2}) \cdot d\mathbf{r}. \tag{14.4-1}$$

It will be convenient to use the symbol β for the quantity v/c. Then

$$\frac{d}{dt}(\mathbf{v}/\sqrt{1-\beta^2})\cdot d\mathbf{r} = \frac{d}{dt}(\mathbf{v}/\sqrt{1-\beta^2})\cdot \mathbf{v}\, dt$$

$$= \beta^2 c^2 \frac{d}{dt}(1/\sqrt{1-\beta^2})\, dt$$

$$+ c^2 \beta \dot{\beta}/\sqrt{1-\beta^2}\cdot dt$$

$$= \frac{d}{dt}(c^2/\sqrt{1-\beta^2})\, dt. \qquad (14\cdot4\text{--}2)$$

Hence

$$\int_{\mathbf{r}_0}^{\mathbf{r}_1} \mathbf{F}\cdot d\mathbf{r} = m_0 c^2/\sqrt{1-\beta^2}\, \Big]_{\beta_0}^{\beta_1}. \qquad (14\cdot4\text{--}3)$$

It is therefore plausible to take the relativistic kinetic energy in the form

$$K = m_0 c^2/\sqrt{1-\beta^2} + C, \qquad (14\cdot4\text{--}4)$$

where C is a constant. In other words we must include an additive constant which can be so chosen as to give K the simplest possible form. Thus we naturally wish to have $K = 0$ when $\beta = 0$. This can be achieved by taking $C = -m_0 c^2$. Then we write definitively

$$K = m_0 c^2 [1/\sqrt{1-\beta^2} - 1] \qquad (14\cdot4\text{--}5)$$

or in the simpler form

$$K = (m - m_0)c^2. \qquad (14\cdot4\text{--}6)$$

The above expressions for the kinetic energy certainly look unfamiliar. Yet K must reduce to the usual classical mechanical expression when β becomes very small. If we expand $(1 - \beta^2)^{-1/2}$ in $(14\cdot4\text{--}6)$ in a series (Peirce's *Tables* No. 750) we get

$$K = \frac{m_0 v^2}{2} + \frac{3}{8} m_0 \frac{v^4}{c^2} + \cdots. \qquad (14\cdot4\text{--}7)$$

Since here $v \ll c$, the second term is enormously smaller than the first and the same is true of all subsequent terms in the series. Hence K reduces to the classical expression for the kinetic energy in the limit of velocity small compared with the velocity of light.

A result of more importance for modern physics is obtained by rewriting $(14\cdot4\text{--}6)$ in the form

$$m = m_0 + K/c^2. \qquad (14\cdot4\text{--}8)$$

Here the variable mass of the moving particle is seen to be made up of the invariable rest mass m_0 plus the contribution K/c^2. This may be taken to mean that a part of the mass we must associate relativistically with a moving particle is associated with its kinetic energy: a gain in kinetic energy by whatever means means an increase in mass and a loss in kinetic energy a loss in mass. This is the basis of the famous generalization of Einstein, associating with the total energy E of any particle whatever an inertia value corresponding to mass m where

$$E = mc^2 \qquad (14\cdot4\text{--}9)$$

The quantity m_0c^2 is sometimes referred to as the *intrinsic* energy of the particle. Eq. (14·4–9) is the fundamental mass-energy relationship which has proved of such importance in nuclear physics and is at the basis of nuclear energy and the atomic bomb.

14·5. Relativistic Conservation of Energy and Momentum. The Compton Effect.

An interesting illustration of the conservation of energy and momentum in relativistic mechanics is provided by the Compton effect. This is the change in wave length or frequency experienced by X rays when they are scattered by electrons in atoms.

From the standpoint of the quantum theory, light is looked upon as corpuscular in nature and composed of particles called " photons," which have no mass but carry energy $h\nu$ and momentum $h\nu/c$, where ν is the frequency of the light and h is Planck's constant of action (see Sec. 3·11) having the value 6.55×10^{-27} erg sec. As usual c is the velocity of light in free space. Suppose a photon of frequency ν_0 moving along the positive x axis collides with an electron at rest with respect to a certain set of rectangular axes. Fig. 14·2 indicates the situation in schematic form, with the incident photon indicated by $h\nu_0$. The original position of the electron is shown as e. After the collision it is assumed that the electron moves off with velocity v in a direction making angle θ with the positive x axis, whereas the photon travels in a direction making angle ϕ with the same axis as shown, and has its frequency altered to ν. The problem is to find the relation between ν, ν_0, and the angles.

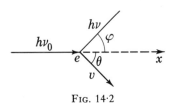

Fig. 14·2

We proceed to apply the conditions that energy and momentum must be conserved in the collision. Since the rest or intrinsic energy of the electron, from Sec. 14·4, is m_0c^2 and after the collision its energy is mc^2, where $m = m_0\sqrt{1 - v^2/c^2}$, conservation of energy demands

$$h\nu_0 + m_0c^2 = h\nu + mc^2. \qquad (14\text{·}5\text{--}1)$$

Conservation of momentum is a bit more complicated, since momentum is a vector, and the momentum components both in the x direction and at right angles thereto must be conserved. From Sec. 14·4 we recall that the relativistic expression for the momentum is $m\mathbf{v} = m_0\mathbf{v}/\sqrt{1-v^2/c^2}$. Hence for conservation of momentum in the x direction we have

$$\frac{h\nu_0}{c} = \frac{h\nu}{c}\cos\phi + mv\cos\theta, \qquad (14\text{·}5\text{--}2)$$

whereas at right angles to the x direction the corresponding equation is

$$0 = \frac{h\nu}{c}\sin\phi - mv\sin\theta. \qquad (14\text{·}5\text{--}3)$$

It is left to the reader to show that by the elimination of θ from these three conservation equations, one can obtain the following equation connecting ν_0, ν, and ϕ

$$\frac{m_0c^2}{h}(1/\nu - 1/\nu_0) = 1 - \cos\phi. \qquad (14\text{·}5\text{--}4)$$

It is usually simpler to express this in terms of the change in wave length $\Delta\lambda$ experienced by the photon as a result of the collision. Thus

$$\Delta\lambda = \lambda - \lambda_0 = (c/\nu - c/\nu_0) = \frac{h}{m_0c}(1 - \cos\phi). \qquad (14\text{·}5\text{--}5)$$

This is the fundamental equation of the Compton effect. The quantity h/m_0c, usually referred to as the Compton wave length, has the approximate value 0.0242 Å (where the angstrom unit is 10^{-8} cm).

PROBLEMS

1. If a spherical light wave starts at time $t = 0$ to move with velocity c from the origin of a fixed system of axes (x, y, z), at time t (as measured in this system) it will have reached the surface of a sphere whose equation is

$$x^2 + y^2 + z^2 - c^2t^2 = 0.$$

Show that the equation of this sphere has the *same* form in the system of axes (x_0, y_0, z_0) moving with respect to the first with constant velocity v along their common z axes. (The origins of the two systems are assumed to pass each other at time $t = t_0 = 0$.) That is, using the Lorentz-Einstein transformation equations (13·2–12), show that the expression above becomes

$$x_0^2 + y_0^2 + z_0^2 - c^2t_0^2 = 0.$$

Note that the theory of relativity supposes that c is a universal invariant. Comment on the physical significance of the result of the transformation.

2. Show that if l is the length of a rod measured in the system with respect to which it is at rest, the length l' in the system S' with respect to which it moves with velocity v is

$$l' = l \sqrt{1 - v^2/c^2}.$$

This is the basis for the relativistic contraction of moving objects.

3. Prove that if one clock is stationary in S and another is stationary in S', the time interval $\Delta t'$ on the clock stationary in S' is related to the time interval Δt, as measured on the clock stationary in S, between the same two events, by the relation

$$\Delta t' = \sqrt{1 - v^2/c^2} \cdot \Delta t.$$

This is the basis for the relativity statement that a moving clock runs slow.

4. Show that on the theory of relativity if a particle has velocity u relative to system S, its velocity relative to system S' is not $u' = u - v$, but rather

$$u' = \frac{u - v}{1 - uv/c^2}.$$

Comment on the significance of this for $u = c$.

5. Recalling that the hyperbolic tangent obeys the following identity

$$\tanh (\alpha - \beta) = \frac{\tanh \alpha - \tanh \beta}{1 - \tanh \alpha \cdot \tanh \beta},$$

show that the relativistic law for the composition of velocities given in the preceding problem (Problem 4) can be written in the form

$$\text{arc tanh } u'/c = \text{arc tanh } u/c - \text{arc tanh } v/c$$

Comment on the physical significance of this result.

CHAPTER 15

WAVE AND QUANTUM MECHANICS

15·1. De Broglie's Wave Mechanics. No book on physical mechanics would be complete without a brief introduction to the application of mechanical ideas to the study of atomic particles and atomic structure which formed so large a part of physics during the second quarter of the twentieth century.

We have already seen (Sec. 3·11) how the Bohr-Rutherford theory considers a neutral atom to be composed of a nucleus charged with positive electricity about which move electrons equal in number to the number of positive charges on the nucleus. These electrons move in orbits according to the laws of classical mechanics, but with the significant difference that not all mechanically possible paths are allowed, but only those for which certain so-called *quantum conditions* are satisfied (recall particularly eqs. 3·11–1). The latter serve to fix the possible orbital dimensions and energy values of the nucleus-electron system. (Recall also the corresponding problem for the electron in simple harmonic motion: Sec. 10·7.) Now it is important to note that in this theory the electron is still considered as a mass particle whose motion is to be treated largely as a classical mechanical problem. L. De Broglie has however suggested a quite different method of approach to this problem. He begins by assuming that an electron is not an entity localized in space but a *periodic phenomenon extending throughout all space.* More specifically, let us consider a *free* electron, that is, one not subject to any external force. De Broglie supposes that in the inertial system with respect to which the electron is at rest it is to be represented by an expression of the form

$$u(x_0, y_0, z_0, t_0) = f(x_0, y_0, z_0)e^{2\pi i \nu_0 t_0}. \qquad (15\cdot1-1)$$

In this expression we are using x_0, y_0, z_0, t_0 to denote position and time in the system in which the electron is at rest. The right-hand side represents a simple harmonic pulsation with frequency ν_0 and amplitude $f(x_0, y_0, z_0)$, the phase being the same at all points in space.[1] Both ν_0 and $f(x_0, y_0, z_0)$ must now be looked upon as something

---

[1] The use of the complex form is for convenience only. Either real or imaginary part could be used equally well.

429

fundamental for the physical significance of the particle.   At first sight this point of view appears rather barren of meaning.   However, let us next refer the electron to a reference system with respect to which it is moving with constant velocity v, say for convenience along the z axis. What will be the mathematical representation of the electron in this new set of axes which may be regarded as *fixed* from the standpoint of a hypothetical observer of the electron?

To solve this problem we need only use the Lorentz-Einstein transformation equations of special relativity, already developed in Sec. 14·2 (eq. 14·2–12) which we may now write in the form

$$x_0 = x, \quad y_0 = y, \quad z_0 = \frac{z - vt}{\sqrt{1 - v^2/c^2}}, \qquad (15\cdot1\text{–}2)$$

$$t_0 = \frac{t - vz/c^2}{\sqrt{1 - v^2/c^2}},$$

where now we denote the electron's frame of reference by the subscript zero rather than by the prime (as in Sec. 14·2) and we have chosen the motion in the z rather than the x direction.

To solve the problem of De Broglie we must now substitute from (15·1–2) into (15·1–1).   However, in so doing we must not overlook the fact that v_0, being a frequency, depends on the time and must also undergo transformation.   Thus, if we concentrate on a particular value of z, corresponding intervals of time in the two inertial systems from the last of eqs. (15·1–2) will be given by

$$dt_0 = \frac{dt}{\sqrt{1 - \frac{v^2}{c^2}}},$$

and therefore v_0, which is proportional to $1/dt_0$, will transform to v, where

$$v = \frac{v_0}{\sqrt{1 - \frac{v^2}{c^2}}}. \qquad (15\cdot1\text{–}3)$$

On finally carrying out the indicated transformation we get for the representation of the electron in the system with respect to which it moves with constant velocity v

$$u'(x, y, z, t) = f\left(x, y, \frac{z - vt}{\sqrt{1 - v^2/c^2}}\right) e^{2\pi i v \left(t - \frac{v}{c^2} z\right)}. \qquad (15\cdot1\text{–}4)$$

We recognize this at once (Sec. 11·5) as a *plane progressive harmonic wave* of frequency ν moving in the positive z direction with velocity

$$V = \frac{c^2}{v}. \tag{15·1–5}$$

The amplitude f is, of course, variable in space and time. *Thus in the inertial system with respect to which it is moving with constant velocity v, the electron appears to be equivalent to a harmonic wave.* It is interesting to note from (15·1–5) that the velocity of this wave is never less than the velocity of light, since $v \leqq c$ for a particle, a fact that is one of the consequences of the special theory of relativity. The fact that $V \geqq c$ might seem to detract from the value of De Broglie's viewpoint. However, he was able to show that if one considers the particle to be represented not by a single wave but by a whole *group* of harmonic waves with slightly different frequencies clustered about an average frequency ν and moving in the same direction with slightly different velocities, the velocity of the point of phase agreement of such a group, i.e., the so-called *group velocity* (see Sec. 11·8), is precisely equal to the particle velocity v. The reader should work this out for himself. (See Problem 1 at the end of the chapter.)

De Broglie further assumed that there is a fundamental relation between the *energy* of the electron considered as a particle moving with respect to the fixed axes and its frequency considered as a wave. This relation is the famous quantum theory equation

$$E = h\nu, \tag{15·1–6}$$

where h is the universal constant of Planck (Secs. 3·11, 10·7, and 14·5).

Now we have seen that on the theory of relativity the energy of a freely moving particle (i.e., the kinetic energy) is given by

$$E = mc^2, \tag{15·1–7}$$

where m is the mass of the particle with respect to the system in which it is moving with velocity v, and is given by

$$m = m_0/\sqrt{1 - v^2/c^2}, \tag{15·1–8}$$

where m_0 is the rest mass, i.e., the mass in the frame of reference in which the particle is at rest. The combination of (15·1–5), (15·1–6) and (15·1–8) yields an important relation for the wave length λ of the wave representing the electron. Thus

$$\lambda = \frac{h}{mv} = \frac{h}{p}, \tag{15·1–9}$$

where we use p to denote the momentum of the electron. Experiments in which electrons are reflected from the surfaces of single metal crystals have verified eq. (15·1–9) and hence the wave nature of the electron.[1]

Let us go back to De Broglie's idea that an electron might well be represented not by a single monochromatic wave like (15·1–4) but rather by a group of waves to form a kind of wave packet. In Sec. 11·9 we noted an important consequence of the superposition of a set of waves of different frequencies and different velocities. This is the relation between the length of the corresponding wave pulse or packet and the spread in the wave parameters of the various components of the pulse necessary to produce the pulse. Eq. (11·9–8) expresses this. If we rewrite this in terms of wave length λ, we get

$$\Delta(1/\lambda)\cdot\Delta x \geqslant 1. \qquad (15\cdot1\text{--}10)$$

Now we have just seen that the De Broglie wave length λ is given in terms of the electron momentum by (15·1–9). If we substitute this into (15·1–10) the result is

$$\Delta p\cdot\Delta x \geqslant h. \qquad (15\cdot1\text{--}11)$$

The result of representing an electron by a group of waves of wave lengths clustered about the value of λ given in eq. (15·1–9) is thus an indeterminacy relation of the form (15·1–11), in which Δx now represents an uncertainty in the position of the electron and Δp the corresponding uncertainty in its momentum. For Δx is the length of the wave packet, and the electron associated with it may lie anywhere within this interval. It is therefore undetermined to the extent measured by Δx. At the same time Δp is proportional to the variation in the reciprocal wave length of the component waves making up the packet. Hence the momentum of the electron may lie anywhere in an interval of this length. Suppose it is desired to locate the electron to an accuracy of 10^{-8} cm. Then

$$\Delta p \geq 10^8 h = 6.55 \times 10^{-19} \text{ gm cm/sec.}$$

This may seem to be a very small indeterminacy indeed. The corresponding indeterminacy in the velocity of the electron, however, is very large, since the rest mass of the electron is of the order of 9×10^{-28} gm. This would yield Δv of the order of

$$7 \times 10^8 \text{ cm/sec.}$$

15·2. Operator Method in Quantum Mechanics. The considerations of the preceding section apply primarily to a free electron, i.e., one not subjected to any force. The generalization of the treatment

[1] See, for example, Max Born, *Atomic Physics*, Hafner, New York, 1957.

to the case of an electron in a force field — e.g., that due to a positively charged nucleus as in an atom — is the subject matter of what is now called quantum mechanics, which indeed strictly speaking covers the behavior of atomic particles of all kinds and in all circumstances. Its basic postulate is that electrons and atomic systems in general can exist only in certain energy states characterized by great stability and that such systems can gain or lose energy only by passing from one specific state to another. One of the basic problems of quantum mechanics is the determination of the allowed energy states of atomic systems. We have already noted the method of solution of this problem by the earlier Bohr quantum conditions technique (Secs. 3·11 and 4·3). Modern quantum mechanics handles this in more powerful fashion.

We shall illustrate the quantum mechanical method first by means of the simple harmonic oscillator. Essentially the method consists in writing the energy equation for the oscillator in Hamiltonian form (Sec. 13·4) and transforming this into a differential equation by replacing the momentum by a special differential operator. Thus the energy equation of the oscillator is

$$\frac{p^2}{2m} + \frac{kx^2}{2} = E, \tag{15·2–1}$$

where p is the momentum of the oscillator and E is its total mechanical energy. The quantity k is the *stiffness* of the oscillator. As we have seen in Sec. 2·3 it is related to the frequency ν of the oscillator by the equation

$$k = 4\pi^2\nu^2 m. \tag{15·2–2}$$

Eq. (15·2–1) is of course an algebraic equation. We can turn it into a differential equation by replacing p by the operator

$$p = \frac{h}{2\pi i}\frac{d}{dx}, \tag{15·2–3}$$

where h is still Planck's constant. This means that if ψ is any differentiable function of x, we have

$$p\psi = \frac{h}{2\pi i}\cdot\frac{d\psi}{dx}, \tag{15·2–4}$$

and

$$p^2\psi = -\frac{h^2}{4\pi^2}\frac{d^2\psi}{dx^2}. \tag{15·2–5}$$

The quantum mechanical interpretation of the energy equation (15·2–1) then is this: if we operate on any function $\psi(x)$ with the operator

$$\frac{1}{2m}\left(\frac{h}{2\pi i}\right)^2\frac{d^2}{dx^2} + \frac{kx^2}{2}, \tag{15·2–6}$$

the result is the same as multiplying $\psi(x)$ by the constant E. But this yields at once the second-order ordinary differential equation

$$\frac{d^2\psi}{dx^2} + \frac{8\pi^2 m}{h^2}(E - \tfrac{1}{2}kx^2)\psi = 0. \qquad (15\cdot2-7)$$

Comparing this equation with Eq. (11·6–30) we see that it may be interpreted as the wave equation for plane harmonic waves traveling along the x axis with variable wave length

$$\lambda = \frac{h}{\sqrt{2m(E - \tfrac{1}{2}kx^2)}}. \qquad (15\cdot2-8)$$

Eq. (15·2–7) is then taken as the wave equation, the so-called Schrödinger wave equation,[1] associated with the simple harmonic oscillator.

Now that we have our wave equation, what are we going to do with it? In the case of the wave equation for a finite stretched string discussed in Sec. 11·6 we sought for a solution giving the displacement of the string as a function of x and t subject to *certain boundary conditions.* Now this is precisely what Schrödinger does with the eq. (15·2–7). He looks for a solution giving ψ as a function of x (it is already assumed to be harmonic in time) which satisfies the general boundary condition that it shall be *finite, continuous and single-valued for all x and shall vanish at infinity.* The solution of this type of problem has long been familiar to mathematicians under the general name of *boundary value problem.* It is a little too lengthy for us to embark on here. It will be sufficient to say, however, that the analysis shows that it is impossible to obtain solutions of (15·2–7) which satisfy this boundary condition for *all* values of the energy E. In fact it develops that such solutions are obtained only for values of the energy of the following form

$$E_n = (n + \tfrac{1}{2})h\nu, \qquad (15\cdot2-9)$$

where $n = 0, 1, 2, \ldots$ These are then called the *eigenvalues* or *characteristic values* of the simple harmonic oscillator. Physically speaking they are the allowed energy values of the oscillator and correspond to the quantization of the motion. It is very interesting to compare the result of the Schrödinger quantization with that of the Bohr quantum condition method — (eq. 10·7–10). It is seen that the two are alike save that $n + \tfrac{1}{2}$ in the former replaces n in the latter. Experimental applications indicate that (15·2–9) is more in accord with observed facts than (10·7–10). It is however important to note that the quantization process

---

[1] See, for example, R. B. Lindsay and H. Margenau, *Foundations of Physics*, Dover Publications Inc., New York, 1957, Sec. 9·6.

in both cases results from the imposition of a boundary condition: in the Bohr theory this is the quantum condition applied to the classical mechanical motion, while in the Schrödinger wave mechanics it is a condition analogous to those imposed on the wave equation representing a vibrating string.

Since the quantum mechanical method may seem a bit mysterious, it will pay to give another example in which the details are relatively simple and can be presented here. This example concerns a single particle of mass m constrained to move along the x axis between $x = 0$ and $x = l$. The potential energy of the particle is assumed to be $V(x)$, but it is assumed that $V(x) = 0$ for $l > x > 0$ and $V(x) = \infty$ for $x < 0$ and $x > l$. This means that the particle is effectively restricted to the interval between 0 and l, since it would have to climb an infinitely high potential barrier in order to get out. Inside the interval it moves freely under no force.

The Hamiltonian energy equation of the particle then is

$$\frac{p^2}{2m} + V(x) = E, \tag{15·2--10}$$

and the corresponding Schrödinger equation becomes (with the technique described above)

$$\frac{d^2\psi}{dx^2} + \frac{8\pi^2 m}{h^2}[E - V(x)]\psi = 0. \tag{15·2--11}$$

The simplest way to solve this subject to the boundary conditions cited is to assume that $V(x) = V_0$ inside the interval and $V(x) = V_1$ outside the interval in which the particle is to be confined. In the final solution we hope we can then safely let $V_0 \to 0$ and $V_1 \to \infty$. Since $E > V_0$ (E being taken to be positive) inside the interval, the solution there is

$$\psi = Ae^{ikx} + Be^{-ikx}, \tag{15·2--12}$$

where A and B are arbitrary constants and

$$k^2 = 8\pi^2 m(E - V_0)/h^2. \tag{15·2--13}$$

Outside the interval we shall assume that $E < V_1$, since we shall ultimately make V_1 infinitely great. Hence for the solution outside we take

$$\psi = A'e^{k'x} + B'e^{-k'x}, \tag{15·2--14}$$

with

$$k'^2 = 8\pi^2 m(V_1 - E)/h^2. \tag{15·2--15}$$

In order to satisfy the conditions on ψ for all x, both inside and outside the interval, it is necessary that both ψ and $d\psi/dx$ shall be continuous at the ends of the interval.   This gives

$$A + B = A' + B', \tag{15·2–16}$$

$$ik(A - B) = k'(A' - B'). \tag{15·2–17}$$

In order to prevent ψ from becoming infinitely large as x becomes infinitely large negatively in (15·2–14) it is necessary to take $B' = 0$. Moreover, when we let V_1 become infinitely great, k' does likewise. To keep the left-hand side of eq. (15·2–17) finite means then that A' must vanish.   Hence eq. (15·2–16) becomes

$$A + B = 0, \tag{15·2–18}$$

which means that ψ must vanish at $x = 0$ to satisfy the imposed boundary conditions.   The same argument may be used to show that ψ also vanishes at $x = l$.   Hence in addition to (15·2–18) we must have

$$Ae^{ikl} + Be^{-ikl} = 0. \tag{15·2–19}$$

The combination of (15·2–18) and (15·2–19) yields

$$\sin kl = 0, \tag{15·2–20}$$

which in turn means that

$$kl = n\pi, \tag{15·2–21}$$

where n is any integer.   From (15·2–13) we therefore conclude that the allowed values of the energy are

$$E = V_0 + \frac{n^2h^2}{8ml^2}. \tag{15·2–22}$$

and for $V_0 = 0$

$$E = \frac{n^2h^2}{8ml^2}, \tag{15·2–23}$$

Here again we encounter a discrete series of quantized energy values like in this respect the eigenvalues of the oscillator.   Once more it is of interest to compare the energy eigenvalues computed from the Schrödinger equation with those given by the use of the Bohr quantum conditions.   If we quantize the momentum in the usual way we get

$$\int_0^l p \, dx = nh, \tag{15·2–24}$$

where n is an integer.   Since in this problem p is constant, eq. (15·2–24) yields

$$p = \frac{nh}{l}, \tag{15·2–25}$$

and the corresponding energy values are given by

$$E = V_0 + \frac{n^2 h^2}{2ml^2},$$ (15·2–26)

which differ numerically from (15·2–23), though the form is the same. If in the Bohr quantum condition we were permitted to use half-integer quantum numbers, the two sets of allowed energy values would be identical.

The true physical meaning of the Schrödinger wave equation can be appreciated only after a comprehensive study of the foundations of wave mechanics which is really a new method of attacking physical problems in the atomic domain. All the problems worked out by the Bohr theory (such as the hydrogen atom and atoms of more complicated structure) have been solved also with quantum mechanics and the results have been remarkably successful. Our aim in this section has been merely to provide a brief and somewhat formal introduction to this new discipline and in particular to indicate what an essential role a clear understanding of classical mechanics plays in its elucidation.[1]

PROBLEMS

1. Consider a group of plane harmonic De Broglie matter waves moving in the z direction with frequencies included in the range $\nu - \delta\nu$ to $\nu + \delta\nu$, where ν is a *mean* frequency and $\delta\nu \ll \nu$. Any particular wave in the group may be represented by

$$A (\nu + \epsilon) \cos 2\pi (\nu + \epsilon) \left[t - \frac{z}{V (\nu + \epsilon)} \right],$$

where $\nu + \epsilon$ is the frequency and $\epsilon \leqq |\delta\nu|$. The velocity of the wave is $V (\nu + \epsilon)$ and is supposed to be a function of frequency. Consider particularly *two* waves in the group for which $\epsilon = \epsilon_1$ and ϵ_2 respectively. Show that if they agree in phase at some point z at a certain t, this point of phase agreement will move with velocity

$$V_g = \frac{1}{\dfrac{d \left(\dfrac{\nu}{V} \right)}{d\nu}},$$

the *group* velocity of the group of waves. Prove that for the case of De Broglie waves $V_g = v$, where v is the velocity of the particle represented by the wave group.

[1] See, for example, R. B. Lindsay and H. Margenau, *Foundations of Physics*, Dover Publications, New York, 1957, Chap. 9; also D. Bohm, *Quantum Theory*, Prentice-Hall, Englewood Cliffs, N.J., 1951.

2. In Sec. 3·11 we found that the Bohr quantum condition for an electron moving about the nucleus of the hydrogen atom in a circular orbit of radius r is

$$p_\theta = rp = \frac{nh}{2\pi},$$

where p_θ is the angular momentum of the electron in its circular path, while p is the actual momentum (mv) along the path.

Assume that the momentum p is given by the De Broglie wave mechanical relation (14·1–9). By substitution find the relation between the wave length λ of the electron and the radius of the corresponding Bohr orbit. What physical significance can be attributed to this result?

3. Show from Sec. 6·4 that the moment of momentum (or angular momentum) of a particle revolving about the z axis can be written in the form

$$xp_y - yp_x,$$

where p_x is the linear momentum associated with motion in the x direction, etc. Hence find the corresponding quantum mechanical operator.

4. Write the Schrödinger wave equation for a particle revolving about the fixed z axis. Express it in terms of polar coördinates by the transformation $x = r \cos \theta$ and $y = r \sin \theta$. Solve the equation to find ψ as a function of θ. By imposing the condition of single-valuedness on ψ, i.e.,

$$\psi(\theta) = \psi(\theta + 2\pi),$$

show that the angular momentum is quantized in the same way as in the simple Bohr model.

5. Generalize the discussion in Sec. 15·2 to apply to the motion of a particle of mass m confined to a parallelepiped of sides l_1, l_2, l_3.

Show that the quantized energy values have the form

$$E = \frac{h^2}{8m} \left[(n_1/l_1)^2 + (n_2/l_2)^2 + (n_3/l_3)^2\right],$$

where n_1, n_2, n_3 are any triplet of integers. What is the physical significance of increasing the size of the box?

SUPPLEMENTARY PROBLEMS

1. Use the method of " dimensions " to derive the functional dependence of the period P of a simple pendulum on g and the length of the string. Discussion: Recall that with every mechanical quantity there is associated a dimensional formula involving the three fundamental dimensions of mass, length and time, represented symbolically by M, L, and T. Thus the dimensional formula for velocity is L/T or LT^{-1}; that for acceleration is LT^{-2}; that for force, MLT^{-2}, etc. To have physical meaning, every equation in mechanics must be consistent dimensionally; that is, both sides must have the same dimensions.

In the present example, if l = length of string, m = mass of bob and θ = angular amplitude of swing, assume that P is represented by the formula

$$P = l^x m^y g^z \theta^u.$$

P has the dimensions of T and hence the right-hand side must have the same dimensions. From this fact find the relations that x, y, z, u must satisfy in order to make the equation dimensionally consistent. Thus show that $P \propto \sqrt{l/g}$. The factor 2π in the actual formula is undetermined by the dimensional method. It is, of course, dimensionless. For a detailed account of dimensional analysis, see the interesting book by P. W. Bridgman *Dimensional Analysis* (Yale University Press, 2d ed., 1931).

2. Derive the functional form of Kepler's third law by the use of the method of dimensions. Do the same for Jurin's law for the rise of a liquid in a capillary tube (Sec. 12·8).

3. Show that when a mass particle moves in a circular path with a constant speed equal to that which it would gain in freely falling under gravity a distance equal to one-half the radius of the circle, the centripetal force on the particle is equal to its weight. This result is due to Huyghens (1629–1695) and is of considerable historical interest since it marks the beginning of the clear distinction between mass and weight.

4. A particle is constrained to fall under gravity from the highest point of a vertical circle along a chord of the circle. Prove that the time of descent is the same for *every* chord passing through the highest point. Prove also that the time of descent from all points on the circle is the same along the chords from those points passing through the lowest point of the circle.

5. Consider the parabola with equation $y = a - kx^2$ with the xy plane vertical. A particle moves from rest under gravity from the focus. If it is constrained to move along some line extending from the focus to the parabola, find the equation of the line along which it will meet the parabola most quickly. Show that the length of this line is equal to that of the latus rectum.

6. A particle moves in a circle of radius R under the attraction of a force varying inversely as the square of the distance from the center of the circle.

Use the expression for the centripetal force to derive Kepler's third law of planetary motion for this special (i.e., degenerate) case.

7. In the motion of a comet about the sun in a parabolic orbit, prove that the comet crosses the orbit of any given planet with a velocity $\sqrt{2}$ times that which the planet has at the same place (assuming that the orbit of the latter is approximately circular).

8. The solution of Kepler's equation [Sec. 3·9 eq. (3·9–28)], viz.,

$$M = E - \epsilon \sin E,$$

where E is the eccentric anomaly, ϵ the eccentricity and M the mean anomaly, is of great importance, both in celestial mechanics and in the Bohr theory of atomic structure. The desired solution consists in finding E as a function of M and hence of t. This is equivalent to finding the radius vector r as a function of t. Indicate how a graphical solution may be obtained by plotting a sine curve and a straight line and getting their point of intersection. In this way construct graphical plots of E as a function of M for values of $\epsilon = 0.1$, 0.3, 0.5, 0.8.

9. A particle moves in an elliptical orbit in a central field of force varying inversely as the square of the distance from the force center (one focus of the ellipse). Calculate the time average of the radius vector in terms of the major axis and eccentricity of the orbit. Apply numerically to the case of the earth and sun.

10. A particle moves in an elliptical orbit in a central field of force varying directly at the distance from the force center (the center of the ellipse). Calculate the time average of the radius vector in terms of the constants of the orbit. What is the expression for the period of revolution in this type of motion? Mention a physical illustration of this motion. Cf. Sec. 3·5.

11. A particle moves in a plane orbit with polar equation

$$r = \frac{\epsilon p}{1 - \epsilon \cos \gamma\theta},$$

where γ is a dimensionless constant very close to unity. Show that this orbit represents an ellipse of eccentricity ϵ and parameter p, whose perihelion slowly rotates. Find the rate of perihelion motion and make a sketch of the orbit. Assuming that the particle moves in a central force field, find the expression for the law of force, and in particular note the deviation from the inverse square law. All the planets show this perihelion motion to a certain extent, that of Mercury being the largest (574 seconds of arc per century). Classical Newtonian mechanics has been unable to account for the whole of this as being due to the perturbing influences of other planets. The theory of general relativity of Einstein has seemingly removed the difficulty (cf., e.g., R. B. Lindsay and H. Margenau, *Foundations of Physics*, Dover Publications, New York, 1957, Chap. 8). It is interesting to note that the application of special relativity mechanics to the motion of an electron about a nucleus in the Bohr theory leads to an orbit of precisely the form indicated above with $\gamma = \sqrt{1 - 4\pi^2 e^4 Z^2/k^2 h^2 c^2}$, where e is the charge on the electron, Z is the number of positive charges on the nucleus, c is the velocity of light, h is Planck's constant, and k is any integer. See Ruark and Urey, *Atoms, Molecules and Quanta*, McGraw-Hill, New York, 1930, p. 132.

12. A force $\mathbf{F} = \mathbf{i}F_0 + \mathbf{j}kte^{-at}$ acts on a particle, where F_0 is constant and equals $10/e$ dynes, $a = 1/20$ sec^{-1} and $k \doteq 200$ dynes/sec. Find the momentum produced (direction and magnitude) in $1/10$ second. Plot the magnitude of F as a function of t.

13. An alpha particle with initial velocity 2×10^9 cm/sec is shot *directly* at a nucleus of atomic number $N = 80$ (i.e., charge on the nucleus is 80 e):

(a) Assuming that the nucleus stays at rest, find the minimum distance of approach.

(b) What is the potential energy of the alpha particle at the minimum distance?

14. Find the way in which the central force must vary with the distance from the force center in order that a particle may describe the equiangular spiral

$$r = e^{a\theta},$$

the force center being assumed to be at the pole (a is a constant). Use the law of areas to find the expression for the resultant velocity of the particle as a function of r. Solve the same problem for the spiral of Archimedes for which $r = a\theta$ (a is again a constant).

15. A particle of unit mass moves under the influence of no force save a resisting force of the form $A + Bt$ where A and B are constants. If the particle comes to rest in time t_0, find the total distance traversed and show that it is equal to $\displaystyle\int_0^{t_0} t(A + Bt)\, dt$. Try to generalize this result.

16. In a straight rod of length l, the line density varies linearly from ρ_0 at one end A to ρ_1 at the other end B. Find the mass of the rod and the position of the center of mass. Also find the gravitational force with which the rod attracts a unit mass at point P such that PA is perpendicular to the rod and equal to h. Through what point of the rod does this force pass?

---

17. Find the law of density distribution in a sphere so that its attraction for a particle on its surface shall be independent of the size of the sphere.

18. A particle of mass m moves in a straight line subject to an attractive force directed toward a fixed point on the line and varying inversely as the square of the distance from the point. It is assumed to start from rest at distance a from the fixed point. Discuss the motion and in particular find the possible energy values of the motion consistent with the Bohr quantum condition $\oint m\dot{x}\, dx = nh$

(Sec. 3·11 and Sec. 4·3). These paths are the so-called " pendulum orbits " of the Bohr atomic theory. It should be shown that the quantized energy values agree with those obtained for elliptical motion in an inverse square field for $n_1 + n_2 = n$. Physically speaking, these orbits are ruled out since they involve collision with the force center, i.e., the nucleus in the atomic problem.

19. An electron moves in a quantized elliptical orbit about a positive nucleus as in the Bohr theory of the hydrogen atom. Find the expression for the fraction of the whole period of revolution which the electron spends on the average in a spherical shell of thickness dr at distance r from the nucleus.

Hint: Use the expression for the eccentric anomaly, Sec. 3·9. Hence show that if the electron's motion is assumed to be equivalent to a spherical distribution of negative charge about the nucleus the *average* fraction of the total charge e in the spherical shell dr at distance r is $de = \dfrac{er\,dr}{\pi a^2 \sqrt{\epsilon^2 - 1 + \dfrac{2r}{a} - \dfrac{r^2}{a^2}}}$.

Plot the distribution function. Integrate over r to get the total charge; this of course should be e.

20. Calculate the expression for the *potential* produced at any point distant r from the nucleus by the spherical distribution of the previous problem (Problem 19). Note: Electrical potential is calculated in the same way as gravitational potential. Care should be taken to distinguish between the potentials due to a given shell at points *inside* and *outside* the shell (Sec. 4·4). Use appropriate numerical values and plot the potential as a function of r.

21. Find the force acting on a particle of unit negative charge at point r in the field produced by a positive nucleus and the spherical distribution of negative charge described in Problem 19 above. This type of calculation has been of value in the Bohr theory of the structure of atoms with more than one electron. (Consult Ruark and Urey, *Atoms, Molecules and Quanta*, p. 200.)

22. Use Gauss' law (Sec. 4·5) to show that Laplace's equation, viz.,

$$\frac{\partial^2 V}{\partial x^2} + \frac{\partial^2 V}{\partial y^2} + \frac{\partial^2 V}{\partial z^2} = 0$$

in spherical coördinates ($x = r \sin \theta \cos \phi$, $y = r \sin \theta \sin \phi$, $z = r \cos \theta$) becomes

$$\frac{1}{r^2} \frac{\partial}{\partial r}\left(r^2 \frac{\partial V}{\partial r}\right) + \frac{1}{r^2 \sin \theta} \frac{\partial}{\partial \theta}\left(\sin \theta \frac{\partial V}{\partial \theta}\right) + \frac{1}{r^2 \sin^2 \theta} \frac{\partial^2 V}{\partial \phi^2} = 0.$$

Hint: Apply the law to the volume element in spherical coördinates, viz., $r^2 \sin \theta \, d\theta \, d\phi \, dr$, whose surface consists of two spherical elements, two conical elements, and two plane elements.

23. A sphere of radius a contains electric charge distributed throughout its volume with constant density ρ. Use Gauss' law (Sec. 4·5) to obtain the magnitude of the electric intensity due to this charge distribution (i.e., the force on a unit charge) at any point distant r from the center of the sphere. Thus show that for a point *inside* the sphere, the intensity has the magnitude $\dfrac{4\pi\rho r}{3}$, while *outside* it has the value $\dfrac{4\pi\rho a^3}{3r^2}$. Hint: Recall Çoulomb's law of force for electric charges and compare with the gravitational analysis of Secs. 4·4 and 4·5.

24. In the preceding problem (Problem 23) calculate the electric potential (Sec. 4·2) for a point distant r from the center of the sphere both inside and outside. Thus obtain $V_i = -\tfrac{2}{3}\pi\rho(3a^2 - r^2)$ and $V_0 = -\dfrac{4\pi\rho a^3}{3r}$. Prove that these satisfy Poisson's and Laplace's equations respectively [eqs. (4·5–19) and (4·5–20)]. Hint: Use the latter expressed in spherical coördinates as in Problem 22 above. Work the same problem for the case of gravitational attraction.

25. A sphere of radius a contains electric charge distributed throughout its volume with density $\rho = k(a^2 - r^2)$. Show that $k = \dfrac{15Q}{8\pi a^5}$, where Q is the total charge. Find the magnitude of the electric intensity at points inside and outside the sphere and do the same for the potential. Check by substitution into Poisson's equation.

26. Consider a conducting sphere of radius a. A point charge $+e$ is placed at the point P distant u from the center of the sphere, O, where $u > a$. Prove that if a charge $e' = -ae/u$ is placed at a point on OP inside the sphere distant $b = a^2/u$ from O, the potential at all points on the sphere will be zero. The charge e' is called the *electrical image* in the sphere of the charge e. The use of electrical images is very valuable in the solution of problems in electrostatics.

27. A boat with mass 2 tons (including that of the passenger) is moving through the water with an initially constant velocity of 20 ft/sec with respect to the shore. The passenger throws a 2-lb ball with an initial velocity of 30 ft/sec relative to the boat in the direction of motion of the boat. How much work does the man do in throwing the ball?

28. A gun and its carriage of mass M rest on a rough horizontal surface for which the coefficient of friction is μ. If the gun is fired horizontally so that the initial velocity of the projectile of mass m relative to the gun is V, find the distance which the carriage recoils.

29. A particle of mass m is acted on by a force $\mathbf{F} = kr^{-3}\mathbf{r}$ where k is a constant. How much work is done by the force when the particle moves in the xy plane in the arc of a circle from the position

$$\mathbf{r}_1 = a\mathbf{i}$$

to the position

$$\mathbf{r}_2 = a\mathbf{j}?$$

Obtain the answer in two different ways.

---

30. Two forces act on a given particle. Prove that if the sum and difference of the two forces are perpendicular to each other, the two forces are of equal magnitude. Prove also that if the magnitudes of the sum and difference respectively of two forces are equal, the two forces are perpendicular. Hint: Use the scalar product of two vectors.

31. Two electrostatic point charges $+2e$ and $-e$ are at a distance a apart. Find the neutral point, i.e., that at which a unit charge would be in equilibrium under the action of the two given charges.

32. A particle is constrained to lie on the convex side of a smooth ellipse and is acted on by forces of magnitude F_1 and F_2 directed toward the two foci respectively, and a force of magnitude F_c directed toward the center. In what position will the particle be in equilibrium?

33. A particle is placed at point P distant $r_1, r_2, \ldots r_n$ from the fixed points $O_1, O_2, \ldots O_n$. Forces act on the particle directed along $O_1P, O_2P, \ldots O_nP$ and are in magnitude proportional respectively to $r_1, r_2, \ldots r_n$. Use the principle of virtual work to show that the surface on which the particle will be in equilibrium in all positions is a sphere.

34. A flexible cord is suspended from two fixed points on the same horizontal line. What must be the law of variation of the mass per unit length in order that its shape may be a semicircle whose diameter is horizontal?

35. Prove that the resultant of several non-coplanar couples has a moment which is the resultant of the moments of the individual couples.

36. Find the center of mass of a sector of a plane uniform circular disk the arc of which subtends an angle of 30°. Also find its moment of inertia about an axis perpendicular to its plane and passing through the center of mass.

37. A plane ABC intersects the three coördinate axes in the points A, B, C respectively, forming the tetrahedron O–ABC. Four forces act normally to the faces of the tetrahedron along the three coördinate axes respectively and along the normal to ABC passing through O. These forces are proportional in magnitude to the areas of the faces to which they are respectively normal. Prove that they are in equilibrium. Generalize the result to the case of *any* tetrahedron. State the connection between the result of this problem and the laws of hydrostatics.

38. A uniform triangular plate with two sides equal to 10 cm and 15 cm respectively and the included angle 30° has a mass of 100 grams. It lies in a horizontal plane, suspended from a fixed point 25 cm above the plane by three strings attached to the corners. Find the tension in each of the strings. In particular find the relation between these tensions and the lengths of the strings.

39. A thin uniform rod has a length l and mass m. It is suspended by a vertical thread attached to its center O. A particle of mass M is placed at point P distant r from O so that OP makes the angle θ with the rod. What is the total force moment about the axis of suspension due to gravitational attraction?

40. A bar magnet of magnetic moment M (equal to ml where m is the strength of the poles, assumed to be concentrated at the ends of the magnet, and l is the length of the magnet) is suspended by a wire perpendicular to the lines of force of a uniform magnetic field of intensity H (that is, H dynes per unit pole or oersteds). What torque or force moment is required to hold the magnet at an angle θ with respect to the direction of the field? How much work is done in the motion of the magnet from a position parallel to the field to a position making angle θ with the field?

If the magnet has moment of inertia I about a perpendicular axis through the center, find the frequency of the vibrations it will make if displaced slightly from its position of equilibrium with respect to the field and then let go.

41. Prove that the analytical conditions for the equilibrium of a rigid body retain the same form if oblique axes are used instead of rectangular axes.

42. Use the theorem of Pappus on centroids to find the expression for the volume of a torus or anchor ring.

43. A uniform brass cylinder of radius 1 cm and length 50 cm is allowed to swing in a vertical plane about one end through an angle of 30° each side of the plumb line. Find the period of its oscillations.

44. A heavy block of wood is suspended by a stiff but massless vertical wire. A bullet is fired into the block. Indicate how the velocity of the bullet may be obtained. Derive the formula

$$v = \frac{2(M + m)k\sqrt{gh}\ \sin\ \theta/2}{mp}$$

where: m = mass of the bullet; M = mass of the block; k = radius of gyration of the block with the bullet in it; v = velocity of the bullet; p = the distance of the line of motion of the bullet from the point of suspension of the block; h = the distance of the center of mass of the block from the point of suspension; θ = the angle through which the block is deviated from the vertical. This arrangement is known as a *ballistic pendulum*.

45. A uniform thin hemispherical shell is constrained to move with its pole fixed. Find the equation of the momental ellipsoid.

46. A particle is projected with velocity V on a smooth horizontal plane. Show that because of the rotation of the earth the particle will describe an arc of a circle of radius $\dfrac{V}{2\omega\ \sin\ \lambda}$, where ω is the angular velocity of the earth and λ is the latitude. Work out a numerical example.

47. The contour of an elliptical plate of unit thickness has the equation $Ax^2 + Bxy + Cy^2 + Dx + Ey + F = 0$. Find the moment of inertia of the plate about a diameter parallel to the x axis.

48. A thin circular sheet of radius r and mass m falls from rest in a vertical position to a horizontal floor. If the bottom in contact with the floor does not slip, with what kinetic energy will it strike and what will be the velocity of the top end?

49. What is the kinetic energy of rotation of a right circular cone with height 1 meter and radius of base 20 cm if it rotates at constant angular velocity 10 rev/sec about its principal axis? What angular velocity would be necessary to give it the same kinetic energy if it were rotated about an axis through the vertex perpendicular to the principal axis?

---

50. Two particles A and B with masses m_A and m_B respectively move subject only to their mutual interaction. What is true of their instantaneous velocities? Specialize to the case where they are initially at rest. If A moves in a circle of radius r_A with constant angular velocity, show that B must likewise move in a circle with the same angular velocity. What is the radius of this second circle? Specialize to the lowest energy state in the Bohr model of the hydrogen atom and give numerical values.

51. Two particles B and C with masses m_B and m_C respectively move subject only to their mutual interaction. Find the expression for the acceleration of C *relative* to B in terms of the acceleration of C in the reference frame. Find the relative fractional acceleration of C. What are its maximum and minimum possible values?

What will be the effective relative mass, i.e., the mass of a particle which, moving with the *relative* acceleration, has the same unbalanced force acting on it as acts on B and C themselves?

52. Prove that $\int_{V_0}^{V_1} p \, dV$, where p is the excess pressure and V the volume, represents the work required to compress a fluid from volume V_0 to volume V_1. If the fluid is an ideal gas and the compression is adiabatic, calculate the work. If the fluid is a liquid, obtain an expression for the work by the use of the bulk modulus.

53. The energy of a single molecule of a fluid when in a state of compression from volume V_0 to volume V may be expressed in terms of the series

$$E = E_0 + (V - V_0)\left(\frac{dE}{dV}\right)_0 + \frac{(V - V_0)^2}{2} \left(\frac{d^2E}{dV^2}\right)_0 + \cdots,$$

where E_0 is the equilibrium energy in the uncompressed state and $\left(\frac{dE}{dV}\right)_0$ is the derivative referring to equilibrium conditions. If equilibrium corresponds to minimum molecular energy, what value must be assigned to the second term on the right? Derive the following expression for the bulk modulus of the fluid

$$k = V_0 \, N \left(\frac{d^2F}{dV^2}\right)_0,$$

where N is the number of molecules in volume V_0. Discuss the physical significance of the requirement which the positive nature of k places on $\left(\frac{d^2E}{dV^2}\right)_0$.

54. If in Problem 52 the change in volume from V_0 to V is that involved in the change from liquid to solid state, the work done may be expected to be approximately equal to the heat of fusion. Test this hypothesis by application to the following substances: lead, bismuth, ethyl alcohol, and tin.

55. The critical temperature of a substance may plausibly be defined from the kinetic theory point of view as the temperature for which the average energy per molecule equals the energy required to separate the molecules completely. The latter may be calculated from the result of Problems 52 and 53. Thus get an estimate of the order of magnitude of the critical temperature of water on this hypothesis.

56. A possible equation of state of a liquid has been given in the form

$$p\,(V - V_0) = 3NkT,$$

where V_0 is the *minimum* possible volume for the closest packing of the molecules. The other symbols have their usual significance as in Chapter 7. How does the pressure vary with depth for such a liquid under isothermal conditions?

---

57. Discuss the motion of the bob of a simple pendulum in a medium which resists the motion with a force varying directly as the velocity. Also discuss the case where the resisting force varies as the square of the velocity.

58. A bead moves on a smooth circular wire of radius a; the plane of the wire is inclined at an angle ϕ to the vertical. Find the frequency of the small oscillations of the bead about the lowest point of the wire.

59. The motion of the bob of a simple pendulum when first observed has an amplitude of 6 cm. Eight minutes thereafter the amplitude of swing has decreased to 4 cm. Find the decay modulus. How long a time must elapse before the amplitude has diminished to 2 mm? If the length of the pendulum is 50 cm, calculate its natural frequency and compute the error involved in neglecting the effect of the dissipation. What is the logarithmic decrement?

60. In a special arrangement of Atwood's machine both particles have the same mass, so that the system is originally in equilibrium. One of the particles is then pulled aside a short distance in the original plane of the system and allowed to swing in this plane as a simple pendulum. Discuss its motion.

61. A perfectly flexible string of length l and line density ρ is stretched with tension τ. Show that when it is displaced transversely, the total kinetic energy and total potential energy (neglecting dissipation) may be expressed in the following way

$$T = \tfrac{1}{2} \int_0^l \rho \dot{\xi}^2 \, dx,$$

$$V = \tfrac{1}{2} \int_0^l \tau \left(\frac{\partial \xi}{\partial x} \right)^2 dx.$$

Here ξ represents the displacement at distance x along the string from one end chosen as origin. Taking the solution for a progressive wave along the string, i.e., $\xi = A \cos(\omega t - kx)$ (from Sec. 11·5), evaluate T and V.

62. Consider a perfectly flexible circular membrane of radius a which is fixed at the periphery. Imagine it depressed by a uniform pressure p. If the superficial tension, i.e., force per unit length (Sec. 12·8), is τ (assumed to remain constant under the displacement), show that the displacement of a point on the membrane distant r from the center is given approximately by

$$\xi = \frac{pa^2}{4\tau} \left(1 - \frac{r^2}{a^2} \right).$$

Hint: Discuss the static equilibrium of the ring element $2\pi r \, dr$. What is the maximum displacement ξ_0 and what is the shape of the deformed membrane?

63. Find the expression for the total kinetic energy of the membrane in the previous problem (Problem 62) if it is depressed and let go, assuming that ξ is always given by the expression above, and that the instantaneous velocity of the center is $\dot{\xi}_0$. In this way prove that the *effective* mass of the membrane is *one-third* of the actual mass. N.B. The effective mass, m_e, is that for which $\tfrac{1}{2} m_e \dot{\xi}_0^2$ is equal to the total kinetic energy.

64. Referring again to Problem 62 show that the potential energy of the circular membrane to the approximation there assumed is

$$V = \frac{8\pi\tau}{a^2} \left(\frac{a^2}{4} \right) \frac{\xi_0^2}{2},$$

so that the effective stiffness coefficient of the membrane is $f = 2\pi\tau$. (N.B. The effective stiffness coefficient is that such that $\tfrac{1}{2} f \xi_0^2$ is equal to the total potential energy.) Hence show that the natural frequency of vibration of the membrane is $\nu_0 = \dfrac{1}{2\pi} \sqrt{\dfrac{6\tau}{\rho a^2}}$, where ρ = surface density of membrane. It should be noted that the last three problems refer to an approximate theory of the circular membrane. According to the more exact theory, the membrane has a whole set of natural frequencies (recall the stretched string) of which ν_0 is a first approximation to the fundamental. (See Lindsay, *Mechanical Radiation*, McGraw-Hill, 1960, p. 131.)

65. A perfectly flexible string of length l is stretched in a horizontal line with tension τ and loaded at equal intervals a with n particles of mass m, so that $(n + 1)a = l$. One of the masses is displaced slightly in the vertical plane. Using the general method of Sec. 10·8 write the equations of motion of the system, assuming that the mass of the string itself is negligible. Show that if the vertical displacements of the particles are denoted by $q_1 \ldots q_n$ respectively

$$q_j = \sum_{k=1}^{n} A_k \sin \frac{(j-1)k\pi}{n+1} \cdot \cos (\omega_k t + \epsilon_k),$$

where j runs from 1 to n, satisfies the equations, provided that

$$\omega_k = 2 \sqrt{\frac{\tau}{ma}} \sin \frac{k\pi}{2(n+1)}.$$

The latter are known as the *characteristic frequencies* of the loaded string. Compare with the special case of Sec. 10·8. Take a special case and calculate numerical values.

66. In the diagram m_1 and m_2 are masses joined to the rigid supports C_1 and C_2 respectively by the two springs with stiffness f_1 and f_2 respectively. Moreover, the masses are joined with a spring of stiffness f. Assuming that the

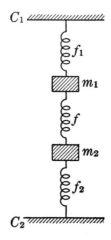

motion of the masses is confined to the vertical direction, write the equations of motion of the system when it is given a slight displacement from equilibrium. Neglect the mass of the springs. Determine the frequencies of the motion.

67. The diagram indicates a massless, inflexible rod, 1 meter in length, hinged at one end and carrying a mass $m = 500$ grams at the other end. The rod is supported by a vertical spring of stiffness 1 kilogram wt per cm attached 25 cm from the hinge. When the mass m is displaced vertically a *small* distance and let go, the amplitude of motion is found to be reduced to $1/e$th of its original value in 10 sec.

(a) What is the natural frequency of the vibrations of m?

(b) What is the logarithmic decrement of the motion of m?

(c) If the system were to be driven at its resonance frequency by a periodic force with a maximum value of 100 grams wt, at what rate would it dissipate energy?

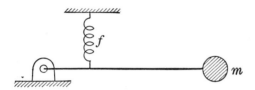

68. Consider a pair of coupled oscillators like those described in Sec. 10·8 and for which the displacements are given by

$$\xi_1 = A \cos (\omega_1 t + \epsilon_1) + B \cos (\omega_2 t + \epsilon_2),$$

$$\xi_2 = A \cos (\omega_1 t + \epsilon_1) - B \cos (\omega_2 t + \epsilon_2).$$

Suppose the system is started from rest by giving the first component the initial displacement ξ_{10} while the second has zero displacement. Show that the resultant motion can be expressed in the form

$$\xi_1 = \xi_{10} \cos \frac{(\omega_1 + \omega_2)}{2} t \cdot \cos \frac{(\omega_1 - \omega_2)}{2} t,$$

$$\xi_2 = -\xi_{10} \sin \frac{(\omega_1 + \omega_2)}{2} t \cdot \sin \frac{(\omega_1 - \omega_2)}{2} t.$$

Discuss the physical significance of this result.

69. The point of suspension of a simple pendulum moves with constant velocity in a circle in the plane of the pendulum's motion. Write the equations of motion and solve them for the case in which the circle is very small.

70. A condenser of capacitance C is charged through a resistance R by a constant source of e.m.f. E. Find the relaxation time, i.e., the time required for the charge on the condenser to rise to within $1/e$ of the static value.

71. Write the relaxation equation (cf. eq. 10·2–47) corresponding to the imposition of a constant excess pressure p_e on a fluid of mean density ρ_0. This is the differential equation for the excess density ρ_e. Find the expression for the relaxation time.

Do the same problem when the excess pressure is a harmonic function of the time and solve to find p_e/ρ_e in terms of the relaxation time. What physical significance can be associated with this ratio? (cf. eq. 12·6–38.)

72. A uniform steel cylindrical rod of length l_1 and radius a is suspended horizontally at its mid-point from a steel wire of length l_2 and radius b. Find

the ratio of the number of oscillations per second of the bar (eq. 11·2–17) at temperature T_1 to the number at temperature T_2. Consult physical tables for necessary numerical data.

73. A solid cylindrical rod of radius a rolls without slipping inside a hollow cylindrical pipe of radius $b(> a)$. If the angle of roll is small, find the frequency of oscillation.

Write the energy equation for the case of arbitrary amplitude.

---

74. Given two homogeneous media separated by a plane boundary. Let us suppose that all particles move in the first medium in straight line paths with constant velocity V_1 and in the second medium with constant velocity V_2. Find the path of a particle between point A of the first medium and point B of the second medium satisfying the condition that it shall be traversed in the minimum time. (Note: This is the famous principle of Fermat for the propagation of light. It should be shown that Snell's law of refraction follows from the condition cited.)

75. A cubical box of side a is supposed to be filled with electromagnetic radiation in the form of plane harmonic waves which, however, must satisfy the boundary condition that the displacement is zero on all faces of the box. Show that the allowed frequencies are given by

$$\nu = \frac{c}{2a} \sqrt{n_1^2 + n_2^2 + n_3^2},$$

where c = velocity of the waves, and n_1, n_2, n_3 form a set of any three integers. Hint: Use the expression for the characteristic frequencies of a stretched string (Sec. 11·6).

76. Referring to the previous problem (Problem 75) prove that the number of possible modes of oscillation inside the cubical space having frequencies included in the frequency region ν to $\nu + \Delta\nu$ is given by $4\pi a^3/c^3 \cdot \nu^2 \Delta\nu$. Hint: Represent each possible frequency by a point in a three-dimensional lattice space with coördinates the integers n_1, n_2, n_3. The number of such points lying in any given volume of this space will be numerically equal to the volume, approximately. If each mode of oscillation has attached to it the amount of energy kT (where T is the absolute temperature and k is Boltzmann's gas constant), show that the energy density of the radiation in the frequency interval ν to $\nu + \Delta\nu$ is $\Delta E_\nu = \dfrac{8\pi\nu^2 kT}{c^3} \Delta\nu$. Express this in terms of wave length.

This gives the Rayleigh-Jeans law for the frequency distribution of energy in the radiation from a perfect radiator of electromagnetic radiation (i.e., a black body). Unfortunately the result does not agree with experiment. This discrepancy was instrumental in the introduction of the quantum theory by Planck in 1900.

77. The displacement in a plane harmonic acoustic wave progressing in the x direction may be written in complex form as $\xi = Ae^{i(\omega t - kx)}$ where A is the amplitude, $\omega = 2\pi\nu$, where ν is the frequency and $k = \omega/c$, where c is the wave velocity. Find the expression for the ratio $p/\dot{X}$, where p is the excess pressure in the wave and $\dot{X}$ (the so-called volume current) $= S\dot{\xi}$, S being the area of cross-section of the wave front. This ratio is called the *acoustic impedance* of the wave. Hint: Use the definitions and theory in Sec. 12·6.

78. A plane harmonic acoustic wave $\xi = Ae^{i(\omega t - kx)}$ progresses through a cylindrical tube of cross-sectional area S_1 in the x direction (i.e., from left to right). At a certain point there is an abrupt change in the area of cross-section from S_1 to S_2. Show that the fraction of the incident energy at the boundary which is reflected is $\left(\dfrac{S_2 - S_1}{S_2 + S_1}\right)^2$. For this purpose utilize the boundary conditions that at the boundary there exists continuity in pressure p as well as in volume current $\dot{X}$. Assume that there is no wave in the negative x direction in the tube to the right of the boundary.

79. Show that the wave equation for spherical acoustical waves diverging from or converging to a point may be written in the form

$$\frac{\partial^2 (r\phi)}{\partial t^2} = c^2 \frac{\partial^2 (r\phi)}{\partial r^2},$$

where ϕ is the velocity potential and r the distance from the point in question. Hence show that the general solution has the form

$$\phi = \frac{1}{r}\left[f_1(ct - r) + f_2(ct + r)\right].$$

Considering the velocity potential for spherical harmonic waves in the form

$$\phi = \frac{A}{r} e^{i(\omega t - kr)},$$

deduce the expression for $p/\dot{X}$ (see problem 77), i.e., the acoustic impedance, and compare with that for a plane wave. What is the limiting value of the acoustic impedance of the spherical wave as $r \to \infty$?

80. A torsional wave travels along an infinitely long uniform cylindrical solid rod. Show that the velocity of propagation is $\sqrt{\mu/\rho}$, where μ is the shear modulus and ρ is the density.

81. A conical horn is in the form of the frustum of a right circular cone with slant height h. If both ends of the horn are open, show that its characteristic or resonance frequencies for spherical acoustic waves are given by $\nu = nc/2h$ where n is any integer. Compare with the case of the stretched transversely vibrating string and with the cylindrical organ pipe.

82. Harmonic acoustic waves pass through a tube with rigid walls and of varying cross-section S (i.e., a horn). The diameter is supposed to be everywhere smaller than the wave length. Show by setting up the equation of motion and the equation of continuity for the fluid (e.g., air) in the tube and by making the usual acoustic approximations (Sec. 12·6) that the approximately valid differential equation for the acoustic excess pressure in the tube is

$$\frac{\partial^2 p}{\partial x^2} + \frac{1}{S}\frac{dS}{dx}\frac{\partial p}{\partial x} + k^2 p = 0,$$

where $k = 2\pi/\lambda = 2\pi\nu/c$ in the usual notation. Solve this equation for the special case of a conical tube. This differential equation is basic for much of modern acoustical horn theory.

83. A semi-infinite solid rod of cross-sectional area S is traversed by harmonic compressional elastic waves of frequency ν in both directions. Show that the complex volume current $\dot{X}$ (i.e., product of particle velocity $\dot{\xi}$ and area S) and the complex excess stress T (due to the waves) at any point may be represented by

$$\dot{X} = \left[\dot{X}_1 \cos kx + \frac{iT_1 S}{\rho_0 c} \sin kx \right] e^{i\omega t},$$

$$T = \left[T_1 \cos kx + \frac{i\dot{X}_1 \rho_0 c}{S} \sin kx \right] e^{i\omega t},$$

where $\dot{X}_1$ and T_1 are the complex volume current and excess stress at $x = 0$ respectively, ρ_0 = mean density of the material of the rod and c = velocity of the waves. As usual, $k = 2\pi/\lambda = \omega/c = 2\pi\nu/c$.

84. The solid rod in the preceding problem (Problem 83) is loaded at equal intervals of length $2l$ with concentrated weights of mass m. By setting up the usual boundary conditions (see Problem 78 above) involving continuity of pressure and volume current, and making use of the recurrent nature of the structure show that, if $\dot{X}_n$ and T_n are the volume current and excess stress halfway between the $(n - 1)$st and nth loads, we have the relations

$$\dot{X}_{n+1} = \dot{X}_n e^{-iW},$$

$$T_{n+1} = T_n e^{-iW},$$

where $\cos W = \cos 2kl - \dfrac{m\omega}{2\rho_0 cS} \sin 2kl$. Hence show that the structure behaves like a low frequency pass filter for compressional waves, allowing the free transmission only of those waves whose frequencies satisfy the condition

$$-1 \leqq \cos W \leqq 1.$$

85. The accompanying schematic diagram represents an infinite succession of cylindrical tubes of cross-sectional area S_1 and S_2 respectively and lengths l_1 and l_2 respectively. If plane harmonic waves travel along this structure in both directions, show by the use of boundary conditions as in Problem 78 that the structure is a low pass filter and find the conditions for transmission and attenuation bands.

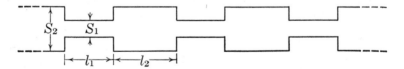

86. The accompanying figure represents a section of an elastic fluid medium extending in the x direction. Consider the two elements of length AB and BC both equal to Δx. If the medium is given a small displacement so that the layer at A moves through ξ, show that there is a change in density such that, in the displaced element $A'B'$, the density is to a first approximation

$$\rho = \frac{\rho_0}{1 + \dfrac{\partial \xi}{\partial x}},$$

where ρ_0 is the mean equilibrium density.   Find $d\rho$ and (by the use of Hooke's law for longitudinal extension) deduce the equation of motion in the x direction in the form

$$\ddot{\xi} = Y/\rho_0 \cdot \frac{\partial^2 \xi}{\partial x^2} \Big/ \left(1 + \frac{\partial \xi}{\partial x} \right)^2.$$

To what form does this reduce when $\left| \dfrac{\partial \xi}{\partial x} \right| \ll 1$?   Discuss the physical significance of this.

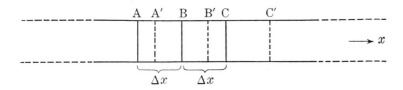

87. Two waves of intensity I_1 and I_0 respectively are said to differ by D decibels if

$$D = 10 \log_{10} I_1 / I_0.$$

When the intensity of a wave diminishes through absorption by the medium, the intensity I at distance r from the place where the intensity is I_0 is given by

$$I = I_0 e^{-\alpha r}$$

Find the loss in decibels per cm (db/cm) in terms of α.   Apply to Problem 29 of Chapter 12.

88. In the schematic sketch AB denotes an infinitely long hollow tube of radius a with rigid walls and with axis along the x direction. MM' is a thin membrane stretched across the tube with surface tension T.   The membrane has surface density σ.   If a plane harmonic sound wave for which the displacement is

$$\xi = \xi_0 \cos(\omega t - kx)$$

impinges on the membrane from the left, find the ratio of the sound intensity transmitted to the right of the membrane to that incident on the membrane from the left.   Hint: Use the simple membrane theory set forth in Problems 62, 63, 64.

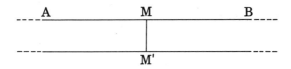

89. Two horizontal flexible strings of length 25 cm, but having line densities of 0.2 gram/cm and 0.4 gram/cm respectively are joined together.   The opposite ends are then fastened so that the resulting composite string is stretched horizontally with a tension of 10^6 dynes.   Find an expression for the harmonics of this stretched string.

90. If the string in the preceding problem (Problem 89) is pulled aside a distance of 0.2 cm from its horizontal position at the junction point of the two separate strings and then let go, find the amplitudes of the first two harmonics of the resulting stationary wave pattern.

91. In Sec. 12·6 we showed that the excess pressure in a small-amplitude sound wave in a fluid is given by

$$p_e = \rho_0 c^2 s,$$

where ρ_0 is the equilibrium density, c is the velocity of sound, and s is the condensation. A better approximation for a more intense wave would replace ρ_0 by the actual density $\rho = \rho_0 (1 + s)$, by the definition of condensation and write

$$p_e = \rho_0 (1 + s) c^2 s.$$

Calculate from this the average excess pressure in a harmonic wave for which the condensation is expressed by

$$s = s_0 \cos (\omega t - kx).$$

Show that

$$\bar{p}_e = \frac{\rho_0 c^2 s_0^2}{2}.$$

This static excess pressure is called the radiation pressure.

92. Derive the relation between the velocity of sound in an ideal gas and v_m, the r.m.s. molecular velocity. Under what conditions are the two velocities approximately the same? Comment on the physical significance of the relationship.

93. Derive the expression for the velocity of sound in a van der Waals gas, i.e., one having the equation of state

$$(p + a/V^2) (V - b) = RT,$$

where a and b are constants.

94. Determine the dependence of the velocity of sound on temperature and pressure in a real gas whose equation of state can be put in the form

$$pV = RT \left(1 + \frac{B}{V} + \frac{C}{V^2} + \cdots \right),$$

where B, C, etc., are the second, third, and higher *virial* coefficients. Apply to the case of carbon dioxide at atmospheric pressure and temperature 30° C.

95. A shock front is a thin layer of fluid moving in the direction of its thickness in such a fashion that the fluid flow velocity, density and pressure on one side of the layer differ by finite amounts from the corresponding quantities on the other side of the layer. If the appropriate quantities behind the shock front are u_1, ρ_1, p_1 respectively and ahead of the front are u_2, ρ_2, p_2 respectively (measured in a coördinate system that moves with the front), show from the application of conservation of mass flow and momentum that

$$u_1 = \frac{1}{\rho_1} \sqrt{\frac{p_1 - p_2}{1/\rho_2 - 1/\rho_1}}$$

$$u_2 = \frac{1}{\rho_2} \sqrt{\frac{p_1 - p_2}{1/\rho_2 - 1/\rho_1}}.$$

Also show from the conservation of energy in the motion of the front that

$$u_2 - u_1 = \sqrt{(p_2 - p_1)(1/\rho_1 - 1/\rho_2)}.$$

Show that if $p_1 - p_2$ and $\rho_1 - \rho_2$ are very small compared with p_1 and ρ_1 respectively, the velocities u_1 and u_2 become equal and reduce to the normal velocity of sound in the medium.

---

96. The surface of a liquid is in the form of a cylinder of length h and radius R. Show that the internal pressure necessary to keep the liquid cylinder in equilibrium is T_s/R, where T_s is the surface tension.

97. An air bubble is formed in water by forcing air through a vertical tube whose open end is 2.91 cm below the water surface. The radius of the tube orifice is 0.025 cm. If the excess pressure in the bubble at the moment of its breaking away, as measured by a manometer, is 9.15 cm. of water, find the surface tension of the water.

98. A thin circular disk of radius a is suspended so that its lower surface touches a liquid which wets it. Show that the force with which it is necessary to pull upward to remove the disk from the liquid is given by $2\pi a^2 \sqrt{\rho g T_s}$, where ρ is the density of the liquid, g is the acceleration of gravity and T_s is the surface tension. Carry out the numerical calculation in the case of water for a disk of radius 10 cm.

99. According to Rayleigh (*Theory of Sound*, par. 353) the velocity of surface waves of moderate amplitude in an ideal, incompressible fluid under gravity and surface tension is given by

$$c = \sqrt{(g/k + T_s k/\rho) \tanh kl},$$

where $l =$ depth of fluid, $T_s =$ surface tension, $\rho =$ fluid density, $k = 2\pi/\lambda$, where $\lambda =$ wave length, and $g =$ acceleration of gravity.

If the fluid is water, find the expression for the *group* velocity for the following special cases: $kl \ll 1$; and $kl \gg 1$. Specialize the second case to both large and small λ. Introduce numerical values where possible. Comment on the physical significance of the results.

100. Show that the differential equations of the stream lines of a fluid in steady flow are

$$\frac{dx}{u} = \frac{dy}{v} = \frac{dz}{w},$$

where u, v, w are the rectangular components of flow velocity. If one confines one's attention to two-dimensional flow in the xy plane, find the stream lines corresponding to $u = Cy$ and $v = -Cx$, where C is a constant.

101. How will the Poiseuille formula for steady flow of a viscous fluid through a cylindrical tube (eq. 12·7–12) be modified if the viscosity is a linear function of the flow velocity, i.e., $\eta = \eta_0 + Cu$, where C is a constant?

102. Use the method of dimensions to find the dependence of the resistance offered to a solid body of definite shape moving at constant velocity through an infinite fluid on the linear dimensions of the body, the velocity and the viscosity of the fluid. Thus show for small velocities that

$$R = \phi \eta v l,$$

where η is the viscosity, v the velocity, l the linear dimension, and ϕ is a function of the shape. If the restriction to small velocities is abandoned, what other quantities conceivably might enter into the expression for R?

103. Starting with the Newtonian equation of motion for the case of one degree of freedom and assuming that the force is conservative, derive Hamilton's principle, i.e., show that

$$\delta \int_{t_0}^{t_1} (T - V)\, dt = 0,$$

the variation having the meaning of Sec. 13·1.

104. Show that Hamilton's principle for a conservative system may be stated in the following form: A conservative dynamical system moves in such a way that the time average of the potential energy over any time interval differs least (or most) from the time average of the kinetic energy over the same interval. Find the expressions for $\overline{T} - \overline{V}$ in the special cases of the harmonic oscillator, motion in a uniform field and motion in a central inverse square field.

105. The Hamiltonian for a simple harmonic oscillator of mass m and stiffness k is (see Sec. 13·4)

$$H = \frac{1}{2m} p^2 + \frac{k}{2} q^2,$$

where q is the coördinate and p the conjugate momentum. Introduce the transformation from the coördinates p, q to P, Q where

$$q = \sqrt{\frac{2}{m\omega}}\, \sqrt{P} \sin Q,$$

$$p = \sqrt{2m\omega}\, \sqrt{P} \cos Q.$$

Here ω is a parameter. Find the form of the Hamiltonian in the new coördinates, and show that the canonical equations of motion

$$\frac{\partial H}{\partial q} = -\dot{p}, \quad \frac{\partial H}{\partial p} = \dot{q}$$

now become

$$P = \alpha, \quad Q = \omega t + \beta,$$

where α and β are arbitrary constants and $\omega = \sqrt{k/m}$. Hence show that the solution to the problem is

$$q = \sqrt{\frac{2\alpha}{m\omega}} \sin \left(\sqrt{\frac{k}{m}}\, t + \beta \right).$$

The transformation here considered is called a *canonical transformation* and is of much importance in problems of atomic mechanics.

106. From the theory of relativity show that the total energy E of a free particle can be written in the form

$$E^2 = p^2c^2 + m_0{}^2c^4,$$

where $p = $ the momentum mv, and m is the variable mass. What is the momentum of an electron with 2×10^6 electron volts energy? (The electron volt is the energy gained by an electron in falling through a potential difference of 1 volt.)

107. Write and solve Lagrange's equations for a particle which moves in a plane subject only to a constant force in the x direction.

108. Mass particles m_1, m_2, m_3 are attached to a vertical flexible string as indicated in the diagram. If the particles are displaced arbitrarily from the

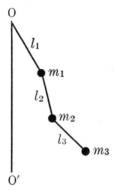

vertical equilibrium position (in the same plane) and released, write Lagrange's equations for the subsequent motion.

INDEX

459